74/-

D1485537

WITHDRAWN

THE NEUROPSYCHOLOGY OF LASHLEY

McGRAW-HILL SERIES IN PSYCHOLOGY

HARRY F. HARLOW, *Consulting Editor*

BEACH, HEBB, MORGAN, AND NISSEN · The Neuropsychology of Lashley
BARKER, KOUNIN, AND WRIGHT · Child Behavior and Development
VON BÉKÉSY · Experiments in Hearing
BERLYNE · Conflict, Arousal, and Curiosity
BLUM · Psychoanalytic Theories of Personality
BROWN · The Psychodynamics of Abnormal Behavior
BROWN AND GHISELLI · Scientific Method in Psychology
CATTELL · Personality
CRAFTS, SCHNEIRLA, ROBINSON, AND GILBERT · Recent Experiments in
    Psychology
DEESE · The Psychology of Learning
DOLLARD AND MILLER · Personality and Psychotherapy
DORCUS AND MILLER · Handbook of Employee Selection
FERGUSON · Personality Measurement
FERGUSON · Statistical Analysis in Psychology and Education
GHISELLI AND BROWN · Personnel and Industrial Psychology
GILMER · Industrial Psychology
GRAY · Psychology Applied to Human Affairs
GRAY · Psychology in Industry
GUILFORD · Fundamental Statistics in Psychology and Education
GUILFORD · Personality
GUILFORD · Psychometric Methods
HAIRE · Psychology in Management
HIRSH · The Measurement of Hearing
HURLOCK · Adolescent Development
HURLOCK · Child Development
HURLOCK · Developmental Psychology
JOHNSON · Essentials of Psychology
KARN AND GILMER · Readings in Industrial and Business Psychology
KRECH AND CRUTCHFIELD · Theory and Problems of Social Psychology
LEWIN · A Dynamic Theory of Personality
LEWIN · Principles of Topological Psychology
LEWIS · Quantitative Methods in Psychology
MAIER AND SCHNEIRLA · Principles of Animal Psychology
MILLER · Language and Communication
MISIAK AND STAUDT · Catholics in Psychology: A Historical Survey
MOORE · Psychology for Business and Industry
MORGAN AND STELLAR · Physiological Psychology
PAGE · Abnormal Psychology
REYMERT · Feelings and Emotions
SEASHORE · Psychology of Music
SHAFFER AND LAZARUS · Fundamental Concepts in Clinical Psychology
SIEGEL · Nonparametric Statistics: For the Behavioral Sciences
STAGNER · Psychology of Personality
TOWNSEND · Introduction to Experimental Method
VINACKE · The Psychology of Thinking
WALLEN · Clinical Psychology: The Study of Persons
WATERS, RETHLINGSHAFER, AND CALDWELL · Principles of Comparative
    Psychology
ZUBEK AND SOLBERG · Human Development

John F. Dashiell was Consulting Editor of this series from its inception in
1931 until January 1, 1950. Clifford T. Morgan was Consulting Editor of this
series from January 1, 1950 until January 1, 1959.

Karl Spencer Lashley
1890–1958

The Neuropsychology of Lashley

SELECTED PAPERS OF K. S. LASHLEY

Edited by
FRANK A. BEACH
DONALD O. HEBB
CLIFFORD T. MORGAN
HENRY W. NISSEN

McGRAW-HILL BOOK COMPANY, INC.
1960   New York   Toronto   London

THE NEUROPSYCHOLOGY OF LASHLEY

04202

PREFACE

In April of 1955, just before Lashley's retirement as Director of the Yerkes Laboratories of Primate Biology, four of his former students and colleagues began corresponding to lay plans for an appropriate memorial to his manifold scientific contributions and his signal influence on experimental and physiological psychology. This memorial volume has taken longer to prepare than we had hoped, and in the meantime, Lashley passed away in Poitiers, France, on August 7, 1958. Two months before he died, however, he was apprised of the plan and expressed his pleasure with it.

At first the possibility of publishing a traditional *Festschrift* was considered, but this was soon discarded in favor of a more attractive and functional alternative. Lashley had never published a systematic account of his work following his experimental monograph *Brain Mechanisms and Intelligence* (1929). Hence scholars who wish to gain some appreciation of the reach and breadth of his contributions to science must consult dozens of different journals in which the original experimental and theoretical articles are published. It occurred to the self-constituted committee that it would be exceedingly desirable and useful if a selected sample of Lashley's original papers could be assembled and republished in book form.

The aims of our selection procedure were to choose a group of papers that would reflect the range of Lashley's interests and achievements, to avoid duplication, and to hold the size of the final product within reasonable limits. When the final choices were agreed upon, the committee felt that it had not merely made a representative selection of Lashley's contributions, but that it had assembled a number of publications still highly significant for current problems—ones that should be available for study by any student of behavior.

This collection consists of thirty-one articles from a total bibliography of more than a hundred titles, not counting book reviews. It represents, we believe, four dominant themes characterizing four different phases of Lashley's career as a professional investigator: (*a*) laying the foundations, (*b*) the grand attack on connectionism, (*c*) experimental studies of sensory representation (chiefly vision), and (*d*) general theory. We have not attempted to separate the papers into these four categories, for some papers fit into both; but the reader will be able to see the themes in the chronological sequence of papers.

Nearly all of the articles selected are here reprinted without any substantial deletions. A few pages have been omitted from two articles— numbers 1 and 26—to reduce their length. For the same reason, one or more tables have been omitted from articles 3, 4, 18, 22, and 27. In order to avoid duplication, or because suitable copy for reproduction was not available, one or more figures had to be omitted from articles 1, 4, 16, 18, 19, and 29. The text has been edited to reflect these minor omissions; tables, figures, and footnotes have been renumbered as necessary. For the sake of consistency, the bibliographies of the various articles have been edited and rearranged, where possible, according to the former policy laid down in the Publication Manual of the American Psychological Association without, however, altering their contents. The sections of articles 1, 8, 10, 11, 24, and 27 appearing in small type were set that way in the original publications. Again for consistency, the editors have also designated sections of the following articles for small print: 3, 4, 5, 7, 12, 17, 18, and 19. Otherwise, a minimum of editorial changes or comments have been made.

When the problem of introductions to the volume was raised, it seemed appropriate to make explicit recognition of the fact that Lashley's scientific contributions have not been limited to the field of psychology. Accordingly, Professor Boring was invited to write one introduction dealing with Lashley's impact on psychology, and Professor Cobb was asked to contribute his views as a neurologist. The fine introductions these two gentlemen graciously prepared enhance the value of the book, and the committee expresses its deepest thanks for all their contributions. It also wishes to thank Miss Anne Christake who assisted in getting together copies of Lashley's papers; Mrs. Murray E. Townsend, office manager of the Yerkes Laboratories, for helping in various ways; and Mrs. Jean S. Morgan for typing and preparing the manuscript for publication. We are also grateful to the various publishers who kindly granted permission to reproduce the articles; specific credit is given at the beginning of each article.

It is hoped that this volume will stand as a modest tribute to Karl S. Lashley, man and scientist, and that it will constitute a useful addition to the scientific literature.

Frank A. Beach
Donald O. Hebb
Clifford T. Morgan
Henry W. Nissen

CONTENTS

INTRODUCTION

LASHLEY AND CORTICAL INTEGRATION
Edwin G. Boring

The mass of evidence . . . shows conclusively that it is the pattern and not the localization of energy on the sense organ that determines its functional effect (29, p. 492).[1]

The alternative to the theory of the preservation of memories by some local synaptic change is the postulate that the neurons are somehow sensitized to react to patterns or combinations of excitation. It is only by such permutations that the limited number of neurons can produce the variety of functions that they carry out. . . . But speculation about this mechanism without direct evidence is likely to be as futile as speculation concerning changes in resistance in the synapse has been. . . .

The conclusion is justified, I believe, . . . that all of the cells of the brain are constantly active and are participating, by a sort of algebraic summation, in every activity. There are no special cells reserved for special memories (29, p. 500).

That was Karl Lashley in 1950, summing up thirty-three years of his own research but perhaps not yet stating the position of contemporary neuropsychology, which is only just beginning to accept this new interpretation for the psychological functions of the cerebral cortex.

Now we may ask, how did Lashley arrive at these views? The answer will emerge if we run quickly through the history of Lashley's thinking from 1917 on, the course of discovery and insight, of which the details are printed in this volume. After that we can enquire into the place of this activity in the history of science.

Lashley's earliest published researches (1912–1916) were done at The Johns Hopkins University under the influence of H. S. Jennings and John B. Watson. They had to do with the instinctive behavior and the learned discriminative behavior of animals. The first two papers (1, 2) in

---

[1] EDITORS' NOTE: The numbers appearing in parentheses in the introductions by Professors Boring and Cobb refer to Lashley's articles as numbered and listed in the Table of Contents. Parenthetical numbers elsewhere refer to the end-of-chapter references.

the present volume treat of unlearned organized behavior and thus provide a setting for what Lashley later had to say about instinct.

In 1917 Lashley became associated with Shepherd Ivory Franz, who was then at St. Elizabeths Hospital in Washington. The line of descent for those who believed in exact cerebral localization in the nineteenth century (1861–1900) may be said to have been Gall, Broca, Fritsch and Hitzig, Ferrier, and Munk, whereas the doubters and negativists were Flourens, Goltz, and presently Franz. Since 1901 Franz had been working on the functions of the mammalian cerebrum by the method of the ablation of parts and had found, among other things, that a lesion in the frontal lobes does not abolish learned behavior unless the destruction of tissue is great, that long-established habits appear to persist in any case, and that habits lost by the extensive destruction of tissue can be relearned. So now in 1917 Lashley seized the opportunity to publish with Franz (5), using the rat, which was destined to become Lashley's favorite subject. They obtained results similar to Franz's earlier ones.

Afterwards Lashley took this problem over from Franz. It was to be his life work. We can follow the development of his thought by citing only the papers printed in this book. First we note the work of 1921 on the visual cortex of rats (7). In these experiments it was found that the visual habits disappeared when the visual area was removed, thus suggesting the existence of a center for vision. Lashley discovered, however, that neither the boundaries nor the disturbances of function were exact. It might be said that an intermediate finding of "inexact localization" was the result. Later Lashley was to know more about this function.

In 1923 he reported the inconstancy of localization in the motor area of the monkey's cortex (10). One day's mapping would no longer be valid on the morrow, yet might be found again at a later time. Presumably remote conditions operate to change the function of a particular spot. In 1924 he found that the retention of motor habits is not dependent on keeping the "motor" area intact (8). In that same year he attacked the generally accepted theory that learning occurs by the lowering of the resistance of the synapses by use (9). In 1926, working with D. A. McCarthy, he showed that neither the learning of the maze habit nor its retention is affected by the destruction of the cerebellum (11). Thus he was tending to establish learning as an *action propre* of the cerebrum as a whole and an *action commune* within the cerebrum in respect of its different parts. These are Flourens' old terms for specific localization and unlocalized function. In 1929 with J. Ball, Lashley showed that the maze habit can persist when the sensory tracts are interrupted by cervical sections of the cord (12). As a consequence he argued that the cerebral organization of the habit must be independent of the excitation of the exteroceptors.

It was at this time (1926 *et seq.*) that Lashley substituted a positive theory for his own and Franz's earlier negatives. He established the concepts of *equipotentiality* and *mass action* to account for the absence of precise or persistent localization of function in the cortex, and he summarized the *status quo* in his *Brain Mechanisms and Intelligence* (1929), a monograph too long to be reprinted in this book. "Equipotentiality of parts," he wrote, is the "capacity of any intact part of a functional area to carry out, with or without reduction in efficiency, the functions that are lost by the destruction" of other parts. This property "is not absolute but is subject to the law of mass action whereby the efficiency of performance of an entire complex function may be reduced in proportion to the extent of the brain injury within an area whose parts are not more specialized for one component of the function than for another" (p. 25). Later he was to be less cautious in reserving the possibilities for specific localization, but this was 1929.

It was now clear that Lashley's experiments were, for the most part, producing evidence to confound nineteenth-century mechanism. Psychology had been caught in the toils of associationistic connectionism. The conception that learning occurs by the association of ideas, a view that goes back to John Locke (1690) and David Hume (1740), was paralleled by the neuron theory (1891), which pictures the brain as a mass of neurons connected by synapses. This similarity of a synapse to an association proved irresistible, but Lashley's experiments denied such simple connectionism and brought him over toward the camp of the gestalt psychologists. In the monograph under discussion we find him raising the question of how simple neural or associative connectionism can possibly account for the fact of perceptual transposition—the response to the relation like the brighter or the larger of a pair and not to the specific related items themselves. During the next two decades the mutual support between Lashley's researches and the experiments of the gestalt psychologists became more and more obvious.

In 1929 Lashley delivered the Presidential Address of the American Psychological Association before the Ninth International Congress of Psychology at New Haven, Connecticut (13). It was called "Basic Neural Mechanisms in Behavior," and in it Lashley cited research and struck out against reflex theory:

> The frantic search for sources of motivation and of emotion in visceral activity, though initiated by introspective analysis, has been supported by the faith that the nervous system is only a conductor having no sources of energy within itself. Our preoccupation with analysis of learning by trial and error, the denial of association by similarity, the belief that the transfer of training can occur only through the training of common synapses—these are the result of the belief that learning is simply a linking together of elementary reflexes. The

doctrine that the intelligent solution of problems results only through random activity and selection, and that intelligence itself is an algebraic sum of multitudinous capacities, is largely a deduction from reflex theory (13, p. 207).

Psychology is today a more fundamental science than neurophysiology. By this I mean that the latter offers few principles from which we may predict or define the normal organization of behavior, whereas the study of psychological processes furnishes a mass of factual material to which the laws of nervous action in behavior must conform (13, p. 207).

It was in 1930 that Lashley invented the technique of the jumping stand for the learning of discrimination by rats (14). Actually the invention, by speeding up discrimination, made possible a discovery that told against connectionism, for it showed that the mere concurrence of stimuli is not adequate to conditioning. What the rat perceives is the total pattern.

In 1933 he discussed at length the integrative functions of the cortex (15). It was now clear that the mind-body problem had come to be integration, not localization. There never was much meaning to localization as a theory anyhow. You assign a function to a spot in the brain, and what then? What does that tell you about how it works? Why is it there? What else might happen if you changed the conditions? It is at best a remnant, not merely of phrenology as Franz said in 1912, but of the philosophy that demanded a seat for the soul. Precision of cortical localization, said Lashley, is much less than was supposed. Specificity is greatest in the visual area, less elsewhere. Then in 1934 he worked out the facts for retinal projection on the visual cortex, a one-to-one correspondence, but even here there was overlap and the specificity was imperfect.

Next Lashley showed (1934) that the rat's visual perception of distance is innately organized and not learned, for rats raised in darkness up to 100 days of age, when trained on the jumping stand, are able at once to adjust the strength of their jumps to the distances to be jumped (17).

In 1935 Lashley again reinforced the theories of equipotentiality and mass action. He found that cerebral lesions do not destroy the latch-box habits of rats although large lesions do retard this kind of learning (18). Now it has been argued that the effect of lesions upon maze learning is not crucial evidence because the maze habit is so complex that we may here be faced with a simple case of vicarious function. The latch-box habit is, however, more conclusive. Lashley was also able at this time to bring under these principles the simple reaction of rats to light: they chose the lighter passage and rejected the darker (19). Not much chance for vicarious function in so simple a reaction as that.

In 1937 he summed up the *status quo* (20). We have to consider that there are fields of force operating in the brain, he said. This is a move of his still further in the direction of gestalt psychology and of field theory, the alternative to connectionism and simple mechanism.

The next year Lashley was found examining the thalamic theory of emotion, Head's notion that the thalamus provides the pleasantness and unpleasantness in emotion (21). He concluded that there is no solid ground for this view. Presumably the thalamus does sometimes have to do with expressive movements, like sham rage, but that is all.

Also in 1938 Lashley turned to an examination of instinctive behavior (23), which, he contended, is plainly a matter of sensory organization that is formed without dependence on stimulus organization. Motivation plays a role in it and the organization may be hormone reinforced.

Next Lashley returned to the problem of the visual cortex, the area that shows the greatest specificity. In 1939 he demonstrated that a very small remnant of the rat's visual cortex, as few as 700 neurons, is sufficient to permit the discrimination of visual figures (24). The visual function is not disturbed provided some bit of the crucial tissue is left, nor does it matter which bit is spared. This finding tells more for equipotentiality than for localization, though it must be admitted that the visual area as a whole does indeed have some slight *action propre*, but not its parts. In 1943 he discovered that the visual cortex is as important in learning a maze as in seeing it, for he found that completely blind rats have difficulty in learning a maze when the visual area has been disturbed (27). The area contributes to an integration that is independent of visual perception, contributes equipotentially with respect to its various parts.

In 1947 we find Lashley discussing the evolution of animal intelligence before the American Society of Naturalists (28). The evolution of mind, he said, consists in increasing the capacity of the organism to discover relations, to form novel integrations, to effect new neural patterns. Field theory thus comes out on top in the developmental hierarchy.

The best summary of Lashley's total contribution is his own "In Search of the Engram," published in 1950 (29). At the beginning of this Introduction, I have quoted from it.

Also in this volume is Lashley's contribution to the Hixon Symposium of 1948, *Cerebral Mechanisms in Behavior*, published in 1951. Lashley called his paper "The Problem of Serial Order in Behavior" (30), and in it he marshaled the evidence that the integrations which determine behavior are structured in time as well as in simultaneity. Long sequences are predetermined as wholes. We have to deal, said Lashley, with "the syntax of action."

So that is Lashley—an integrationist, a field theorist, if you will, and, like the gestalt psychologists, an opponent of mechanism and connectionism. He fits into the continuous course of the history of science and more specifically of neuropsychology. Nevertheless he occupies in scientific history a place of distinction—of great distinction, I should say—for he did so much more than anyone else in this third of a century to bring cerebral neurology away from the neurology that applies at the periphery of the nervous system and to bring it toward a field dynamics of the brain.

Modestly Lashley remarked, in answer to the applause of his distinguished colleagues when they had heard his paper at the Hixon Symposium, that discovery occurs when the times are ripe for it, that the individual investigator is discovery's agent rather than its genius. That is not quite right. Lashley told the naturalists that the capacity to perceive relations does indeed increase with evolution. Just so there are among adult investigators individual differences in the capacity to perceive relations. Lashley, it is true, fits the times, but also he seems to me to lead them. If Newton had not discovered the spectrum, some one else would have done so eventually; yet all honor to Newton who was the first man strong enough to defy assured convention and say that white is complex and not a simple color.

So with Lashley. The major movement is from mechanism to field theory, from *Undverbindungen* to *Gestalten*, from atomism to emergent wholes. The psychologists were caught in atomism and mechanism by their long affiliation with associationism. They are being pulled out now by the gestalt psychologists, although William James (1890) and John Dewey (1896) started them in that direction even before Wertheimer (1912). The neurologists were captured by the improvement of the microscope which revealed so many small structures, by the discovery of the synapse and the establishment of the neuron theory, by the many discoveries that neurons at the body's periphery do indeed act as isolated conductors with sequential linkage at the synapses. Physics went through the same process. Newton's mechanics had eventually to be altered, great as was its power. Field theory starts with Faraday, was established by Clerk Maxwell, passed on through Max Planck to Einstein. When Köhler was asked what person had most influenced his intellectual life when he was a graduate student, he said, of all people, Max Planck. Was gestalt psychology then born of physics? No; remember James and Dewey, and in Germany Ehrenfels, Külpe, and Wertheimer. Nevertheless the new physics and the latest psychology were consistent with each other and with the times, which in the twentieth century were themselves set against the mechanism of the nineteenth. Physics and psychology would seem to have pulled neuropsychology along with them, but all this change needed leaders, and Lashley was certainly a leader, a man with the insight to see new relationships, an organism who had especially benefited by evolution. Or, if he were to insist that he is but an agent and not a creator, then he was the agent of nature, for the impressive thing about the papers in this volume is the way in which discovery leads speculation, not speculation discovery.

A SALUTE FROM NEUROLOGISTS
Stanley Cobb

The professional introduction to these collected papers of Karl S. Lashley has appropriately been written by a psychologist, because Lashley was primarily a psychologist and a leader in the field. But inasmuch as he always had a consuming interest in finding out how the brain works, we can claim him as a neurologist.

In a personal letter written in 1957 commenting on the paper (31) he had written for the Association for Research in Nervous and Mental Diseases in 1956, Lashley said:

The present paper really dates from ideas of 1910, even before I had heard of behaviorism. Queer how early problems persist. As a laboratory boy in zoology in 1907 I found in a box of trash abandoned by J. B. Johnston when he went to Minnesota a series of Golgi stained sections of a frog's brain. I proposed to Reese, his successor, that I work out all the connections among the cells so that we might know how the frog works. It was a shock to learn that the stain is selective, but I have never escaped from the problem.

Yes, it is queer how problems persist, but it is fortunate for mankind when a problem of such importance persists in such a fine mind as Lashley's for over fifty years! In his contribution of 1956 on "Cerebral Organization and Behavior" (31), he summarizes as follows:

As long as mind is thought of as a special kind of being, obeying an all-or-none law in its presence or absence, or as some special type of energy, such as Sherrington sought and failed to find, so long will its relation to the brain be incapable of investigation. Mind is a complex organization held together by interaction of processes and by the time scales of memory, centered about the body image; it has no distinguishing features other than its organization. The mental phenomena must be subjected to an analysis as complete and detailed as that which is being made of neural activities. Only as progress is made in such an analysis and as the picture of the brain's activities is completed, will it be possible to make significant correlations between the two organized systems. Meanwhile, there is no logical or empirical reason for denying the possibility that the correlation may eventually show a complete identity of the two organizations.

In the early days at Johns Hopkins he used to come over to the Phipps Psychiatric Clinic and talk to us informally about the psychological work that he was doing with J. B. Watson. He fascinated us by the breadth of his interest and by his flair for ingenious and adventurous experimentation. He took great pleasure in exploring and living in the field to carry out his work. At about this time he was going to the Tortugas off Florida to study the homing reactions of terns (1). This work on the homing and nesting instincts, of course, brought up many problems which were close to psychiatry, although many of us in psychiatry were not then wise enough to see the connections.

During the next forty years Lashley was to be the psychologist most frequently chosen by neurologists and psychiatrists to come to their meetings to give a paper or to discuss the papers of others. Some of his most important contributions have been presented at these special symposia. Perhaps the best example is the one held at the California Institute of Technology in September, 1948. This was financed and arranged by the Hixon Foundation which brought together such scientists as Halstead, Klüver, Köhler, McCulloch, Von Neumann, and Lashley to consider "Cerebral Mechanisms in Behavior." They gave papers which were discussed by Gerard, Liddell, Lindsley, Lorente de Nó, Neilsen, Weiss, and others. Lashley's contribution was a long paper entitled "The Problem of Serial Order in Behavior," which is included in the present volume (30). His discussions of the papers by the other men were equally important. Perhaps Lashley's most famous contribution at a symposium is "In Search of the Engram" presented before the Society for Experimental Biology in 1949 and published in the society's fourth volume of symposia in 1950. This paper also is included in the present volume (29).

Many neurological and psychiatric societies made use of Lashley as a speaker and contributor to discussions at their meetings. The American Neurological Association made him an honorary member in 1952, and some examples of his great usefulness to this association indicate how much he was appreciated by the clinicians and medical scientists. In 1949 at the American Neurological Association a session was devoted to functional localization in the cerebral cortex. There were contributions from several surgeons,—Ericson and Penfield and Pool—and physiologists such as Wilbur Smith and John Fulton. The papers had to do with new refinements in human cerebral localization, for example, the supplementary motor and sensory areas. Lashley was asked to read the last paper in this group and he produced a masterful, short contribution entitled "The Problem of Interaction of Cerebral Areas." A discussion of his paper was opened by Kurt Goldstein, who spoke from his great clinical experience with head injuries in World War I. He accepted Lashley's point of view saying, "It is clear that we are facing here a problem which is pertinent for the decision whether we are dealing with isolated areas in the cortex which come only secondarily in connection with each other, or whether the cortex functions always in its entirety." Lashley closed the discussion with a remarkable extemporaneous talk showing his intimate knowledge of the anatomy of the human brain as well as the brain of various laboratory animals. He added, "I once went through the entire literature on motor aphasia, trying to get together cases in which I could estimate just roughly the amount of destruction and the severity of the aphasia; the amount of destruction in the third central convolution and the severity of aphasia. In that whole list I got less than eighteen cases which satisfied such very simple requirements and those eighteen cases gave me a correlation of .9 between the extent and severity of symptoms." He went on to discuss the problem of individual variation and concluded by saying that up to that time he had no clue as to what may be the mechanism of integration.

Again at a symposium on "The Brain and the Mind" at the American Neurological Association in June, 1951, papers were read by von Bonin, Magoun, Jasper, Cobb, and Penfield. At the close Lashley was the most important participant in the discussion and gave us a sample of his virtuosity as impromptu speaker. During my paper I had thrown on the screen a short piece of music ("The Sun Shines Bright on my Old Kentucky Home") in order to illustrate the idea that sequence in time was important in integration. Lashley picked this up, whistled the tune as written, and then whistled it backwards, saying:

Both Drs. Cobb and Penfield have stressed the importance of the problem of the temporal organization of behavior. This is, I think, the most fundamental and the most troublesome problem in neurology today. I feel that its solution may be found by studying the translation of temporal orders of action into spatial patterns, and the reverse. It is possible to represent a short temporal sequence in terms of spatial dimensions, to manipulate those dimensions, and by scanning them in various ways, to re-translate them into another temporal pattern. Perhaps I can demonstrate this with Dr. Cobb's little melody. [Dr. Lashley whistled the tune as it was presented on the slide, then whistled it backward.] I think that what must happen in such a case is that the afterdischarge of the sensory excitations persist with a spatial distribution in the brain, which can be scanned by some other mechanism.

I am less impressed with the analogies between various machines and neural activity, such as are discussed in *Cybernetics*. There has been a curious parallel in the histories of neurological theories and of paranoid delusional systems. In Mesmer's day the paranoid was persecuted by malicious animal magnetism, his successors by galvanic shocks, by the telegraph, by radio, and by radar, keeping their delusional systems up to date with the latest fashions in physics. Descartes was impressed by the hydraulic figures in the royal gardens and developed a hydraulic theory of the action of the brain. We have since had telephone theories, electrical field theories, and now theories based on the computing machines and automatic rudders. I suggest that we are more likely to find out how the brain works by studying the brain itself and the phenomena of behavior than by indulging in far-fetched physical analogies. The similarities in such comparisons are the product of an oversimplification of the problems of behavior. . . .

Finally, I should like to speak a word of warning against the present tendency to ascribe very complex functions to the thalamus and brain stem. These are regions of relatively few cells and poorly developed internuncial systems. . . .

It should be a fundamental principle of neural interpretation of psychological functions that the nervous activities are as complex as the psychological activities which they constitute. . . .

Many incidents like these when put together make a picture of Lashley as seen by his medical confreres: the wiry, enthusiastic youth of 1917 with many exciting expeditions and intellectual explorations ahead of him; the forty years of his challenging and helpful appearances by invitation at our neurological and psychiatric meetings; and most recently the mature formulations of the great problems common to his field and ours.

And so, in paying Karl Lashley our homage, we claim at least a tithe of his work for neurology!

1. NOTES ON THE NESTING ACTIVITIES
OF THE NODDY AND SOOTY TERNS[1]

ORIENTATION IN THE NEST LOCALITY

In the report of his extensive studies of the activities of the noddy and sooty terns Watson raises the question of the method by which the birds recognize their nests and young and records the results of a few experiments bearing upon the problem. The terns breed in great numbers upon Bird Key, an island in the Tortugas group somewhat less than 5 acres in area. Their nests, of which there were more than 10,000 in 1908, are in many cases closely crowded together, as many as 30 sooty nests being found in an area of 100 square feet, and the nests and eggs are almost indistinguishable to the human observer. Indeed, the island suggests a city of 10,000 houses, all much alike, unnumbered and set down at random, without streets or definite landmarks. The birds choose their own nests, without error, from among hundreds of similar ones, and under normal conditions never show the slightest hesitation in making their choice.

In testing the sensory factors involved in nest recognition, Watson found that he might change the appearance of the nest and egg without disturbing the birds in the least. Very great changes in the appearance of objects near the nest did not alter the quickness and accuracy of orientation. When, however, the slightest alteration was made in the horizontal position of the nest, when it was moved only a few inches to one side, the birds were much confused, refused to occupy the nest in its new position, and reacted positively to the original nest site even when no trace of the original nest remained. . . .

In view of the remarkable ability of the terns to return to their nests from great distances the problem of the sensory factors involved in their recognition of the nest locality and orientation in the neighborhood of Bird Key becomes of considerable importance as offering a possible aid to the understanding of more distant orientation.

[1] EDITORS' NOTE: From *Carnegie Instn. Publ.*, 1915, 7 (211), 61–83. Reproduced by permission of Carnegie Institution of Washington. The work reported here was done under the auspices of the marine biological laboratory of the Carnegie Institution of Washington.

At the suggestion of Professor Watson I attempted to gain further evidence upon the problem of proximate orientation in the terns during a six weeks' residence on Bird Key. The work has not furnished any clue to the mechanism of distant orientation, but the details of the birds' behavior in finding and recognizing their nests seem worth recording as exemplifying the extremely complicated habit-systems which wild animals may develop under a normal environment, and, also, as showing that, whatever the mechanism of distant orientation may be, proximate orientation is readily explainable in terms of visual and kinesthetic habits. . . .

Detailed descriptions of the nests and eggs have been given by previous writers, and the following brief notes are included only for the sake of a clearer presentation of the experimental control of orientation.[2]

The nest of the sooty consists usually of a shallow depression in the sand, of about the depth and diameter of a large saucer. The birds hollow it out by a sort of wallowing movement, turning around and around and pushing the sand away with their breasts. In this depression a single egg is laid. Rarely two eggs are found in a single nest, but whether both are laid by a single bird, or one is stolen from a neighboring nest, is uncertain. . . . The nests of the noddies are loose masses of sticks piled among the branches of the low shrubs which cover the greater part of the island. They are frequently lined with bits of coral and shells, and, like the nests of the sooties, rarely contain more than a single egg.

The key upon which the nests are built is roughly triangular, about 500 yards in length and half as broad. . . . Its greatest elevation is not more than 6 feet. The key was formerly overgrown thickly with bay cedars, but the greater number of these were killed by the hurricane of 1910 and only a few living cedars remain, for the most part near the center and western end of the key. These grow to a height of 5 feet and make many irregularities in the profile of the key which are probably important as landmarks for the birds. Where the bay cedars have been washed out the sand is covered by low fleshy herbs resembling the common tumble-weed. At the beginning of the nesting season large numbers of these weeds were torn up and piled along the beach to give the sooties nesting space in the center of the island.

At the western end of the island are some buildings, the warden's house and the old detention hospital, which are the most conspicuous objects upon the island. The group of buildings is about 50 feet in length and has a maximum height of 15 feet. Three cocoanut palms . . . grow near the buildings. The buildings, the palms, the clumps of bay cedars, and the piles of brush along the beach present extremely complex visual stimuli to

---

[2] EDITORS' NOTE: Several drawings and photographs have been omitted from this selection primarily because of difficulties in reproducing them. References to figures have been edited and renumbered accordingly.

the birds coming home from sea. Even at the most isolated nests the environment presents a countless number of possible visual stimuli and it is never practicable to control more than a very few of the stimuli which may be potent factors in the birds' orientation. Long-continued study of a single nest is prevented by the fact that the birds soon become hopelessly confused by the changing conditions of the experiment and cease to react definitely to the nest or nest environment. The situation at every nest presents a distinct problem and in no case has it been possible to reconstruct the entire process of reorientation from the data obtained at a single nest. The relation between particular stimuli and the orientation of different birds has been determined, and a combination of the results of observations at many nests gives a fairly complete picture of the mechanism of orientation in the immediate neighborhood of the keys. The experiments recorded in the following pages are typical of a large number carried out at other nests and will serve to illustrate the chief phases in the recognition of the nest and nest site.

EXPERIMENTS WITH SOOTIES

Recognition of the Nest Site

The sooties become accustomed to the experimenter's presence very quickly and often become so tame as to interfere seriously with the experiments, refusing to be driven more than a few feet from the nest. After they have been disturbed a few times their return to the nest is very prompt . . . [see Table 1.1].

Table 1.1. Average Time of Six Brooding Sooty Terns to Return to Nest after Being Driven Off *

Trial	Time, sec.
1	56
2	25
3	30
4	18
5	12

* Title supplied by editors.

The accompanying table gives the time elapsing from the moment when the brooding sooty was driven from the nest until it had again covered the egg. The time given is based upon the average of 6 birds during 5 successive trials at intervals of 5 minutes. The average time which a tame sooty requires to rise from the nest, fly 15 or 20 yards and return, is 12 seconds. This is not appreciably changed by the substitution of a strange egg for the one in the nest, or by the filling in or remodeling of the nest by the experimenter, so long as the egg remains in nearly its original position. A very slight change in the lateral position of the egg, however, causes a very great increase in the time required by the bird to return to the nest and begin to brood the egg. In adjusting to such changes the sooties show a very accurate localization of the original position of the nest, even when all traces of it have been completely obliterated. The following notes give a description of a typical instance of adjustment to a lateral displacement of the egg.

Experiment 1. 10:50 A.M. I drove a sooty from her nest, obliterated the nest, and made a new one with a noddy egg in the same place. In 1 minute the bird returned and in 2 minutes covered the egg, after driving away two trespassers.

10:53 A.M. I obliterated the old nest and made a new one, 1 foot south of the first position. The bird alighted at the old nest and turned around as if to adjust the egg. She then caught sight of the egg in its new position and went over to the new nest, then returned to the old one. She then made 4 more trips back and forth between the new nest and the original nest site, and finally settled down at the latter, hollowing out the sand to form a shallow nest. After a minute she went to the egg, adjusted it, and settled down on it. Another sooty attacked her and she drew back from the egg without defending it, looking back to the old nest site. She next went to the old nest, then back to the egg, which she covered for 30 seconds. After one more trip to the old nest she seemed reconciled to the egg in the new position. The total time required for this readjustment was 10 minutes.

11:05 A.M. I drove her away again. She returned in 1 minute, alighted between the first nest position and the new one, went first to the egg, then to the old nest site, then back to brood the egg. Two minutes later she paid a brief visit to the old nest.

11:10 A.M. Driven away again, the bird alighted near the old nest site and ran directly to the egg. After 30 seconds she visited the old nest site, and again after 2 minutes. She was driven away 6 times during the next half hour and at the end of this time showed an almost perfect adjustment to the changed conditions, returning to the egg in 15 seconds. The egg was then returned to its original position. The bird accepted it at once and paid not the slightest attention to the new nest which she had just been occupying.

In this case the substitution of noddy egg and artificial nest for the original egg and nest did not affect the bird's reaction in the least.

Experiment 2. In another case the egg was taken from a nest, a piece of black cloth 3 feet square was spread over the nest, and the egg was replaced on top of the cloth. The bird alighted in a few seconds and walked immediately to the edge of the cloth. It showed a good bit of hesitation in stepping on the cloth, and walked around it, looking at the egg for many seconds. In less than a minute, however, it ventured upon the cloth, seemed to lose all fear immediately, ran to the egg and covered it contentedly. The total time required for adjustment to the new situation was less than a minute.

Other instances of similar indifference to the appearance of the nest
and egg are recorded in later experiments and make it clear that, except
under unusual conditions, the individual characters of the nest and egg do
not play any important part in orientation. The birds react positively to
any nest at the chosen site. In contrast to this the birds are almost always
very greatly disturbed by a lateral displacement of the nest of only a few
inches and react to the original nest site much as did the bird described
in experiment 1. The time required for readjustment to such slight
changes varies greatly with different birds, even under quite similar
conditions.

Experiment 3. The same birds whose average time of adjustment to disturbance is given . . . [in Table 1.1] were used for a comparison of the times
of adjustment to a change of position of the nest. The nests were similarly
located in open, rather thickly populated areas, but so far apart that no two
of the birds under observation were disturbed at the same time. In each case
the nest was obliterated, a new nest was constructed 1 foot from the old nest

Table 1.2. Time Required for Each of Six Brooding Sooty Terns to Return to
a New Nest Site after Being Driven Off *

No. of trial	Time in seconds					
	Bird no. 1	Bird no. 2	Bird no. 3	Bird no. 4	Bird no. 5	Bird no. 6
1	240	480	300	†	30	100
2	15	60	270		20	100
3	120	240	30		90	50
4	150	120	40		‡	50
5	15	65	55			40
6	50	75	30			20
7	15	300	36			30
8	10	90				50
9	10	30				40
10	15	30				

* Title supplied by editors.
† Did not find egg in half an hour.
‡ Undisturbed by change.

site in the direction most free from other nests, and the egg was placed in this
artificial nest. The birds were allowed to find the new nest and settle down
quietly over the egg each time before being frightened away again. Table 1.2
shows the time required for each bird to readjust to the new situation. The
birds were driven away at intervals of 5 or more minutes.

In each case but one the birds were greatly confused by the change in the position of the nest and all showed a tendency to settle down at the original nest site. As it was clear that the nest itself was not the stimulus to the localization of this area, an attempt was made to control the immediate surroundings of the nest. The following experiments with objects near the nest give some insight into the mechanism of nest recognition:

Experiment 4.[3] . . . It was found [in this experiment] that recognition of a nest is to some extent dependent upon the relative positions of the nest and other objects in the neighborhood, in this case an artificial nest. Other factors not brought out by the experiment seem, however, to play a still more important part in orientation. The constant alighting place and path to the nest furnish a clue to other factors in orientation which appear more strikingly in other experiments.

Experiment 5. A nest in an open space near a short stake was obliterated and replaced by two nests a foot apart. The bird chose the northern egg. Both eggs were moved a foot to the northward. The bird alighted and chose the northern egg without hesitation. Her mate came and covered the southern one. Both were driven off. The first returned and alighted at a place four feet to the eastward, then walked for three feet straight toward the original position of the nest. When still a foot away she seemed to catch sight of the eggs in the new position, turned sharply from her course, and went straight to the northern egg. She soon became dissatisfied, went back to her alighting place, and returned to the northern nest, but this time directly. She then went to the southern nest, returned to the northern and covered the egg. Her mate came back and again took the southern nest.

Both nests were again moved, with the stake, 2 feet to the northward. The first bird alighted as usual near the bushes, walked to the original nest site, looked about, and went directly to the new southern nest. Her mate came and walked about the old nest site. She got up and went to him, and then returned to the nest.

The stake was then moved back to its first position, the nests being left undisturbed in the northern position. The first bird came to her alighting place and started directly to the new site, then seemed to catch sight of the stake and turned toward it, then back to the alighting place, toward the stake, back again to the alighting place, then finally to the new nest. The path followed . . . shows clearly the struggle between the motives offered by the sight of the stake and that of the egg. . . .

This series of observations offers several interesting points:

(a) In comparison with the sooties in crowded localities, the bird under observation showed a remarkable plasticity. Attempts to duplicate the experiment in crowded districts failed completely.

---

[3] EDITORS' NOTE: Details of this experiment have been omitted.

(b) The constancy of the place at which the bird alighted is very striking. How this place was recognized could not be determined, but it was near an open place in the bushes which offered many more visual criteria than did the immediate surroundings of the nest. The certainty with which the direction was taken from this position to the nest is also unexplained. It was to a certain extent independent of the appearance of the immediate vicinity of the nest. The question of orientation from the alighting place will be taken up later.

(c) The relative force of the egg and stake in determining behavior gives some insight into the bird's habits with respect to the nest environment. The stake had been planted two weeks before to mark the site of another nest, at that time destroyed. In 2 weeks it came to occupy an important place in the bird's recognition of her nest, perhaps taking the place of the obliterated nest in her system of habits. That it was not the fundamental factor in locating the nest is shown by the fact that after a few failures to reach the nest by going to the stake the bird paid little further attention to the latter.

Experiment 6. A nest in a rather crowded area was chosen for this experiment. It was 8 inches north of a stake which had been planted a week before to mark another nest, and near the center of a triangle the northern side of which was formed by a line of very dense weeds, the western by a very dense clump of weeds and the stem of a palm leaf, the southern side being open. . . . I drove the bird from the nest—she circled above the island and came back immediately, alighted 6 feet to the eastward of the nest, and walked almost straight to it. . . . This was repeated twice, her path in returning being each time the same.

The stake was by far the most conspicuous object near the nest, and to test its effect upon the bird's reaction I moved it from its position south of the nest to an equal distance north of the nest. I also constructed a new nest, north of the stake. . . . The relation between this nest and the stake was now the same as the relation of the [old] nest . . . and the stake had been before the change. The bird's own egg was placed in the [new] nest and a strange egg was placed in [the old nest]. The bird returned by the path [formerly taken] and took its own nest . . . after some hesitation. The change in the position of the stake was a disturbing factor, but was not sufficient to determine the choice of nests.

The line of weeds forming the northern boundary of the triangle was next moved a foot to the northward. The bird returned by its customary path without the slightest hesitation. This landmark played no part whatever in orientation. . . .

The weeds to the northward were cleared away and the [old] nest was moved 18 inches to the northward of [the new nest]. The leaf and weeds were likewise shifted to the northward, so that the original relations of the nest and two objects were now duplicated, nearly 3 feet from the original position. The bird returned and covered the southern egg; 3 minutes later she got up, went to the new [formerly old] nest, adjusted the egg, and covered it. I watched her for half an hour longer, during which time she remained contentedly on the nest, which she occupied during the whole of the following day.

From this . . . account it is clear that the final orientation was determined wholly by the visual stimulus of two objects in the neighborhood of the nest. Neither the palm leaf nor the clump of weeds alone was sufficient to determine the choice of the nest, but both together called forth a definite reaction, regardless of all other objects in the vicinity.

Watson found that considerable changes could be made in the vertical position of the nest without affecting the bird's reaction in the slightest. His experiments have been repeated, but always with negative results. The following notes illustrate the type of reaction obtained:

Experiment 7. A nest near that described in experiment 5 was placed in a pan of sand, 1 foot square and 2 inches deep, so that it was raised 2 inches above its former level. The owner of the nest always alighted 6 feet to the eastward and walked by a somewhat zigzag path to the nest. When the pan of sand was first put in place she approached, walked around it, and inspected it carefully. She next stooped, peered about in all directions, then stepped up to the higher level. She did not cover the egg, but walked about in the pan and finally backed over the edge and fell out. She spent some time standing near the pan, then stepped up on it again, and after 8 minutes covered the egg. Half an hour later she was driven away. She returned at once, spent 2 minutes in preening her feathers, then stepped up into the pan, and covered the egg immediately.

The pan was next raised to a height of 6 inches from the ground. The bird returned to her alighting place, walked toward the pan, hesitated, walked around it several times, but made no attempt in half an hour to get up on it. With the pan in this position she could not see the egg from the ground. The pan was then lowered to a height of 4 inches. The bird came from her alighting place to the pan, climbed into it with difficulty, putting one foot in it and fluttering up, and covered the egg in 2 minutes. The nest was left in this position until the following day, when the experiment was resumed. The bird was then driven off several times and each time returned to her usual alighting place, walked to the edge of the pan, then fluttered up to the egg. The nest was raised to 5 inches and was taken immediately. It was next raised to a foot from the ground. The bird walked around it for 5 minutes before flying up and covering the egg. It was left in this position for an hour and was then raised to a height of 2 feet. The bird returned to her alighting place, walked to the foot of the post supporting the nest, and seemed very much puzzled by the new condition. She walked round and round the post, looking up at the nest, but in 10 minutes made no attempt to fly up to the pan. The pan was lowered to 6 inches and was occupied immediately. . . .

[Sometime] later the same bird was upon the nest. The egg had hatched in the meantime. The pan was raised to the top of a post 2 feet above the ground. The bird walked around the post for half an hour without seeming to look up at all. She then flew away and was not seen for the remainder of the day. The next day she was again in the nest. When driven off she returned and alighted directly upon the nest.

The pan was raised to a height of 5 feet. The bird came to the ground and walked around under the pan for several minutes, looking up. Then came the most interesting part of her entire series of reactions. She flew up to a height of 2 feet and went through the motions of alighting just as though the pan was still at this height, then dropped back to the ground. She repeated this five times in exactly the same way, then walked about for a few minutes, looking up, and finally flew up to the pan and covered the nestling. She was frightened away again, returned to the ground, and flew up to the pan immediately.

This experiment brings out three facts quite clearly. First, adjustment to changes in the height of the nest is not made any more readily than to changes in the horizontal position. Second, shifting the nest along the pathway toward the alighting place disturbs the birds less than a change in the position of the nest in any other direction. Third, there is a strong tendency to replace visual motor reactions by habits based upon kinesthesia, resulting in reactions like those shown by the rat in an adjustable maze.

Clearly, in all these experiments the birds were influenced to some extent in the recognition of their nests by visual objects in the immediate neighborhood. Such objects were other nests, debris which had been in place since the nest was made, and objects recently added to the situation. It appears that long-familiar objects influence more than those added after the laying of the egg. The birds pay more attention to the nests of others than to any other class of objects.

In the case of some other nests, particularly those in crowded areas, I could find nothing in the immediate neighborhood of the nest which seemed to influence the birds' orientation. At one time a nest was shifted 1 foot from its original position and practically every object within a radius of 3 feet was moved for the same distance in the same direction. The sand in this area was smoothed out to change its appearance. Thus the original environment was duplicated with 1 foot lateral displacement. The bird came back to the position of the original nest, now completely obliterated, and gave nearly the same set of reactions as that of the bird described in experiment 1. In this case the recognition of the nest locality was upon the basis of some other stimulus than that provided by the immediate environment. The same was in part true of the nests described in experiments 4 and 5.

The Alighting Place

The clue to the method of orientation in such cases is given by the behavior of the bird described in experiment 5 in passing from her alighting place to the nest. It seemed that this bird took its direction from some

objects at the alighting place and depended upon this place for reorientation when confused by changes in the position of the nest. The following
observations bring out the importance of the alighting place and the path
from this to the nest.

Experiment 8. At the edge of the beach two piles of brush were thrown together in such a way as to leave a small overarched passage extending half way
through between the piles and opening on the beach to the westward. A pair
of sooties had their nest at the inner end of this passage. The bird studied
alighted always at the southern end of the brush pile, where there was another
nest, and then followed the western side of the pile to the opening of the nest.
The path was complicated by a dead bay-cedar branch, which projected from
the face of the pile and forced the bird to stoop and turn out to the left. The
bird was seen to follow this path accurately in five successive trips to the nest.
I broke off the branch and removed it, leaving a clear path. On the next two
trips to the nest the bird went through exactly the same movements of stooping
and turning out which had been required by the presence of the dead
branch. . . .
The path was then blocked by piling brush [where the bay-cedar branch
had been]. The bird alighted [as usual], started along the path, came to the
pile of brush, and seemed to be completely lost. She wandered about for a
long time and finally came to [another] nest at the other end of the brush
pile. She crawled into the brush and inspected this nest, then turned and scur-
ried around to her own nest as fast as she could run. The nest at [the end of the
brush pile], like that at [the beginning of the path], served as a landmark.

Under normal conditions a nest near the alighting place furnished the
bird a clue to the direction of its own nest and the path to the latter was
followed almost wholly by a series of kinesthetic-motor habits. The bird
was able to reorient from other visual stimuli when the usual method was
prevented.

Experiment 9. An isolated nest upon the beach, just at the foot of a steep
sand bank covered with dead bay-cedar bushes, was chosen for observation.
. . . The brooding bird was driven off several times and her return noted. She
never alighted upon the beach, but always upon the top of the bank, among
other nests, at a distance of more than 8 feet from her own. From this point
she walked to her nest, following a winding path about 12 feet in length. . . .
Moving the nest along the bank at a distance of 2 feet in either direction did
not seem to affect the bird's behavior in the least. A piece of canvas was placed
against the face of the bank so as to cover the bird's path from the top to the
foot. . . . The bird returned, seemed frightened, but in 5 minutes alighted
and walked upon the canvas. She started down the bank in the right direction,
but became confused as soon as she got upon the canvas, and returned to her
usual alighting place. She made several more false starts, became accustomed
to the canvas, and walked upon it without hesitation, but never walked the
full distance to the foot of the bank. . . . After a great number of failures she

finally reached the foot of the bank, seemingly by chance, half an hour after the canvas was placed in position, and from this place she followed her customary path to the nest. An hour later she was driven from the nest (she probably made many trips to and from it during the interval). She returned to her original alighting place at the top of the bank and flew from it across the canvas to the foot of the bank, then walked to the nest.

In this case the alighting place was far from the nest. Blocking the path between the alighting place and the nest was sufficient to destroy orientation. The immediate neighborhood of the nest was reached by chance, but was recognized at once. Readjustment to the changes in the path followed very quickly.

From many observations I am convinced that practically every sooty has a special alighting place and path which is invariably followed in the return to the nest under normal conditions. In some cases the path seems unaccountably complicated. . . .

In many cases it is evident that after orientation is gained the path to the nest is determined largely by motor habits irrespective of the immediate visual stimuli. Little direct evidence upon the recognition of the alighting place has been gained, and the attempt to trace back orientation beyond this point must be postponed until data from experiments with noddies has been presented.

EXPERIMENTS WITH NODDIES

The Nest and the Perch

As in the case of the sooties, Watson found that the noddies locate their nests readily when the appearance of the surroundings has been completely altered and that the substitution of an artificial nest and egg for the originals does not disturb the birds in the least. He found also that very slight changes in the position of the nest confuse the noddies and that after such changes the birds still react positively to the old nest site. The nests of the noddies are always built upon the bay cedars and any great change in the appearance of the nest and environment involves not only a great deal of labor but also the destruction of many other nests. For this reason no great number of experiments upon the nest recognition of the noddies were carried out. Such experiments as the following, together with a large number of observations upon the flight of the birds to their nests, give, however, a fairly complete picture of the mechanism of orientation.

Experiment 10. A pair of noddies had built their nest in a dead cedar bush near the smaller of [two] palm trees. When both birds were at the nest, one or the other was always seen to be perched on the middle row of a low leaf of the palm. The nest was torn from its position and fastened on top of a stake,

3 feet farther from the perch than its original position. At this time only one bird was present at the nest. It was frightened away and did not return for some minutes after the change was effected. It was first identified again as it hovered over the old nest site. Thence it flew to the perch, then back to the first position of the nest. This was repeated several times.

Without paying the least attention to the nest [on the stake], the bird flew to the large palm, circled close around its stem and darted back to the perch. Without alighting here it turned and dropped quickly to the bushes where the nest had been. This was repeated many times until it seemed quite certain that sight of the large palm furnished the clue to the position of the perch and that the change in direction of flight from the perch to the nest was effected largely in terms of kinesthesia.

Three points were brought out by these observations. First, the existence of a well-localized perch corresponding to the alighting place of the sooty; second, the use of other very conspicuous objects (in this case, the large palm) as points from which orientation is gained; third, the importance of kinesthetic-motor habits even in determining the direction of flight. The perch seemed to be recognized partly by its appearance and partly by its relation to the neighboring palm tree.

Experiment 11.[4] . . . The method by which the noddies recognize their nests is very similar to that of the sooties, the only difference being the manner of approaching the nest—in the one case by flying, in the other by walking. The perch has for the noddies much the same relation to the nest as the alighting place has for the sooties. Recognition of the noddy perch seems to be partly in visual terms, partly in the relation of the perch to other very conspicuous visual objects, such as the palm in experiment 10.

Destruction of both the alighting place and nest gave no very definite results. In one instance the birds flew back and forth along the edge of a row of bushes in which the nest and perch had been located, and made swift flights out around a number of tall stakes which had been planted to mark other nests. In almost every instance the destruction of the perch and removal of the nest brought out some antecedent factor in orientation, such as the stakes mentioned above, but these factors were so widely distributed and varied as to be practically beyond experimental control.

Orientation in Approaching the Island

In the two experiments recorded it seems clear that the birds gained their first orientation from the visual stimulus afforded by the palm trees and buildings, and from a large number of observations I feel certain that all the birds, on approaching the island, determine their direction with

---

[4] EDITORS' NOTE: The description of experiment 11 has been omitted.

all animals, vision tends to be replaced by kinesthesia as habits become
~~ked~~, but the process is relatively slow and plays no great part in orien-
~~.tion~~.

~~R~~ECOGNITION OF THE YOUNG

Closely related to the problem of orientation and recognition of the
~~n~~est in the terns is that of the recognition of the young, and in this respect
~~t~~he two species show much greater differences than in nest recognition.
~~T~~he noddies do not distinguish their own young from other young noddies
~~a~~nd I have been unable to discover any difference in their active behavior
~~t~~oward either strange noddy or sooty young.

Experiment 12. I placed a sooty chick, 24 hours old, in the nest of a noddy,
~~t~~aking out the noddy egg which was just hatching. The noddy came back to
~~t~~he nest and covered the young sooty immediately. I watched the nest at fre-
~~q~~uent intervals throughout the day. The noddy brooded the young sooty con-
~~s~~tantly, but was not seen to feed it. On the second and third days the noddies
continued on the nest, but were not seen to feed the sooty, which on the third
day was considerably smaller than other chicks of the same age. On the fourth
day, when the noddies were driven from the nest, the chick was found dead,
apparently from starvation. Another sooty chick, 4 days old, was placed in the
nest. The noddies continued to brood it for 3 days. On the fourth day the
chick was dead and the noddies had abandoned the nest.

The noddies accept sooty chicks in exchange for their own young of
any age, as was determined by a number of such substitutions. In no case,
however, was a noddy seen to feed a young sooty. Apparently the peculiar
behavior of the young noddy is required to call out from the adult the
instinctive act of regurgitation and feeding.

Experiment 13. Two 2-day-old noddy chicks were placed in a nest which
already contained a 3-day chick. One of the younger chicks was white, the
other black. The older chick was black. The adult noddy returned and covered
the three chicks immediately. The nest was observed regularly for 15 days,
when the work was interrupted by heavy storms. The three young chicks were
fed by the single pair of adults and throve as well as chicks which were alone in
the other nests. On the eleventh day one of the chicks disappeared. The others
were still in the nest when observations were interrupted.

During the first days after the hatching of the egg the noddies do not
distinguish their own young from those of other birds and react to them
only because of their presence in the nest. On the fourteenth day, or
earlier, the young noddies leave the nest and lie hidden in the bushes
during the day. In the evening they are fed, returning to the nest to meet
their parents. Watson states that at this time the noddies distinguish
their own young. I have no clear evidence upon this subject, but it seems

respect to the more prominent visual features of buil
bushes. The paths followed by the birds coming in from
the best evidence of this. . . .

When the birds are frightened they run from their ne
air, and fly against the wind until they reach a height
feet, then turn quickly and fly with the wind until well a
land. If not badly frightened, they turn when 20 to 200 y
the island, and fly back rapidly against the wind to tl
nest. Birds in open areas may be kept in sight constantly
and time and time again are seen to follow the same path
nest. The great majority of birds in short flight return b
pathways. . . . [These] lead directly to the chief nestin
preponderance of birds following them may be due sim
In each case, however, the path is near a conspicuous
buildings and opening in the bushes), and the birds fre
their direction of flight after passing [this]. . . . It seems
that these prominent visual objects are the directing factors
tion of the birds when approaching the island.

Summary of Work on Nest Recognition

The general method by which the birds reach their
summarized as follows: Coming in from the sea, they dir
by the more conspicuous features of the island, the buildir
bushes, etc. From these the direction is taken along the
the edge of the cleared nesting area to the alighting plac
offers prominent visual stimuli. From this the path to the ne
either by a series of visual-motor habits built up around
debris, etc., or by a series of kinesthetic-motor habits irresp
ternal stimuli. Study of orientation at night is practically im
because of the difficulty of identifying the birds and, chiefl
their increased timidity. During the breeding season, howeve
are never so dark as to render the chief landmarks invisible a
and, with direction gained from these, the birds' kinesthetic-
are adequate for further orientation.

The study of orientation in the nest locality has given no
dence upon the method of orientation at greater distances fr
but it does furnish two negative points of some importance.
nest locality the birds are dependent upon visual and kinest
for orientation and show no evidence whatever of the posses
special sense of locality, such as a magnetic sense, functional v
flights. Second, kinesthetic-motor habits are formed with no su
as to suggest that the birds can retrace a path by memory of its
directions and distances when these have been experienced onl

probable that, as in the case of the sooties, the recognition is rather due to a dovetailing of the habits of parents and young than to a visual or auditory recognition.

Unlike the noddies, the sooties give prompt reaction both to the appearance of the chicks and to the number of chicks in the nest. They will not usually accept noddies under any circumstances. In one instance a sooty which had been given a noddy egg hatched it and brooded the chick for a few hours in the morning, but in the evening both adult and chick were gone. Usually where a young noddy is placed in a sooty nest the old bird throws it out and drives it far away into the bushes. The reaction is to the visual stimulus, and is purely instinctive, as is shown by such results as the following:

Experiment 14. (a) I interchanged a sooty egg, just ready to hatch, and a 24-hour chick. The parent of the egg accepted the chick immediately. The other hesitated in covering the egg, looked about, walked to and fro for several minutes, and finally settled down upon the nest.

(b) I replaced a pipped sooty egg with a noddy. The sooties attacked the young noddy and drove it from the nest. A third sooty from another nest came and helped in the attack and I was forced to interfere to save the chick's life.

Such reactions are by no means invariable. A sooty will sometimes refuse to accept a sooty chick in exchange for its egg or again will fail for some minutes to notice the presence of a young noddy in its nest; but in general the different appearance of the chicks of the two species calls out different instinctive behavior in the adult sooties.

The greatest variation in the behavior of the adult sooties occurs in their reaction to strange chicks of their own species. Ordinarily they do not distinguish between their own young and other sooty chicks of about the same age during the first few days after hatching.

Experiment 15. I placed a 3-day chick in a nest with another of the same age. The parent returned to the ground near the nest, rushed forward and threw out the nearest chick (her own), drove him into the bushes, then walked back and covered the other. I placed the abandoned chick in the nest with another of about the same age. One of the parents of this chick returned and accepted both young. Three days later both chicks were still in the nest.

Chicks from 1 to 4 days of age may almost always be interchanged without inducing any marked change in their parents. Many such exchanges were made and almost without exception the changelings were adopted without hesitation. Until the age of 4 days the sooty chicks are not recognized individually by their parents. At about that age a change takes place in the behavior of the young sooty. Before this time it feigns death when attacked by the adult birds or when removed from the nest to strange surroundings. On the fourth or fifth day it becomes much more active, attempts to crawl out of the nest and hide in the bushes at the experimenter's approach, and attempts to run away when attacked in the open by older sooties. After the age of 10 days it spends most of the daylight hours lying hidden among the weeds and bushes near the nest and comes out only in the evening to receive food from the parents. With its increasing activity it seems to form a set of habits with respect to its nest very similar to those of the adult birds. In its own nest it lies quiet when attacked by strange adults, which happens frequently, for the sooty rarely misses an opportunity to take a sly dig at her neighbor's chick; but outside its own nest the chick, after the fourth day, scrambles away actively when attacked. This seems to furnish the first criterion by which the adults recognize their own young.

Experiment 16. (*a*) I interchanged a 1-day and 6-day chick. The parents at both nests were much disturbed, refused to cover their nests, and poked the young ones with their beaks. The younger chick lay still in her nest and after a short time seemed to have been adopted. The older chick started to run away and was immediately attacked savagely and driven away among the bushes.

(*b*) I exchanged a 3-day chick and a 5-day chick. The younger bird was accepted immediately by the parents of the other. They did not seem to note the change. When the adults returned to the other nest the 5-day chick ran away. They attacked it at once and drove it away to a distance of 4 feet, where it received so much abuse it gave up and refused to run further, feigning death. I returned it to the nest. The adults examined it and pushed it away roughly. This time it lay quite motionless, however, and the older birds, after driving away a trespasser, adopted it.

The tendency of these chicks to run away from the strange nests no doubt determined the parents' final action toward them. In the first experiment recorded here, the difference in the appearance of the chicks, differing in age by 5 days, was sufficient to cause some disturbance in the behavior of the parents, but was not great enough alone to cause the rejection of the chick.

On the seventh or eighth day after the eggs hatched, the birds began to distinguish their own chicks from younger or older ones by their appearance alone.

Experiment 17. (*a*) A 2-day chick was placed in a nest instead of a 7-day chick which belonged there. The adults pulled it out of the nest and forced it to crawl away. It was immediately adopted by a bird whose nest had been robbed of a young chick upon the previous day.

(*b*) A 1-day chick was placed in a nest instead of an 8-day chick. The parent of the 8-day chick returned and refused to cover the nest for 10 minutes. She continually pecked at the chick although not savagely. When she showed a tendency to leave the nest, I replaced the young bird with one 3 days old. The parent returned, pecked the chick, and when it started to run away, attacked it furiously. Her own chick was replaced and accepted at once. After a time I substituted a 10-day chick for this one. It was attacked and driven away at once.

The parent sooty here seemed to distinguish its own young, 8 days old, from 1-, 3-, and 10-day chicks which were substituted for it. But the recognition at this time is by no means certain, as is shown in the following observations:

Experiment 18. A 6-day-old chick and a young egg were interchanged. The parent of the egg drove the chick away immediately. The nest from which the chick was taken was under a clump of bushes. The owner of the nest examined the egg, came out from under the bushes, went back and covered the egg, then came out again. She began to show an interest in the cries of her chick, which was being abused by the egg parent about 3 feet away. She went over and defended the chick, and finally covered it, about 4 feet from her own nest. . . .

I placed a chick a very little larger than [a] 5-day chick in the nest under the bushes and a 5-day chick in the egg nest again. The parent started to defend her own chick in a half-hearted manner, caught sight of the chick in the nest, went to it and covered it. A moment later she drove it out of the nest and stood for 5 minutes in the empty nest. I put both chicks in her nest. She pecked the larger, but as it did not run away she covered both.

Half an hour later both chicks were still in the nest. I placed the strange one in the egg nest, where it was promptly attacked. Its foster mother paid no attention to it, but went to her own chick and nest. I interchanged the chicks. She rushed to defend her chick, covered it, and paid no further attention to her own nest.

The reactions of this adult bird are rather conflicting and hard to interpret, as is true, indeed, of much of the behavior of the birds in tests upon recognition of the young. Seemingly, there is here the beginning of recognition of the chick, based in part upon its appearance, in part upon its "feel" in the nest, its cries, and its reactions to the parent. None of these alone seems sufficient to form the basis of an absolutely positive recognition, and it is probable that the conflicting behavior of the bird is due to the imperfect integration of some such groups of impulses as the following:

(a) Positive reaction to the appearance of the nest and its contents, and to the nest locality.

(b) Disturbance of this caused by the changed appearance of the young and leading to greater sensitivity to other stimuli.

(c) Positive reaction to feel of chick in the nest; this likewise disturbed by the substitution of the larger chick.

(d) Positive reactions to the cries of the chick.

(e) Defending reaction to the situation, chick attacked by adult.

(f) This defending reaction is established as a habit which temporarily exceeds even (a) in force.

All these factors are apparent in the activities of this bird and stand out more or less clearly in the reactions of most of the sooties to their own and to other young. Recognition of the young at this stage thus appears to be the result, in part, of the pattern of visual and tactual stimuli offered by the chick; in part, of the behavior of the chick in the nest region (experiment 16). Complete recognition is the result of a complex of many sensory-motor reactions, not merely of a single type of stimulus. . . .

Watson has shown that when the appearance of adult birds is completely altered, as by painting their breasts and heads with brilliant colors, they are at first rejected by their mates, but this rejection is not permanent and the disfigured birds are finally accepted by their mates by reason of their persistence in their normal activities in the region of their nests. The "recognition" through the interrelation of habits overcomes the disturbance produced by the changed visual situation. For the recognition of the young, the same complex of reactions must be established. The visual stimulus provided by the young at the nest calls out the normal brooding activities. A slight change in the appearance of the young interrupts the normal series of activities and leads to trial movements. If the situation remains otherwise unchanged—if the behavior of the young gives the customary series of stimuli—the changed appearance comes to be disregarded.

INSTINCT AND HABIT IN THE NESTING ACTIVITIES

Modifiability of Instinctive Activities

The activities of the birds centering around the nest during the breeding season may be roughly divided into mating, selection of the nest site, construction of the nest, laying, incubation, and rearing of the young. During each of these periods a special group of instinctive acts is called into play and the behavior of the birds is modified quite suddenly at the transition from one period to the next, as in the sudden appearance of the constant brooding activities after the egg is laid. Watson found that birds which are quite timid become aggressive as soon as the egg is laid and either refuse to be driven from the nest or attack intruders actively. . . .

I have obtained a small amount of evidence bearing upon this question, but the data are fragmentary and a great deal more time may be spent profitably upon this particular aspect of behavior. Owing to the lateness of the season when the work was begun no observations were obtained upon mating or the construction of the nest.

Experiment 19. After some difficulty a newly completed noddy nest was found. The building activities of the owners had almost ceased, but no egg had been laid and one bird was perched on a dead limb near the nest and the other was not in the neighborhood. A noddy egg was placed in the nest. This was early in the morning. No change in the activity of the bird at the nest was observed during the day. It disappeared occasionally, but did not show any reaction to the egg. The mate was not seen.

On the following morning a bird was found brooding the egg. Its mate was on the dead limb near by. When I approached both birds defended the nest, the one on the perch flying into the air and striking at me, the sitter refusing to leave the nest. I caught the latter and marked it with a spot of paint. The marked bird was occupying the nest when it was observed later in the day.

On the third day only the unmarked bird was seen at the nest. It spent the day sitting on the perch or on the edge of the nest, paying no attention to the egg.

On the fourth day the marked bird was again observed at the nest. Both birds were upon the nest, the marked one brooding the egg, the other standing on the edge of the nest. Both flew up at my approach. The marked bird returned immediately and covered the egg. The unmarked one returned, hovered about for a short time without alighting, and then flew out to sea.

On the following day the marked bird was observed on the perch. At this time the unmarked bird was on the nest over the egg. For as long as I watched, this bird did not assume the brooding position, but stood upright and turned about, moved to the edge of the nest, and flew away rapidly when disturbed, thus showing the behavior of the layer rather than of the sitter.

The marked bird was on the nest for the greater part of the sixth day. The unmarked bird was seen on the edge of the nest, but did not cover the egg.

On the seventh day a second egg had been deposited and the unmarked bird spent the day in brooding the eggs. After this time the birds seemed to take turns regularly in brooding the eggs.

In this case it seems clear that only one of the birds was stimulated to the brooding phase of activity by the sight of the egg. The other retained almost wholly the behavior of the layer up to the time when the second egg was deposited. There can be little doubt that this second bird was a female, that the stimulus in the case of the male was purely visual and tactual, while in the case of the female the act of laying was necessary before the brooding phase could appear.

It is generally stated by the natives of the region that the sooty will lay a second egg if the first is taken from the nest. I was unable to verify this. The eggs were taken from ten nests and in no case was a second egg deposited; the nests were all abandoned after a few days. However, none of these nests was less than a week old, and it is possible that the loss of the egg at an early period may serve as a stimulus to further oviposition.

An attempt was made to find out how long incubation might be interrupted by removal of the egg without leading to the abandonment of the nest. Eggs were taken from a number of nests and returned at regular intervals, from 0 hours to 4 days. Brooding activities were resumed by the birds after 4 days. The experiment had to be interrupted here because of stormy weather.[5] From rough observations, however, I believe that after a week's interruption the birds will not resume incubation. The time is certainly less than the time required for the loss of the brooding instinct of birds in captivity, as might be expected from the greater opportunity which free birds have to form new habits toward the colony.

After the hatching of the egg the parental instinct seems to be even more dependent upon the stimulus of the chick in the nest. In some cases nests in which the chicks were removed seemed to be wholly abandoned after 48 hours.

The second marked change in the behavior of the nesting birds occurs at the hatching of the eggs. The incubation period of the noddies is given by Watson as 32 to 35 days, that of the sooties as 26 days. I made attempts to shorten and to lengthen the time required for incubation in order to test the extent to which intraorganic factors are concerned in the changes from incubation to brooding activities. The experiments are very unsatisfactory, chiefly because the age of very few nests was known.

Substitution of young chicks for noddy eggs of any age was not followed by any marked change in the behavior of the adult birds. They were never seen to attack the chicks, but I could not determine how soon such chicks are fed. It seems certain, however, that the incubation period of the noddy may be shortened by at least one-fourth without serious interference from an intraorganic rhythm.

Attempts to shorten the incubation time of the sooties have not been carried out fully, but there is more evidence that the length of the incubation period is determined, to some extent, by internal factors. Parents whose eggs are less than two weeks old will not adopt young chicks. The data at hand are not conclusive beyond this point. Adults whose eggs are pipped will sometimes refuse to accept young birds in exchange for them, but usually during the last week of incubation such changes may be made without difficulty.

The period of incubation may be also lengthened to some extent, but this differs in different birds and its limit was not determined.

In some 10 nests younger eggs were substituted for pipped ones. After 2 days one of the nests was abandoned. During the following 5 days 6 of the eggs hatched. The remaining birds were still sitting at the end of 77 days, when observations had to be discontinued.

A dead egg was substituted for a pipped one, somewhat earlier in the

---

[5] Experimental work with the colony was made almost impossible during the last 10 days of June, at a time when the young birds were in the most interesting stage of development. High winds and heavy rains, with a considerable lowering of the temperature, made it advisable to disturb the colony as little as possible, as the birds frightened up from the ground were instantly blown far out to sea and at times could not regain the island for hours.

season. Upon the following day it was found that the parents had adopted a 3-day-old chick and were brooding both it and the egg.

This observation and the abandonment of the single nest in the other experiment suggest that the length of the incubation period is conditioned by an internal rhythm, which does not determine, however, an exact period of 26 days, but permits a range of variation of 2 weeks or more around this period.

Integration of Complex Habits

Two of the most striking features in the colonial life and behavior of the terns are the enormous number of habits which they exhibit and the disconnected, impulsive character of their activities. The number of habits involved in the process of orientation has been illustrated in the earlier experiments. By the time that the experimental work had been carried far enough to give an insight into the mechanism of orientation the eggs were laid and the birds had been reacting to the situation at the nest for some weeks. Hence there was little opportunity for such study of the formation of the habit complexes. In general, as might be expected in a colonial bird, the most definite and firmly established reactions are associated with other birds or their nests. The chief landmarks used by many sooties for the final location of their nests are the nests of their neighbors, and it is apparent that the presence of these neighbors, defending their nest areas, tends to give a greater stimulating value to the nests. The birds whose nests were in very crowded areas showed a much lower plasticity in adapting to changed conditions than those whose nests were somewhat isolated, hesitating to occupy nests only a few inches from their own nest sites and offering little defense of such nests against trespassers. The behavior of the birds suggests that in the early part of the nesting season exchanges of nests must be of relatively frequent occurrence. An interesting example of the diffidence of the birds in appropriating new nests is given in the following:

Two sooty nests, 18 inches apart, were obliterated and both eggs were placed in a new nest half way between them. The parents of both eggs returned to their nest sites, missed the eggs, and began to look about for them. One caught sight of the eggs in the new nest and covered them. The other at once drove her off and took the nest. The first, after standing for a few moments at her nest, returned to the new nest and drove off the second. This was repeated several times, the bird occupying the nest offering little resistance to the attacks of the other but returning fiercely to the attack after a visit to her own empty nest. Finally one bird rolled an egg back to its nest and both settled down contentedly.

In small matters, such as changes of a few inches in the position of the nest, changes in the appearance of the egg, young, or nest, the habits of the birds may be quite readily modified, but this seems to hold true only within certain limits. Many attempts were made to shift nests to the edge of the beach with the purpose of transferring them to rafts in the hope of ultimately transplanting a part of the colony to other keys, but however slowly such shifts were made (6 inches or so per day) the nests were either abandoned when moved 4 feet or less from their original position, or the eggs were rolled back as fast as they could be moved forward.

NOTE: This moving of the egg back to the original position of the nest has been mentioned before in connection with other experiments. It might seem to involve very complex processes, memory of the relative position of the egg and nest and an attempt to restore their relation. I watched the entire procedure in a dozen or more instances and believe that there is little implicit behavior involved in it. The bird, returning to the empty nest, misses the egg, looks about, and catches sight of it a few inches away. She starts toward it rapidly, but goes more and more slowly as she approaches, sometimes turning back before reaching it. Perhaps after several such hesitating starts she gets close to the egg, stops as soon as she can reach it with her beak and rolls it back under her body. In this way the egg is moved for 2 or 3 inches at each trip from the old nest site to the egg. That it is moved in the direction of the old nest site seems to be the result of the fact that the bird always faces away from the latter as she approaches the egg. There is no real evidence of implicit behavior in this case, even of a delayed reaction in which orientation is held as the egg is moved.

In all its activities, where reaction to a new situation is involved the behavior of the birds has a peculiarly impulsive character. One group of stimuli seems to gain momentary control and determine the bird's reaction in spite of contradictory elements in the situation as a whole. If a chick is taken from its nest and put down among strange adults they are at once attracted by its cries and crowd around it. Several of them attack it and immediately others rush forward to defend it. The fight becomes general and may give the chick a chance to escape. After a time some of the adults are driven away and leave the victors to strut about. If one of these catches sight of the chick, he attacks it and the fight is soon renewed. I have seen the same bird alternately attack and defend a chick through a number of fights; the sight of the strange chick calls out movements of attack; the sight of an adult attacking a chick calls for defense of the chick. Young chicks, when attacked by adults, either feign death or sprawl about helplessly, without being able to escape. In the latter case they sometimes force their way under the body of the adult. When this happens it practically always produces a marked change in the behavior of the adult bird. His aggressive attitude drops away suddenly, he shuffles about for an instant, looks down at the chick, tucks it under him with his beak, and assumes the brooding position. If he is at some distance from his nest his brooding reaction is of short duration; he soon grows restless, gets up and turns around several times, and finally returns and attacks the chick with renewed savagery.

The same lack of coordination in reactions to complex situations is seen in the choice between two nests, in the reorientation in the path to the nest, and in the reaction to changes in the appearance of the path. The reactions are to separate groups of stimuli and there is clearly no analysis of the situation as a whole. The birds do what a man would only consider doing under like circumstances; that is, they carry out in overt activity many of the same processes which in man are restricted to the language mechanism. In subjective terms, they show little or no evidence of "ideational processes" in their activities.

2. INHERITANCE IN THE ASEXUAL REPRODUCTION OF HYDRA VIRIDIS[1]

Do heritable variations commonly occur among the offspring of a single individual multiplying asexually? May selection among such offspring produce strains differing in hereditary characters? The investigation here resumed is designed to contribute data toward the answer to these much debated questions.

A number of specimens of *Hydra viridis,* taken at random from wild populations, gave rise by asexual reproduction to clones differing from one another in their average number of tentacles and in other characters. As a test of whether such differences are the result of internal factors or of environmental differences two clones were bred in large numbers for a period of five months, during which time the members of the two clones were kept under environmental conditions as nearly as possible the same. Each polyp was kept in a separate culture dish and food was distributed uniformly to all. The number of tentacles was recorded at the time when the polyps began their independent life after separation from the parents (the initial number of tentacles), and records were kept, also, of changes in the number of tentacles of parents.

The two clones kept under parallel conditions gave the following results. The average number of tentacles of 1,353 members of one clone (A) bred during the first three months was 6.463 ± 0.013; the average number of tentacles of 1,395 members of the other (D) was 5.793 ± 0.011; the difference between these averages is 0.724 ± 0.017. At the end of three months a single polyp was taken from each clone and used to found another clone. The average number of tentacles of the subordinate clone obtained in this way from clone A was 6.907 ± 0.026; that of the clone derived from D was 5.844 ± 0.029; the difference is $1.063 \pm$

[1] EDITORS' NOTE: From *Proc. nat. Acad. Sci.,* Wash., 1915, 1, 298–301. Reproduced by permission of the National Academy of Sciences. Presented to the Academy, March 17, 1915. From the zoological laboratory, the Johns Hopkins University.

24

0.039, in the same direction as before. At different times during the history of the clones the number of tentacles of the buds fluctuated considerably, but the difference between the averages of the buds produced at the same time by the two remained fairly constant. The minimum difference in any one week of cultivation was 0.449 ± 0.042, the maximum difference, 1.063 ± 0.039. Small groups of polyps from the two clones were kept in mass cultures under partly controlled environmental conditions, such as reduced food supply. Under such conditions the difference persisted so long as the two clones were kept under the same environment.

These clones differed in other respects besides the average number of tentacles. The polyps of clone A were, on the average, more than twice as large as those of clone D, the average for the two being: A = 0.869 ± 0.021 cu. mm; D = 0.322 ± 0.022 cu. mm; the average difference is 0.547 ± 0.023 cu. mm. Polyps of clone A began to produce buds at an average age of 3.74 ± 0.074 days, those of clone D at 4.81 ± 0.10 days, a difference of 1.06 ± 0.13 days in the average age at reproductive maturity.

At no time during their history did the two clones show an identity of characters. There were no constant differences in the environmental conditions under which they were cultivated and it is certain that the differences between the clones were the result of some internal factors. The clones represented hereditarily diverse races. Other diverse races showing somewhat less well marked differences have been found and seem to be of rather frequent occurrence in wild populations. No direct evidence upon the origin of such diverse races or their relation to sexual reproduction has been obtained.

The inheritance of variations in the number of tentacles within the clone was studied by statistical methods and by the continued selection of variates. A comparison of the variations in the initial number of tentacles of parent and offspring by the use of the coefficient of correlation shows no significant resemblance between parent and offspring. The coefficients obtained are such as the following:

No. of parents	No. of offspring	Coefficient of correlation
251	1395	0.0038 ± 0.018
78	439	−0.0342 ± 0.032
164	859	0.0011 ± 0.023
28	204	0.0314 ± 0.047
18	153	−0.2420 ± 0.051
51	154	−0.0750 ± 0.054

As is well known, the number of tentacles of Hydra changes during the life of the individual. When the number of tentacles of each bud is compared with the number borne by the parent at the time when the bud was produced there is a slight correlation in the variations of parent and offspring. For the first clone recorded above this is 0.096 ± 0.016. There is also a slight positive correlation in the variations of the buds produced by a single parent, as is shown by the following:

No. of pairings	Fraternal coefficient of correlation
12099	0.161 ± 0.004
10766	0.077 ± 0.006

A study of the relation of variations in the number of tentacles to environmental changes shows that unfavorable conditions tend to reduce, or to prevent increase in, the number of tentacles of parents and at the same time lead to a reduction in the number of tentacles of the offspring of these parents. Thus, wherever diversities of environment occur in cultures of Hydra there should be produced a likeness between parent and offspring that is not the result of heredity. To test this, the period of cultivation of the two clones giving the above fraternal correlations was divided arbitrarily into five-day periods and the buds produced within each of these periods were compared. From this comparison it appears that unrelated buds produced under like conditions of cultivation resemble each other as much as do the offspring from a single parent. The coefficients of correlation between the unrelated buds produced at the same time were:

No. of pairings	Coefficient of correlation
95141	0.0774 ± 0.0015
101872	0.1313 ± 0.0014

It thus appears that the slight resemblance found between parent and offspring and between members of the same fraternity within the clone may be due either to an inheritance of variations or to the like action of environment upon individuals produced at nearly the same time. Statistical methods do not suffice to distinguish between the two possibilities.

Twenty-five variates from a single clone were selected for seven or more tentacles, and twenty-five for six or less, the mean of the clone lying between six and seven. Selection was continued for six or more generations. At the end of this time records were kept of all buds produced by the last selected generation. Those produced by parents from the series selected for few tentacles were found to have somewhat fewer tentacles than those from parents of the other series, but the difference appeared only in the first six buds and did not persist in the later buds produced by the same parents. The average number of tentacles of the first six and of later buds produced by the last selected generation is shown in the following table:

Buds of the Last Selected Generation

	Average of all	First six	Later buds
Selected for many tentacles	6.695 ± 0.023	6.677 ± 0.029	6.712 ± 0.030
Selected for few tentacles	6.605 ± 0.026	6.460 ± 0.034	6.782 ± 0.037
Difference	0.090 ± 0.035	0.217 ± 0.044	−0.070 ± 0.047

Continued selection at first seemed to have produced a change in the hereditary character of the two groups but this did not persist even through a single generation. Complete regression appeared as soon as the polyps reached maturity.

An almost identical result was obtained in an earlier experiment on the effects of injury. Polyps which had regenerated the mouth and tentacles showed a marked reduction in the number of tentacles of the buds which they produced immediately after regeneration, but the average number of tentacles of successive buds formed after regeneration increased until at the end of two weeks, when four to eight buds had been produced, the polyps had returned to the normal condition of the clone from which they were derived.

The similarity of these results makes it certain that the only effect of selection was a temporary change in the vigor of the selected polyps (the selection of individuals with few tentacles involving the selection of weaker polyps) and that there is no cumulative inheritance of variations in the number of tentacles within the clone. Races of Hydra differing in their hereditary number of tentacles exist but individual variations do not involve changes in the hereditary constitution of such races.

Some evidence that the same conclusions apply to the inheritance of size was obtained, but the relation of variations in size to environmental changes has not been investigated thoroughly.

3. REFLEX SECRETION OF THE HUMAN PAROTID GLAND [1]

Discovery of the importance of internal secretions for physiological psychology is leading to a widespread interest in the conditions governing secretion. The difficulties of studying the activity of the ductless glands in man are at present almost insurmountable and their relation to the nervous mechanism and to the changing habit systems of the individual must be judged largely from the conditions in other animals or from analogy with such glands as can be studied directly in man. In an earlier paper I have summarized the work which has been done upon the reflex secretion of the human salivary glands and outlined the problems of psychology which a study of human salivary reactions may help to solve. The chief interest of these glandular reactions for psychology lies in the complex nature of some stimuli to secretion and in the formation of conditioned reflexes (habits of secretion). Before a study of these complex activities can be undertaken it is necessary that we have a fairly complete knowledge of the simpler stimuli influencing secretion. The existing studies of unconditioned secretion in man are too incomplete to give this and are, hence, inadequate as a foundation for work upon conditioned reflexes. The experiments reported in the following pages were undertaken in preparation for a study of the relation of secretion to the more complex activities of the individual and have been directed, primarily, toward the discovery of the stimuli which may influence the secretion of the parotid gland directly or indirectly. While the data obtained are largely physiological, some of the reactions observed seem to rival the complexities of the language mechanism and place the topic of reflex secretion very near the border line between the sciences of physiology and psychology.

For suggestions concerning the general plan of the work I am indebted to Professor J. B. Watson. In many of the tests, also, in which more than one observer was required and in those in which I have acted as subject he has given generously of his time in conducting the experiments.

[1] EDITORS' NOTE: From *J. exp. Psychol.*, 1916, 1, 461–493. Reproduced by permission of the American Psychological Association. From the department of psychology, the Johns Hopkins University.

Technique

The only method of obtaining the secretion of the parotid gland in normal human subjects that has been used by physiologists is that of draining off the saliva from a small canula inserted into the mouth of Stenson's duct. As Orⁿstein (12) states, this method is not very suitable for quantitative work for the reason that one never can be sure that some of the secretion is not leaking past the canula. The expanding walls of the duct also frequently let the canula slip out. A few tests with small canulas quickly convinced me that the method is not practicable for long-continued work.

Finally the instrument shown in Fig. 3.1 was devised and has proved quite satisfactory for the study of the secretion of the parotid gland. It consists of a metal disc 18 mm. in diameter in which two concentric chambers, a and b, are cut. The inner of these is 10 mm. in diameter and 3 mm. deep; the outer, in the form of a circular groove, is 2 mm. wide and 3 mm. in depth. The two

Fig. 3.1. Drainage tube used for collecting the secretion from Stenson's duct.

chambers open through the back of the disc into two separate tubes, c and d, of about 2 mm. bore and 15 cm. length. The tubes are of silver, soft-drawn for greater flexibility, and the disc is heavily silver-plated. In use, the instrument is placed against the inner surface of the cheek so that the central chamber covers the mouth of Stenson's duct and the air is exhausted from the outer chamber by a suction pump, when the disc clings tightly to the cheek. The saliva is free to flow into the central chamber and thence through the tube, c, to a suitable measuring device, without constriction of the duct or unusual resistance. When the mouth is closed the tubes lie between the cheek and the upper molars and pass out through the corner of the mouth. The instrument interferes little with talking or eating and may be worn for several hours without discomfort.

For the submaxillary glands a slight modification of the instrument has proved fairly useful. In this the tubes are directed at right angles to the surface of the disc and are bent sharply to pass over the lower incisors. The close proximity of the mouths of Wharton's ducts to the mandible makes it necessary to have the central chamber eccentric so that the suction chamber is reduced to a width of 0.5 mm. on the side next to the mandible. The ducts of the two submaxillary glands open so close together that both must be covered by the instrument and their secretions can not be obtained separately. The great sensitivity of the mucosa of this region and the necessity for depressing the tongue in swallowing make this instrument less satisfactory than that for the parotid.

Various methods of recording the quantity of secretion have been tried, but for the present work the mere counting of the drops as they fall from the drainage tube has seemed sufficiently accurate. The drops vary in size with changes in the rate of secretion and the viscosity of the saliva. With the drainage tube used in the greater part of the work the size of the drops varies from a minimum of 0.06 c.c. to a maximum of 0.07 c.c. with extreme changes in the viscosity of the secretion. For more detailed study of the quantitative relations of the secretion than has been undertaken here measurements of both the quantity and chemical composition of the saliva will be necessary.

The Normal Rate of Secretion of the Parotid

Before the rate of secretion of the parotid in the absence of extero-stimulation can be determined the stimulating effect of the method of collecting the saliva must be tested. Where a fistula exists, such stimulation is improbable but where a canula or suction cup is placed in the mouth some excitatory effect is to be expected. The effect of mechanical stimulation from the drainage tube can be tested only indirectly; and excitation from the suction cup described earlier seems ruled out by the following facts: (a) The presence of a large glass rod or other tasteless object in the cheek with the drainage tube does not increase the rate of secretion. (b) Mechanical stimulation of the cheek and gums, where not covered by the drainage tube, does not call out reflex secretion until it becomes strong enough to excite reflex avoiding movements. (c) Manipulation of the drainage tube after adjustment, while it may force out a few drops of secretion from the receiving chamber, does not increase the rate of secretion as measured in successive minutes. From this evidence it seems safe to conclude that the secretion collected from the drainage tube represents fairly the normal secretion of the gland.

To determine the variation in secretion under conditions of as little stimulation as possible I have tested a number of subjects in a quiet state, computing the rate of secretion from a half hour's observation during which the flow remained fairly constant. Measurements were made at different hours in order to control, to some extent, the enteric stimuli. In each case the subject remained quiet, with mouth closed, but without inhibition of the swallowing reflex or of movements adjusting the position of the body. The results of the tests are summarized in Table 3.1. The children tested give a secretion considerably less than the average for adults. The great amount of individual variation makes it impossible to be certain of the sex differences noted by Tuczek (15).

The data shown in the table can not be considered as showing the rate of secretion in the absence of stimulation. Marked extraorganic stimulation is lacking but the gland is subject to almost constant stimulation from the receptors of the mouth and throat. Table 3.2 shows the variations in the rate of secretion in a subject remaining quiet for twenty minutes and partially inhibiting the swallowing reflex. Swallowing is seen to result in an accelerated flow,

Table 3.1. Rate of Secretion of the Left Parotid Gland without
Extero-stimulation

Subject		Secretion, c.c. per hour	Condition of test
Age	Sex		
26	♂	3.81	11:30 A.M. No food for 12 hours
		7.74	1:00 P.M. After lunch
35	♂	1.47	12:00 A.M. Before lunch
		1.98	1:00 P.M. After lunch
38	♂	3.47	1:30 P.M. Under alcohol
		3.24	11:30 A.M. Before lunch
		6.98	2:00 P.M. After lunch
24	♂	1.90	9:00 A.M. No breakfast
		1.30	5:00 P.M. Before dinner
		3.00	7:00 P.M. After dinner
25	♀	0.39	11:30 A.M. Before lunch
		0.65	1:30 P.M. After lunch
		1.19	10:00 A.M. Two weeks later
27	♀	4.64	12:00 Before lunch
		6.60	1:00 P.M. After lunch
8	♂	0.60	3:30 P.M.
12	♀	0.43	4:00 P.M.

persisting for some minutes, and movements of the body also seem to have a slight stimulating effect.[2]

In some subjects, when particularly quiet, the activity of the parotid may cease completely for five or more minutes. Whether this is due to the absence of stimulation or to some inhibitory process is difficult to determine. The data upon paralytic secretion show that after destruction of its nerve supply the submaxillary gland continues to secrete for some months until it finally degenerates. Bradford (4) failed to obtain this paralytic secretion from the parotid in dogs whence it seems that in the absence of stimulation the parotid does not secrete. No observations on man after section of the nerve supply of these glands are available.

The Relative Activity of the Two Parotid Glands. Colin (8) states that in the ruminants the parotid glands function alternatively, not only when food is being chewed on one side of the mouth but even in the absence of food. In man, for the most part, the glands secrete equally and simultaneously. Drainage tubes were placed over both of Stenson's ducts and the subject was allowed to remain without extero-stimulation for fifteen minutes. The average number of drops per minute secreted by the two

[2] From the tests reported later in this paper it seems probable that the apparent excitatory effect of shifting the position really acts by removing the inhibitory effect of muscular tension.

Table 3.2. Variations in the Rate of Secretion Due to Swallowing

Drop	Time *	Drop	Time *	Drop	Time *	Drop	Time *
1		13	60	25	80	35	55
2	4	14	73	26	120	36	145
3	4	15	152	27	185	37	155
4	9	16	135	28	215	38	155
5	13	17	173	29	209	39	110
6	10	18	204	Shifted position		40	67
7	10	19	125			Swallowed	
8	15	Swallowed		30	88	41	15
Sucked cheeks		20	7	Swallowed		42	15
9	10	21	4	31	19	43	56
10	20	22	16	32	14	44	67
11	31	23	30	33	30	45	83
12	39	24	38	34	20	46	172

* The figures represent the time in seconds intervening between the formation of successive drops. The rapid rate at first is the result of an acid stimulus given to make sure that the instrument was properly adjusted.

glands was: right parotid 1.92; left parotid 1.92 drops. The quantity of secretion from the two glands was thus almost exactly the same (the ratio in the size of the drops from the two drainage tubes being as 49 to 50) and the variations in rate were the same for both. Table 3.3 shows the relative reactions of the two glands to various stimuli. The reactions of the left seem to be somewhat more vigorous than those of the right, which accords with the fact that the subject habitually chews on the left. Bilateral stimulation affects both glands equally. Stimulation of one side of the mouth stimulates the gland of that side to a greater extent than the other. Each gland seems to be most intimately associated with the receptors of its own side.

Reflex Secretion to Stimulation of the Mouth

The direct reflex of the parotid seems to be excited only by stimulation of the receptors within the digestive tract, chiefly those within the mouth. A number of diverse stimuli applied here will excite the reaction and the chief problems are concerned with the distribution of sensitive areas and the quantitative relations of the secretion.

Thermal Sensitivity. Wulfson,[3] Popielski (14), and Brunacci (5) have raised the question of the excitability of the parotid by thermal stimuli. The work of the latter shows excitability only by temperatures above 55 and below 15 degrees Centigrade. These results are confirmed by the following results of my own.

[3] Cited from Babkin (2).

Table 3.3. A Comparison of the Activity of the Right and Left Parotid Glands *

Stimulus	Total secretion in drops		Time required for the secretion recorded, min.
	Right	Left	
No stimulation	29	29	15
Chewing tasteless cube:			
Between incisors	13	16	2
Between right molars	15	6	2
Between left molars	4	19	2
Between right and left molars	14	17	2
Sodium chloride, 10% solution:			
Uniformly distributed	18	20	2
In right cheek	6	6	1
In left cheek	8	8	1
Hydrochloric acid, 2.50%:			
On right side of tongue	19	12	1
On left side of tongue	12	30	1
In right cheek	15	7	1
In left cheek	4	12	1
Uniformly distributed	19	21	1
Tongue scraped with pointed rod:			
Right side	6	3	1
Left side	6	10	1

* The ratio of size of the drops from the right and left sides is 49 to 50.

The subject, L, whose normal rate of secretion from the left parotid during experiments is about 1 drop per minute, was required to take three sips of water (about 10 c.c.) in quick succession at each of the following temperatures. The number of drops secreted during the three minutes following stimulation was recorded as follows:

Temperature of water, degrees	*Drops of saliva*
66	13
61	10
55	6
52	7
41	5
36.5	7
25	7
18	7
13	10
10	8
0	10

Increased secretion above that resulting from mechanical stimulation of the mucosa appears only with temperatures above 55 and below 18 degrees. These are well beyond the limits determined by Head and Sherren (9) for protopathic sensation and suggest the absence of any direct reflex connection between the thermal receptors of the mouth and the parotid glands.

Mechanical Sensitivity. Mechanical stimulation of the oral mucosa is considered by most investigators to be an efficient excitant of parotid secretion. A careful test of this without interfering stimuli and with the possibility of conditioned reflexes reduced has failed to confirm this view. Table 3.4 shows the reflex secretion from the left parotid gland obtained from two subjects after mechanical stimulation of the mouth. Stimulation of restricted areas of the mucosa is seen to have little effect except at the back of the tongue and soft palate, where nausea is produced. Some summation of stimuli is apparent in stimulation of the tip of the tongue with a stiff brush, the individual bristles of which gave less violent stimulation than the sharp points of the dividers. In general it seems that very little reflex secretion is obtained from the parotid in response to mechanical stimuli.

The Effects of Chewing. The experimental literature shows little agreement as to the excitatory effects of chewing movements upon the parotid and no one has attempted an analysis of the relative influence of the different end organs stimulated when some solid object is chewed. A few tests of the effects of chewing convinced me that the adequate stimulus is more complex than any of the previous workers has suggested. A series of experiments was made to distinguish the elements in the constellation of stimuli involved in chewing that are effective in exciting secretion. The tests are summarized in Table 3.5. From the data in this and the preceding table the following conclusions seem justified: (*a*) Contractions of the muscles of the mandible or changes in the tension of its ligaments do not excite secretion. (*b*) Pressure on the teeth is, alone, not an effective stimulus. (*c*) No amount of mechanical stimulation of the mucosa excites as much secretion as light contraction of the teeth upon a foreign object. Chewing does not excite secretion solely by stimulation of the mucosa. (*d*) Combined mechanical stimulation of the tongue and pressure on the teeth are not so effective as less violent stimulation of the same sort when some object is held between the teeth. (*e*) Active secretion is excited by the presence of a foreign object held between the teeth.

The reaction seems to be to the total situation rather than to any simple stimulus. The following observation is especially difficult to explain as a reaction to a simple stimulus. With lips drawn back and tongue depressed the subject apposed the first pair of incisors on the left and continued strong rhythmic con-

Table 3.4. Reactions to Mechanical Stimulation of the Oral Mucosa [*]

Subject	Stimulus	Secretion	
		Before stimulation	During stimulation
H	Blunt glass rod rubbed against:		
	Lower lip	0	0
	Tip of tongue	0	0
	Side and back of tongue	1	1
	[Side and back of tongue] with tongue-movements	0	1
	Soft palate	1	2
L	(Stimulus applied for 30 seconds)		
	Blunt ivory rod rubbed against:		
	Lips	3	2
	Tip of tongue	2	5
	Middle of tongue	2	5
	Back of tongue	2	12
	Gums at right	2	5
	Hard palate	2	8
	Soft palate (nausea)	2	13
	Stimulation with points of dividers:		
	Lips	2	2
	Tip of tongue	2	3
	Middle of tongue	2	5
	Hard palate	2	5
	Stimulation with stiff brush:		
	Tip of tongue	3	7
	Middle of tongue	2	9
	Stimulation with tasteless cube:		
	Lower surface of tongue	2	3
	Rubbed violently between tongue and left molars	2	5
	Between tongue and hard palate	2	4
	Stimulation with 1 c.c. of fine sand rubbed between tongue and hard palate	3	8

[*] The effect of the stimulus is shown by the increase in secretion between the minute before and the minute during stimulation.

tractions of the masseters for two minutes, exerting considerable pressure on the teeth and breathing the while through the nose. In the two minutes preceding these movements 3 drops of saliva were secreted; in the two minutes during chewing 4 drops. A disc of hard rubber 2 mm. in thickness was then placed between the same two incisors without contact with the lips or tongue and the

Table 3.5. Experiments on the Stimulus from Chewing [*]

Stimulus	Secretion			
	Before stimulation, min.		During stimulation, min.	
	1	2	1	2
Chewing movements with contact on normal facets	3	3	3	3
Chewing without contact between teeth	4	5	4	5
Rhythmic contraction of masseters, mouth closed	4	3	3	3
Chewing movements with contact on unused facets	3	3	3	3
Tongue chewed violently between left molars	3	2	10	2
Tongue chewed violently between right molars	3	2	5	2
Foreign object in the mouth (For stimulation of mucosa see Table 3.4)				
Hard rubber cube held lightly between second molars on left	1	1	5	1
Same, [except] gripped tightly	2	2	10	2
Same, [except] chewed lightly	4	1	13	1
Same, [except] chewed violently	2	2	38	2

[*] The stimulus was continued in each case for one minute. The total number of drops secreted by the left parotid during and after stimulation until the rate returned to normal was found: For comparison the number of drops secreted during an equal time before stimulation is given. The tongue was depressed and unstimulated except where noted.

chewing rhythm was renewed with the same strength as before. In the two minutes preceding chewing 4 drops of saliva were secreted; in the two minutes during chewing 13 drops. The stimuli added to the local situation by the hard rubber disc were first, tactile, from the particular type of mechanical stimulation transmitted through the teeth, and second, kinesthetic, from the slightly greater separation of the jaws by the disc. The last is ruled out by further tests with discs of different thickness, to all of which the gland secreted equally. It is not possible to distinguish between the elements of the tactile stimulation at present. Irregular and varying pressure on the teeth is not alone an effective stimulus. The stimulus to secretion seems to be no less complex than that by which knowledge of a foreign object between the teeth is gained.

Colin (8) and Zebrowski (16) have found that chewing on one side of the mouth excites chiefly the gland of that side. My observations bring out the additional fact that when chewing occurs on both sides at the same time, less secretion is produced than when one side only is stimulated.

Two equal cubes of hard rubber were used with the drainage tube on the left Stenson's duct. One cube was placed between the left second molars, chewed for two minutes, and then removed. When the rate of secretion returned to normal both cubes were placed between the second molars on the right and left respectively and chewed for two minutes. This was repeated three times with the following results:

Stimulus	Drops of secretion per min.
Cube on left	12.0
Cubes on left and right	5.0
Cube on left	7.0
Cubes on left and right	3.0
Cube on left	8.0
Cubes on left and right	2.0
Average, cube on left	9.0
Average, cubes on left and right	3.3

The reduction of secretion with bilateral stimulation must be due either to an inhibitory effect of stimulation of the molars of one side upon the gland of the opposite side, or to some peculiarly effective stimulus arising from asymmetrical movements. Unequal tension on the ligaments of the jaw seemed to fulfill the latter alternative but both passive and active twisting of the jaw are alone without effect so that alterations in the tension of the ligaments seem excluded.

The stimulus offered by chewing has been dwelt upon at some length because the reaction to it illustrates, perhaps better than any other, the complex integration involved in the salivary reflex. Chewing upon a tasteless object excites profuse secretion yet no single element in the complex of stimuli is capable of calling out any marked reaction. The reflex secretion to the stimulus of chewing can not be considered the sum of lesser reactions to the individual components of the stimulus; it is rather a reaction to a particular pattern of stimuli, occurring not at all when any element of the pattern is omitted. This pattern seems no less complex than that by which we recognize the presence of an object between the teeth. The reaction is, however, dissociated from the language mechanism in that it is automatically adjusted to the position of the foreign object in the mouth and is not conditioned by the ordinary inhibitory processes which affect the reactions of striped-muscle.

There is some evidence for an equal complexity in other unconditioned salivary reflexes, particularly in the relations of the stimuli to reflex swallowing and to secretion but the analysis of these is as yet incomplete.

Reactions to Gustatory Stimuli. A number of extensive studies of reflex secretion to gustatory stimuli have been made. Those of Popielski (14) and Zebrowski (16) are the most complete available. Sensitivity to acids, salts, alkalis, fats, and to a large number of food substances has been demonstrated. Popielski has shown that the quantity of secretion elicited by an acid is rather accurately proportional to the degree of ionization of the acid but failed to obtain any uniformity in the reactions to other substances. From tests with sand and water he concluded that the amount of secretion is directly proportional to the quantity of the stimulus-substance used. Zebrowski, from experiments in which his subjects chewed and swallowed measured quantities of bread, concluded that the amount of secretion is proportional to the square root of the intensity of the stimulus. Brunacci (5) points out the complexity of the stimulus involved here and thinks that the ratio applies only to the particular case. . . .

The Relation of the Quantity of Secretion to the Intensity of the Stimulus. The difficulties in the determination of the excitatory effects of different concentrations of chemical solutions are practically the same as those met with in the study of the effects of different quantities. The experiments on man have shown no more than that strong solutions are more effective salivating agents than weak ones. Accurate results have been made almost impossible by the difficulty in removing the stimulating agent from the tongue at a specified time, the presence of a constant secretion after strong stimulation of the gland, and the possibility of paralysis of the receptors by high concentrations of the solutions.

The last of these is illustrated by the following experiment: Small discs of cotton, 1 cm. in diameter, were saturated with acid solutions and placed, one after the other, over the same group of papillae on one side of the tongue. The cotton was allowed to remain in place for one minute and the record of drops was taken for this minute only. The same solutions were applied with a brush to a small group of fungiform papillae. The following quantities of secretion were obtained:

Stimulus		Drops on side of tip	Drops on fungiform papillae
HCl	0.25%	4	2
	0.50	4	3
	1.00	6	2
	2.50	8	3
	5.00	11	6
	7.50	8	5
	10.00	6	4

The decrease in the quantities of secretion with solutions of more than 5.0 per cent is the result of injury to the taste buds. Desquamation of the stimulated areas followed the experiment.

A series of tests was carried out with solutions of hydrochloric acid and of sodium chloride. Other taste substances, quinine sulphate in particular, could not be used because of the difficulty of removing them from the surface of the tongue without prolonged washing. In the tests with salt and acid the following technique was adopted. Thirty seconds before each test 5 c.c. of water were placed in the subject's mouth to dilute the mucus present and the mouth was cleared of saliva as well as possible by swallowing. The remaining procedure was the same as that described [earlier]. Each test was delayed until the secretion returned to normal (about 1 drop per minute).

Table 3.6 shows the results of these tests. In no single case were the reactions proportional to the square root of the stimulus intensity. In the

Table 3.6. Relation of the Quantity of Secretion to Intensity of the Stimulus [*]

Subject		Stimulus	Drops of secretion in 3 min.	Average of trials
L	HCl	0.25%, 1 c.c.	12.8	5
		0.50%, 1 c.c.	17.0	3
		1.00%, 1 c.c.	20.0	3
		2.50%, 1 c.c.	28.7	4
		5.00%, 1 c.c.	40.5	2
		0.25%, 2 c.c.	16.0	2
		0.50%, 2 c.c.	20.0	2
		2.50%, 2 c.c.	42.0	2
	NaCl	0.20%, 1 c.c.	8.0	1
		1.00%, 1 c.c.	10.0	1
		5.00%, 1 c.c.	14.0	1
		25.00%, 1 c.c.	17.0	1
		0.20%, 3 c.c.	11.0	1
		1.00%, 3 c.c.	14.0	1
		5.00%, 3 c.c.	17.0	1
		25.00%, 3 c.c.	24.0	1
B	HCl	0.50%, 1 c.c.	2.5	2
		1.00%, 1 c.c.	7.0	4
		2.50%, 1 c.c.	13.0	2
		5.00%, 1 c.c.	17.0	2

[*] Drainage tube on the left duct. Stimulus applied for one minute and the total secretion during this and the following two minutes recorded.

majority of cases the range of variation of secretion for different intensities is less than would be expected from Zebrowski's formula. Weber's law of constant increment seems to express the results more exactly, but the control of stimuli is not accurate enough for the computation of any definite ratio. The technique employed is subject to almost all the objections outlined above and the experiments are reported in their present form only because they suggest that with an adequate technique a very accurate correlation of the intensity of stimulus and reaction may be demonstrated.

Stimulation of Restricted Areas in the Mouth. The intensity of reaction to stimulation of restricted areas of the mouth has been investigated only by Heyman,[4] working with the dog. His results show a differential sensitivity of different areas of the mucosa to mechanical and chemical stimuli, with considerable variation between different types of distribution of taste buds in man. His original publication is not available but it seems that only gross areas were stimulated.

In man a rather close restriction of stimulation to individual papillae is possible so that a comparative study of the effect of different chemicals upon the end organs of the same region may be undertaken. Some preliminary tests to this end have been completed, the following technique being used.

The surface of the tongue was mapped out roughly and a regular series of movements of the tongue was adopted in order to control the nongustatory stimuli. Before each stimulation the mouth was cleared of saliva, the tongue protruded as far as possible without strain, and the surface of the tongue was wiped from tip to base with a soft cotton cloth to erect the papillae and remove adherent saliva. The taste substance was then applied to individual papillae in the usual manner with a camel's hair brush. The tongue was next retracted and held depressed so that the taste substance was not spread by contact with the palate. After one minute the mouth was rinsed with 3 c.c. of water and the next test was delayed until the rate of secretion returned to normal.

The most extensive tests were carried out with three points on the dorsal surface of the tongue. These were: (a) a group of three filiform papillae on the right margin of the tip; (b) two fungiform papillae just to the right of the mid-dorsal line, 5 cm. from the tip; (c) one circumvallate papilla on the left at the base of the tongue. The quantities of secretion obtained after stimulation of these areas [were recorded]. In the tests the rate of secretion before stimulation varies from 1.3 to 2.3 drops per minute. Where the stimulus has little effect the initial rate affects the results considerably and for this reason I have used the increase in rate rather than the absolute secretion in comparing the excitability of different areas.

The data are not extensive enough for certain conclusions but suggest that the tip of the tongue is relatively more sensitive to water, acid, and salt than to other gustatory stimuli; that the base of the tongue is relatively most sensitive to sugar and quinine; that the fungiform papillae are most readily stimulated by salt. In the case of all but protopathic stimulation, however, the proximal regions of the tongue excite a greater secretion than the distal, irrespective of the quality or intensity of the stimulus.

[4] *Ibid.*

The effect of acid upon other parts of the mouth was tested by the same method. Stimulation of the hard palate, cheeks, lips, and uvula with acid excites no stronger secretion than is obtained with water. The soft palate is considerably more excitable to acid than to water.

The Rate of Recovery of the Gland from Excitation

The time required for recovery from stimulation varies with the intensity of stimulation. Table 3.7 shows the number of drops of saliva from the left parotid obtained in successive minutes during and after stimulation with salt and acid. In each test the stimulus solution was held in the mouth for one minute, then the mouth was rinsed with a pipette of water. The time required for the rate of secretion to fall to 1 or fewer

Table 3.7. Duration of Excitation of the Parotid °

	Stimulus	Successive minutes									Total secretion after cessation of stimulus
		1	2	3	4	5	6	7	8	9	
HCl	(Subject B) 0.50%	3	0	0	0	1	0	0	..	..	1
	1.00%	4	0	0	1	0	0	..	..	..	1
	1.00%	4	2	0	1	0	0	..	..	..	3
	1.00%	7	2	0	0	1	0	0	..	..	3
	2.50%	8	4	2	1	1	1	0	..	..	9
HCl	(Subject L) 0.25%	6	5	1	1	1	1	..	..	..	9
	0.50%	14	4	2	1	1	2	..	..	..	10
	2.50%	18	8	3	3	2	1	..	..	..	17
	5.00%	31	7	3	3	2	3	..	..	..	18
	0.50%, 1 c.c.	12	1	1	3	1	1	..	..	..	7
	0.50%, 2 c.c.	14	5	3	2	2	1	..	..	..	13
	0.50%, 3 c.c.	17	4	2	2	2	1	..	..	..	11
NaCl	0.20%	5	1	2	2	1	0	..	..	..	6
	1.00%	6	3	1	1	1	1	..	..	..	7
	5.00%	8	4	2	1	2	1	..	..	..	10
	25.00%	10	5	2	2	1	1	..	..	..	11
After 1% HCl continuously for ten minutes		..	9	9	2	2	6	2	2	3	..

° The amount of secretion, in drops, obtained during successive minutes after different intensities of stimulation is given. The stimulus was applied for one minute (1 in table) in each case, then rinsed from the tongue with water.

drops per minute after the removal of the stimulus was roughly proportional to the intensity of stimulation. As a corollary of this the quantity
of secretion after cessation of the stimulus is proportional to the intensity
of stimulation (last column, Table 3.7). After intense stimulation the
heightened secretion may persist for ten or more minutes.

Fatigue of the Unconditioned Reflex

The possibility that fatigue of the direct reflex might interfere seriously
with quantitative studies of the secretion led to a series of tests with
continued stimulation. These were carrried out as follows:

1. Two glass tubes were placed in the mouth in such a way that a
constant stream of dilute hydrochloric acid could be directed against the
soft palate and allowed to drain off from the tip of the tongue. The
stimulating substance could thus be constantly renewed and the question
of its dilution eliminated. With 0.25 per cent acid continuous stimulation
was given for ten minutes; with 1.0 per cent acid for five minutes. The
weaker solution excited in ten successive minutes a secretion of 18, 24, 18,
16, 15, 12, 11, 13, 12, 12 drops. The stronger solution gave in five successive minutes 28, 27, 30, 32, 30 drops. In this short time there is little
evidence of fatigue. The series with the weaker solution is complicated
by the fact that just before the end of the first minute the subject choked
and swallowed some acid. The decrease in the rate of secretion following
probably represents the recovery from this stimulation of the throat, rather
than a fatigue of the reflex.

2. One cubic centimeter of 1.0 per cent hydrochloric acid was placed
in the subject's mouth at the beginning of each minute for 20 successive
minutes. The quantities of secretion obtained during this time [were
recorded]. The secretion obtained during the second ten minutes [was]
practically the same as that during the first ten. There [was] no evidence
of fatigue.

3. A 5.0 per cent solution of sodium chloride was applied in the same
way for ten minutes. The quantities of secretion in successive minutes
were 6, 7, 6, 5, 5, 6, 5, 5, 5, 6 drops. There is here a reduction of only
7.0 per cent from the average secretion of the first to that of the second
five minutes.

Under the conditions of these tests the direct salivary reflex fatigues
very slowly if at all.

Excitation of the Glands by Stimuli from Other Parts of the Digestive Tract

Jänicke (10) and earlier workers believed that stimulation of the
mucosa of the stomach excited salivary secretion. Buff (7) failed to obtain
any increase in secretion by stimulating the walls of the dog's stomach
with acid introduced through a fistula and held that reflex excitation of

A serious defect in these experiments arises from the fact that the protopathic stimulus modifies the movements of the mouth and may prevent the usual distribution of the gustatory stimulus. The subject was warned to keep the distribution of the acid on the tongue uniform, but there is no certainty that this was done. Where rather large quantities of concentrated solution are used this source of error is certainly less important than where threshold intensities are used as in the experiments of Brunacci and DeSanctis reviewed below. The results of the tests with protopathic stimulation are consistent and it seems probable that there is an actual inhibition of secretion with very intense stimulation.

The Influence of Mental Work and Emotion upon the Rate of Secretion

Brunacci and DeSanctis (6) have studied the effect of mental work upon the secretion of the parotid, finding a smaller quantity of secretion during activity than during repose. I have been unable to verify this result and believe that the apparent inhibition resulted from the technique used by these investigators. They stimulated their subjects once per minute with a very dilute solution of acetic acid and recorded the resultant secretion when the subjects were at rest and when they were translating from a foreign language or computing. A diminished secretion during mental activity was interpreted as evidence for inhibition. The importance of the distribution of the stimulus solution in the subject's mouth has been emphasized already. Any distraction may alter this distribution, which depends largely upon the movements of the tongue. The solutions used by Brunacci and DeSanctis were near the threshold intensity and there is no evidence from their experiments that the reduction of secretion was not due to a limited distribution of the stimulus solution when the subjects were occupied.

The following experiment shows an excitatory rather than an inhibitory effect of mental work upon the normal secretion of the gland: The subject was required to square three-place numbers without visual assistance for twenty minutes, to remain quiet for twenty minutes, and then to resume computation for twenty minutes more. The intensity of concentration is assured by the fact that the subject, who had had no experience with this type of computation, returned correct answers to three of twelve problems and made errors of only one figure in five other products. The average rates of secretion obtained were:

	Drops per min.
During first period of multiplication	1.80
During period of rest	1.23
During second period of multiplication	1.88

The rate of secretion during each of the periods was almost constant. An unmistakable increase in secretion resulted from the intense mental application. Similar, but less pronounced results have been obtained with other subjects

the glands from the stomach does not occur. Ordenstein's data (12) upon secretion measured for twenty-seven consecutive hours show some increase in glandular activity after the subject had eaten but the author does not discuss this point.

In the tests reported above upon the rate of secretion without extero-stimulation five subjects were examined immediately before and at intervals ranging from ten to sixty minutes after eating (Table 3.1). In every case the rate of secretion was greater after the meal than before. Stimulation from particles of food remaining in the mouth was excluded, leaving the alternatives of stimulation from the stomach and intestine or persistent reaction to the long-continued oral stimulation in eating as possible explanations of the heightened rate of secretion. The latter seems to be excluded by the following observation:

The rate of secretion of the first subject recorded in Table 3.1 was tested without extero-stimulation for fifteen minutes and found to be constant at 3.60 c.c. per hour. The subject then chewed "Zwieback" for fifteen minutes without swallowing any of it, then cleared the mouth of adherent particles and returned to the apparatus. His rate of secretion during the following twenty minutes was found to be 3.60 c.c. per hour, exactly the same as before the oral stimulation. From this it seems that the increase in secretion following a meal is not the result of oral stimulation but is a reflex from some other part of the digestive tract.

The Effect of Olfactory Stimulation

The fact that the odor of food is sufficient to produce salivation has been commented upon frequently (2, p. 24) but I have been unable to find record of any experiments upon the direct reflex to odors in man. Zeliony [5] after ablation of the cerebral lobes of the dog was unable to obtain any glandular reaction to odors; a result which favors the view that the secretion observed by other investigators was a conditioned reflex.

The reactions of the human parotid to odors have been tested with several subjects. . . . The subjects, with eyes closed, were stimulated for thirty seconds with each of [several] odorous substances . . . and asked to identify the odors. The stimuli were given at intervals of six or more minutes, and the number of drops of saliva obtained during the three minutes preceding and the three minutes following stimulation [were recorded].

In no case did any marked increase in secretion follow the stimulation. Amyl alcohol and oil of peppermint seemed to accelerate secretion but both irritate the mucosa of the pharynx, the former producing coughing, and the reaction is probably to this rather than to the odor. The range

[5] *Ibid.*

of odors was fairly broad and the experiments seem to prove that there is no unconditioned reflex secretion to olfactory stimulation.

Inhibition and Reinforcement of Secretion

The data of Aschenbrandt (1) upon salivary secretion after irritation of the conjunctival sac and Pawlow's observations (13) upon inhibition of secretion by injury to the viscera in the dog have been disputed by Buff (7). He himself lays great stress upon movements of the body as excitants of salivary secretion but gives no experimental evidence in support of his view. The statements of these men and the experiments of Brunacci and DeSanctis (6), which will be considered later, constitute the only data available upon the indirect modification of the unconditioned reflex.

The series of tests summarized in Table 3.8 were carried out to test the effect of muscular activity upon the secretion of the parotid. Three

Table 3.8. Influence of Muscular Activity upon Secretion of the Parotid

Subject L

	Average drops of secretion per min.	
Stimulus	Left parotid	
Subject lifted and held 50-pound weight above his head:		
Before exertion, 4 min.	0.75	
During exertion, 2 min.	0.00	
After exertion, 3 min.	1.25	
"Setting up exercises":		
Before exertion, 3 min.	1.25	
During exertion, 5 min.	0.40	
After exertion, 3 min.	1.00	
	Right parotid	Left parotid
Arms held extended:		
Before exertion, 3 min.	2.0	2.3
During exertion, 5 min.	0.6	0.6
After exertion, 3 min.	1.6	1.6

types of activity were used, violent effort, rapid movement, and prolonged strain. In each case there was an inhibition of secretion during activity. During activity of this sort movements of the tongue and throat are largely inhibited, but such movements have normally very little effect and it seems improbable that the suspension of secretion is due wholly to the change in the stimuli coming from the mouth. There seems to be an active inhibition of secretion during violent muscular effort.

A further series of tests was carried out with violent protopathic The subject's finger tips were placed against a knife electrode an current, strong enough to induce profuse perspiration, was directed t fingers. The rate of secretion with and without faradic stimulatio termined. Brunacci's technique was then adopted, the subject being gi of 0.20 per cent hydrochloric acid in the first second of each minute d experiment. The reaction to the acid with and without faradic stimula determined. In one instance tickling of the subject's nose and lips wa tuted for the faradic stimulation. The results of these tests are shown i 3.9. The protopathic stimulation in every case led to a reduction in the

Table 3.9. Effect of Protopathic Stimulation upon the Rate of Secretio

Stimulus	Average drops per min.	Duration of test, min.
Test I.		
Normal rate without stimulation	1.00	10
With faradic stimulation of fingers	0.75	10
Test II.		
Before faradization	12.30	4
During faradization	8.60	5
After faradization	9.20	5
Test III.		
Before faradization	11.80	11
During faradization	9.00	10
Test IV.		
Lip and nose tickled with a feather:		
Before stimulation	12.10	7
During stimulation	7.60	5

* The rate was determined before, during, and after intense protopathic stimulation continued for the time intervals indicated. In tests II, III, and IV, 1 c.c. of 0.20% HCl was given at the beginning of every minute.

secretion. In test II (Table 3.9) complete recovery from the depression did not take place during the five minutes following the faradization, although the rate of secretion increased slightly with the cessation of stimulation. This is not surprising, however, since the electric stimulation was severe, leaving the subject badly shaken. A ten-minute rest, test III, resulted in complete recovery of the normal glandular activity.

Where the acid was given continuously the possibility of fatigue of the direct reflex must be considered. The data [above, however,] show that within the time limits of this experiment the direct reflex does not fatigue. Moreover, the change in the rate of secretion at the beginning of faradic stimulation was not gradual, as would be expected in fatigue, but abrupt. . . .

having a lesser rate of secretion without extero-stimulation. In one case reduced secretion appeared during computation. This subject obviously used the fingers largely in computation while the others seemed to rely wholly upon the speech mechanism. This suggests a possible correlation between the implicit system employed and the effect of mental work upon secretion.

The inhibition of salivary secretion during fear has been noted frequently but there is no definite evidence as to the effects of other types of emotion. Colin (8) states that salivary secretion is increased during sexual excitement. Von Bechterew (3, p. 452) says: "Every pleasant sexual excitation is undoubtedly accompanied by salivary secretion; it is questionable only whether this is a reflex from the genitals or (as seems to me more probable) a psychic effect." Since a certain grade of erotic emotion is easily aroused in the laboratory it seemed worth while to test the extent to which the statements of these authors, who give no experimental evidence, can be applied to the parotid gland. For the stimulus to sexual excitement a collection of pornographic literature and pictures was used. The rate of secretion of the subjects while quiet or reading indifferent material was determined. They were then given the erethitic material and the rate of secretion while this was examined was determined. Finally a second determination of the normal rate was made. Table 3.10 shows the

Table 3.10. Inhibitory Effect of Erotic Emotion *

Subject	Secretion with indifferent material, drops per min.	Secretion with erethitic material, drops per min.
B	0.36	0.11
B	0.77	0.00
T	0.80	0.36
M	0.20	0.10

* The average secretion in drops per minute is recorded. The subjects read indifferent material for 20 minutes or more (first column), then examined the erethitic material for 10 minutes (second column).

effect of the erotic emotion. In every instance it resulted in a reduction of the rate of secretion. The exciting effect of the material used has been tested in other experiments and there is no doubt of its erethitic nature. The tests seem extensive enough to establish the inhibitory effect of erotic emotion.

A second effect of this emotion seems to be an almost complete inhibition of the swallowing reflex. The secretion accumulates in the mouth and subjects have been seen to drool saliva while reading the pornographic literature although the secretion of the parotid glands was partially suppressed. This probably accounts for the statements of Colin and von Bechterew, whose observations do not seem to have been made upon isolated glands.

It has not been possible to obtain strong emotion of other types in the laboratory. In one instance, when a long series of tests was made with a disagreeable mixture of hydrochloric acid and sugar, the subject became rebellious and, when the experimenter insisted on continuing the work, angry. The reactions of the parotid became less intense and quite irregular under these conditions.

Conditioned Reflexes Appearing without Training

None of the students of human parotid secretion has been able to demonstrate conditioned reflexes. The reason for this is, perhaps, that they have made no attempt to reproduce in the laboratory the environment in which the subjects were accustomed to obtain food. Early in my own experiments it became evident that no increase in secretion followed the mention of food. As it seemed possible that lack of real hunger was responsible for the absence of secretion, the first test for the conditioned reflex was made under rather severe conditions. The subject abstained from food for three days, the drainage tube was then placed over the left Stenson's duct and a list of fifty-three words, fifteen of which were names of foods, the others indifferent, was read to him. The words were given at two-minute intervals and the secretion recorded in drops per minute. The average secretion following the names of foods was 2.00 drops per minute; following the indifferent words it was 2.10 drops per minute. There is absolutely no evidence of a conditioned reflex.

With the sight of food as a stimulus quite different results were obtained. In this test the subject abstained from food for twenty-four hours and was then shown a variety of foods. No increase in secretion appeared with the sight of food. The subject was then allowed to eat a single raw oyster, rather heavily seasoned with paprika. An immediate change in the salivary reaction to the sight of food followed. This may be illustrated in detail by a test with a bar of almond chocolate, which shows the extreme sensitivity of the reflex. In the [table on p. 49] the number of drops of saliva secreted during successive minutes is given on the right, the conditions of stimulation are given on the left.

Like results were obtained in other tests but varied with the particular food used. . . . Where no secretion was excited by the sight of food, raising the food toward the mouth was sufficient to excite secretion, except in the case of the peppermint which the subject dislikes.

Tests involving the same movements of hands and mouth as those used with the food but in which inedible substances were held resulted in no increase in secretion, so that it seems quite certain that the results obtained with food substances are due to conditioned reflexes to the visual and olfactory characters of the the food.

During [some of] the experiments reported . . . [above] the formation of conditioned reflexes to the sight of the bottles of acid and other objects used in giving gustatory stimuli was noted but discussion of these must be postponed to a later paper.

No extero-stimulation	1, 0
Chocolate placed in subject's hand	4, 3
Subject smelled chocolate	5
Brought chocolate to lips but kept mouth closed	9
Held chocolate at arm's length	4, 3, 3
Told to eat but stopped as chocolate reached lips	7, 6, 2
Chocolate snatched away	0, 0, 3
	2, 2, 1
Chocolate given back and held at arm's length	4, 3, 4
	3
Chocolate snatched away	1, 1
Chocolate given back	4, 2, 4
Chocolate eaten	32, 13

Summary

The experiments reported form a preliminary survey of the conditions affecting the secretion of the parotid gland. Only the direct reflex has been considered extensively but the data obtained upon this phase of secretory activity furnishes a basis for an investigation of some of the acquired reflexes of the human autonomic nervous system. While all classes of stimuli which may affect secretion have not been tested it is probable that those employed embrace the ones which are most influential and which might enter as conflicting elements into studies of acquired reflexes. Chemical analysis of the saliva has not been possible but the first tests of conditioned secretion may be restricted advantageously to quantitative experiments which will not be affected seriously by this lack.

The experiments thus far reported seem to justify the following conclusions:

1. Direct reflexes of the parotid gland are excited by mechanical, chemical, and protopathic stimulation of the oral mucosa. Lack of an adequate method of limiting the distribution of chemical stimuli has prevented accurate quantitative experiments.

2. There is probably no direct reflex to thermal stimuli unless they are of protopathic intensity.

3. The secretion produced when a foreign object is chewed involves a specific reaction to a complex group of stimuli.

4. The reaction of the parotid is most intense when the homolateral mucosa is stimulated.

5. The quantity of secretion varies with different chemical stimuli applied to different parts of the mucosa but is usually greatest when the proximal region of the tongue is stimulated.

6. The presence of food in the stomach excites secretion.

7. There is no direct reflex to olfactory or to ordinary visual, auditory, or tactile stimulation.

8. Parotid secretion is partially inhibited by violent muscular activity. Mental work (involving movements of the tongue and throat?) increases the secretion.

9. Erotic emotion reduces the quantity of secretion.

10. Reflex secretion is excited by the sight and odor of food but is conditioned by hunger, by the previous experience of getting food under the conditions of the experiment, and by complex emotional factors which have not been analyzed.

REFERENCES

1. Aschenbrandt. Ueber reflectorischen Speichelfluss nach Conjunctivalreizun, sowie über Gewinnung isolirten Drüsenspeichels, *Arch. ges. Physiol.*, 1881, **25**, 101–111.

2. Babkin, B. P. *Die äussere Sekretion der Verdauungsdrüsen.* Berlin: Springer, 1914.

3. Bechterew, W. von. *Die Funktionen der Nervencentra.* Jena: Gustav Fischer, 1909–1911.

4. Bradford, J. Some points in the physiology of gland nerves, *J. Physiol.*, 1888, **9**, 287–316.

5. Brunacci, B. Sulla funzione secretoria della parotide nell'uomo: Nota I. Influenza della qualita dello stimolo sulle proprieta fisicochimiche della saliva parotidea, *Arch. Fisiol.*, 1910, **8**, 421–457.

6. Brunacci, B., and DeSanctis, T. Sulla funzione secretoria della parotide nell'uomo: Nota II. Influenza inibitrice dell'attivita psichica sulla quantita e qualita della saliva secreta, *Arch. Fisiol.*, 1914, **12**, 441–454.

7. Buff, R. Revision der Lehre von der reflectorischen Speichelsecretion, *Beitr. Anat. Physiol.*, 1888, **12**, 1–39.

8. Colin, G. *Traité de physiologie comparée des animaux domestiques.* T. i–ii. Paris: Baillière, 1886–1888.

9. Head, H., and Sherren, J. The consequences of injury to the peripheral nerves in man, *Brain*, 1905, **28**, 116–338.

10. Jänicke, A. Untersuchungen über die Sekretion der glandula parotis. *Arch. ges. Physiol.*, 1878, **17**, 183–214.

11. Lashley, K. S. The human salivary reflex and its use in psychology, *Psychol. Rev.*, 1916, **23**, 446–464.

12. Ordenstein, L. Ueber den Parotidenspeichel des Menschen, *Beitr. Anat. Physiol.*, 1860, **2**, 103–122.

13. Pawlow, J. Ueber die reflectorische Hemmung der Speichelabsonderung, *Arch. ges. Physiol.*, 1878, **16**, 272–292.

14. Popielski, L. Ueber die Gesetze der Speicheldrüsentätigkeit, *Arch. ges. Physiol.*, 1909, **127**, 443–473.

15. Tuczek, F. Ueber die vom Menschen während des Kauens abgesonderten Speichelmengen, *Z. Biol.*, 1876, **12**, 534–557.

16. Zebrowski, E. von. Zur Frage der sekretorischen Funktion der Parotis beim Menschen, *Arch. ges. Physiol.*, 1905, **110**, 105–173.

4. THE ACCURACY OF MOVEMENT IN THE ABSENCE OF EXCITATION FROM THE MOVING ORGAN [1]

For psychology the problem of motor activity has been largely one of the perception of movement. Discussion has centered about the questions of the receptors which are excited differentially by changes in extent and force of movement, about the psycho-physics of the constant error, the influence of the emotions upon the perception of movement, the relation of the "will impulse" to the perception of movement; with the result that the equally important questions of the nervous mechanism of initiation, continuation and cessation of adaptive movements have been dealt with only incidentally as throwing light upon this perception. Whether such an attitude on the part of investigators is the result of the general concept of psychology which would restrict its scope to the study of sensation, or is a consequence of the relative ease with which the problems of sensory and motor physiology may be attacked, the result has been an almost total neglect of the neurological problems presented by skilled movements.

In many cases the perception and control of movement may be one and the same phenomenon, but certain experimental data and facts of everyday experience indicate a certain degree of independence of the accuracy of movement from any stimulation resulting from the movement itself. Such is the accuracy of automatic movements as seen in the production of steps of uniform length, or more strikingly, the swift movements of the musician, many of which are made more quickly than the briefest cortical reaction time. These movements are frequently regulated in extent and force with the utmost nicety, under conditions where any reflex control from excitations arising in the moving hand seems excluded. Again, the evidence obtained by Bowditch and Southard (1), Loeb (4), Woodworth (6, 7), and others, while by no means conclusive, indicates a partial independence of the motor control from afferent processes originating in the moving organ. The reestablishment of walking movements

[1] EDITORS' NOTE: From *Amer. J. Physiol.*, 1917, 43, 169–194. Reproduced by permission of the American Physiological Society. From the Johns Hopkins University and the Government Hospital for the Insane.

in the dog after section of the dorsal root gives further evidence for the same view.

Clearly the ideal opportunity for the study of these relations would be given by a case of complete sensory anesthesia in man with no more impairment of motor functions than would necessarily arise from the anesthesia. A partial condition of this character is occasionally reported in tabes dorsalis and the complete absence of afferent impulses in rare cases of spinal lesion. Through the courtesy of the staff of the Government Hospital for the Insane, I have had opportunity to examine a number of patients showing various degrees of anesthesia and to carry out the experiments reported in the following pages with one who showed a condition particularly adapted to answer some of the questions centered about the control of movement.[2]

The present paper is devoted to a study of the sensory and motor condition of this patient. He is a young man of more than average intelligence who has, as a result of a gun-shot injury to the spinal cord, a partial anesthesia of both legs with motor paralysis of the muscles below the knees. The anesthesia of the left leg is much more extensive than that of the right. Rough preliminary tests indicated a sensitivity to movements of all joints except the left knee and ankle, and the paralysis of the muscles controlling the latter made it necessary to restrict the study to movements of the knee. The experiments were arranged for investigation first, of excitations from movements at this joint; second, of the accuracy of the control of such movements as failed to excite afferent impulses from the limb.

Physical Condition of the Subject

Neurological examination shows the left leg, with the greater part of the left groin and gluteal region, to be insensitive to the light touch, temperature, and to protopathic stimulation. The extent of the area of cutaneous anesthesia is shown in Fig. 4.1. Except for the rather large areas in the gluteal region and the somewhat smaller areas on the calf (shown in white in Fig. 4.1) there is complete loss of cutaneous sensitivity of this leg. The loss of sensitivity to deep pressure is much less extensive, complete anesthesia to deep pressure involving only the foot and anterior surface of the lower leg (cross-striated area in Fig. 4.1), but in the regions retaining sensitivity this is reduced much below normal. The minimum amount of pressure that can be detected in the region of cutaneous anesthesia is 900 grams on an area ½ inch in diameter in the region of

[2] I wish to express my obligation in particular to Superintendent W. A. White, who has given me every opportunity for investigation, and to Dr. S. I. Franz, who first brought the patient to my attention and who has given important suggestions concerning the control of the experiments. Finally my greatest debt is to the subject of the present study who has worked tirelessly, and who has himself suggested improvements in technique which were essential for the success of the experiments.

the groin and this increases to 2000 grams over the greater part of the thigh and calf. The thresholds to deep pressure over the anesthesia area are shown in Fig. 4.2. Except in the gluteal region in the groin and on the calf, localization of deep pressure is very inexact, the average error

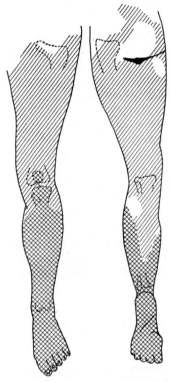

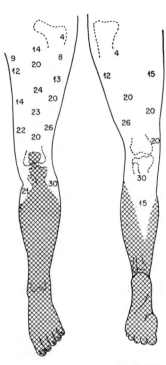

Fig. 4.1. The extent of anesthesia of the left leg of the subject studied. White areas, cutaneous sensitivity; light-shaded areas, cutaneous anesthesia with deep sensitivity to pressure; dark-shaded areas, complete anesthesia to all stimulation.

Fig. 4.2. Threshold of sensitivity to pressure applied over an area one-half inch in diameter. Shaded area completely insensitive. The figures give the sensitivity of other regions in 100-gram units.

of localization being about 8 inches. No amount of pressure that I was able to apply excited deep pain.

There is slight sensitivity to vibration (50 per second) in the femur. A small area of the patella also seems sensitive to this type of stimulation, but its sensitivity is probably due to the transmission of the vibration to the femur. There is no sensitivity to this type of stimulation in the region below the knee.

The cutaneous and tendon reflexes of the leg are completely abolished but a slight degree of tonicity is retained by the muscles of the thigh. We do not know the exact extent of the lesion and no detailed clinical history of the operation to remove the bullet is available, but the clinical picture indicates an extensive destruction of the dorsal bundles in the second or third lumbar segment of the cord with invasion of the dorsal horns or injury to afferent roots in the sacral region sufficient to abolish the tendon reflexes. The determination of the exact extent of the lesion is not essential to the present work since the conclusions depend wholly upon the experimental determination of the extent of anesthesia to movement.

Sensitivity to Position and to Passive Movements

Preliminary tests had indicated that in spite of the sensitivity to pressure retained by the subject, his sensitivity to flexion and extension of the knee was abolished. Before a study of the accuracy of active movements could be undertaken it was necessary to establish this point beyond question. A number of experiments was therefore carried out with a view to revealing any sensitivity to movement which might play a part in determining the accuracy of adaptive movements.

In all the tests on movement the subject was seated on a soft cushion in a rather high chair with his left thigh supported by a padded rod, 3 inches behind the knee, so that his foot could swing freely from the knee through an arc of about 130 degrees from complete extension to the point where the heel came in contact with the rungs of the chair. The foot was attached by a cord to the carriage of a modified form of the Münsterberg movement apparatus, so that rate and extent of movement could be recorded. The subject was blindfolded during all the tests and precautions were taken to eliminate any auditory stimulation from the recording apparatus which might serve as a clue to the extent of movement. The distance moved was recorded in centimeters read directly from the recording device. A slight inaccuracy is introduced here, since the measurement was in straight lines while the movement was about the perimeter of a circle. In the records 1 cm. is equal to approximately 1.28 degrees rotation about the knee.

Detection of Passive Movements. The experimenter grasped the subject's foot in his right hand and, holding his left hand on the subject's knee to detect unintentional movements of the thigh, flexed and extended the knee passively through angles varying from 10 to 130 degrees. The subject was asked to describe the distance and direction of movement whenever he felt that any movement had been made. The rate of the passive movements was varied from about 2 cm. to 100 cm. per second.

When the passive movements were made at a rate of less than 20 cm. per second, the subject was unable to detect any movement, however great its extent, and throughout a series of fifty such movements gave no reaction except when the movements resulted in hyperextension of the knee. More rapid movements were detected in about 50 per cent of the trials but reports of their direction and extent seemed to be wholly a matter of chance.

Fifty passive movements of the foot at a rate of more than 20 cm. per second were made under conditions where auditory cues were eliminated. The subject was asked to give the direction of movement and position of the foot whenever he felt that it was moving. Twenty-four of the movements brought no reaction. The remaining 26 were detected as movements; 4 were described as of uncertain direction, 22 brought definite statements of direction of movement which were, however, quite inaccurate. Seven movements of extension and four of flexion were described correctly. Five movements of extension were described as flexion and six movements of flexion were described as extension. The description of the position of the foot was equally inaccurate. The subject usually denied any knowledge of its position and in the instances where he ventured a definite statement he was as frequently wrong as right. Thus, in 3 out of 6 cases flexion at 70 degrees was described as complete extension and in 2 of 5 cases hyperextension was described as flexion.

When the knee was hyperextended the subject invariably stated that the knee was being moved. His knee was alternately hyperextended and flexed a number of times and he was asked to describe the movements. Only those of extension were detected and these the subject alternately stated to be extensions and flexions. Flexing movements brought no reaction. From this it seems that the reactions to hyperextension were to the strain on the joint or ligaments and not to the movement as such.

An attempt was made to locate the source of stimulation by which rapid movements were detected. Slight flexion of the hip (elevation of the knee through a distance of 2 cm.) was for the first three trials interpreted as an extension of the knee, twice as a movement of the knee of uncertain direction, and remained undetected in more than 20 cases. Heavy pressure above the knee was once described as a movement of extension but later failed to elicit any response. The patient was instructed to contract the antagonistic muscles of the thigh so as to increase the tension upon the knee joint and fix the leg at the thigh. When this was done no passive movements were detected, unless they produced flexion of the hip. The quick movements which brought reactions were frequently described as "jerks" and I could not be certain that any of the movements that were detected did not involve a certain amount of strain upon the muscles of the trunk.

These tests suggest the absence of any afferent excitations from the leg during slow passive movements of the knee which may stimulate verbal reactions to the direction or extent of the movements. From them it seems probable, also, that the recognition of quick passive movements is not based directly upon excitations from the moving to adjacent parts of the body. Whatever may be the basis of the reactions to rapid passive movements the stimuli involved are not differentiated enough to allow the subject to determine the direction or extent of the movement.

Maintenance of Position. The preceding tests required chiefly reaction to movement with, possibly, very little stress upon local signs from the position of the leg. A further series of tests was made with the emphasis upon position.

The subject's knee was hyperextended and he was asked to maintain that position as long as he could against the force of gravity. The quadriceps became tense and the leg was kept extended for about ten seconds, then dropped to vertical with a series of spasmodic twitches. The subject, when questioned, stated that he was still holding the leg extended and one minute later said, "Now I am letting it down," the leg, in the meantime, hanging lax. The test was repeated a number of times and gave similar results in every case. There was momentary maintenance of position, relaxation without recognition of the movement, and later an illusion of relaxation.

Other positions than that of hyperextension could not be maintained at all. When the subject's foot was placed passively in any other position and he was asked to hold it there, the leg dropped back to the vertical as soon as the support was removed, jerking back and forth spasmodically for a few seconds, and then came to rest in the vertical position, the subject asserting, without certainty, that he was holding the leg still.

Reaction to the Position. With the weight of the subject's foot wholly supported by the experimenter, the knee was flexed, starting from 105 degrees, until the recording carriage moved 10 cm. The subject was told that his foot would be moved back to the starting position and was asked to indicate verbally when it reached that position. The movements from the starting position were made at a uniform rate; the rate and direction of the "returning movements" were varied. The subject was warned in each case that the displacement of the foot was completed and that the experimenter was returning it to the starting point. In five series different procedures were employed: (a) The foot was moved back very slowly toward the initial position; (b) it was returned to the initial position at the same rate at which it had been displaced; (c) it was moved back very quickly; (d) the displacing movement was continued so as to bring the foot farther from the starting point; (e) the foot was held motionless after being displaced.

The positions stated by the subject to be the one from which the foot was originally displaced are given in Table 4.1. Slow return was overestimated, quick return underestimated, and lack of movement or movement in the wrong direction was not detected. The subject stated that he was depending upon the time interval after the warning that the foot was being returned to its original position, and the relation of the position identified as the starting point to the rate of passive movement confirms his statements. The results of the tests show clearly that there were no afferent excitations capable of arousing a reaction to position.

Table 4.1. Reactions to Position of the Leg °

Foot displaced, cm.		Extent of second movement, cm.		Error in identification of position, cm.	Rate of second movement
Backward	10	1.4	Forward	− 8.6	Very slow
Backward	10	12.2	Forward	+ 2.2	Same as that of displacement
Backward	10	22.5	Forward	+12.5	Quick
Backward	10	0.0	Forward	−10.0	No movement
Backward	10	25.5	Backward	−35.5	Quick
Forward	10	2.1	Backward	− 7.9	Very slow
Forward	10	8.3	Backward	− 1.7	Same as that of displacement
Forward	10	16.7	Backward	+ 6.7	Quick
Forward	10	0.0	Backward	−10.0	No movement
Forward	10	8.5	Forward	−18.5	Quick

° A constant position of the knee (105 degrees extension) was adopted as a "starting point." The subject's foot was displaced passively 10 cm. from this and he was asked to indicate when it had been returned by a second movement. The figures, each based on the average of five trials, give the distances and the directions traversed by the foot in the second movement before the subject indicated that the starting position had been reached.

Duplication of Passive Movements. The data presented thus far indicate that any excitations from the position or from slow passive movements of the leg are subliminal for the language mechanism of the subject. It seemed possible that the excitations from passive movements might still be above the threshold for the reflex control of active movement and to test this experiments were carried out in which the subject was asked to duplicate the extent and direction of a passive movement by making an active movement.

The position of the subject described above was used. Distances of 2 and 10 cm. were selected as pattern movements, and the subject's foot was moved backward or forward through these distances at a rate of less than 10 cm. per second. The subject stated that he could not tell when the pattern movement was made, so he was warned each time his foot was moved and was asked to continue the movement through the same distance and in the same direction as the passive movement. . . .

The relation of the direction of the subject's movements to the direction of the pattern set . . . [was tabulated]. The direction was interpreted wrongly in almost 50 per cent of the trials, which indicates that the direction of the subject's movements was wholly a matter of chance. The lengths of the movements varied from 0 to 27 cm. (the maximum movements permitted by the subject's foot). . . . The variations in two series of tests are shown in Fig. 4.3, other tests giving similar results.

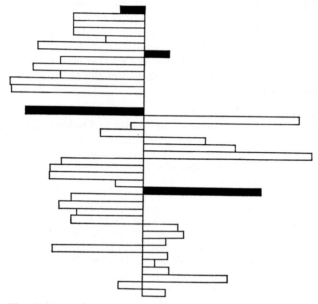

Fig. 4.3. Record of attempts to duplicate by active movements a pattern set by passive movement of the leg. The direction and extent of the passive movements are shown by the solid rectangles; the active movements of the subject are shown by those in outline. The pattern was repeated before each active movement.

There is no correlation either in direction or extent between the active movements and the passive pattern which they were intended to reproduce.

The subject's failure to give any precise or constant reaction to the position or movement of his knee seems to prove that the anesthesia of the leg is sufficiently extensive to exclude any reflex control of the accuracy of movement based upon cortical excitations arising from the moving limb. The one remaining possibility of excitation from the limb calls for the postulation of receptors in the muscles which are stimulated by active contraction and not by passive tension. To test this the relative lengths of the voluntary movements which the subject estimated as equal when different amounts of resistance were opposed to the movement were measured.

Afferent Excitation from the Contracting Muscles

Rough tests were first carried out with different amounts of resistance opposed to the subject's active movements. He was asked to flex his knee so that his foot was drawn back 3 inches from a given position (120 degrees extension) in which his leg was held by the experimenter and to indicate verbally when he had moved his foot through this distance. The latter precaution was taken to test the relation between the duration of the motor innervation and any excitation of the language mechanism which might exist.

In the first trials the foot was allowed to move only at a rate about 1 cm. per second. The average distance moved and reported as 3 inches under this condition was 1.65 cm. with a range from 0.9 to 2.5 cm. (ten trials). In the next ten trials the pull against the subject's movements was increased to such an extent that the knee was extended slightly during his attempts to flex it. In these tests an average forward movement of 1.04 cm. with a range of 0.5 to 1.5 cm. was reported as a backward movement of 3 inches. During these tests the subject reported that he felt resistance but had increased the force of his movement until he had compensated for it completely. The mechanism by which the resistance was detected was not determined. It may have been due to a residual joint or tendon sensitivity that was too slight to be stimulated by unresisted movements, or to the deep muscle sensitivity to pressure, or to certain stimulation from strain on the muscles of the trunk which could not be altogether eliminated. The subject indicated his knee as the source of stimulation, but was very uncertain. Whatever the locus of excitation, the stimulus was not specific enough to give a clue to the extent of movement of the foot. In a third series of tests the active movement of the subject was accelerated by the experimenter, the subject being asked, as before, to stop the movement and indicate when his foot had moved 3 inches. The average of distances moved in ten trials was 28.94 cm. with a range 26.0 to 30.5 cm. This was practically the maximum extent of movement allowed by the position of the subject.

The same tests were repeated with a better control of the amount of resistance offered to the movement, and with virtually the same results. The subject's foot was supported to 120 degrees extension by a spring exerting 100 grams for each 4.5 cm. extension and he was asked to draw his foot back 3 inches. The initial tension on the spring was varied from 266 to 1,380 grams. In other tests the foot was held motionless, in others the knee was extended during the attempt at flexion, and finally the spring was set to flex the knee. As far as possible the subject was kept in ignorance of the procedure. He was asked to indicate verbally when he had carried out the instructions. . . . The distances moved vary inversely with the resistance encountered but not in direct ratio. The foregoing tests seem to show that there are no excitations from the actively moving limb which are specific enough to give a clue to the extent of the movement.

A certain amount of adjustment to the resistance is indicated by the fact that the extent of movement is not inversely proportional to the resistance. The work done in extending the heavier springs (computed as distance times weight lifted) is greater than that performed with the lighter springs. Such a method of considering the data is misleading, however, for it considers that no work is done unless external resistance is opposed to the movement, whereas a certain amount of work is done in the contraction of free muscles, in the stretching of the antagonistic muscles, and in overcoming the resistance at the joint. It is impossible to estimate the amount of force expended in this way, but if we assume that the work done in moving the leg without external resistance is the equivalent of lifting 50 grams for the distance moved, the total amount of work done in moving against each of the resistances recorded . . . is practically the same. There is no jusification for assigning this particular value to unresisted movement, but there is also no certain evidence that there was any compensation for the different resistances encountered.

There remains the subject's statement that he felt resistance and made an adequate allowance for it by giving a harder pull. How much of the apparent increase in work done was due to this cannot be determined without more data than are available at the present time upon the internal resistance to movement of muscle and joint.

Such imperfect compensation for resistance as the subject may have made is irrelevant to the problem in hand since the subject failed to distinguish the extent of movement. No difference between a flexion of 16 cm. and an extension of as much as 10 cm. was detected except in the amount of resistance encountered. The recognition of resistance was evidently not based upon excitation which could give evidence upon the direction and extent of movement.

We may conclude that we are dealing with an anesthesia to passive and active movements of the knee which is practically complete for a rate of movement of less than 20 cm. per second within an arc of 45 degrees in each direction from the right angle. With this established it is possible to test the accuracy of voluntary movements within these limits with the certainty that the intensity and duration of the innervation involved in them are not reflexly controlled by afferent excitations from the moving limb.

Direction of Movement. In the preceding tests where active movements were requested the subject made no errors in the direction of his movements. Only twenty additional trials were given in a formal test of accuracy in the direction of active movements, in all of which movements, however, I have never seen the subject make a mistake in direction, except where he misunderstood instructions. It seems certain that the voluntary excitation of a specific group of muscles is possible in the absence of afferent excitation from it.

Extent of Movement. Two somewhat different methods were used for testing the accuracy in control of extent of voluntary movements. In the first experiments the subject was asked to move his foot through a given distance (an estimated inch, 2 inches, etc.) while the experimenter gave a slight nearly constant support to the backward moving foot in order to control the inability of the relaxed quadriceps to support it against the pull of gravity. The inaccuracy of this method has been considered . . . [above]. The resistance was applied only to the backward movements, probably accounting for the fact that they are slightly shorter than the corresponding forward ones . . . and does not influence the extent of the forward movements, which are equally accurate. When a movement was made its extent was recorded and the foot was brought back passively to its initial position, usually about 110 degrees extension. None of the subject's active movements exceeded the rate of 20 cm. per second so that the controls for slow rates of passive movement apply to all the active movements studied.

In the first experiment the subject was asked to make ten attempts to move his foot through distances which he judged to be ½, 1, 2, and 3 inches. The averages for the different distances are given in Table 4.2. The movements were all longer than the distance asked for but there was practically no overlapping between the movements estimated as different. The pattern set by the first voluntary movement was duplicated rather accurately in later movements.

Table 4.2. Average Distances, Each Based on Ten Trials, through Which the Subject Moved His Foot when Asked to Move through a Distance Which He Judged to Be That Given at the Left

Attempt to move foot, in.°		Average distance moved, cm.	
½	Forward	2.88 ± 0.37	Forward
1	Forward	3.86 ± 0.14	Forward
2	Forward	5.16 ± 0.50	Forward
3	Forward	13.42 ± 0.87	Forward
2	Forward (later test)	7.00 ± 0.27	Forward
½	Backward	1.46 ± 0.25	Backward
1	Backward	3.40 ± 0.24	Backward
2	Backward	7.34 ± 0.68	Backward
3	Backward	11.17 ± 0.57	Backward

° Inches were used because [subject] was not familiar with the metric scale.

In these tests the ten trials for each distance and direction were given successively and it seemed possible that this might contribute something to the accuracy of the movement through the establishment of a rhythm of motor excitation. A series of tests was made therefore in each of which movements through distances of from ½ to 6 inches were made successively. The results of five such tests . . . [are omitted here]. In only one of the five tests, which began with the shortest and progressed to the longest movement, was a movement shorter than one preceding it. . . . The subject was not told that he had made an error, yet an apparent compensation appeared in the next movement, which is the longest made for that distance.

A third series of the same general character was carried out in which all the movements of a given estimated distance were made successively but the different distances to be estimated were taken in irregular order so that an estimate of the absolute distance moved rather than a comparison of the length of successive movements was required. The order in which they were taken up was ½, 6, 1, 3, and 2 inches. The averages for the different distances with their standard deviations . . . [were calculated].

In all these tests there is a surprising accuracy in the extent of the voluntary movements. Too few trials were given at each distance to lend much significance to the coefficients of variation for the attempts to estimate given distances, but in every series of tests the average distances moved are roughly proportional to the distances which the subject was asked to estimate. The pattern set by voluntary movement could be graduated in a series of distinctly different steps.

Comparison of Accuracy of Movement with That of a Normal Subject. For the determination of the variability of movements when the subject was asked to copy a pattern set by his own active movements and for a comparison of this with the normal variability, it was necessary to eliminate any influence which the experimenter might exert in supporting the subject's foot. This was done by supporting the foot by a light spring so that the knee was partially extended. The subject was then asked to draw his foot back through a given distance and then allow it to swing forward freely. The carriage of the recording apparatus was arranged to stop at the limit of the backward movement.

Series of twenty or more trials were obtained for estimated distances of 1, 2, and 3 inches. The average extent of movement for these three distances with the standard coefficient of variations are given in Table 4.3. . . . For comparison, the results of a similar experiment on an apparently normal individual are included in the table. . . . This subject, a physician, was selected at random, the instructions and method of supporting the foot and recording the extent of movement were the same as those employed with the anesthetic subject so that the results with the two subjects may be taken as closely comparable. There is a surprising similarity in the results obtained with the anesthetic and with the normal subject. The movements of both showed wide errors from the distances which they were asked to estimate and the normal subject was not greatly superior to the anesthetic in this respect. In the variability of the movements estimated as equal there was no constant superiority of either subject. The normal individual gave more uniform movements of the longer distance but varied more in estimation of the shorter ones.

We may conclude that the anesthetic subject's control of his movements is not significantly less accurate than that of the normal individual, and it is not clear that for the simple movement studied the afferent impulses from the moving limb contributed anything to the accuracy of

Table 4.3. Variation in the Extent of Movements Estimated as Equal by the Anesthetic Subject and by a Normal Individual

	Distance estimated, in.	Average extent of movement, cm.	Standard coefficient of variation	Error from distance estimated, cm.	Number of trials
Anesthetic subject	1	4.62 ± 0.08	0.254	+ 2.12	84
	2	14.40 ± 0.26	0.122	+ 9.40	21
	3	23.98 ± 0.44	0.167	+16.48	38
Normal subject	1	2.04 ± 0.09	0.476	− 0.46	50
	2	11.24 ± 0.21	0.193	+ 6.00	50
	3	22.30 ± 0.16	0.076	+14.80	50

movement in the normal subject. The chief mechanism for the control of movement is located in some other body segment than that of the moving organ.

The Relation of Rate to Accuracy of Movement

Earlier studies of movement, particularly those of Loeb and Dellabarre, have indicated that the duration of movement may serve as a clue to its extent, in place of the changing pattern of stimulation from the moving limb. It seemed possible that the subject of the present experiments was depending upon the duration of movement by maintaining a constant motor discharge during time intervals corresponding to the distances through which he was asked to move. In the following tests the rate of movement was recorded with the distance.

The subject's foot was suspended with the knee extended to 110 degrees by a spring having a coefficient of 100 grams for each 4.5 cm. extension. He was asked to draw his foot back through distances at a rate suggested by the experimenter. The results of the tests are summarized in

Table 4.4. From this it will be seen first, that the duration of movement is not proportional to the distance when the subject is allowed to choose his own rates but that the rate of long movements is less than of the short ones (tests A, B, and C); second, that the movements may be made of equal extent, although the rate is quite different (tests D and F); third, that, except in test A, the variability in the time of movement is considerably greater than that of its extent; and fourth, that the variation in both extent and time of movement decreases with increasing rate. The experiments thus show a degree of independence in the rate and extent of movement which precludes the possibility that the extent of movement is determined merely by the control of the duration of the excitation of motor pathways. They indicate, on the contrary, that there is a control

Table 4.4. Variation of the Rate of Movement Compared with Variation in the Extent of Movement

Test *	Average distance, cm.	Standard coefficient of variation	Average time, sec.	Standard coefficient of variation	Distance required, in.
A	4.27	0.334	0.69	0.272	1
B	8.05	0.156	2.19	0.216	2
C	11.52	0.153	3.97	0.398	3
D	12.59	0.121	1.44	0.324	3
E	9.87	0.119	0.80	0.264	3
F	11.41	0.115	0.68	0.235	3
Average		0.166		0.285	

* In tests A, B, and C the subject was allowed to select his own rate of movement; in test D he was asked to move quickly; in E, still more rapidly; and in F, to jerk his foot back as quickly as possible. The averages are each based on ten trials.

of the intensity of motor discharge which is independent both of the duration of excitation and of the effects of the discharge upon the effectors. The increase in accuracy with increased speed is in accord with the results obtained by Woodworth (6) in his study of the accuracy of automatic movements and confirms his assumption that rapidity of normal movement interferes with its accuracy only by reducing the influence of the "current control" of the excitations aroused by the moving organs.

The time records showed further that the slow movements were not the result of a single muscular contraction but consisted, in practically every case, of a series of from two to five successive contractions, resulting in alternate acceleration and retardation of the movement. This furnishes additional evidence against a temporal control of movement and also raises the question whether an initial set is adequate to account for an accurate movement which is excited by a series of innervations, without some controlling mechanism which is active continuously during the course of the movements.

Reactions to Error of Movement

In occasional instances the subject stated that a given movement was longer than he intended. Records of only eight such movements have been obtained but in every case the recorded movement was considerably greater than other movements of the series in which it occurred. The recognition of such movements is ascribed by Woodworth (6) to sensory elements arising from the movement. If, as seems established by the tests recorded, the subject of the present experiments was anesthetic to movements of the knee, the detection of error must be ascribed to some mechanism other than the receptor system of the moving organ. This demands a distinction not only between the initial set or intention of movement and the final adjustment due to sensory stimulation, but also the recognition of a third factor in the control of movement, the capacity of reaction to the intensity of innervation which is independent of both the initial set and the excitations from the moving organ. This suggests the old doctrine of the feeling of innervation, although an alternative hypothesis must be considered. This is outlined . . . [below].

Effects of Fatigue

In some of the earlier tests, after many repetitions of a given movement, the subject complained of feeling resistance to his movements and at the same time increased their length. It seemed that this might be the result of fatigue and a number of series of movements was therefore made to test this more thoroughly. The subject was required to repeat a movement of a given length from 20 to 85 times. Resistance to the movements was offered by a spring which drew the foot back to the starting point after each movement.

. . . In each case repetition of the movement led to a considerable increase in its extent. The progression in the length of movement in two series . . . [was clear cut]. During the later trials of the long series the subject stated that he felt tired and that it seemed to require a greater effort to move his foot than had been necessary at first.

We can scarcely interpret such data at present. The progressive increase in the length of movements estimated as equal seems almost certainly the result of the frequent repetition of the movement. From the subject's statement it seems probable also that the increase resulted from some feeling of resistance or of increased effort necessary for the movement, which led to an overcompensation. The source of the stimulation leading to this compensation offers an interesting problem. It does not seem probable that with the extensive anesthesia to all other forms of stimulation there should still persist a normal sensitivity to chemical changes in the muscles which give rise to the feeling of fatigue. The alternative seems to be some cortical mechanism by which the increase in the threshold of excitability of the motor cells resulting from fatigue directly modifies the behavior of other action systems besides the one which is immediately involved in the movement.

The Interaction of Different Muscles in the Control of Movement

Owing to the lack of adequate means for determining the degree of tension of the muscles of the subject's thigh, it was not possible to determine the relative functions of the flexors and extensors in controlling movement, but a few crude observations indicate that much of the normal complex interplay of the muscles is retained. In quick flexing movements a preliminary contraction of the quadriceps extensor is detectable although the inertia of the subject's foot prevents the appearance of a form of reaction movement similar to that first described by Smith (5) for finger movements. There is also, seemingly, an increase in the tension of the quadriceps as the limit of movement is approached.

When the subject is asked to contract both flexors and extensors, to "make his leg tense," an apparent fluctuation in the intensity of innervation results in oscillations of the foot, yet a given degree of extension is maintained much longer than when he is merely asked to hold his leg extended as in the experiment described . . . [earlier]. In the latter case only the extensors are in active contraction so it seems that the simultaneous excitation of both flexors and extensors permits of a steadier and much longer motor discharge than is possible when only one set of muscles is innervated.

The complete loss of the tendon reflexes and the great reduction in the tone of the muscles makes a reciprocal innervation of the antagonistic muscles improbable and suggests that the interaction of antagonistic muscles in the control of movement is regulated by some part of the nervous mechanism cephalad to the spinal segment from which the muscles are innervated.

The Influence of Training

The final question arises as to whether the condition of control of movement in this subject is comparable to that of a normal individual or whether some mechanism of control has been developed by practice which was not functional at the time of the lesion. The present observations were made five years after the spinal injury but the subject's history scarcely supports the view that his control of movement has been reacquired by practice during this time. For the first year after injury he practiced daily walking with crutches for two hours but he made such little progress that he became discouraged and gave up all attempts to recover the lost functions, spending his time either in bed or in a wheel chair. Except for this relatively brief practice, which aimed only at a visual control of movement, there is no history of any activity which could develop an active control of short, slow movements.

Discussion

Every adaptive movement seems to involve three physiologically distinct processes when we attempt to analyze its neurological mechanism. These are (a) the initiation of motor excitation resulting in muscular contraction; (b) its continuation by a series of disturbances propagated either in the central nervous system, or reflexly as a result of the motor discharge; (c) the cessation of excitation of the protagonists and excitation of the antagonists. The first of these has much in common with the simple reflex twitch and is not of moment in the problem of control of accuracy of movement unless in some way the extent of movement may be determined by the initial excitation of the motor pathway. The continuation of the movement implies the production of a series of tetanic contractions arising from successive nerve impulses, which have been excited by a single momentary stimulus. The duration of the tetanus varies with the extent of the contraction. Curiously enough, no more than vague suggestions have been advanced to account for this change from brief to long-continued excitation. The demonstration by Forbes and Gregg (2) that a single strong stimulus may induce the propagation of two or more waves of disturbance in the nerve may furnish the clue to the continuation of movement, but the increase in duration of excitation which they have shown is very slight and seems inadequate to account for movements continued for several seconds. Upon this the present work gives no data except the probable elimination of circular reflexes by which a contracting muscle might stimulate its own contraction, a possibility perhaps adequately disproved already by operative experiments.

The cessation of movement is no more explicable today than its continuation. To be useful, a movement must end with the attainment of a result which is specific for a given stimulus; it must reach a determined distance, exert a determined force, etc. In many cases the stimulus to cessation or inhibition of movement evidently comes from exteroceptors and does not directly involve the receptors of the moving organs, but in the experimental duplication of a pattern set by active movement no extero-stimulation is present to determine the cessation of movement and its duration and extent must be determined wholly within the organism, either by excitation of proprioceptors or by processes carried out wholly within the central nervous system. Several alternative hypotheses to account for the cessation of movement in such cases have been formulated in such a way as to make experimental test possible.

The first of these appeals to the local sign, assuming that the extent of movement is determined by a change of one pattern of stimulation in the moving organ to another. It seems to demand a vast if not infinite series of specific reactions to different patterns of stimulation (3, p. 408).

A second assumes that the extent of movement is determined by the amount of excitation coming from the moving organ, the amount varying with the extent of movement. The hypothesis seems to demand the assumption of priming or preliminary integration of efferent neurones before the initiation of movement.

Third, there may be purely intracortical control by some spreading of excitation, of whose nature we can form no concept at present.

Some evidence bearing upon the role of excitations from the moving organ in the control of accuracy has been obtained by other experimenters. Lack of space prevents any extensive summary of the literature and the thorough review of Woodworth (7) makes this unnecessary. Indications of the relative independence of motor discharge from direct control by circular reflexes come chiefly from three sources: (*a*) The discovery by Bowditch and Southard (1) that the reproduction by movement of a pattern distance set by visual stimulation is more accurate than that of one set by kinesthetic stimulation gives evidence of the importance of the preliminary set for accurate movement, although it throws no light upon the mechanism of the preparation of movement. (*b*) The observation of Loeb (4) upon the inequality of simultaneous movements of the two arms indicates that the movements of the two have a common source of control the action of which is relatively independent of the extent of movement. (*c*) In his study of automatic movements Woodworth (6) found that the accuracy of movement increased in direct ratio to the speed. From this he concluded that such movements are controlled by the initial set.

The significance of the results of the present study depends upon the validity of the evidence obtained for anesthesia to slow movements. The various tests recorded have shown that (*a*) the subject is unable to determine the position of his leg (except occasionally when the knee is hyperextended); (*b*) he cannot detect the extent, duration, direction, or even the presence or absence of passive movements of the knee, if such movements are made at a rate of less than 20 cm. per second; (*c*) he is unable to detect the movements and changes in degree of active contraction of muscles of the thigh occurring during his attempts to hold the knee in a given state of contraction against the pull of gravity; (*d*) he is unable to determine whether or not his attempts to bend his knee have resulted in movement when various amounts of resistance are opposed to the movement. In the face of this evidence we can scarcely hold that he retains a sufficient sensitivity to movement to make possible a reflex control of the extent of movement or a distinction between the extent of actual movement and the intended extent, based upon any stimulation of the receptors of the leg. We are rather forced to the conclusion that the phenomena observed are independent of afferent excitations from the moving organ.

The experiments have shown that the subject is able to control the extent of his movements with almost normal accuracy, to vary the speed and extent of movement independently, and to make rhythmic alterations of flexion and extension. The evidence for anesthesia makes it necessary to assume that all these activities may be carried out in the absence of excitation from the moving organ. The mechanism of control must be sought either in the central nervous system or in some other body segment. Data on the accuracy of movement at different rates show that in the present case its extent is not determined solely by its duration. This makes it necessary to assume some regulation of the intensity of motor discharge which is independent of its duration. Is this determined immediately by the incoming stimulus to movement resulting in a "set" [3] by which a given intensity of motor excitation is aroused explosively without further possibility of control, or is there such a spreading of the motor impulse that some control of its intensity is possible during the discharge? A certain amount of evidence bearing upon this question has been obtained. It comes from three sources. First, very slow movements were not made by the subject as a steady contraction of the muscles but by a series of impulses following each other at intervals of one-tenth second or more. Second, the subject was able to detect the excessively long movements of a series and to state that they were longer than he intended to make them. Third, he complained of fatigue at the same time that he showed objective signs of some disturbance in the normal conditions of movement, while chemical sensitivity to fatigue products in the muscles of the anesthetic leg seems improbable. These points are not at all firmly established by the data at hand but all indicate that there is a spreading of the motor excitation which plays a part in the control of movement and may perhaps lead to some phenomenon such as that described as the feeling of innervation. The hypothetical explanation of such a condition which is most open to experimental test is that assuming a spread of the motor impulse to other action systems with reflex control from them. It may, perhaps, be tested by a study of the possibility of controlled movements within intervals less than the minimum cortical reaction time.

[3] It would be profitless to discuss here the nature or existence of attitude or set. Whether it be a priming of reflex pathways, the assumption of an altered muscular tonus, or what not, it seems distinguishable from the condition in which control of movement occurs after the initiation of the motor impulse.

Experiments to this end are now in progress. As evidence for the importance of the initial set, on the contrary, there is the fact, emphasized earlier by Woodworth (6) for automatic movements, that the accuracy of movement increases directly with the rate. The evidence at hand is not adequate to rule out either alternative.

Summary

Active movements of the left knee were studied in a subject having a complete anesthesia to movements of the joint. Evidence bearing upon the nature of the control of movement in such a condition suggests the following conclusions.

1. Accurate movement of a single joint is possible in the absence of all excitation from the moving organs. The interaction of the various muscles concerned in the movement is not obviously different from that found in normal subjects.

2. In contrast to reflexly controlled movements, the accuracy of movements under such conditions is in direct ratio to their rate, that is, within the time tested, the quicker the movement the more accurately it is made.

3. The control of accuracy of the movements is relatively independent of their duration; movements of different lengths do not result from a uniform excitation continued for varying time intervals but from variations in the intensity of motor discharge.

4. It is probable that a control of the intensity of motor discharge after its initiation is possible in the absence of excitation from the organs activated.

5. The normal phenomena of fatigue occur when it is highly probable that the chemical sensitivity of the fatigued muscles is reduced.

REFERENCES

1. Bowditch and Southard. *J. Physiol.*, 1881, 3, 232–245.
2. Forbes and Gregg. *Amer. J. Physiol.*, 1915, 39, 172–235.
3. Ladd and Woodworth. *Elements of physiological psychology.* New York: 1911.
4. Loeb. *Arch. ges. Physiol.*, 1897, 41, 107–127.
5. Smith. *Mind*, 1903, 12, 47–58.
6. Woodworth. *Psychol. Rev.* (Monogr. Suppl.), 1899, 3 (114).
7. Woodworth. *Le mouvement.* Paris: 1903.

5. THE RETENTION OF HABITS BY THE RAT AFTER DESTRUCTION OF THE FRONTAL PORTION OF THE CEREBRUM [1]

Much has been written regarding the neurology of learning and especial attention has been directed to the cerebrum. Comparatively little evidence has been adduced to show what cerebral elements are used in the formation of habits, although recent experimental investigations show that the frontal portions of the cerebrum are utilized by monkeys, dogs, and cats.[2] In only those animals with a highly developed brain is there a distinct differentiation of the frontal (as an association area) from the central (so-called motor and sensory-kinesthetic) area, and in fact the possibility of the histological differentiation of numerous areas of the brains of many of the lower animals is slight. The relatively simple and homogeneous character of the cerebral cortex in the rodents makes their cerebral physiology worthy of study, and there is the added advantage that the animals acquire habits rapidly and much information is at hand regarding their normal reactions.

At the same time, on account of their low cost and ease of housing, many different experiments on the brain may be made which are not possible with animals having larger and more highly developed brains. Such experiments on rats may be expected to give results of at least suggestive value respecting the functions of corresponding parts of more highly evolved brains. Thus, if it is found that these animals can acquire habits after the removal of certain small or large parts of the cerebrum, but not after the removal of other parts, or if they can retain but cannot acquire habits after certain cerebral destructions, there will exist a basis for further extensive and intensive work on the so-called higher animals. The present work was undertaken with those objects in view.

[1] EDITORS' NOTE: S. I. Franz and K. S. Lashley, authors. From *Psychobiology*, 1917, **1**, 3–18. Reproduced by permission of Williams and Wilkins Co. From the Government Hospital for the Insane and the psychological laboratory of the Johns Hopkins University.
[2] For most of the evidence: S. I. Franz. *The frontal lobes.* New York: Science Press, 1907.

Several questions were posed, although the facts to answer only a few parts of these questions are now available. Some of the questions are: Do rats retain habits of recent formation after the destruction of certain cerebral regions? Do they retain habits of long standing, or those in which there has been an overtraining or overlearning? Can rats learn after the whole removal of the cortex? If learning and retention are possible after destruction of parts of the cortex, how much and what parts of the brain are necessary for, and what parts are normally used in the formation and retention of habits? At the present time there are available results of experiments in which the frontal portions of the brain have been destroyed, and in which there have been destructions of two-thirds or more of the whole cortex (that of the cerebral convexity), but only those experiments dealing with the effects of frontal destruction will be reported here.

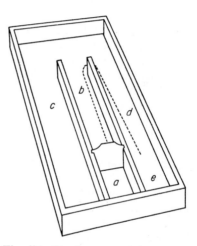

When the experiments were undertaken there was available a large number of rats which had been trained in a simple maze for other purposes and it was decided to use them in preliminary tests. The maze was built after the pattern of the Yerkes discrimination box (Fig. 5.1). It consists of a starting compartment (a) leading by a sliding door to a central alley (b), which at its outer end offers the alternatives of the cul de sac (c) and the alley (d) leading directly to the

Fig. 5.1. Simple maze. (a) Starting compartment, (e) food. The dotted line shows the path taken by well-trained animals, keeping close to the right-hand partition and cutting close around the corner.

food (e). A maze of this character had decided advantages for the training of large numbers of animals but is not altogether suitable for tests on retention on account of the speed with which it is learned and the degree of probability that any given correct trial is the result of chance. Incidental observations on the behavior of the animals in the maze are therefore of great importance for the determination of the retention of the habit.

Two activities of the animals in the maze are to be especially noted, as their characteristics are evidences of learning or lack of learning, and of retention of the maze habits. These activities relate to the reactions at the door of the starting box and to the shortening of the path to the food.

When first introduced into the starting compartment of the maze the rat sniffs at the wire cover, sides, and corners of the compartment and pays no particular attention to the door. When the door is first raised he usually stands erect and sniffs at its lower edge before venturing into the first alley. With practice his reactions become centered on the door; he tries to push it up or sniffs at the crack under it. The moment that the experimenter touches the door to open it the rat turns with his head in the right front corner of the starting compartment and as soon as the door is raised high enough to admit his body crawls out into the alley. This behavior is noted in the records of the different animals as "normal orientation to opening door." In his first trials in the maze the rat spends much time in sniffing at the wire cover, the walls, and particularly the corners of the maze. The trained rat can go from the starting compartment to the food in 1.2 seconds. The minimum time on the first trial for any of the sixty rats that have been trained has been eight seconds and the modal time is about thirty seconds, most of which is spent in exploratory sniffing. With practice these exploratory movements disappear and the animal runs to the food without a pause. Many animals come to follow the path marked by the dotted line in Fig. 5.1. That is, they keep close to the right-hand wall of the middle alley and keep close to the end of the partition in rounding the turn. This cutting down of excess distance and the absence of exploratory sniffing are characteristic of the later stages of learning, and when they appear in retention tests are therefore conclusive evidence for at least a partial retention of the motor habits of the maze.

In training, ten successive errorless trials were taken as evidence for learning (rarely more than six errors are made in the hundred trials following the achievement of this record). Some of the rats were then given an overtraining of from one to two hundred trials before the destruction of the frontal lobes. Others were operated upon on the day following that on which learning was completed.

The operations were performed under ether anesthesia, and at the end the cut scalp was closed with sutures and was covered with a cotton and collodion dressing.

In some cases a transverse opening about 4 by 8 mm. was made in the skull just back of the fronto-parietal suture, and the frontal area of the brain was destroyed by passing a narrow scalpel diagonally forward to the region of the olfactory bulbs and thence cutting out to the sides of the cranial cavity. In other cases two small trephine holes were made in the region of the suture and a spear-pointed needle was inserted through these, pushed through the frontal area and drawn to the sides to cut away the frontal regions. Owing to the small operative field it is not possible to determine the extent of the lesion at the time of operation but the possibility of using a large number of animals and of later determination of the extent of the destruction of tissue makes it possible to obtain records of some animals in which the exact lesion desired has been produced.

Most of the animals have been kept for two weeks or more after the operation and in many cases the absorption of the clot has progressed to such an extent that it seems advisable to wait until histological examinations of the brains can be made before describing the lesions. Fourteen animals have been operated upon for destruction of the frontal lobes and of these eight have been autopsied. In these the gross lesion has been in every case as extensive as that indicated in Fig. 5.2, and in three of the animals has extended back so as to involve the anterior two-thirds of the cortex.

Brief records of the animals studied are given below. Whenever possible, fifteen trials in the maze were obtained from each animal on the day following the operation. The time consumed in each of these trials in going from the starting compartment to the food dish and the numbers of errors, either of entering the cul de sac or of turning back upon the true pathway, were recorded. In the following records the total time consumed in these fifteen trials and the total number of errors are compared with the total time and errors of the first fifteen trials made by the same

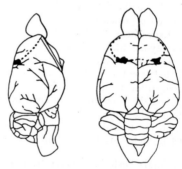

Fig. 5.2. Diagram of the extent of the lesion in rat H1♀, as determined by gross dissection.

rat in its first training in the maze. The time and number of errors of the rats' first trials in the maze at the begining of training are also compared with those of the first trial of the retention tests. In addition to this observations are reported on the general behavior of the animals in the maze.

Animals Tested for Retention without Overtraining

Experiment 1. G2♀. Ninety-four days old at the beginning of training. Learning was completed in fifty-four trials at ten trials per day. No overtraining.

Operation through two trephine holes, followed by extensive hemorrhage. Retention was tested twenty-four hours after the operation. The animal was constantly irritated by inflammation of the nasal sinuses but was otherwise in good condition. Orientation in starting compartment was normal. In every trial except the second one the animal kept close to the right-hand wall of the middle alley and cut close to the end of the partition. On the second trial she turned into the entrance of the cul de sac but did not advance more than two inches. Various tests suggest that she was anosmic. . . .

Experiment 2. G1♀. Ninety-four days old. Learning was completed in twenty-three trials with two trials per day. No overtraining.

Operation through large transverse opening, followed by considerable hemorrhage but with recovery of motor coordination within half an hour. Retention was tested twenty-six hours after the operation. The rat was very weak, falling over when attempting to make quick turns or to scratch the dressing on her head. She oriented in the starting compartment and gave no evidence of exploratory sniffing in the maze. On the first trial she turned into the cul de sac and wandered back and forth for a few seconds, then went directly to the food. A second error was made on the eleventh trial. The other trials were made correctly but at a rather slow rate. The rat made frequent long stuporous pauses and spent a good bit of time also in scratching at the dressing on her head. On the following day she was given twenty trials in the maze and in every case reached the food without error and in less than four seconds. . . .

Experiment 3. H1♀. Ninety-two days old. Learning was completed in twenty-one trials with two trials per day. No overtraining.

Operation through two trephine holes, with little hemorrhage. Retention was tested twenty-four hours after the operation. The rat oriented in the starting compartment, ran promptly and without exploratory smelling, and never explored the maze in a way comparable to that of normal animals in their first trials. She entered the cul de sac on the first, fifth, eleventh, and thirteenth trials but turned back promptly before reaching the end of it. On the errorless trials she followed the path marked in Fig. 5.1. . . .

Animals Tested after Overtraining

Experiment 4. G1♂. Seventy-three days old. Learning was completed in twenty-one trials with ten trials per day. Training was continued for 170 trials.

Destruction of frontal lobes through large transverse opening, followed by little hemorrhage. Retention was tested twenty hours after the operation. The rat oriented correctly in the starting compartment and advanced promptly when the door was opened. On the first trial he turned into the cul de sac and stopped with his head in the first corner, then backed out and went directly to the food. He made a second error on the fourteenth trial. The other trials were correct but delayed by a peculiar reaction. When he reached the first corner after passing the turn he would pause with his nose close in the corner (but without apparent sniffing), then back away and turn down the alley to the food. Tests made by pulling his vibrissae while he was eating indicated that these organs were lacking in tactile sensitivity. . . .

Experiment 5. F1♀. Seventy-five days old. Learning was completed in ninety trials with ten trials per day. Training was continued for 120 trials. Operation through a single trephine hole on the left with little hemorrhage. Retention was tested twenty-six hours later. The rat oriented in the starting compartment, and in the majority of trials followed the path indicated in Fig. 5.1. On the third and fifth trials she retraced a part of the direct pathway to the food and on the tenth trial she swerved so that her head was in the cul de sac, but she never ventured entirely off the direct pathway. . . .

Experiment 6. F2 ♂. Sixty-nine days old. Learning was completed in twenty-four trials with two trials per day. Training was continued for 170 trials.

Operation through large transverse opening with very severe hemorrhage. Retention was tested twenty-three hours after the operation. The rat was active and oriented correctly in the starting compartment. In four trials the rat returned to the starting compartment after advancing for his own length into the middle alley, but he did not leave the pathway once in fifteen trials. . . .

Experiment 7. G3 ♂. Seventy-three days old. Learning was completed in twenty-four trials with ten trials per day. Training was continued for 170 trials.

Operation through trephine holes with little hemorrhage. Retention was tested twenty-four hours after the operation. He oriented correctly to the opening of the door, ran quickly and followed the path of Fig. 5.1 in all but the first and second trials. In the first trial he entered the cul de sac but turned back without exploratory sniffing. In the second trial he put his head into the entrance of the cul de sac, but did not enter it. He appeared to be anosmic. . . .

Experiment 8. F2 ♀. Seventy-five days old. Learning was completed in twenty-five trials with two trials per day. Training was continued for 200 trials.

Operation by transverse opening with severe hemorrhage. Retention was tested twenty-six hours after the operation. The rat was very weak and her movements were, as a rule, slow and hesitating but without marked pauses at the entrance of the cul de sac. On the first trial she explored the cul de sac quickly, but without exploratory sniffing, and had some difficulty in finding the food in the dish. On the tenth and thirteenth trials she again entered the cul de sac but did not go to the end. On the other trials she followed the most direct path and cut close around the end of the partition. . . .

Experiment 9. D1 ♀. Sixty-nine days old. Learning was completed in forty-eight trials with ten trials per day. Training was continued for 200 trials.

The frontal lobes were destroyed by a transverse incision. Retention was tested twenty-four hours after the operation. The rat oriented correctly in the starting compartment, attempting to lift the door by thrusting her nose under it. Two errors were made on the fifth trial. The others were run correctly and by the shortest possible path. There was no exploratory sniffing. . . .

Experiment 10. B1 ♂. Sixty-seven days old. Learning was completed in seventy trials with ten trials per day. Training was continued for 200 trials.

The frontal lobes were destroyed by a transverse incision. Retention was tested twenty-eight hours after operation. On the first trial the rat explored the maze hurriedly without pausing to sniff. In the later trials he usually paused and swayed back and forth at the end of the first passage but entered the cul de sac only once, on the seventh trial. He oriented in the starting compartment. . . .

Experiment 11. F3 ♂. Sixty-nine days old. Learning was completed in sixty trials with ten trials per day. Training was continued for 200 trials.

The anterior third of the cortex was destroyed. Little hemorrhage. Retention was tested twenty-two hours after the operation. On the first trial the rat turned into the cul de sac and ran half way to the end, then turned back and went directly to the food. He made no other error in the fifteen trials of the test, and followed the most direct route to the food. . . .

Experiment 12. G4 ♂. Seventy-three days old. Learning was completed in sixteen trials with two trials per day. Training was continued for 200 trials.

Frontal lobes were removed by a transverse incision in the region of the frontal-parietal suture. Retention was tested twenty-four hours after the operation. The animal was very weak and spastic. He reacted promptly to the maze, however, orienting in the starting compartment and never hesitating at the turn in the maze. He had some little difficulty finding the food, pushing under instead of above the edge of the dish. After ten trials he began to show evidence of fatigue so the remaining trials for retention were postponed for two days when he had gained almost normal strength. . . .

Experiment 13. G2 ♂. Sixty-nine days old. Learning was completed in twenty-four trials with two trials per day. Training was continued for 200 trials.

Frontal lobes destroyed by a transverse incision. Retention was tested twenty-two hours after the operation. The animal was very weak and spastic. He had great difficulty in finding the food and gnawed at the edge of the dish as much as at the bread. Nevertheless he followed the direct path to the food with never a suggestion of reaction to the entrance to the cul de sac. During the trials there were many stuporous pauses (one of fifty seconds' duration, which accounts for the long time consumed in the fifteen trials . . .) so, after five trials the rat was returned to the home cage and the tests continued two days later when he had recovered strength. . . .

Experiment 14. F4 ♂. Sixty-nine days old. Learning was completed in eighteen trials with two trials per day. Training was continued for 120 trials.

Frontal lobes destroyed by a transverse incision through a small trephine hole on the left. Retention tested twenty hours after operation. The animal had developed a left hemi-paresis and failed to leave the starting compartment of the maze in an hour on each of three consecutive days. Autopsy showed an extensive clot over the orbital surface of the right hemisphere, extending back to the pons.

Summary of Results of Experiments

The records of time and errors have been summarized in Table 5.1. From the averages it appears that the rats which were not overtrained required 29 per cent less time for the first fifteen trials after the destruction of the frontal lobes and made 53 per cent fewer errors than they did in learning the maze. This in itself is evidence for a partial retention of the habit. When considered in connection with the data on their behavior in the maze it shows that there was little if any loss that cannot be accounted for by the distracting effects of the head bandages and the general shock effects of the operation. None of the animals showed the exploratory sniffing at cracks and corners which is so characteristic of the untrained rat in the maze. All were tested immediately after the retention tests by being placed in a strange cage with food and all spent at least thirty seconds in exploring the cage before pausing at the food, so that the lack of exploratory activities in the maze must be looked upon as due to retention of the habit and not to a general sluggishness resulting from the operations. The three rats which were not overtrained oriented in the starting compartment and two regularly followed the path marked in

Table 5.1. Time Required for Reaching Food; and Number of Errors Made by Rats in Learning Maze and in Retention Tests after Destruction of Frontal Lobes

	Animals without overtraining					
	Learning			Retention		
	First 15 trials		First trial	First 15 trials		First trial
Number	Time, sec.	Errors	Time	Time, sec.	Errors	Time
G2 ♀	188	5	15	54	1(?)	2.6
G1 ♀	117	8	10	159	2	45
H1 ♀	85	2	10	64	4	8
Totals	390	15	35	277	7	55.6
	Animals overtrained					
G1 ♂	1018	21	34	92	2	12
F1 ♀	640	19	15	44	2	4
F2 ♂	93	7	13	68	0	6
G3 ♂	359	11	11	55	1	8
F2 ♀	203	7	60	115	3	18
D1 ♀	566	23	18	57	3	1.8
B1 ♂	1797	33	32	137	2	12
F3 ♂	428	11	175	50	1	11
G4 ♂	135	2	20	51	0	2
G2 ♂	134	3	31	123	0	8
Totals	5408	137	399	791	13	82.8

Fig. 5.1. The abnormality of behavior of the third (G1 ♀) was probably due to loss of sensitivity of the vibrissae.

The animals which were overtrained required 87 per cent less time for the first fifteen trials after operation and made 90 per cent fewer errors than in their initial learning. This, in addition to the data on individual behavior in the maze, shows that there was practically no loss of the habit resulting from the destruction of the frontal lobes.

There is an apparent difference in the amount of retention between animals which were overtrained and those which were trained only until they had learned the problem. This difference is probably not so great as is indicated by the averages because the long time spent by the non-overtrained group is the result of the inclusion of the rat G1 ♀ which spent a great deal of time trying to remove the dressing from her head.

Only one animal did not show evidence of the maze habit after removal of the frontal portions of the brain. This animal showed such an amount of muscular weakness, or apathy, that the running of the maze was not attempted by it even after the fashion of an untrained animal. With this exception the tests gave indisputable evidence of the retention of the habit after the frontal portion of both hemispheres has been excised. Moreover, the evidence is more compelling because of some obvious behavior disturbances in a number of the animals. Thus, it has been reported of the second animal, G1 ♀, that although the time for running the maze after the operation was greater than in the training series its other behavior relating directly to the maze was retained. The time variation (lengthening) was due entirely to changes in its physical condition other than those necessarily related to its maze activities. That this is so will be realized when it is remembered that the delays were made up of periods of scratching its head-dressing and of long stuporous or apathetic pauses. In the fourth animal the sensibility of the vibrissae was decreased, perhaps they were anesthetic, and the short times for running the maze after the operation are especially noteworthy. The twelfth and thirteenth animals were weak and spastic, and exhibited abnormal reactions in connection with the food dish, but both managed to find the correct path quite promptly. The time for the first fifteen trials of the thirteenth animal, G2 ♂, after operation was only slightly less than that of the corresponding period of training, but the long stuporous pauses account for much of the time that was taken.

As a whole, therefore, the experiments show that in the white rat the removal of large parts of the frontal portions of the brain does not greatly interfere with a learned reaction. This is the more remarkable since it seems probable that the so-called motor area is in that region and that in most, if not all, of the cases there was a destruction or abolition of the motor connections. While it cannot be concluded with certainty, it seems likely that the motor derangements which were exhibited by many of the rats were due to the interference with the normal efferent impulses and not to the general anemia (from the hemorrhage of the operation). Some of the animals also showed obvious disturbances of sensibility, the observations indicating that in some the stimuli to the vibrissae and olfactory stimuli did not give normal effects. In the view of the importance of these two forms of sensibility in the rat's reactions, we are led to wonder whether these retain their predominance in the animal's learned activities, or are replaced by other forms of sensibility, such as the general kinesthetic. Although the results give plain evidence of noninterference (relative, to be sure) with learned reactions when the frontal portions of the brain have been destroyed they also suggest that the habit reaction is not necessarily cortical in these animals. Other experiments which have been performed bear out this conclusion, but it seems best to reserve the account of these other tests until careful cerebral examinations have been completed.

6. A SIMPLE MAZE: WITH DATA ON THE RELATION OF THE DISTRIBUTION OF PRACTICE TO THE RATE OF LEARNING [1]

A Test of the Validity of Results Obtained with the Simple Maze

The use of complicated mazes for the study of learning in animals originated in an effort to determine the limits of educability of the lower mammals. The problem of habit formation in animals soon expanded, however, to include the more general problem of the mechanism of learning and this led to a search for a method of comparing individual differences in learning ability and average differences for groups trained under diverse conditions. The application of the complicated maze to the determination of individual differences followed as a matter of course, since it provided a practicable technique for the training of animals. But in none of the pioneer work, nor, indeed, in any of the studies thus far recorded, has there been a thorough test of the applicability of the maze technique to the particular problems studied by its aid. This is true also of the various problem boxes and other apparatus used for training animals in complex habits.

The study of habit formation in animals has now advanced to a stage where accurate work is possible and where statistical methods can and should be employed for the evaluation of data. Many problems require the comparison of the rates of learning of numerous animals trained under diverse conditions, as in studies of the action of drugs. If the animals are trained in complex habits the experiment frequently requires an expenditure of time out of proportion to the results obtained, and the necessary restriction of the data to a few subjects leaves the experimental results inconclusive. A simpler technique is therefore desirable; one by which the subjects may be trained rapidly and data gathered upon a large number

[1] EDITORS' NOTE: From *Psychobiology*, 1918, **1**, 353–367. Reproduced by permission of Williams and Wilkins Co. From the Johns Hopkins University and the University of Minnesota.

within a reasonable time. The training of larger numbers might, perhaps, be accomplished by the use of automatic training and recording apparatus but the apparatus of this character that has been devised is bulky, expensive, and not altogether dependable. Further, many animals seem to be much more disturbed by mechanical contrivances in the training box than by manipulation in the hands of the experimenter and the preliminary training necessary to accustom them to moving doors, and the like, nearly counterbalances the advantages of automatic training. The alternative method for gathering larger amounts of data involves the training of the animals in some easily acquired habit for which no great expenditure of time will be required by any one animal.

A widely accepted objection to the use of simpler habits arises, however, from the possibility that these may fail to demonstrate individual differences which would appear in more complex forms of learning. This is perhaps true where the primary interest of the study is in the comparative intelligence of the animals but where the problem is primarily that of the mechanism of learning, the nervous changes involved in the reintegration of conduction paths, the phenomena resulting from the complexities of the habit only serve to confuse the data and make it impossible to distinguish between the effects of simple reintegration and those resulting from the simultaneous formation of a number of habits. This confusion is illustrated by the results of studies of the effects of the distribution of practice upon the rate of learning. Such results, as I have shown in previous articles (2, 3) are due at least in part to the interference of simultaneously formed habits and, as the present study indicates, are probably always due to the complexity of the habit and not to any fundamental character of the learning process. The failure of a simple habit to reveal a difference which appeared when more complex habits were studied should indicate, therefore, that the difference found was due to some factor introduced by the formation of several habits simultaneously, rather than that training in the simple habit failed to reveal any fundamental differences in the processes of learning.

In view of the need for a simpler technique it seemed that a study of the adaptability of some simple habit to a comparative study of the rate of learning in diverse groups of animals would be of value. Since the rat is the animal most studied and perhaps best fitted for laboratory study it was chosen for a test of technique. Various attempts were made to adapt the methods of study of the conditioned reflex to the rat, but without much success, and finally a simple maze was adopted as offering a possible technique for comparative work. It was modeled after the Yerkes discrimination box, offering a choice between a single cul de sac and an alley leading to food (see Fig. 5.1).

The questions to be answered by the study were: When differentially treated animals learn the simple maze are differences in the rate of learning as evident as in the formation of complex habits? If such differences appear, are they of the same character as those revealed in complex habits? How great an economy of the experimenter's time is made possible by the use of the simple maze?

It seemed advisable to use some conditions of training which have been tested already in complicated mazes, and of these the use of practice periods of diverse length was selected as a condition whose general results are well established and whose details are capable of wide variation.

Twenty-five rats were trained in the simple maze with ten trials per day and twenty-four with two trials per day. Entering the cul de sac or turning back along the true path was counted as an error and ten successive trials without error were required as a criterion of learning. The general precautions to secure uniformity in the groups compared were those which I have described in an earlier study of the circular maze (4). The conditions of feeding were varied somewhat within the groups: details of this will be considered in the second part of this paper.

The average number of trials required for learning by the animals having two trials per day was 21.5 ± 0.81. The average number for the animals having ten trials per day was 57.8 ± 4.70. The difference is 36.3 ± 4.76 trials in favor of the group practicing with fewer trials per day, a saving of about 60 per cent as a result of the distributed practice. This result is in accord with the data obtained by Ulrich (8) in his study with the circular maze and indicates that the simple maze is as well adapted to bring out group differences of this character as is the more complicated apparatus.

When the animals had learned the maze they were used in operative experiments. Portions of the cerebral cortex were destroyed and retention of the maze habit was tested after the operation. In this type of work also the simple maze proved useful (5).

With respect to the time consumed in training, the simple maze offers a great advantage over the more complicated apparatus. The average time consumed by each of the forty-nine animals in actual practice in the maze was 7.4 minutes. The average time required in practice by a group of thirty-two normal animals trained previously in the circular maze was 47.1 minutes. That is, more than six times as much time must be spent in training animals in the circular maze as in the simple maze, yet the results of the former method are in no way more reliable than those of the latter.

The saving of time is probably of less importance than these figures suggest, for a great deal of time is consumed in placing the animals in the starting compartment, in waiting for them to enter the maze, in recording their behavior, and in caring for them between training periods, so that the time spent in actual training is only a small per cent of that demanded by experimental work. Even so, the item of forty minutes saved in the training of each animal is not to be neglected.

It seems then that the simple maze offers a dependable method of comparing individual differences in learning ability, not inferior to that proved by training in more complex habits, and that it affords a significant economy of the experimenter's time.

Data on the Effects of the Temporal Distribution of Practice

The relative simplicity of the habits that must be formed for the accurate running of the simple maze has made it possible to distinguish certain types of behavior which seem correlated with the effects of the temporal distribution of practice and may contribute something to our knowledge of the way in which long practice periods retard habit formation in the rat. The experiment was originally planned to test the effects of a variety of methods of training other than variations in the distribution of practice. The unexpected result appeared that the diverse methods of training produced different effects, conditioned by the distribution of practice, and it is in these different effects that the chief interest of the experiment lies.

For training the animals were divided into four groups with which diverse methods of training were used. With one of the groups (A) the customary methods of training were employed. Food was placed in the end of one alley (Fig. 5.1e). The animals were confined in the end of this alley and fed there on three days preceding training. During training they were allowed to reach the food at every trial; that is, to correct errors made in the cul de sac.

The second group (B) received similar training except that the animals were allowed to explore the entire maze, without food, for twenty minutes on the day before training was begun.

The third group (C) was treated like the first except that the animals were not allowed to correct their errors but were returned immediately to the starting compartment if they entered the cul de sac or turned back along the correct path. Each time that they were returned to the starting compartment a trial was recorded, whether or not they had reached the food.

The fourth group (D) was trained like the first except that a dish of food, covered with fine wire netting so that the food could not be reached, was placed in the end of the cul de sac.

Each of these groups was subdivided into two, one of which received ten, the other two trials per day. A summary of the groups is given in Table 6.1.

Training was continued until the animals made ten successive trials without error. In some cases training was continued beyond this point

for as much as two hundred trials. None of the animals so trained made
more than 5 per cent of errors in these later trials, so that the criterion
may be looked upon as indicating practically perfect learning.

The average numbers of trials per day required by the different groups
are given in Table 6.2. Under all the various conditions of training the
animals which were trained with only two trials per day learned more

Table 6.1. Conditions of Training for Animals Tested in the Simple Maze

| | | Number of animals | |
| | | --- | --- |
Group	Variations from customary methods of training	Two trials per day	Ten trials per day
A	Normal	10	9
B	Preliminary exploration	5	5
C	Errors not corrected	5	5
C	Screened food in cul de sac	5	5

rapidly, per unit of practice, than those which were trained with ten
trials per day. The average difference for all the groups resulting from
the different distributions of practice is 36.3 ± 4.8, and as this is nearly
eight times its probable error indicates a real effect of the distribution of
practice.

But among the groups trained by different methods the effects of distribution of practice vary enormously, from a minimum of 53 per cent to
a maximum of 338 per cent increase in practice required for learning
following equal lengthening of the practice periods. The relatively slight
individual variation within the groups, indicated by the small probable
errors, makes the differences significant.

The methods of training most effective in producing variations from
the rate of learning determined in the customary way were preliminary
exploration of the maze without food and presence of screened food in
the cul de sac. The significant differences found are:

	Two trials per day		Ten trials per day	
A-B	1.9	2.0	22.3	5.6
D-A	4.1	2.5	58.7	10.6

(C and A are practically identical.)

The influence of these different methods of training was in the same direction for both concentrated and distributed practice, but only in concentrated practice were marked effects produced.

The simplicity of the movements involved in traversing the maze made it possible to record the behavior of the animals in detail and to distinguish characteristic differences in the behavior of the different groups which seem to be correlated with the rate of learning. The variations in behavior relate chiefly to two instinctive modes of response to the maze problem.

1. When given food in a somewhat unfamiliar environment the rat will almost invariably explore the neighborhood of the food before eating. In the circular maze the exploration usually includes the food compartment and the alley surrounding it. If the animal is not restrained after

Table 6.2. Average Number of Trials Required for Learning the Simple Maze by Animals Trained under Diverse Conditions

Group	Average trials at 2 per day		Number of rats	Average trials at 10 per day		Number of rats	Difference (trials)	
A	21.1	0.8	10	51.7	4.3	9	30.6	4.4
B	19.2	1.9	5	29.4	3.6	5	10.2	4.14
C	22.6	1.7	5	44.6	2.7	5	22.0	3.2
D	25.2	2.4	5	110.4	9.7	5	85.2	9.9
All	21.5	0.8	25	57.8	4.7	24	36.3	4.8

reaching the food it is almost certain to go through this exploration on the first trial of each day's practice. Once the exploration is completed the animal will go directly to the food in the succeeding trials. The same tendency appears in the simple maze with an extension of the area explored to include almost the entire maze. This is shown by the following analysis of the path followed by the animals during their first and second trials in the simple maze.

The data are taken from fifty-two animals with which training was begun in the simple maze. Three of these were discarded because of illness; the remaining forty-nine are those described above. Of the fifty-two, twenty-five avoided the cul de sac on the first trial. This is one less than the expectation from chance, since only two alternative paths were offered. Of these twenty-five, chance should have led one half to enter the cul de sac and one half to avoid it on the second trial and, if the principle of recency were an important factor in learning, more than half should have gone directly to the food. Instead of this, however, seventeen of the animals entered the cul de sac on the second trial and only eight went directly to the food. This result seems to indicate an instinctive tendency to varied activity, or to a thorough exploration of the environment.

The tendency to explore the maze becomes much more pronounced if the animals are frightened at any time during training and this leads to additional errors and an apparently increased learning time.

2. The second factor of importance in prolonging the learning process in concentrated practice is emotional disturbance in the food compartment. Unless the animals have been handled a great deal they will give avoiding reactions when the experimenter attempts to pick them up and readily learn to avoid places where they have been caught. The following behavior is typical of the animals in the groups which showed marked retardation in concentrated practice.

The animal reaches the food and begins to eat. The experimenter puts his hand into the food compartment to transfer the rat to the starting box. The rat retreats and is caught. On the next trial he advances toward the food, pauses, extends his head upward toward the place whence the hand came before, makes several false starts, and finally advances timidly to the food, giving evidence of increased tonus and readiness for flight. Under the usual conditions of training (group A) this behavior rarely appears on the first trial, becomes marked on the third to fifth, and disappears by the end of the practice period. It seems as though several trials were required to set up the association between the food compartment and the avoiding reaction, in each day's practice, and several more to fatigue the conditioned emotional reflex so established. This is shown clearly by the following average times required for successive trials on the second day of training by the animals in group A:

Trial	1	2	3	4	5	6	7	8	9	10
Seconds	18	22	57	37	28	15	13	13	17	16

The increased time in the second to fifth trials is characteristic of many of the records and is correlated with the flight reactions near the food compartment.

The chief importance of these two factors in favoring distributed practice lies in the fact that their effects are shown in the later trials of each day's practice. When only two trials are given there is not time for the summation of the exploratory and flight impulses and so fewer errors due to these causes are made. That they were important factors in determining the effects of distribution of practice is shown by the differences in the behavior of the animals in the three groups which differed in the number of trials required for learning. The rats in group B, which had been allowed to become thoroughly familiar with the maze, rarely gave

the flight reactions in the food compartment and there was slight indication of a summation of emotional disturbance such as appeared in
group A. Familiarity with the maze reduced the tendency to emotional
disturbance. This is shown by the following average times for successive
trials in group B (ten trials per day) on the second day of practice:

Trial	1	2	3	4	5	6	7	8	9	10
Seconds	38	22	20	17	22	8	5	5	5	13

The time of successive trials falls steadily throughout the practice period.
The rats in group D, on the contrary, showed a much more marked tendency to flight reactions in the food compartment than did those in the
other groups. They would frequently advance to the food dish, then turn,
run quickly into the cul de sac, and gnaw for some time at the wire cover
of the food dish there. Apparently owing to the presence of the screened
food in the cul de sac, as offering the stimulus of food without associated
handling, these animals frequently persisted in their avoidance of the
food compartment and in their efforts to get at the food in the cul de sac
throughout the practice period. This is shown by the following average
times for successive trials in the second day's practice:

Trial	1	2	3	4	5	6	7	8	9	10
Seconds	14	34	33	11	27	22	35	20	36	154

The prolonged time toward the end of the day's practice is characteristic
of the early days of practice of this group.

The summation of the exploratory impulse and of emotional disturbance thus seems to be characteristic of the groups showing marked
retardation of learning in concentrated practice. Further, the extent to
which such summation occurred varied with the different conditions of
training and resulted in corresponding variations in the amount of
retardation. It thus seems clear that a great part of the retardation resulting from concentrated practice is due to this summation of instinctive
reactions. Even in group B, which showed the least loss of efficiency in
ten trials practice per day, there was some indication of a tendency for the
animals to avoid the place where they had been caught and it seems
probable that a large part of the retardation shown by this group is due
also to the interfering effect of this emotional factor. The greater retardation shown by the other groups (in excess of 53 per cent) is due, almost
certainly, to this one factor of summation of instinctive reactions.

The Bearing of the Results upon Theories of the Neurological Basis of Learning

Experimental work upon the effects of the distribution of effort in learning has given uniform results for practically every process studied. Within

limits as yet undetermined concentrated practice is less efficient than distributed. But no satisfactory explanation of this seemingly universal phenomenon has yet been advanced. In an earlier paper (2) I have listed seven different possible explanations for the superiority of distributed practice found in archery, between which it is not possible to choose on the basis of the existing evidence, and the list then given was certainly not exhaustive.

The universality of the phenomenon might be taken to indicate that it is due to some fundamental process in the formation of new functional connections in the nervous system and this is the view which seems to be most generally held. For example, Starch says (7): "Why are shorter and more numerous periods economical? The main reason, no doubt, is the well known fact that a period of rest after newly formed associations gives them a chance to become settled and fixed." Colvin (1) makes much of this hypothesis, also, and gives it the rank of a general law that "it takes a certain amount of time for associations to fix themselves," and this is used to explain not only the effects of distribution of practice but also retroactive inhibition and the facts included under Jost's law.

From the standpoint of neurological theory the truth or falsity of this hypothesis is of extreme importance. If there is a gradual strengthening of associations during periods of nonpractice there is implied a continuation of chemical changes within the nerve cells, initiated by the passage of a neural impulse through new channels and persisting for hours or even days without the influence of continued impulses. If, on the contrary, no such gradual fixation occurs, the problem of the neuro-chemistry of learning is simplified by admission of the hypothesis that the effects of the passage of the neural impulse upon later conductivity are direct and immediate. This hypothesis is more in accord with such facts as are known concerning the alteration of conductivity in regions of decrement (6), where the learning process may, perhaps, be located ultimately, and with the generally established facts of the deterioration of function through disuse.

The experimental evidence upon which the belief in a gradual fixation of associations is based is far from convincing. It consists primarily of the facts expressed in Jost's law, of occasional records of improvement in complex functions during periods of nonpractice, and of the data upon the effects of distribution of practice. All of this can be explained equally well by other hypotheses and, in view of the extreme importance of the point for physiological explanation, we should be careful not to accept the assumption of a "gradual setting" of new functional connections until some real evidence is advanced in support of it.

In studies of the mechanism of learning the processes of adjustment and of fixation must be distinguished as absolutely independent variables.

The former is, in lower animals and probably in primates also, solely the production of varied random activity, through which the first adjustment to a new situation is brought about; the latter is a process by which the recurrence of certain of the random activities in future trials is rendered more probable. Slow improvement in any function may result either from difficulty in discovering efficient methods of performance or from failure to fix as habits the methods which have been hit upon by chance. In an earlier paper (3) I have shown that a part of the superiority of short over long practice periods is due to the fact that distributed practice permits of greater variability of response and hence greater probability of discovering new and successful modes of attacking the problem, than does concentrated practice. The influence of the distribution of practice is here exerted upon the process of adjustment to the new situation and not upon that of fixation of the random acts.

In the study cited it was not possible to determine the extent to which this one factor was responsible for the effects of the distribution of practice. The present study makes it possible to estimate the importance of conflicting habits under different distributions of practice a little more accurately, although the conflicting reactions are of a somewhat different character from those dealt with in the first study. The retardation in concentrated practice in group D amounted to 338 per cent, that in group B to only 53 per cent of the effort required for learning in distributed practice. The difference, 285 per cent, is clearly due to conflicting habits which affect the efficiency of performance and not the formation of associations. The animals of group B gave some evidence of avoiding reactions in the neighborhood of the food dish, and since a slight exaggeration of this reaction was able to increase the retarding effects of concentrated practice to 145 per cent in group A, we are justified in assuming that a large part of the 53 per cent retardation found in group B is due to the same factors which were effective in groups A and D.

When allowance is made for the influence of stereotyped reactions upon random activity and for the establishment of habits which actively interfere with efficient performance, there may yet remain a slight reduction in efficiency in concentrated practice which is due to the influence of the distribution of effort upon the process of fixation of new functional nervous connections. Such a remainder can be demonstrated only by a process of elimination of agents which modify behavior in problem-solving or efficiency of performance and this can be done only by a more complete control of experimental methods than has yet been undertaken. In the existing evidence there is no reason for the belief that any such remainder will be found, at least in maze-learning. The agents acting upon other processes than those of fixation are adequate to account for all the effects of concentrated practice revealed by experiments and there is no foundation for the assumption that there is any "gradual process of fixation" which is influenced by the distribution of practice. Whether or not the concept is more applicable to other forms of learning, such as those involving implicit activity, is a matter for experimental investigation. The existing studies demonstrate the superior efficiency of distributed practice but give no clue to the reason for it.

The inferences drawn from studies of the rat in the maze can not be extended to embrace learning of other types without further study. But the studies with the maze are the only ones in which definite evidence as to the mode of action of the distribution of practice has been obtained. The experiments reported here and in the previous study seem to demonstrate that the greater part, if not all, of the effect of concentrated practice in maze-learning is due to the development of habits which interfere with efficient performance, either by limiting trial movements or by causing actual avoidance of the correct path. In both cases the interference is with the process of adjustment and not with that of fixation.

In other forms of learning there are many agents such as fatigue and loss of interest in long practice periods which may interfere with efficient performance and so prolong the apparent learning time, while with verbal habits the possibility of practice outside of the experimental practice periods has not been altogether eliminated where short practice periods were used. There is thus a possibility that in all forms of learning the results of distribution of practice are due, not to any fundamental principle in the fixation of nervous integrations, but to wholly incidental factors arising from the particular conditions of training in each case studied. The evidence obtained with the maze lends some probability to this view; sufficient, at least, to preclude the use of such a blanket explanation as the gradual "setting" of new nervous connections before the influence of other factors has been investigated.

Summary

1. The simple maze, including a single cul de sac, provides as reliable an index to the rate of fixation of habit in differentially treated groups of animals as does the more complicated circular maze.

2. The use of the simple maze makes it possible to train larger numbers of animals and so gain a better control of individual variations.

3. In the formation of the maze-habit distributed practice is more efficient than concentrated.

4. This is due to factors which arise from the particular methods of training used, peculiar to the maze problem, and not to the influence of the time relations upon the process of fixation of new functional nervous connections.

5. The same is probably true of all cases where the distribution of

effort has been found to influence the rate of learning. There is no reliable evidence for a gradual "setting" of the nervous connections formed during learning.

REFERENCES

1. Colvin, S. S. *The learning process.* New York: 1911.

2. Lashley, K. S. The acquisition of skill in archery, *Carnegie Instn. Publ.,* 1915, 7 (211), 107–128.

3. Lashley, K. S. A causal factor in the relation of the distribution of practice to the rate of learning, *J. Anim. Behav.,* 1917, 7, 139–142.

4. Lashley, K. S. The effects of strychnine and caffeine upon the rate of learning, *Psychobiology,* 1917, 1, 141–170.

5. Lashley, K. S., and Franz, S. I. The effects of cerebral destruction upon habit-formation and retention in the albino rat, *Psychobiology,* 1917, 1, 71–139.

6. Lucas, Keith. *The conduction of the nervous impulse.* London: 1917.

7. Starch, D. Periods of work in learning, *J. educ. Psychol.,* 1912, 3, 209–213.

8. Ulrich, J. L. Distribution of effort in learning in the white rat, *Behav. Monogr.,* 1915, 2 (10), 1–51.

7. STUDIES OF CEREBRAL FUNCTION

IN LEARNING. *II. The Effects of*

Long-continued Practice upon

Cerebral Localization [1]

The automatization of habits through long practice has offered a problem of especial interest to psychologists because of its bearing upon theories of the physiological basis of consciousness, and the literature contains many speculations and dogmatic assertions concerning the changes in localization through which automatic movements are eliminated from consciousness. For the most part these statements are vague in their anatomical reference, as when James (5) says, "In an habitual action, mere sensation is a sufficient guide, and the upper regions of the brain and mind are set comparatively free." Here we can only infer that by upper regions of the brain the author means the cerebrum, although his application of the term "different heights" to the cerebrum and thalamus makes it fairly certain that this is his meaning. Some other writers have expressed the concept more explicitly. Münsterberg (8) asserts that "Die Mechanisierung des Übergangs von centripetaler zu centrifugaler Erregung bedeutet die Ausbildung subkortikaler Verbindungen, vermöge deren die von der Peripherie kommende Erschütterung zu Ausführungsbahnen hingeleitet wird, noch ehe sie den psychophysischen Rindenapparat überhaupt erreicht." Similar statements occur frequently in current discussions of automatic movements.

The view seems to rest almost solely upon the conception that cerebral processes are conscious processes and that any activity that ceases to be conscious must necessarily lose its cortical representation. We might disregard such discussions as futile but for the fact that they have led to the general acceptance of the theory that conditioned-reflex arcs, originally traversing the cortex, may be short-circuited in the brain stem. The truth

[1] EDITORS' NOTE: From *J. comp. Psychol.*, 1921, **1**, 453–468. Reproduced by permission of the Williams and Wilkins Co. From the department of psychology, University of Minnesota.

or falsity of such an hypothesis is important for an understanding of the physiology of learning, since it involves the concept that the cortex offers greater ease of reintegration of reflex arcs than do subcortical centers, which are, nevertheless, capable of that reintegration. This, in turn, implies that the cortex is in some way specialized for learning. . . .

The theory of reduction of habits to subcortical levels is, however, based upon very slight evidence and until recently had no sort of factual support. The results of experimental decerebration by Flourens, Schraeder, Goltz, and others gave no suggestions of retention of automatized habits and no more crucial experiments were available. In 1902 Franz (2) described the persistence in cats of habits of long standing (coming at call) after operative destruction of the frontal lobes which abolished recently formed habits (latch box). In later work (3) he found habits retained in some monkeys and lost in others after frontal lesions and interpreted this as due to the somewhat longer training that the former had received. Since the publication of these results Dr. Franz and I (7) have found that habits may be retained after partial destruction of the frontal lobes in the rat, when total destruction abolishes them, and I have shown that visual and, hence, probably, auditory habits are not mediated by the frontal lobes (6). These data offer an alternative explanation for Franz's earlier results and suggest that they may have been due either to failure to make complete destruction of the frontal lobes or to differences in the sensory components of the habits which were lost from those which were retained.

In 1916, Dr. Franz and I took up this problem with the rat in an attempt to determine whether long practice in the maze and latch box would result in loss of cerebral representation. The results of those experiments were not conclusive. The simple maze habit showed no cerebral localization at any stage of learning. The latch-box habit was abolished by total frontal destruction at all stages of training up to three times the amount of practice required for learning, although it survived partial destruction of the frontal pole (7).

Existing evidence on the reduction of habits to subcortical levels thus seems inconclusive. The clean-cut localization of habits of visual discrimination in the occipital pole of the cerebrum of the rat, which I reported in the first study of this series, offers an excellent opportunity for a final test of the matter. The retention or loss of the habit is easily recognized. The habit involves only a small and well defined area on the occipital pole, and with practice it is soon brought to an accuracy of performance that indicates automatization. Operation in the occipital region produces little shock or interference with habits other than visual. Experiments with vision have thus a decided advantage over those with the kinesthetic-motor habit involved in the frontal pole, for operation in the latter region frequently produces a general deterioration which obscures the specific effects of the injury.

Tests previously reported have shown that destruction of the occipital pole abolished the habit of discrimination between light and dark alleys in the Yerkes discrimination box when twenty successive errorless trials were obtained. In the present experiments I have tested the effects of the same operation after training had been continued until not less than five hundred successive errorless trials were obtained.

The Visual Area in the Rat

In the previous experiment (6) the entire cerebral cortex was explored by a series of partial destructions in animals which had formed the habit of visual reaction in the problem box. Two additional cases have been obtained with injuries in the temporal and orbital regions, which were

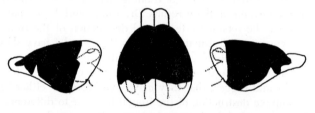

Fig. 7.1. The combined extent of the lesions in a series of animals which showed retention of the habit of visual discrimination after operation. The lesion in each animal included about one-fourth of the total blackened area shown here.

imperfectly covered by the first experiments. Figure 7.1 represents the total extent of the combined lesions in seven animals that retained the habit after operation. The frontal, parietal, orbital, and superior temporal regions are not necessary for the performance of the habit. Figure 7.2 shows the combined lesions of three animals which lost the habit after operation. The area common to the three has been blackened. It seems to represent the only part of the cortex that takes part in the performance of the visual habit.

Methods

Training. The animals used in the present experiments were trained in a discrimination box offering a choice of two alleys illuminated and darkened in irregular alternation. Food was given after passage through the illuminated alley and punishment in the darkened alley. The first three hundred trials were given at the rate of ten per day; thereafter, fifty trials were given daily. Entrance into the dark alley was recorded as an error, but not more than one error per trial was counted. Thus in the records following, errors mean trials in which an error occurred. Training was continued for about fourteen hundred trials.

Operations. The technique of operation was essentially that described in earlier papers, except that the destructions were made with a thermoelectric cautery inserted cold and heated until the tissues began to boil. This method reduces hemorrhages yet produces a thorough destruction.

Retention tests. The animals were first tested twenty-four hours after operation. Ten trials were given, if possible, and the errors made were recorded, together with notes on the general condition of the animal, its orientation in the problem box, reactions to food, etc. No punishment was given in the first thirty trials of the retention tests, but after these the same methods were used as in the original training and retraining was continued with ten trials per day until discrimination was again established.

When a habit is lost following cerebral injury two interpretations are possible. The operation may have resulted in shock which abolished the habit by produc-

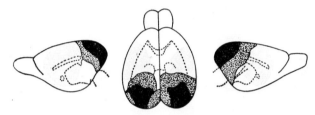

Fig. 7.2. The combined extent of the lesions in three animals that lost the habit of visual discrimination after operation. The stippled area represents the total extent of the destructions; the black area, that destroyed in all the animals.

ing a general deterioration. In such a case the experiment gives no significant data upon localization of function. Or, the loss may be due to the destruction of the particular conditioned-reflex paths involved in the habit. Practically, it is not easy to distinguish between these two possibilities but observations of the general behavior of the animals usually reveal deterioration when it is present.

Some animals after operation do not orient readily in the problem box, enter the dark alley many times in a single trial, have difficulty in finding food, climb out of the box repeatedly, and show other signs of confusion or motor disorganization. Such animals usually clear up in from three to five days and show a sudden drop from 50 to zero per cent error in their reactions. Their temporary loss of the habit is clearly due to operative shock.[2]

Other animals show loss of the specific habit without any evidence of general deterioration. They are normally active, oriented in the problem box, correct their errors without perseveration, find the food readily and retain many kinesthetic-motor habits with reference to the problem box. Their relearning is gradual and requires as long as the original learning. The loss in these cases is

[2] The fact that the so-called motor cortex does not participate in the habit has been emphasized in the first paper of the series. Further data on the point will be published later.

evidently not due to shock but to some specific effect of the operation upon the visual habit. In general, the occipital cases give little indication of operative shock.[3] As a further control of operative shock the orbital and temporal regions of one of the animals of the present series were destroyed while the visual area was left intact. The lesions in this animal are more extensive than those of the occipital cases, and approach more closely the nuclei of the optic thalamus. Its retention records are comparable with those of the occipital cases.

Reconstruction of lesions. Serial frontal sections of the brain were prepared, stained in iron hematoxylin, and mounted in balsam. Sections at intervals of 0.25 mm. were outlined under the camera lucida at a magnification of ten diameters. The extent of the lesions in each section was determined under higher power and indicated on the outline. The level of the section was next determined and the dimensions of the lesions were transferred to the diagrams of the brain by means of proportional dividers. The points so determined were connected by lines and the resultant areas inked in. Only obvious lesions,

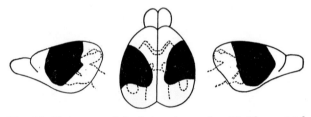

Fig. 7.3. The extent of the lesions in number 13. The parietal and orbital surfaces were destroyed.

absorption of tissue or complete degeneration of the cortex, were recorded, so the diagrams represent the minimal extent of the lesions. The diagrams are probably accurate to within 0.5 mm. when reduced to the dimensions of the brain.

Experimental Data

Four animals were used in these experiments. One (number 13) [4] formed a control in which the orbital surfaces of both hemispheres were destroyed. The others were subjected to occipital injury. The records of the individual cases follow.

Number 13. Orbital Control. Small female, about one hundred days old at the beginning of the experiment. Trained in visual discrimination.

Number of trials required for learning: 100.

Number of errors in successive ten trials during learning: 4:5:5:3:1:3:1:0: 0:1:0:0:0.

[3] These statements are based on the records of about thirty animals which have been tested in the visual habit after operation. These cases will be reported later in detail.

[4] In the first paper of this series visual discrimination was studied in twelve animals. For convenience of reference the animals of the present series are numbered in sequence with those

Training was continued for 1,400 trials after learning.

Number of errors in successive hundreds of trials in overtraining 3:0:2:0:0: 0:0:0:0:0:0:0:1:0:0.

The orbital surfaces of both hemispheres were cauterized. On the first two days following operation the animal showed disturbances of motor coordination, difficulty in locating the food even when placed in contact with the dish, and lack of orientation in the experimental box. She made numerous errors on these days. On the third day the motor difficulties had cleared up, but errors were still made and there was no indication of retention. On the fourth, fifth, and later days discrimination was perfect.

Postoperative retention tests; errors in successive ten trials: 5:2:6:0:0:0:0.

Extent of lesions. Figure 7.3. Right hemisphere: The lesion extends from the level of the knee of the corpus callosum to the level of the anterior margin of the superior colliculus, including all of the orbital and ectorhinal areas. Left hemisphere: The lesion extends from the level of the knee of the corpus callosum to the level of the anterior margin but not extending so far onto the ectorhinal and parietal surfaces as that of the right. The subcortical nuclei of both sides were uninjured.

This animal, after destruction of the orbital surfaces of the hemispheres, gave evidence of operative shock, but recovered in three days and then showed perfect retention of the visual habit.[5]

Number 14. Small Female. About one hundred days old at the beginning of the experiment. Trained in visual discrimination.

Number of trials required for learning: 80.

Number of errors in successive ten trials during learning: 6:3:5:4:4:2:2:1: 0:0:0.

Training was continued for 1,200 trials after learning.

Number of errors in successive hundreds of trials overtraining: 3:1:1:0:0:1: 0:0:0:0:0:0.

The occipital and parietal lobes were cauterized. The animal was stuporous for five days following the operation and could not be tested. On the sixth day she was active, and when placed in the problem box reacted promptly and seemed well oriented. She never entered the dark alley more than once in a single trial, and, in general, showed retention of the kinesthetic-motor habits. She made many errors, however, and gave no indication of discrimination. Retraining was continued until discrimination appeared. During retraining the animal occasionally gave indication of discrimination, looking back and forth from one alley to another and choosing correctly, but such reactions were rare, and give only questionable evidence of retention. Her behavior was suggestive of some of the cases of partial destruction of the frontal pole studied earlier, which showed interference with, but not complete loss of the inclined-plane box habit. Such fluctuations in retention after cerebral injury in man have been emphasized by Head (4). The lesion in this animal probably did not involve all of the visual area.

[5] EDITORS' NOTE: Italics here and elsewhere in this article are Lashley's.

Postoperative retention tests; errors in successive ten trails: 6:6:5:3:1:4:5:4: 3:2:1:0:0:0.

Extent of lesions. Figure 7.4. Right hemisphere: The lesion begins at the level of the anterior margin of the thalamus and extends caudad to the level of the inferior colliculus, including part of the parietal, occipital, and superior temporal regions. It seems to leave the median and extreme caudal portions of the occipital pole intact. Left hemisphere: The lesion begins at the same level as that on the right, and covers approximately the same areas, but does not extend so far over the temporal area and leaves a little more of the occipital pole uninjured. The subcortical nuclei are uninjured.

After injury to the visual area, this animal gave an occasional sugges-tion of retention but required more practice for reestablishment of perfect discrimination than was consumed in the original training. The operation probably did not destroy all of the visual area.

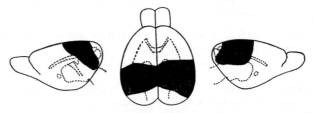

Fig. 7.4. The extent of the lesions in number 14. The occipital pole of both hemispheres is uninjured.

Number 15. Small Female. About one hundred days old at the beginning of the experiment. Trained in visual discrimination.

Number of trials required for learning: 150.

Number of errors in successive ten trials during learning: 7:4:5:5:4:4:7:7: 5:4:1:4:3:3:2:0:0:0.

Training was continued for 1,200 trials after learning.

Number of errors in successive hundreds of trials of overtraining: 1:0:1:0:0: 2:0:0:0:0:0:0.

The occipital regions were destroyed by cautery. Retention was first tested twenty-four hours after operation. The animal was active and the box habits were perfectly retained. She corrected her errors promptly, ran directly to the food, scratched at the door of the starting compartment, but gave no indica-tion of retention of the visual habit for sixty trials of the retention tests. In the original training this animal was unusually timid. The fear reactions disap-peared during overtraining and did not reappear after operation. The fact that relearning was more rapid than the original learning is probably due to this difference.

Postoperative retention tests; errors in successive ten trials: 7:6:3:6:5:5:2:3: 1:0:0.

Extent of lesions. Figure 7.5. Right hemisphere: The lesion begins at the level of the anterior margin of the superior colliculus and extends caudad to the occipital pole, including all the cortex of the dorsal surface. Left hemisphere: The lesion begins at the same level as that on the right, but does not extend to the pole, an area equal to the thickness of the cortex remaining uninjured in the caudal region. The subcortical nuclei are uninjured.

After destruction of the visual cortex this animal showed no evidence of shock, but failed to retain her visual habit. The habit was regained with less practice than was required for the original learning, owing, probably, to the retention of kinesthetic-motor habits and reduction of timidity.

Number 16. Small Female. About one hundred days old at beginning of experiment. Trained in visual discrimination.

Number of trials required for learning: 100.

Number of errors in successive ten trials during learning: 6:7:7:2:3:1:1:1: 0:1:0:0:0.

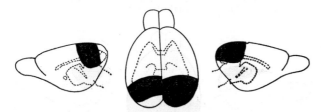

Fig 7.5. The extent of the lesions in number 15.

Training was continued for 1,200 trials after learning.

Number of errors in successive hundreds of trials of retraining: 4:0:0:0:0:1: 0:0:0:0:0:0.

The occipital cortex was destroyed by cautery. Retention was first tested twenty-four hours after operation. The animal was very active and seemed quite normal in all of her reactions. She corrected errors promptly and never hesitated on the way to the feeding compartment. She gave no evidence of retention of the visual habit on this or the following days.

Postoperative retention tests; errors in successive ten trials: 7:4:3:4:5:5:3: 3:4:1:1:0:0.

Extent of lesions. Figure 7.6. Right hemisphere: The lesion extends from the level of the anterior margin of the nucleus habenulae to the posterior limit of the external capsule. All the cortex of the dorsal surface within these limits is destroyed. The cortex of the inferior temporal area and of the extreme occipital pole is intact. Left hemisphere: The lesion begins at the level of the pillars of the fornix and includes approximately the same area as that on the right. The dorsal lobes of the hippocampus are destroyed on both sides. The subcortical nuclei are uninjured.

After destruction of the visual area, this animal showed normal activity, retention of kinesthetic-motor habits, and complete loss of the visual habit. Relearning required a little more practice than learning.

Table 7.1. Errors Made in Retention Tests by Animals after Operation*

Number	Trials for learning	Trials for relearning	Errors in successive ten trials of retention tests
13	100	30	5 2 6 0 0 0
14	80	110	6 6 5 3 1 4 5 4 3 2 1 0 0 0
15	110	90	7 6 3 6 5 5 2 3 1 0 0
16	100	110	7 4 3 4 5 5 3 3 4 1 1 0 0
10	60	100	6 5 5 3 3 0 1 0 2 2 0 0
11	60	74	3 (of 4) 6 4 9 2 0 3 4 0 0

* Five errors in ten trials is the chance expectation and indicates lack of discrimination. Number 13, temporal lesions; numbers 14, 15, and 16, occipital lesions after long training; numbers 10 and 11, occipital lesions after brief training.

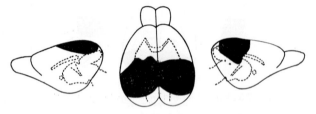

Fig. 7.6. The extent of the lesions in number 16.

The results of these tests are summarized in Table 7.1. The control animal (number 13), with extensive lesions in the orbital regions, showed confusion in three days, then quick recovery with immediate reappearance of the habit. Number 14, after occipital injury, was stuporous for five days, then regained normal activity and kinesthetic-motor habits, but did not make a perfect record until after retraining for 110 trials. Numbers 15 and 16, after occipital lesions, gave no indication of shock from the operation, retained kinesthetic-motor habits, but lost the visual habit.

These had all received 1,200 or more trials of overtraining. The records of numbers 10 and 11 from the earlier experiments are included in Table 7.1. The occipital lobes of these animals were destroyed after less than one hundred trials in the discrimination box. Both show loss of the habit, with relearning as rapid as that of the overtrained animals. The overtraining, therefore, does not increase the power of the habit to survive injury or to be reacquired after the operation.

Early in the retention tests all of the overtrained animals gave evidence of normal activity and retention of the kinesthetic-motor habits of the discrimination box. The loss of the habit in them, therefore, can not be ascribed to general shock resulting from the operation. The direct effect of the operation upon lower visual centers is also ruled out by the facts, first, that these centers showed no microscopically detectable lesions and, second, by the results with number 13, in which the cautery passed close to the pulvinar and external geniculate body on both sides, without abolishing the habit. From this it seems clear that the loss of the habit is not due to shock or to injury to the optic thalamus but is a specific effect of the destruction of the visual cortex.

These considerations lead to the conclusion that overtraining up to twelve hundred trials does not alter the cerebral localization of the habit of visual discrimination. The functional activity of the visual cortex is still necessary to the performance of the habit and there is no indication that subcortical nuclei have taken over any part of the reaction, even sufficient to facilitate relearning. The cerebral area functional in learning seems to retain the same function after prolonged training.

The Question of Automatization

Thus far in the discussion I have taken it for granted that 1,300 trials of practice would produce automatization. That assumption, however, is open to question. The test for automatization in man is the ability to carry on the habitual act while the verbal or other complex mechanisms are making other nonhabitual adjustments. In the rat such a test is not readily practicable and it is necessary to fall back upon indirect methods of judging the degree of mechanization of the habit.

No data upon the amount of practice necessary to automatize a simple visuo-motor habit in man are available, but certainly less than 1,000 trials are sometimes effective. Some of my own automatic reactions, such as changing to a laboratory coat, have been established in less than 500 trials. The habits of shifting the stimulus lights and doors of the discrimination box are automatized by the experimenter long before the animals cease to make errors in discrimination.

It can not be argued then, that 1,300 trials are inadequate to produce mechanization under some conditions. Whether they did so in these experiments can be judged only from general observations on the behavior of the animals. In the early stages of training the rat frequently hesitates at the entrance to the alleys, sways back and forth as though looking at first one, then the other stimulus plate, and finally advances slowly into one alley. Later, these comparing movements disappear, but for several hundred trials they occasionally recur. At this stage of learning, if the animal is disturbed by a noise or jar as it enters the alley, it stops, makes comparing movements or smells at the stimulus plate, and explores the alleys before passing to the food compartment. By the end of the thousandth trial all such reactions had disappeared in these animals. The door of the starting compartment is of glass so that the stimulus plates are visible through it. Seemingly the animals, after a thousand trials, were oriented toward the light before the door was opened and dashed through to the food the moment the door was raised. If they were distracted on the way, they did not stop and make comparing movements, but whirled about and returned to the starting compartment, then rushed back through the illuminated alley. This last bit of behavior is highly suggestive of the human tendency to start an automatized reaction all over again when it is interrupted, and forms the strongest evidence available that the habit was really mechanized. Finally, the regularity and accuracy with which the habit appeared and the fact that none of the animals made more than three errors in the last thousand trials indicate that the reaction was reduced to a condition where it required no very complex adjustments. From these facts it seems almost certain that, after 1,000 trials, the visual habit had reached a stage comparable to that of complete automatization in man.

The Neurological Basis of Automatization

The evidence from pathological cases in man is inconclusive. Occasionally a long-practiced habit, such as the patient's ability to recall his name, persists in an otherwise complete aphasia. But a strong case could be made for the view that these habits persist, not by virtue of long practice, but because they have a deep emotional significance and hence receive a tonic reinforcement that is lacking to other activities. Certainly, hymn singing and profanity are among the most common accomplishments of aphasics. On the other hand, many activities that are certainly automatized in the great majority of individuals fail to survive in apraxia or aphasia from cerebral lesions and so are clearly not mediated by subcortical nuclei. The pathological evidence certainly cannot be advanced as proof of the reduction of habits to subcortical levels.

Many, perhaps the majority of automatized habits in man, have a proprioceptive rather than exteroceptive basis. The present experiments seem adequate to prove that visual habits are not reduced to subcortical levels by long practice. Is the same true of habits having a kinesthetic basis? The work of Franz and the writer indicated that the latch box habit was abolished by frontal destruction after a considerable period of overtraining. Simpler habits, such as that of the maze with a single cul de sac, were undisturbed by frontal lesions even after only a brief period of training. I have since tested retention of the discrimination box habits after extensive lesions involving, in one or another animal, every part of the cerebrum except the ectorhinal area. Irrespective of the position of the lesions these animals have showed fairly perfect retention of the kinesthetic-motor habits of the discrimination box. The simple tactual- and kinesthetic-motor habits have no cerebral localization at any stage of training. Whether they are mediated by diffuse arcs passing through all parts of the cortex or are formed at subcortical levels is uncertain. I have obtained formation of such habits in nearly decerebrate animals, in which only the inferior temporal and ectorhinal areas were intact, but this is not sufficient to settle the question.

Whatever the explanation of these facts, they suggest that for kinesthetic-motor as well as for visual habits, the cortical or subcortical representation is determined at the time of learning and is not modified by subsequent practice.

If long-practiced habits are not reduced to subcortical levels, what is the neurological basis of automatization? The musician may not speak when first learning a difficult movement but later his verbal reactions are dissociated from the manual coordinations so that the two processes may go on simultaneously. It is this capacity to function without exciting reaction systems other than those directly concerned with its performance that characterizes the automatic habit. Such a condition might be brought about by blocking cerebral associative connections, and this seems to be the only alternative to reduction to subcortical levels. An analogous situation is presented by the differentiation of the conditioned reflex to a specific stimulus (1). Whether the confining of impulses to a single path is the result merely of repetition or of some active inhibitory or blocking process can not be decided from existing evidence. Some professional musicians who have never practiced talking while playing do not show the dissociation of the functions, and I have seen the dissociation increased by practice. This would indicate that some active conflict between the reactions is essential to their dissociation, and suggests that, perhaps, the mechanisms of automatization and of dissociation through conflict and repression in the Freudian sense may have much in common.

Summary

Animals were trained in a habit of visual discrimination and were then given additional practice for 1,200 trials. Destruction of the visual area after this training resulted in loss of the habit. Retention of other habits showed that the loss was due to destruction of visual conditioned-reflex arcs and not to operative shock. Long training did not reduce the habit to subcortical levels.

REFERENCES

1. Bechterew, W. v. *La psychologie objective*. Paris: 1913.
2. Franz, S. I. On the functions of the cerebrum: I. The frontal lobes in

relation to the production and retention of simple sensory-motor habits, *Amer. J. Physiol.*, 1902, 8, 1–22.

3. Franz, S. I. On the functions of the cerebrum: the frontal lobes, *Arch. Psychol.*, 1907 (2), 1–64.

4. Head, H. *Studies in neurology.* London: 1920.

5. James, W. *The principles of psychology.* New York: 1890.

6. Lashley, K. S. Studies of cerebral function in learning, *Psychobiology,* 1920, 2, 55–135.

7. Lashley, K. S., and Franz, S. I. The effects of cerebral destruction upon habit-formation and retention in the albino rat, *Psychobiology,* 1917, 1, 71–140.

8. Münsterberg, H. *Grundzüge der Psychologie.* Leipzig: 1900.

8. STUDIES OF CEREBRAL FUNCTION IN LEARNING. V. *The Retention of Motor Habits after Destruction of the So-called Motor Areas in Primates* [1]

Since the area was first described by Fritsch and Hitzig (14), the function of the electrostimulable cortex of the cerebrum has been the subject of almost continuous controversy. The experiments were immediately called in question through criticisms of the technic by Dupuy (9), Sanderson (49), Carville and Duret (6), and others or by abstruse metaphysical deductions such as were advanced by Hermann (19) who objected to the motor area as violating the "unity of mind." The work of Ferrier (11), Carville and Duret and Hitzig soon established the fact of the electrical excitability of limited areas of the cortex, but immediately a new question arose. Fritsch and Hitzig had considered the excitable zone as motor, if we may translate the expression, "entry of single psychic functions into material" by such a term. In this they were followed by Carville and Duret, who described the motor disturbances following lesions in the area as "paralysie de la motricité volontaire corticale." Ferrier also considered the area as motor. But most of the early work had been done with dogs, and the sensory disturbances which appear in this animal after ablation of the stimulable area were emphasized by Schiff (52), Nothnagel (43), Munk (41) and Hitzig (20), who interpreted the disorders of movement variously as due to the loss of muscular and cutaneous sensitivity or to the loss of kinesthetic images of the movements to be performed.

Following the suggestion of Tamburini, Luciani and Seppili (32) advanced the view that the motor areas contained somesthetic projection fibers as well as motor elements, and developed a theory of the sensory-motor function of the sigmoid gyrus and rolandic areas. In this they were

---

[1] EDITORS' NOTE: From *Arch. Neurol. Psychiat.*, Chicago, 1924, **12**, 249–276. Reproduced by permission of the American Medical Association. From the department of psychology, University of Minnesota.

followed by Horsley (22), Mott (38), Dana (8), Rothmann (48) and many others.

De Barenne (1), in particular, has demonstrated the existence of marked sensory disturbances in the cat after application of strychnine to an area which widely overlaps the stimulable area, and the general correctness of Luciani's view for the stimulable areas of lower mammals does not seem open to question, although there may be some doubt as to whether the motor functions of the cortex in these forms are comparable with those of primates.

Recent more critical work with primates, however, shows that in them a further specialization has occurred with the development of the fissure of Rolando as a line of demarcation between centripetal and centrifugal projection areas.[2] The work of Schäfer (51), Mills (35), Grünbaum and Sherrington (17), C. and O. Vogt (58), Lewandowsky and Simmons (29), Hoppe (21), Cushing (7), Franz (13), and Leyton and Sherrington (30), all points to the conclusion that primary excitability is limited to the precentral gyrus and that sensory disturbances rarely result from lesions confined to this area.

These studies have defined the centrifugal function of the cells of the precentral gyrus and have confirmed the view that the area is motor rather than somesthetic, but in spite of the fairly general recent agreement as to the location of "motor" area, there is a wide diversity of opinion concerning the significance of the "motor" function. The area is somehow concerned with the production of movement, but how it acts and what kinds of movement it controls are still debated points. Ferrier (11) emphasized the "automatic" character of movements after destruction of the motor areas and held that "all reactions not so (automatically) organized, and still dependent upon conscious discrimination and exercise of attentive volition are effectually and permanently annihilated." Munk (40) classified movements according to their somatic distribution and maintained that small unilateral adaptive movements (Einzelbewegungen) are permanently lost after destruction of the motor areas. His definition of these movements is by no means clear, but his accounts seem to imply that the movements had been learned, and he denies that a dog can learn to give his paw after destruction of both motor areas. Wagner (59) maintained that the chief function of the motor areas is in learning, and that animals deprived of them are incapable of forming any new habits. Bechterew (2) also refers to experiments leading to the same conclusion.

---

[2] The lack of any persistent paralysis in rodents, carnivora, and ungulates after destruction of the stimulable areas and the occurrence of partial paralyses after destruction of parts of the corpus striatum in lower forms suggest that the differentiation of function of precentral and postcentral gyri in primates may be due rather to the acquisition of primative striate functions by the cerebral cortex than to a division of cortical functions which overlap in lower forms.

He states that after removal of the motor centers associative motor reflexes are lost. "With unilateral destruction of the motor region in dogs the associative motor reflex may be elicited in the homolateral fore-leg, but in the contralateral fore-leg the reflexes learned earlier are forever lost and can not be reestablished even after a number of conditioning associations" (2, pp. 1551 ff.). Gierlich (16) also supports this view of the exclusive motor function of the stimulable areas.

In opposition to these results, several writers have reported the acquisition of habits after the destruction of the motor areas or of the pyramidal tracts. Starlinger (55) trained a dog to give his paw after total destruction of both pyramidal tracts. Rothmann (47) observed learning in a rhesus monkey in which one precentral gyrus had been extirpated and the pyramidal tract of the other had been sectioned in the cervical region. Franz and Lashley (14) and Lashley (25) found learning ability in the rat unaltered by total destruction of the stimulable cortex. This result has been confirmed by Jellinek and Koppányi (24).

In the contradiction of evidence here, we must favor the positive results. Failure to learn may be due to any one of a number of factors in addition to specific destruction of tissue, and a single positive case with certain destruction of the motor area is sufficient to discredit any number of negative findings such as are cited by Bechterew and Munk. It seems quite certain that the formation of conditioned motor reflexes is possible in the absence of the electrostimulable cortex, but this fact fails to reveal the normal function of the area in the performance of complex activities. Both Rothmann and Brown (4) seem to believe that in the intact animal the motor areas form the chief centrifugal path for complex adaptive reactions and that when learning occurs in their absence it is to be considered as due to vicarious function of other parts rather than as an expression of their normal function. On the basis of Brown's work and of clinical evidence, however, Monakow (37) is inclined to minimize the importance of the pyramidal areas for "voluntary" movement. He suggests that "we must give up or essentially modify the view that the precentral convolution alone conducts impulses to voluntary movement. It is probable that the pyramidal areas serve less for the execution of voluntary movements than for the inhibition of the kinetic functions of spinal coordination. Their function seems to be in the class of reflex activity." Lashley (26) has reported the survival of visuomotor habits after the complete destruction of the stimulable area and serious injury to the caudate and lenticular nuclei [3] and has suggested that the primary function of the

[3] When these experiments were reported, I believed that the lesions were largely confined to the caudate nuclei. Dr. J. B. Johnston has since called my attention to the fact that the caudate nucleus in the rat comprises only a narrow median band in the corpus striatum and that the lesions reported actually included a considerable portion of the lenticular nucleus.

stimulable area is the reflex regulation of postural and kinetic mechanisms. Similar results have since been obtained for the stimulable cortex with problem-box and maze habits.

Thus we find in the literature claims that the electrostimulable cortex is motor, that it is sensory, that it is sensory-motor, that its motor function is exercised through the storing of images of movement, that it is the final common path for all voluntary movements, and that it is a reflex center not primarily concerned with voluntary activity.

Much of the literature on the function of the electrostimulable cortex, as on cerebral localization in general, presents an inextricable tangle of physiologic fact and psychologic speculation. The long controversy between Goltz, Munk, and Hitzig was largely due to their inability to grasp each other's psychologic theories, and recent progress in psychology tends to invalidate much of the cerebral localization which was based on older conceptions of mental faculties.

Images have fallen into disrepute, and even the psychologists who still deal with them deny that kinesthetic imagery has any demonstrable relation to the initiation of movement (56). The conception of volitional activity is too vague to have any scientific value. At best it represents an indefinite distinction between more or less complexly conditioned activities, and the conception of conditioned reflexes leaves the distinction without significance. The "will" has been largely discarded in psychology, although it is still in good standing in neurologic discussions. Such a statement as that the stimulable cortex is not motor, but "psychomotor," means no more than that the pyramidal cells excite patterns of spinal motor cells rather than individual cells. It contributes nothing to our understanding of cerebral function. In the present state of psychologic science, we can not do better than follow the dictum of Bubnoff and Heidenhain (5), "Es will uns überhaupt scheinen als müste die Untersuchung der physiologischen Processe in dem Gehirn von den jene Vorgänge begleitenden Bewusstseinsvorgängen möglichst absehen, wenn es sich um eine Deutung physischen Geschehens handelt," and rigidly exclude from neurologic discussion every subjective concept which cannot be translated into objective terms.

There is no evidence for the localization of any "mental function" in any part of the cerebrum. All that can be concluded from the existing evidence is that the conduction pathways concerned in particular kinds of behavior lead from receptor to effector through certain cerebral areas. Cerebral motor localization is a problem of the origin and function of the centrifugal neural impulses of the cortex. Their "volitional" or "automatic" character can be defined only in terms of their complexity of organization and their relative importance in the total motor integration of kinetic melody, and until so defined the terms are meaningless. The "reflex" conception of cerebral function, although still a theory and notably inadequate to account for all the phenomena of cerebral function because of oversimplification in its formulations,[4] is too well supported by evidence on nerve conduction and analogy with spinal functions to be disregarded in favor of any speculations concerning the localization of "psychic" functions.

Statement of Problem

Stated objectively, three mutually incompatible theories concerning the function of the precentral gyrus are to be found in the current literature. They are: (a) This area is the only centrifugal outlet from the cerebral cortex for complexly integrated movements or for movements acquired as a result of training (voluntary movements or conditioned reflexes). (b) In the intact animal, the Betz cells are the principal centrifugal paths, but some neural impulses of like function may descend by extrapyramidal tracts, and these tracts may assume vicariously all the functions of the motor area. (c) The motor area is a part of the mechanism functioning in the regulation of tonus and posture and is not directly concerned in conditioned reflex activity.

The first of these views is definitely ruled out by the evidence cited above for habit formation after destruction of the areas. The evidence for the second and third views, as applied to primates, is inconclusive, although a considerable mass of evidence derived from the cerebral paralyses seems to support the second. The validity of this evidence will be considered after the experimental data are presented.

A simple test of the hypotheses is possible. If after total destruction of the precentral areas an animal shows undiminished ability to carry out activities of all degrees of complexity, acquired before the operative destruction, this will be conclusive evidence that the lesion did not destroy any part of the conditioned reflex arcs involved in the activities, and, as a corollary, that these arcs do not traverse the motor areas. Loss of the conditioned reflexes following the lesion with their later reestablishment through training will support the second view, that the pyramidal cells of the precentral region are the principal efferent paths involved in habitual movements.

Such a test was made with the rat and gave unmistakable evidence against the participation of the motor areas in the activities of the simple maze and visual discrimination box (14, 26). Since the publication of that report, the results have been confirmed for a complex maze and the "double-platform box." As the rat shows no paralysis after lesions to the

---

[4] The data on direct adaptation of unpracticed organs to the solution of problem boxes presented later in this paper seem wholly inexplicable in terms of simple conditioned reflexes.

stimulable areas alone, it is not possible to generalize from it to higher forms which do develop a paralysis. I have therefore repeated the tests in a series of experiments with monkeys.

Experimental Methods

The paralysis which follows lesions to the precentral gyrus in monkeys necessitates a modification of the technic used with the rat. The general procedure was as follows: The animals were trained in rather simple manipulative acts involving a new and easily recognizable pattern and sequence of movements. They were then kept without practice for about two months, at the end of which time their retention of the habits was tested. This gave a measure of the normal loss to be expected from disuse of the habits over a period equal to that required for recovery from cerebral paralysis. After these *preliminary retention tests*, the motor areas were destroyed. The animals were then kept without further practice in the habits until the paralysis was so far improved that they were judged capable of making the movements required. They were then given a final series of retention tests (*postoperative retention tests*) and brought to necropsy.

Training Methods. For training, the familiar problem-box method was used. The animals were confined in a large cage, 5 by 5 feet, to the floor of which a small problem-box containing food was bolted. Three problem-boxes were used:

1. *Pull box.* The animal must reach through a circular hole, 2 inches in diameter, grasp and pull foward a rod which passed transversely 3 inches behind the hole. This released the lid of the box, which was thrown open by a spring.

2. *Crank box.* The animal must grasp and turn a crank projecting from the front of the box. The crank handle described a 6-inch circle. It offered a resistance of about 200 gm. at all points of the circle. It was set at "one o'clock" and must be turned counter-clockwise through 270 degrees, at which point it released the lid of the box. The lid was thrown back by a spring.

3. *Hasp box.* The animal must open an ordinary gate hasp, closed with a wooden plug inserted loosely through the staple, withdrawing the plug and lifting the hasp from the staple, over which it would fall again if released. He must then raise the lid of the box and hold it open while he reached in for the food.

Five trials a day were given with each box; the time spent in each trial was recorded, and detailed notes were made as to the use of right or left hand and the exact method employed in opening the boxes. Training was continued until the latches were released in a stereotyped manner without random movements. Several interruptions of training occurred lasting from one to several weeks, so that the learning curves do not represent the rate for continuous training.

In addition to the problem-box habits, each animal was trained to pick out cubes of banana from among cubes of wood of similar size and appearance. The cubes were scattered in irregular order under a sheet of glass supported 2 inches above the floor of the cage. They were placed about 6 inches back from the edge so that the animals had to reach under the glass to get the cubes, which they could see but could not distinguish by odor.

Operative Technic. Destruction of the motor areas was made under ether anesthesia, with aseptic precautions. The region of the precentral gyrus was exposed by trephining and identified by electrical stimulation. The opening was enlarged by bone-forceps until the precentral gyrus and surrounding areas were exposed. Arm, leg, and face areas were verified by stimulation, and the limits of the excitable area determined. The entire area was then undercut by thermocautery to a depth of about 6 mm. To avoid injury to the longitudinal sinus, a median bridge of bone, 1 cm. in width, was left intact. In one specimen the leg area of this region was undercut by passing the cautery diagonally mediad and downward until the resistance of the falx was felt, then cutting longitudinally across the gyrus. The dural flaps were then replaced and the wound closed. In the cases reported below the wounds healed without infection.

Retention Tests. The animals all showed marked paralysis after operation. This cleared up gradually, and the retention tests were given about two months after the operation. (Numbers 1 and 3, *v.i.*, recovered somewhat more quickly than is usually the case when the lesion is restricted to one hemisphere.) In the postoperative retention tests, the animals were placed singly in the large cage with each of the latch boxes in turn. The time required to open the boxes was noted, and the methods were recorded in detail for comparison with methods employed in learning and in the preliminary retention tests.

Verification of Lesions. When the tests were completed, the operative fields were again exposed and explored by electrical stimulation. Excitable points found were mapped. The brains were then removed, fixed in 10 per cent formaldehyde, and sketches made under a camera lucida. Serial sections of the region of the lesions were then prepared. Camera drawings of these were made and the lesions reconstructed from them.

Protocols

Number 1. This was a small male cebus, trained on the crank box, pull box, and hasp box. The skull was trephined and opened on both sides in front of the precentral gyrus. The openings were extended backward to the fissure of Rolando. The leg, arm, and face areas were located by electrical stimulation and destroyed by cautery. Cauterization extended beyond the stimulable area except in the median line. The wound was covered with mica and closed.

On the following day, there was a partial paralysis of both sides with great spasticity. Coordinated walking movements were possible, but there was great weakness of the legs. The arms were extended toward food. He could not grasp with his left hand. Partial grasping with the right hand appeared, but there was inability to raise food to the mouth. He recognized a banana and made efforts to grasp it. The arms were usually hyperextended.

Four days later, he moved clumsily, his arms and legs spread out frequently, letting him fall prone. He grasped with his right hand, but was unable to hold food or lift it to his mouth. He ate by thrusting his mouth against the bread. He was well oriented in the room. Two weeks before operation he had learned to slip out of the crack as the door was opened and to run into an adjoining room. He did this twice on the fourth day. He had a tendency to stay near a cage containing other monkeys and to hide under it when pursued. There was marked tremor after slight effort.

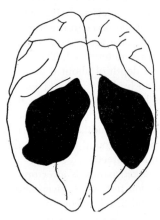

Fig. 8.1. Extent of lesions in animal number 1. Reconstructed from camera sketch and serial sections.

Ten days after operation, he stood and walked without falling, fumbled in grasping, but was able to hold food in his right hand or to lift it to his mouth.

Thirty-five days after operation, he climbed and ran accurately, picked up small pieces of banana with the right hand without noticeable clumsiness, and made quick movements in efforts to catch flies. Retention of the problem-box habits was tested at this time.

The average time per trial in each day's practice (five trials daily) is given in Table 8.1 for each of the problem-boxes. This is followed by the average time per trial on each day of the preliminary retention tests, and similarly for the postoperative retention tests.

Tests for visual discrimination were made. There was no error in 100 trials. At all times following the operation the animal was oriented in the cage and room and, with the exception of the motor disturbance, gave no indication of any deterioration.

Extent of Lesions. The areas destroyed are shown diagrammatically in Fig. 8.1 and in sections in Fig. 8.2.

Left hemisphere: Mediad, the lesion began about 1 mm. behind the end of the fissure of Rolando and extended forward to the level of the knee of the corpus callosum. The cortex of the precentral gyrus was destroyed to within 2 mm. of the edge of the longitudinal fissure, but that of the median surface was uninjured. Caudad, the lesion extended slightly onto the postcentral gyrus

Table 8.1. Average Time in Seconds Per Trial Consumed in Opening Each Problem-Box in Each Day's Practice of Training, Preliminary Retention Tests, and Postoperative Retention Tests

	Training tests			Preliminary retention tests			Postoperative retention tests		
	Pull box	Crank box	Hasp box	Pull box	Crank box	Hasp box	Pull box	Crank box	Hasp box
	136.6	206.2	135.2	1.6	3.2	44.4	2.8	63.6	31.0
	5.4	390.0	34.4	3.0	1.6	81.8	2.2	7.4	57.6
	1.8	47.2	10.0	2.4	11.0	14.0		4.4	
	2.0	12.8	18.0	1.2	2.4			3.8	
	1.6	4.6			5.6				
	1.2	3.8			2.6				
	2.4	10.8			2.7				
	2.0	27.6							
	2.2	2.6							
	1.6	4.8							
		6.0							
		1.8							
		2.8							
		1.6							
		2.2							
		2.6							

but did not involve all of the cortex within the fissure of Rolando. Laterad, it extended to the upper border of the operculum. The parts of the stimulable area left intact were the paracentral gyrus, the cortex within the fissure of Rolando and the lateral part of the face area included on the operculum.

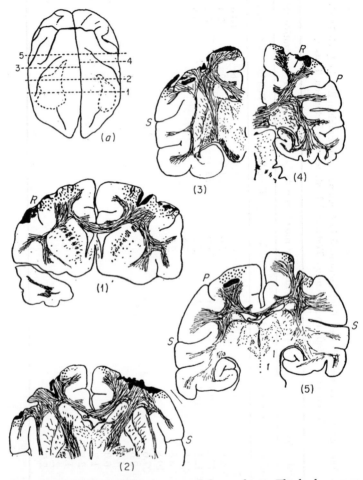

Fig. 8.2. (*a*) Outline of dorsal aspect of the cerebrum. The broken areas outlined indicate the extent of dural adhesions. The transverse broken lines show the level of the sections designated by the corresponding numbers. (1) to (5) Camera sketches of sections showing extent of lesions. Blood clots and scar tissue are indicated in solid black. Obviously degenerated cortex is marked with coarse stippling. *R*, fissure of Rolando; *S*, fissure of Sylvius; *P*, parieto-occipital fissure.

Right hemisphere: The lesion was similar to that on the left but slightly more extensive. The cortex within the rolandic fissure was destroyed, and the lesion extended farther over the operculum.

After destruction of almost all of the arm areas of both sides and of most of the areas of the legs and face, this animal, on recovery from paralysis, showed perfect retention of visual and motor habits acquired before injury. Except for the paralysis and later spasticity, no significant change in his behavior could be noted.

Number 2. This was a small male cebus too wild for training at the beginning of the experiments. The motor area of the right hemisphere was exposed, the arm, face, and leg areas identified and cauterized to a depth of 5 mm., caudad to central fissure, laterad and cephalad to a line 5 mm. beyond the limits of the excitable area.

Following operation, the left leg and arm were not used. The leg was hyperextended and gave some support to the body in standing or sitting, but made no stepping movements. No movements of the hand could be elicited. This complete paralysis of the left hand persisted for two weeks.

Four weeks after operation, the left leg was used almost normally. The left arm could be used to support the animal's weight, but tended to become rigid in hyperextension, and the left hand could not be used for grasping.

Eleven weeks after operation, the paralysis had almost disappeared; the left hand was somewhat clumsy but could be used in grasping food. It was not used when the right hand was unrestrained.

Training on the problem-boxes was begun at this stage of recovery. During the next three months, the problems were learned and retention tests given.

Seven months after the first operation, the left motor area was exposed and similarly explored and destroyed. Paralysis of the right arm and leg followed. It appeared to be as complete as that of the left side following the first lesion. It improved more rapidly, however. Six weeks after operation the right hand was used to pick up food, and, although still somewhat spastic, was judged capable of manipulating the latch boxes. Retention tests were therefore begun. The average time per trial for successive groups of five trials in training, preliminary retention tests, and postoperative retention tests is given in Table 8.2. Visual discrimination was unaffected by the operation.

The short time required for opening the boxes in the postoperative retention tests gives clear evidence for some retention of the habits. Much of the delay apparent was due to the weakness and clumsiness of the right hand. With each problem-box the attack in the postoperative retention tests was directly on the latches. The methods employed were at first those used before operation, and the movements were definitely adapted to solving the problems, although lacking force and accuracy; for example, efforts were all directed to turning the crank counter-clockwise.

The weakness of the right arm led to a surprising readjustment on the part of this animal. The operation on the right hemisphere made the left

Table 8.2. Average Time in Seconds Per Trial Consumed in Opening Each Problem-Box in Each Day's Practice in Training, Preliminary Retention Tests, and Postoperative Retention Tests

Training tests			Preliminary retention tests			Postoperative retention tests		
Pull box	Crank box	Hasp box	Pull box	Crank box	Hasp box	Pull box	Crank box	Hasp box
24 hrs.*	126.0	102.2 †	2.2	28.8	8.8	9.8	14.8	102.5
24 hrs.*	105.0	111.0 †	2.0	1.6	6.4	3.6	11.4	93.4
2,520 sec.	16.0	235.0				1.2	7.2	35.4
24 hrs.*	5.2	184.4						60.6
366 sec.	7.8	19.6						22.8
2.5	7.4	16.0						15.4
1.4	1.4	55.6						
4.5	1.2	6.0						
20.4	2.8	6.6						
1.6								

* Failed to open box while under observation and was left in the cage over night.
† Time with hasp left unfastened.

118

arm weak and spastic during training. In all of the trials of training and preliminary retention tests the left arm was used only as a prop, and the left hand was *not once* used in manipulating the latches of any of the boxes. After the second operation, the right hand was much more affected than the left, which had largely recovered and an almost immediate shift to the left hand in opening all of the boxes occurred.

Pull Box. Postoperative retention test.

Trial 1: Fumbled in hole with right hand, removed hand, peered into hole; again inserted right hand and again pulled lever: twenty-seven seconds.

Trial 2: Right hand, fairly accurately: seven seconds.

Trial 3: He fumbled with right, then inserted left, grasped lever and pulled: seven seconds.

Trial 4: He inserted left hand at once: three seconds.

Trial 5: Left hand used at once: five seconds.

The right hand was used only four times in the succeeding forty trials.

Crank Box. Trial 1: He grasped the crank with his right hand at once and turned counter-clockwise. The crank stuck in the third quadrant. He pushed at it feebly, gave up, returned to the attack from the side of the box and pulled it through final segment: 160 seconds.

Trial 2: He grasped the crank with the right hand. Apparently, he was unable to move it. He grasped it with both hands and swung it around: twenty-five seconds.

Trials 3, 4, and 5: He used only the right hand and turned with difficulty moving to side of box and exerting direct pull instead of his former transverse rotary movement.

Trial 6: He grasped with the left hand and turned counter-clockwise: six seconds. All later trials were made with the left hand only.

Hasp Box. On the first three days of the postoperative tests, he pulled out the plug and disengaged the hasp promptly with his right hand, but lacked strength to lift the lid. He gave up after a few attempts with his right hand.

On the fourth day, he drew out the plug and disengaged the hasp with his right hand, then lifted the lid with his left foot. It fell back as he attempted to reach the food. He lifted it again with his left hand, climbed to the edge of the box, bringing his right side against the lid, so holding it up while he grasped the food with his left hand. On the second trial, he lifted with the left hand and held it up with his left hand, inserting his head for the food. In all later trials, he lifted the lid with his left hand, sometimes holding it back with his left knee or with his head while reaching into the box with his left hand, or with the left hand while reaching with his head. On the eighth and all later trials, he pulled the plug with his left hand and used the right only as a prop.

Throughout the retention tests his activities were centered on the plug, hasp, and lid. He never attempted to lift the lid until the hasp was disengaged. When the lid was raised the next acts seemed definitely directed to holding it up, and though clumsy, the movements were clearly not random.

Effects of Subsequent Destruction of the Corpus Striatum. A broad bladed cautery was next passed through the old lesion into the corpus striatum and drawn back and forth through this nucleus. The wound was closed, and the animal was kept under observation until his death eight days later.

On recovery from anesthesia, the animal showed marked spasticity of the left side. The left arm was usually hyperextended, although in walking or clinging to a perch the arm and leg assumed a normal posture. The left side was very weak, and when he walked the arm and leg frequently collapsed suddenly. He took food with his right hand and placed it in his mouth with the palm of his left hand, but without closing the fingers, which remained hyperextended.

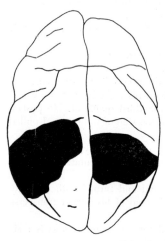

On subsequent days, he used both right and left hands in walking, climbing and grasping food. The left side was spastic and very weak but capable of a variety of fine adaptive movements. The right side showed a coarse tremor, and athetoid movements of the left arm appeared when the right was used. There was marked paralysis of the pharynx. He kept his mouth stuffed with food or shavings but was unable to swallow.

At no time was the paralysis as marked as after the destruction of the cortex. Indeed the condition showed no resemblance to hemiplegia, but, except for the pharyngeal paralysis, was essentially described by Wilson (60) for lesions of the striate nucleus without involvement of the pyramidal tracts. The possibility that the recovery from the initial paralysis was due to vicarious functioning of the striate nucleus seems thus definitely to be ruled out. The animal did not recover sufficiently for retention tests after this operation, but his behavior when released in the laboratory showed that his general orientation was unaffected. When given an egg, he made efforts to break it by pounding it on the floor, as he had done before the operation, and in the performance of this habit both hands were used.

Fig. 8.3. The extent of the lesions in animal number 2. Reconstructed from camera sketch and serial sections. The posterior border of the left precentral gyrus escaped injury.

Extent of Lesions. The extent of the destructions is indicated in Fig. 8.3 and sections through the area are shown in Fig. 8.4.

Right hemisphere. The lesion extended cephalad from the median end of the central fissure to the middle of the superior frontal gyrus, bordering the longitudinal fissure but leaving the cortex of the median surface of the hemisphere intact. Caudad it invaded the postcentral gyrus and completely obliterated the fissure of Rolando. Laterad it extended well onto the operculum. Only the paracentral gyrus and the lateral portion of the face area remained intact.

The second operation destroyed all of the caudate nucleus and the greater part of the lenticular, leaving only the posterior end of the putamen intact.

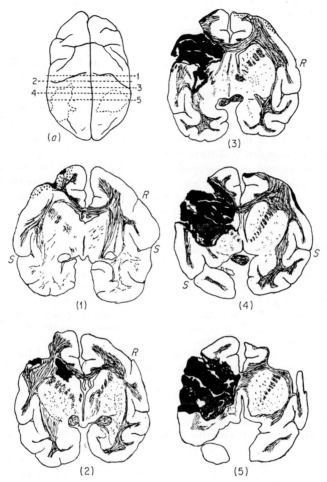

Fig. 8.4. (*a*) Outline of the dorsal aspect of the cerebrum. The broken areas outlined indicate the extent of dural adhesions. The transverse broken lines show the level of the sections designated by the corresponding numbers. (1) to (5) Camera sketches of sections showing extent of lesions. Blood clots and scar tissue are indicated in solid black. Obviously degenerated cortex is marked with coarse stippling. *R*, fissure of Rolando; *S*, fissure of Sylvius; *P*, parieto-occipital fissure.

Left hemisphere. The lesion was less extensive than that on the right. It began 5 mm. in front of the median end of the central fissure and extended to the frontal lobe. All of the cortex of the median surface to the callosomarginal fissure was destroyed. The posterior edge of the precentral gyrus remained intact, for a width of about 5 mm.

In this animal, practically all of the precentral gyrus of the right hemisphere was destroyed. He was then trained in manipulative movements of the right hand. This was followed by partial destruction of the left precentral gyrus. On recovery from paralysis, he gave clear evidence of retention of the habits but owing to spasticity of the right hand, made a direct transfer of the habits to the left hand. The right precentral gyrus was almost completely destroyed, whereas a rather large proportion of the left precentral gyrus escaped injury, but in spite of this, the animal shifted to the use of his left hand in opening the problem-boxes. Subsequent destruction of the greater part of the corpus striatum did not produce a recurrence of the hemiplegic symptoms.

Number 3. This was a large female rhesus trained on problem-boxes and visual discrimination. After retention tests, the motor areas of both sides were exposed, mapped and cauterized. Following the operation the legs and left arm were completely paralyzed. The right arm made clumsy pawing movements. Twelve hours after operation, the animal walked a few feet with staggering gait, then collapsed with arms and legs widely extended, and for several days made no further efforts to walk. The following day she grasped a grape with her right hand and brought it to her mouth after several unsuccessful trials. The movements were clumsy and slow.

Four weeks after operation she seemed sufficiently recovered for retention tests, although still showing a general clumsiness and marked weakness of the left limbs.

The average time per trial for successive groups of five trials in training, preliminary retention tests and retention tests after operation is given in Table 8.3. Visual discrimination was unaffected by the operation.

The time required to open the problem-boxes in the postoperative retention tests gives certain evidence of the retention of the habits. An average of 678.8 seconds was consumed in each of the first five trials of training in opening the boxes by the method of random activity. Only 17.5 seconds' average was required for the first five trials of the postoperative retention tests. The methods of opening the pull and crank boxes were the same before and after the operation. The persistent weakness of the left arm called for a change in method of opening the hasp box. Before operation, the animal had used the same method in twenty consecutive trials. The plug was pulled out of the staple with the right hand. The hasp was lifted from the staple with the right hand, turned back against the lid, and then transferred to the left hand. The lid was lifted with the left hand and the right hand thrust into the box for the food. In the postoperative retention tests, the left hand was not used at all. She first lifted the lid with her right hand, then released it and attempted to grasp the food

Table 8.3. Average Time in Seconds Per Trial Required for Opening Each Problem-Box in Each Day's Practice in Training, Preliminary Retention Tests, and Postoperative Retention Tests

Training tests			Preliminary retention tests			Postoperative retention tests		
Pull box	Crank box	Hasp box	Pull box	Crank box	Hasp box	Pull box	Crank box	Hasp box
68.2	1,595.0	40.4 *	1.0	4.2	24.0	1.0	2.2	49.2
2.6	111.8	373.2	1.0	3.8	6.6	1.0	1.4	9.8
1.0	145.4	124.6		1.6	5.0	2.6	1.4	8.4
1.0	304.2	24.2		1.2	3.6			
	140.0	17.0		1.0	2.2			
	16.8				1.8			

* Time with hasp unfastened.

with the same hand, but the lid falling back prevented this. On the first trial, she finally held the lid back with her right hand, inserted her head in the box and took the food in her teeth. On the second trial, she thrust her head against the lid after raising it with the right hand and so held it open while the hand was inserted in the box. The same method was used on the third and fourth trials. On the fifth trial, she attempted to hold up the lid with her left foot and finally succeeded in this after overbalancing twice. In all later trials, she released the lid and allowed it to fall against her right arm as this was thrust into the box. These various acts were carried out with definite adaptation to the contour of the box and had none of the elements of random pulling and thrusting which characterize the initial stages of learning. As in the case of number 2, there seemed to be an immediate adaptation of movements to opening the box, which had not been employed at any time in the previous practice.

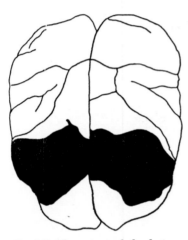

Extent of Lesions. The injured areas are shown in Fig. 8.5 and sections in Fig. 8.6.

Right hemisphere. The lesion began at the posterior median end of the central fissure and included practically all of the precentral gyrus. On the median surface, all of the cortex above the callosomarginal fissure was destroyed. Practically all of the gyrus within the rolandic fissure was involved. Laterad: the lesion included the upper half of the operculum. At most, only the lateral facial area escaped destruction.

Left hemisphere. The lesion was almost coextensive with that on the right. More of the paracentral gyrus was destroyed and somewhat less of the operculum.

Fig. 8.5. The extent of the lesions in animal number 3. Reconstructed from camera sketch and serial sections. Practically the whole of both precentral gyri destroyed, including the paracentral gyrus and cortex within the central sulcus.

After practically complete destruction of both precentral gyri this animal gave evidence of perfect retention of visual habits and habits of manipulation. Direct adaptive changes in behavior were made to compensate for weakness of the left arm.

Discussion of Experiments

After extensive lesions to the precentral gyri of both hemispheres, each of the animals studied gave clear evidence of the retention of patterns of movement which had been acquired before the operative destructions. Evidence of this retention was obtained from a comparison of the time required for opening the problem-boxes in initial training with that for the postoperative retention tests, from the restriction of reactions in the postoperative retention tests to the catches of the problem-boxes, and from the persistence of individual peculiarities of opening the boxes.

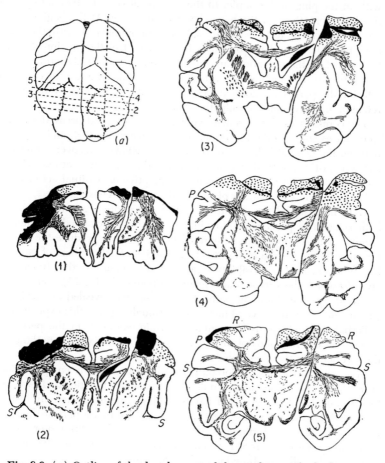

Fig. 8.6. (*a*) Outline of the dorsal aspect of the cerebrum. The broken areas outlined indicate the extent of dural adhesions. In a preliminary examination, the left hemisphere was cut through along the longitudinal dotted line. The sections of its two halves are therefore from somewhat different levels. The transverse broken lines show the level of the sections designated by the corresponding numbers. (1) to (5) Camera sketches of sections showing extent of lesions. Blood clots and scar tissue are indicated in solid black. Obviously degenerated cortex is marked with coarse stippling. *R*, fissure of Rolando; *S*, fissure of Sylvius; *P*, parieto-occipital fissure.

The average time required by all animals for opening each box in the first five trials of training was 584 seconds.[5] An average of only 30.7 seconds was required in the first five trials of the postoperative tests. The animals all failed the hasp box in the preliminary training until first trained without the plug in the staple. In the postoperative tests, they all opened this box promptly with the hasp closed by the plug. At the beginning of the postoperative tests, each animal (except number 3 with the hasp box) used the same hand or hands for each part of the manipulation as he had before the operation, and attacked the latches in his former manner, although the methods of attack were modified rapidly to compensate for the persistent motor difficulties. All the animals showed perfect retention in the visual discrimination test.

These results establish conclusively that the cerebral areas destroyed were not essential to the performance of the habits studied, and observations on the general behavior of the animals following recovery from the paralysis justify the further conclusion that the areas are not essential to the performance of any type of complex adaptive or habitual activity.

Four possible explanations of the results must be considered:

1. In no case did the operation destroy the entire precentral gyrus of both sides. The parts remaining intact may have contained a sufficient number of fibers previously integrated in the habit to produce the conditioned reflexes, in spite of the great destruction of other fibers of equivalent function. Such a possibility is supported by data on other functional areas in which the various parts seem equipotential (12, 25) and by the apparent equipotentiality of parts of the motor area revealed by electrical stimulation (28), but several facts speak strongly against this explanation.

Partial destructions usually entail a certain confusion in the performance of all the functions of an area, which seems to exceed anything of the sort noted in these animals.[6]

In number 3, the destruction on both sides was so nearly complete that only a part of the face areas could have remained functional. If we attempt to explain the survival of habits as being due to the activity of undestroyed parts of the motor area, we must assume that a part of the face area is capable of performing all the functions of the entire motor cortex —an assumption which is as far from the accepted views of localization as is the denial of all habit function to the motor areas.

---

[5] This does not include the failures with the hasp box or the times when number 2 was left in the cage over night.

[6] I am collecting data on this question at present. The evidence is not complete, but there is indication that, e.g., any extensive but incomplete destruction of the visual areas of both hemispheres in the rat is followed by inaccuracy of brightness discrimination, with great variability from day to day, such as has been reported by Franz in 1916 for aphasia, yet without any complete loss of any phase of the visual function. Such loss as appeared in the motor habits of the monkeys was almost certainly ascribable to the simple motor weakness, and gave no indications of any apraxia.

2. It might be urged that in the recovery from the motor paralysis, the vicarious functions assumed by other areas included the movements involved in the problem-box habits; that the habits were relearned during the period of recovery from paralysis. The habits, however, consist of particular patterns of movement associated with the stimuli presented by the latch boxes. During the postoperative period, there was no occasion for the animals to reacquire these particular patterns of movement and no opportunity for the movements to be associated with the latch boxes.

3. The long controversy concerning the sensory-motor function of both the precentral and postcentral gyri suggests that the two may both include centrifugal cells for the performance of habits. The literature cited in the first part of this paper seems to establish the differential function of the two areas, however, and the lack of paralysis after lesions to the postcentral gyrus makes the hypothesis untenable. Nañagas (42) found a few islands of large pyramidal cells in the postcentral gyrus, but the great mass of them was restricted to the precentral. Finally, Brown (4) reported that the destruction of the postcentral gyrus did not abolish learning ability or interfere seriously with habits formed before the operation in the chimpanzee.

4. The only remaining possibility seems to be that the electrostimulable areas do not include the centrifugal elements of conditioned reflex arcs of any sort. (It is of course possible that they contain some such elements, but these cannot comprise any significant proportion of the total number of centrifugal cells, since their destruction leaves the habits completely unaffected.) In this, the experiments confirm for primates the results previously reported for the rat. The neural impulses involved in conditioned reactions do not pass from sensory projection areas to the precentral gyrus and thence to lower centers, but must be conducted by centrifugal cells lying outside of the pyramidal system. In the rat, the evidence points to the view that the centrifugal fibers of the sensory projection area itself are primarily involved in this motor function, since the destruction of any fourth of the cerebrum exclusive of the visual areas does not affect the performance of visual habits.[7] Whether or not the same lack of important transcortical conduction holds true for the monkey is questionable in view of the greater proportionate development of the transcortical association tracts in this animal, but it seems established that the "motor areas" are not concerned in the initiation of habitual movements.

---

[7] Experiments now in progress, which indicate that extensive fronto-parieto-temporal lesions may also abolish visual habits without producing a general deterioration of learning ability, indicate that a mass action of the cerebrum is also somehow involved, but they do not seem to invalidate the conclusion that the efferent fibers of the sensory projection area are primarily concerned in the subcortical initiation of movements associated with the receptor for that area.

The Corpus Striatum and Vicarious Function

All recent students of the question agree that recovery from cerebral paralysis is not due to the assumption of the function of the destroyed motor cortex by the corresponding area of the opposite side. On the contrary, the simultaneous destruction of the areas in both hemispheres seems to be followed by a rather more rapid recovery than follows the destruction of either alone. The fact has been noted by Grünbaum and Sherrington (17), and by Wagner (59). It was apparent in the slower recovery of number 2 from the first operation than from the second. The explanation is probably to be found in the forced practice which diplegia imposes on the paralyzed limbs (44).

Other restricted cerebral areas have also been rather definitely excluded from participation in the vicarious function of the stimulable areas, by the work of Leyton and Sherrington (30) and Lashley (27). Luciani (31) has suggested that recovery may be due to the activity of the corpus striatum, which has homologies with the stimulable cortex. This was tested in animal number 2 of the present series by destruction of the right striatum after recovery from diplegia. Hemiplegic symptoms did not recur, so that we may conclude that the recovery had not been due to the vicarious activity of the striate nucleus.

The Function of the Electrostimulable Areas

The conclusions which may be drawn from these experiments are wholly negative. They seem to prove that the precentral gyrus does not include the efferent paths for learned activities; in the current localization terminology, it is not the center for "voluntary movements," as is almost universally assumed. But if this is true, what is the significance of the movements elicited by electrical stimulation? How may we interpret the cerebral paralyses, and why do they especially affect the finer manipulative movements? A number of lines of evidence may help to answer these questions and clear up the function of the precentral gyri.

The Postural Function of the Stimulable Areas. Many investigators have pointed out the similarity between the movements elicited by cortical stimulation and "voluntary movements." I am convinced that this is an error due to contrasting these movements with those which are elicited by stimulation of motor nerves or spinal cord. In the latter cases, the movements are wholly incoordinated, whereas the movements following cortical stimulation involve synergic groups of muscles. But in all cortical stimulation experiments which I have seen, the movements have been slow and rather massive, i.e., chiefly involving the larger musculature of the limbs. When smaller segments are moved, the movements are never coordinated as they are, for example, in grasping small objects. They never show the fineness of gradation and accuracy of adjustment which is characteristic of the movements of the intact animal. This has been observed by various investigators and interpreted as showing that the finer adjustments are integrated at some higher level and imposed through it on the motor area. But there is no direct evidence that this is the case. The movements following excitation are far more like the gross changes of posture which one may observe in the intact animal—the raising of an arm preparatory to snatching at food, bracing against a pressure, or the like. It seems significant that coordinated movements of the eyes are among the most easily elicited movements on electrical stimulation (although their stimulable points lie outside of the precentral areas), and that these movements in the intact man or animal are almost always a reflex fixation (postural adjustment) called out directly by exterostimulation and, in fact, can not be accurately performed in the absence of such stimulation, as with lids closed.

Wilson (61) has pointed out the similarity of the contractures in cerebral paralysis to the postural reflexes of decerebrate rigidity, and from this it seems certain that a part of the function of the stimulable areas is the regulation of these spinal and cerebellar postures. It seems rather probable that the movements obtained on electrical stimulation are only a further exhibition of this postural activity and are unrelated to the finer coordinations of conditioned motor reflexes, or motor habits.

The Dynamic Function of the Stimulable Areas. The condition following lesions to the precentral gyrus or internal capsule, even in man, should be described rather as an enormous difficulty in making movements than as an absolute paralysis of movement. The degree of paralysis varies somewhat from day to day. Excitement seems to increase motor control (36, 26), and the paralysis may in part or wholly disappear during emotional disturbance, only to recur when the disturbing situation is past. If we may judge from the tonic condition of the muscles, there must be in excitement a general facilitation of lower motor centers which temporarily reinstates cerebral control. Further, if this is the case, in the intact animal in the absence of emotional stimulation cerebral control must likewise be conditioned by some such facilitation derived from the precentral gyrus. The work of Brown (3, 4) and of Leyton and Sherrington (30) has shown that stimulation of the motor area does facilitate the centrifugal paths of other areas, either at cortical or subcortical levels, since stimulation of the precentral gyrus renders the otherwise inexcitable postcentral gyrus excitable for corresponding movements.

After partial recovery from cerebral paralysis, the most prominent symptom is the weakness of the formerly paralyzed limbs. The greater part of their repertoire of movements may be restored, speed may be nearly normal, but only a slight force can be exerted, and fatigue occurs readily. What is lacking in this condition is not an adequate integration of the motor impulses, but a sufficient mass of neural impulses to maintain muscular activity. This may be ascribed either to a reduction in the number of functional nerve cells, or to inadequate facilitation. The ready fatigability is evidence for the latter.[8]

There is evidence that the withdrawal of facilitation derived from other sources will produce similar weakness and fatigability and a tendency not to use the affected parts. Thus Munk (41) has shown that denervation of a limb has such effect, and Sherrington's (53) work has demonstrated that they are due to the withdrawal of impulses derived largely from the denervated muscles.

The importance of such facilitating systems has been emphasized by a number of recent investigators (37, 60, 54, 57, 23). The general conception of these investigators is of a series of hierarchies of motor reflexes, all exerting a facilitating influence on the final common path. These involve at least the following elements:

1. Excitation of the motor cells supplying a muscle by impulses derived from the receptors in the muscle itself (53).

2. Long spinal reflexes from synergic muscles (53, 33).

3. Other proprioceptive and general exteroceptive facilitation whose central mechanism is as yet rather obscure (62, 46).

4. Vestibular and proprioceptive influences exerted through the mechanisms of the cerebellum.

5. Probably facilitation derived from thalamic mechanisms in emotional excitement (18).

6. Kinetic influences of obscure origin integrated in the corpus striatum (60, 23).

Interference with any of these mechanisms is able to produce a change in the excitability of the final common path, and in the intact organism it seems certain that every act involves the participation of all of them, both by excitation and inhibition.

These considerations make it possible to form a tentative hypothesis concerning the function of the precentral gyrus. Its demonstrated facilitating effects and its lack of direct participation in the conditioned reflex arc seem to throw it into a class with these other postural and tonic systems. Cerebral paralysis is, I believe, to be interpreted as showing that a normal function of the stimulable cortex is to supply a substratum of

[8] The all-or-nothing principle of nerve and muscle activity requires the assumption that strength of muscular contraction is dependent upon the number of motor fibers involved and the rate of succession of propagated disturbances. Piper's work (45) indicates that fatigue involves a decrease in this rate rather than a reduction in the total number of muscle cells activated.

facilitating impulses which act in some way to render the final common paths excitable by the more finely graduated impulses, descending from the cortex by extrapyramidal paths and producing the finer shades of adaptive movement. In other words, impulses descending from the precentral gyrus do not initiate the finer adaptive movements through the lower motor neurons, but only "prime" these cells so that they may be excited by impulses from other sources. The source of this activity and the probable interrelations of the stimulable areas with other parts of the motor system and with sensory projection areas present problems too complex for discussion here. Unquestionably, the areas receive excitations from other parts of the cerebrum [9] and it is probable that all parts of the kinetic system [10] are capable of mutual influence. Postural facilitation and inhibition may themselves be habitual responses, but the present experiments indicate that they are rather generalized and not independently organized for each specific manipulative habit.

Recent work in general tends to emphasize the complexity of neural functions. We must hesitate to ascribe an exclusive or precise function to any neural structure, for the evidence points rather to the view that observable behavior is always the product of the interaction of many neural systems and that the function of any system is dependent on its temporary physiologic relation to other systems. This is particularly true of the finer adaptive responses of the intact animal which are subject to inhibition and facilitation by innumerable factors. Their execution depends on preparatory postural adjustments, emotional and other dynamic facilitation, as well as integration of impulses from many exteroceptors.[11] The total mass of excitation is effective both through the specific efferent patterns activated and also through the general dynamic effects which alone are incapable of producing the overt motor reactions elicited. The experiments reported here indicate that the electrostimulable areas are rather more concerned with the maintenance of excitability and the regulation of postural reflexes than with the excitation and control of finely integrated adaptive movements.

[9] I have made several attempts to isolate the area from other parts of the cortex by circumsection but have not yet been successful. The literature on this point is conflicting. Marique (34) reported the same results from circumsection as from excision of the area. Exner and Paneth (10) found similar results but were inclined to ascribe them to interference with the blood supply of the area. Schäfer (50) reported one case of complete circumsection without paralysis. He does not report histologic examination of the lesion, however, and in view of the difficulty of the operation there is not sufficient evidence that the isolation was complete.

[10] In this discussion, I have disregarded the important conception of static and kinetic functions advanced by Hunt (23) because the evidence does not show clearly to which of his systems the electrostimulable cortex is to be referred. The postural influences of the area would indicate a static function. What I have called the dynamic or "priming" function is rather a kinetic function, but is more primitive than the activities implied in Hunt's conception of the neokinetic system.

[11] The statement that every act of the intact organism involves the participation of every neuron within the central nervous system is probably no more of an exaggeration than are the extreme theories of precise localization of function or of isolated conditioned reflex paths.

Summary

The greater part of the precentral gyrus of both hemispheres was destroyed in monkeys which had been trained previously in habits of manipulation and visual discrimination. When the animals recovered from paralysis, it was found that they showed perfect retention of these habits. From this it is concluded that the so-called motor areas are not directly concerned with the performance of complex learned activities. The motor impulses of conditioned reflexes must descend from other areas of the cerebral cortex than the precentral gyri, and the latter cannot be regarded as the source of impulses to "voluntary movements."

Destruction of the corpus striatum subsequent to recovery from diplegia produced only the usual symptoms of striate lesion without recurrence of the symptoms of cerebral paralysis. Recovery from paralysis was therefore not due to vicarious function of this nucleus.

The evidence for considering the precentral gyrus as a part of the kinetic mechanism for reflex control of spinal posture and for maintenance of excitability of lower motor centers is summarized.

REFERENCES

1. Barenne, J. G. D. de. Sensory localization in the cerebral cortex, *Quart. J. exp. Physiol.*, 1916, 9, 355–390.

2. Bechterew, W. v. *Die Funktionen der Nervencentra*. Jena: 1911, Vol. III.

3. Brown, T. G. Studies in the physiology of the nervous system: XXV. 4. On the phenomenon of facilitation: its occurrence in the subcortical mechanism by the action of which motor effects are produced on artificial stimulation of the "motor" cortex, *J. Physiol.*, 1915, 9, 131–145.

4. Brown, T. G. Studies in the physiology of the nervous system: XXVII. 6. The motor activation of parts of the cerebral cortex other than those included in the so-called "motor" areas in monkeys, *Quart. J. exp. Physiol.*, 1916, 10, 103–143.

5. Bubnoff, N., and Heidenhain, R. Ueber Erregungs- und Hemmungs-vorgänge innerhalb der motorischen Hirncentren, *Arch. ges. Physiol.*, 1881, 26, 137–200.

6. Carville, C., and Duret, H. Sur les fonctions des hémisphères cérébraux, *Arch. Physiol.*, 1875, 7, 352–490.

7. Cushing, H. A note upon the faradic stimulation of the postcentral gyrus in conscious patients, *Brain*, 1909, 32, 44–54.

8. Dana, C. L. A study of the functions of the cortex of the motor area of the brain, *J. nerv. ment. Dis.*, 1894, 21, 761–785.

9. Dupuy, E. Expériment sur les fonctions motrices du cerveau, *C. R. Soc. Biol.*, Paris, 1888, 1025–1027.

10. Exner, S., and Paneth, J. *Pflüg. Arch. ges. Physiol.*, 1889, 44, 544–555.

11. Ferrier, E. *The functions of the brain*. London: 1876.

12. Franz, S. I. On the functions of the cerebrum: the frontal lobes, *Arch. Psychol.*, 1907 (2), 1–64.

13. Franz, S. I. Variations in distribution of the motor centers, *Psychol. Monogr.*, 1915, 19, 80–162.

14. Franz, S. I., and Lashley, K. S. The retention of habits by the rat after destruction of the frontal portion of the cerebrum, *Psychobiology*, 1917, 1, 3–18.

15. Fritsch, G., and Hitzig, E. Ueber die elektrische Erregbarkeit des Grosshirns, *Arch. Anat. Physiol.*, Lpz., 1870, 300–332.

16. Gierlich, N. *Ueber Symptomatologie, Wesen, und Therapie der hemiplegischen Lähmung.* Wiesbaden: 1913.

17. Grünbaum, A., and Sherrington, C. S. Observations on the physiology of the cerebral cortex of the anthropoid apes, *Proc. roy. Soc.*, 1903, 72B, 152–155.

18. Head, H. *Studies in neurology.* London: 1920. Release of functions in the nervous system, *Proc. roy. Soc.*, 1921, 92B, 184–209.

19. Hermann, L. Ueber elektrische Reizversuche an der Grosshirnrinde, *Arch. ges. Physiol.*, 1875, 10, 77–88.

20. Hitzig, E. *Physiologische und klinische Untersuchungen über das Gehirn.* Berlin: 1904.

21. Hoppe, H. H. A critical study of the sensory functions of the motor zone (pre-Rolandic area): more especially stereognosis, *J. nerv. ment. Dis.*, 1909, 36, 513–527.

22. Horsley, V. On the analysis of voluntary movement, *Nineteenth Century*, 1891, 29, 857–870.

23. Hunt, R. The static and kinetic systems of motility, *Arch. Neurol. Psychiat.*, Chicago, 1920, 4, 353.

24. Jellinek, A., and Koppányi, T. Lernfähigkeit gehirnverletzter Ratten, *Anzieger Akad. Wiss.*, Wien, 1923 (17).

25. Lashley, K. S. Studies of cerebral function in learning, *Psychobiology*, 1920, 2, 55–135.

26. Lashley, K. S. Studies of cerebral function in learning: III. The motor areas, *Brain*, 1921, 44, 255–286.

27. Lashley, K. S. Studies of cerebral function in learning: IV. Vicarious function after destruction of the visual areas, *Amer. J. Physiol.*, 1922, 59, 44–71.

28. Lashley, K. S. Temporal variation in the function of the gyrus precentralis in primates, *Amer. J. Physiol.*, 1923, 65, 585–602.

29. Lewandowsky, M., and Simmons, A. Zur Physiologie der vordern und hintern Zentralwindung, *Arch. ges. Physiol.*, 1909, 129, 240–254.

30. Leyton, A. S. F., and Sherrington, C. S. Observations on the excitable cortex of the chimpanzee, orang-outan and gorilla, *Quart. J. exp. Physiol.*, 1917, 11, 135–222.

31. Luciani, L. *Human physiology.* London: 1915. Vol. III.

32. Luciani, L., and Seppili, G. *Die Funktion-Localization auf der Grosshirnrinde.* Leipzig: Deutsche Ausgabe, 1886.

33. Magnus, R., and de Kleijn, A. Die Abhängigkeit des Tonus der Extremitätenmuskeln von der Kopfstellung, *Arch. ges. Physiol.*, 1912, 145, 455–548. Magnus, R. Welche Teile des Centralnervensystems müssen für das Zustandekommender tonischen Hals- und Labyrinthreflexe auf die Körpermuskulatur vorhanden sein? *Arch. ges. Physiol.*, 1914, 159, 224–250.

34. Marique. *Brain*, 1885, 8, 536–538.

35. Mills, C. K. The separate localization in the cortex and sub-cortex of the cerebrum of the representation of movements and of muscular and cutaneous sensibility, *J. nerv. ment. Dis.*, 1901, 38, 595–619.

36. Minkowski, M. Etude physiologique des circonvolutions rolandiques et pariétales, *Arch. Suisse Neurol. Psychiat.*, 1917, 1, 389–459.

37. Monakow, C. von. Aufbau und Lokalisation der Bewegungen beim Menschen. *Ber. ueber iv. Kongress exp. Psychol. in Innsbruck*, 1910.

38. Mott, F. W. The sensory-motor functions of the central convolutions of the cerebral cortex, *J. Physiol.*, 1893–1894, 15, 464–487.

39. Munk, H. *Ueber die Funktionen der Grosshirnrinde.* Berlin: 1890.

40. Munk, H. Ueber die Fühlsphären der Grosshirnrinde, *Sitzungsber. Berlin Akad. Wiss.*, 1892, 679–723; 1893, 759–781; 1894, 823–833; 1896, 1131–1159.

41. Munk, H. Ueber die Folgen des Sensibilitätsverlustes der Extremität für deren Motilität, *Sitzungsber. Berlin Akad. Wiss.*, 1903, 1038–1077.

42. Nañagas, J. C. Anatomical studies on the motor cortex of macacus rhesus, *J. comp. Neurol.*, 1922, 35, 67–96.

43. Nothnagel, H. Experimentelle Untersuchungen über die Funktionen des Gehirns, *Arch. path. Anat. Physiol.*, 1873, 57, 184–227.

44. Oden, R., and Franz, S. I. On cerebral motor control: the recovery from experimentally produced hemiplegia, *Psychobiology*, 1917, 1, 33–50.

45. Piper, *Electrophysiologie menschlicher Muskeln.* Berlin: 1912.

46. Richter, C. P. A behavioristic study of the activity of the rat, *Comp. Psychol. Monogr.*, 1922, 1, 1–55.

47. Rothmann, M. Ueber die physiologische Wertung der cortico-spinalen (Pyramiden) Bahn, *Arch. Anat. Physiol.*, Lpz. (Physiol. Abt.), 1907, 217–275.

48. Rothmann, M. Ueber die elektrische Erregbarkeit der Zentralwindungen, *Mschr. Psychiat. Neurol.*, 1912, 32, 489–502.

49. Sanderson, J. B. Note on the excitation of the surface of the cerebral hemispheres by induced currents, *Proc. roy. Soc.*, 1874, 22, 368–370.

50. Schäfer, E. A. *J. Physiol.*, 1901, 26, 23–25.

51. Schäfer, E. A. On the alleged sensory functions of the motor cortex cerebri, *J. Physiol.*, 1898, 23, 310–314.

52. Schiff, M. Untersuchungen über die motorischen Funktionen des Grosshirns, *Arch. exper. Path. Pharmak.*, 1875, 3, 171–179.

53. Sherrington, C. S. *The integrative action of the nervous system.* London: 1911.

54. Sherrington, C. S. Postural activity of muscle and nerve, *Brain*, 1915, 38, 191–234.

55. Starlinger, J. Die durchschneidung beider Pyramiden beim Hunde, *Neurol. Zbl.*, 1895, 14, 390–394.

56. Thorndike, E. L. The mental antecedents of voluntary movement, *J. Phil. Psychol. sci. Meth.*, 1907, 4, 40–42.

57. Tournay, A. Conception actuelle des grandes fonctions motrices, *J. Psychol.*, 1920, 17, 904–930.

58. Vogt, C., and Vogt, O. Zur Kenntnis der elektrisch erregbaren Hirnrindengebiete bei den Säugetieren, *J. Psychol. Neurol.*, Lpz., 1907, 8, 277–456.

59. Wagner, V. Discussion in *Neurol. Zbl.*, 1905, 24, 1022.

60. Wilson, S. A. K. An experimental research into the anatomy and physiology of the corpus striatum, *Brain*, 1913, **36**, 427–492.

61. Wilson, S. A. K. On decerebrate rigidity in man and the occurrence of tonic fits, *Brain*, 1920, **43**, 220–268.

62. Yerkes, R. M. Inhibition and reinforcement of reactions in the frog, *J. comp. Neurol. Psychol.*, 1904, **14**, 124.

9. STUDIES OF CEREBRAL FUNCTION

IN LEARNING. *VI. The Theory that*
Synaptic Resistance Is Reduced by the
Passage of the Nerve Impulse [1]

Among the many unsubstantiated beliefs concerning the physiology of the learning process none is more widely prevalent than the doctrine that the passage of a neural impulse through the synapse somehow reduces synaptic resistance and leads to the fixation of a new habit. All theories which are based upon frequency of repetition imply that in learning there is a preliminary penetration of resistant neural paths by irradiation of propagated disturbances and a subsequent lessening of the resistance by repeated use of the new paths. Various elaborate theories concerning the mechanism of this change in resistance have been advanced, ranging from the chemical absurdities of Robertson (10) to the recent revival of the theory of dendritic growth by Kappers (1), but no direct evidence for changes in synaptic resistance has ever been obtained. The hypothesis is not based upon neurological data but is merely a restatement of the observed fact that increased efficiency follows repeated performance.

On the assumption that spinal reflexes represent the basic mechanism of all neural activity the hypothesis has some justification, being simple and in accord with the more apparent facts. It has led to important experimental studies and has furnished a simple pedagogical formula. But the evidence is far from convincing that the acquisition of a simple function is a gradual process or one dependent upon the passage of nerve impulses. All experiments must deal with complex functions involving the successive acquisition of many elementary connections. Familiar learning curves are obviously an expression of these successive integrations and we have no knowledge of the conditions prevailing in formation of a new simple neural integration. The instantaneous character of simpler associations in man, the "all-or-nothing" law which governs the appearance of some

---

[1] EDITORS' NOTE: From *Psychol. Rev.*, 1924, 31, 369–375. Reproduced by permission of the American Psychological Association. From the University of Minnesota.

conditioned reflexes,[2] and the like suggest that in these cases a single performance serves to fix the habit. If this were the case for every simple reintegration within the nervous system we should still get the appearance of gradual improvement through practice, because of the successive formation of many such simple associations or the successive blocking of interfering integrations such as seems to take place in the perfecting of the conditioned reflex.

The fact of gradual improvement in complex functions cannot therefore be taken as evidence for a gradual wearing down of synaptic resistance by repeated passages of neural impulses and the hypothesis must still be considered as open to question. In recent experiments upon other phases of the neurology of learning, I have made incidental observations of some phenomena which seem altogether incompatible with this theory of the wearing down of synaptic resistance and which indicate that new conditioned-reflex paths may be established under conditions where the passage of significant neural impulses over the arcs in question is precluded during the whole course of learning. The experiments deal with both centripetal and centrifugal paths, in both of which it has been possible to block the peripheral neurons during training and to observe their later functioning in the performance of the habitual acts.

Conditioning of Afferent Paths Which Were Nonfunctional during Practice

In tests of the mutual relationships of the striate areas of the cerebral cortex of the albino rat I effectually blindfolded the left eye of the animal with a velvet-lined wire and adhesive tape mask. The blindfold remained in place for a month during which the animal was trained in a Yerkes discrimination box to avoid the brighter of two lights. When discrimination was perfect (no error in thirty trials) the blindfold was transferred to the right eye. When the animal became adapted to the new adjustment his discrimination with the left eye was tested. He showed perfect discrimination with this eye which had not been used during the formation of the habit.

This result is no more than would be expected when we recall the facility with which we ourselves recognize an object with either eye when it has previously been seen with one eye alone (the common experience of the microscopist who views his field alternately with either eye). Yet this obvious fact has never been brought into relation to learning theory. Neural fibers come from the two retinae and somewhere im-

---

[2] It is characteristic that the conditioned reflex is not built up gradually, but is fully integrated when it first appears. Improvement can be expressed only in terms of the proportion of times when the associated stimulus succeeds or fails to elicit it. It is at first easily inhibited. With practice the inhibition becomes more difficult, but there is some evidence for the belief that this is due to the building up of specific resistances to inhibiting agents rather than to a simple increase in the excitability of the associated reaction.

pinge upon a final common path. In the above experiment fibers from the right eye are integrated with the effector mechanisms of the avoiding reaction during the course of training, in which they have been subjected to retinal excitation. But the neurons of the left optic tract prove to be equally well integrated with the avoiding reaction, although that eye was not subject to photic stimulation during training.

It is not sufficient to say that this result is explained by the fact that fibers from corresponding points of the retina do reach the same central ganglion cells. The corresponding fibers do not anastomose and there is no evidence that they have synapses in common. The wearing down of resistance in one afferent tract could not therefore affect the other. It is possible that the corresponding points activate the same central ganglion cells and that the reintegrations take place between these cells and lower motor neurons. But the following facts make this supposition rather questionable. Destruction of one eye and the contralateral cerebral visual area in the rat does not in the least affect visual discrimination. Destruction of one eye and the homolateral visual area reduces accuracy of discrimination. If the cortex contained ganglia equally integrated with both retinae these operations should produce like effects by destroying the final common path. Since they do not, this hypothetical final common path must lie at a subcortical centrifugal level. (The data on hemianopsia in man also indicate that the final common path, except for pupillary reflexes, is not established at a precortical level.) The impulses to the habitual discrimination must therefore pass through the cortex, since the destruction of both striate areas abolishes visual habits, before they reach such common ganglia and hence the destruction of the striate areas should abolish the functional identity of impulses from the two eyes.

I have repeated the above blindfold experiment with an animal after destruction of the visual area of both hemispheres (occipital third of the cortex). The blindfold was applied to the left eye immediately after the brain operation, so that there was no possibility of the formation of new common associations through the simultaneous use of the two eyes. The results of the test with this animal were the same as with the normal one; effective performance of the habit with the eye which had been blindfolded during training was obtained.

These facts seem to exclude the theory of a simple connection of corresponding points in the two retinae with common ganglion cells and reintegration through the passage of impulses over this final common path. As an alternative, the drainage theory might be appealed to here— the hypothesis that the excitation of a neuron exerts a suction upon all the synapses of that neuron (7, 9), but recent work on the character of the propagated disturbance in the axon has most thoroughly exploded the doctrine of nervous energy or neurin. Moreover, the same phenomenon seems evident in recognitions of tactile stimuli and no one would claim that all cutaneous afferent fibers have synapses in common or that the excitation of one final common path drains energy from all afferent tactile fibers.

It seems, then, that the theory of wearing down of synaptic resistances is inapplicable to this case of learning and that we must seek for some other principle to account for the altered conductivity of the neuron system.

The Utilization of Efferent Paths Which Were Nonfunctional during Learning

More striking data with the same implications have come from studies of the precentral gyrus in monkeys. These have been reported in detail (5) and a single illustration will serve for the present thesis. The right precentral gyrus was destroyed by cauterization in a cebus monkey. A severe paralysis of the left arm and leg followed. The animal was then trained to open a variety of latch boxes with his right hand. During the training there was some recovery from the paralysis but the left arm and hand were used only as a stiff prop to support the body during the manipulations with the right hand and at no time during training did the animal grasp at the latches with his left hand. When the habits were fixed the left precentral gyrus was destroyed, with a resultant paralysis of the trained right hand. The animal was kept without further training until the paralysis of the right hand had so far recovered as to seem to permit manipulation of the latches again. His ability to open the boxes was then tested. In the meantime he had acquired facility in the use of his left hand and the right was now by preference used only as a prop.

When confronted with the problem-boxes he fumbled clumsily at the catches of each during a few trials with his right hand, then attacked the fastenings with his left hand and released them without random movements and almost as quickly as he had formerly done with his right hand after protracted training. There was almost perfect transfer of the habit to the hand which had been paralyzed during training.

Here, as in the centripetal end of the arc, we have evidence of the utilization of neural paths in the performance of a learned reaction which were not activated during the course of learning. In this case the drainage theory is definitely ruled out. Irradiation of impulses to symmetrically placed spinal neurons might account for the results but I have records of other cases where the head or leg was substituted for the arm rendered useless by operation and where, consequently, irradiation cannot explain the transfer of the habit to the unused organ.

It seems certain, then, that we have here two types of habit formation which cannot be explained by any wearing down of synaptic resistance through the passage of nerve impulses. The behavior is of a complex character, approximating what is termed ideational behavior in man. Placing it in this category, however, does not advance our problem, which is to understand the physiology of reintegration. Most familiar cases of learning, even the so-called conditioned reflex, approach this order of complexity so that these cannot be looked upon as exceptional cases but rather tend to discredit the theory as applied to any learning.

An alternative theory is not possible in the present state of the science of neurophysiology but there are suggestions in recent experimental work that such theory must develop in a quite different direction from that which it has thus far taken. Spinal reflexes as they are usually described are such simple diagrammatic affairs that they have captured our imagination to the exclusion of other neurological phenomena and have been taken as the pattern of all nervous activity. As conditioned reflexes they have been expanded to embrace all nervous activity, until the telephone system has come to be looked upon as an adequate analogy for all central nervous function. But the phenomena of equipotentiality of function of cerebral areas (2), of vicarious function without definite localization (3), of mass action of central ganglia (8), of temporal variation in function (4), and the accumulating mass of evidence which indicates that in the intact organism every reaction is an expression of the total activity of the central nervous system, all are difficult to harmonize with a system of anatomically restricted reflex paths defined by varying degrees of synaptic resistance.

Work upon the "all-or-nothing" character of conduction and the refractory period of nerve suggests that the rate at which the neuron may transmit successive impulses is at least as important in determining the direction of conduction as the degree of synaptic resistance. The theories of inhibition of Verworn (11) and Lucas (6) involve the conception of critical frequencies of impulses for each neuron. If this should be verified for the central nervous system we may have to seek for changes in the refractory period rather than at the synapse as the basis of the learning process and for changes in the periodicity of discharge within a syncytium rather than for anatomically defined conduction paths to account for new integrations.

The observations recorded above are more in accord with such an hypothesis than with the current one based upon synaptic resistance, but detailed speculation in this field is futile so long as experimental work is unavailable. I am concerned here only to point out the inadequacy of present learning theory and to emphasize the importance of neurological investigation for the correct interpretation of even such psychological findings as the "Law of Frequency" in learning.

REFERENCE

1. Kappers, C.U.A. Further contributions on neurobiotaxis: IX. An attempt to compare the phenomena of neurobiotaxis with other phenomena of taxis and trophism, *J. comp. Neurol.*, 1917, **27**, 261–298.

2. Lashley, K. S. Studies of cerebral function in learning, *Psychobiology*, 1920, **2**, 55–135.

3. Lashley, K. S. Studies of cerebral function in learning: IV. Vicarious function after destruction of the visual areas, *Amer. J. Physiol.*, 1922, **59**, 44–71.

4. Lashley, K. S. Temporal variation in the function of the gyrus precentralis of primates, *Amer. J. Physiol.*, 1923, **65**, 585–602.

5. Lashley, K. S. Studies of cerebral function in learning: V. The retention of motor habits after destruction of the so-called motor areas in primates, *Arch. Neurol. Psychiat.*, Chicago, 1924, **12**, 249–276.

6. Lucas, K. *The conduction of the nervous impulse.* London: 1917.

7. McDougall, W. The nature of inhibitory processes within the nervous system, *Brain*, 1903, **52**, 153–191.

8. Martin, E. G. The application of the "All or Nothing" principle of nervous conduction to the interpretation of vasomotor reflexes, *Amer. J. Physiol.*, 1922, **59**, 400–412.

9. Meyer, Max. *Fundamental laws of human behavior.* Boston: Badger, 1911.

10. Robertson, T. B. Further studies in the chemical dynamics of the central nervous system, *Folia Neuro-biologica*, 1912, **6**, 553–578; 1914, **8**, 485–507.

11. Verworn, M. *Irritability.* New Haven: Yale University Press, 1913.

10. TEMPORAL VARIATION IN THE FUNCTION OF THE GYRUS PRECENTRALIS IN PRIMATES[1]

In much of the earlier work upon the effects of electrical stimulation of the cerebrum the stimulable points were looked upon as the physiological expression of precisely localized structures having rather simple anatomical connections with lower motor neurons. The points were regarded as absolutely stable and maps of areas in different species were published with the conviction that they represented definite anatomical differences having evolutionary significance.

Recent evidence has tended to discredit this view of precise anatomical localization. Franz (3) mapped the arm and leg areas in a number of rhesus monkeys and found little correspondence in localization of stimulable points among different individuals. Even the two hemispheres of the same brain showed divergence in the localization of points exciting the same movements. This result led Franz to conclude that the apparent localization revealed by electrical stimulation is largely the result of physiological rather than strict anatomical conditions. . . .

Quite similar results were obtained by Stout (6) in studies of the motor area of the cat. This author seems to imply a functional correlation of the extent of the stimulable areas with the habit systems of the individual. . . .

This work demonstrates the existence of extensive individual variations in the localization of function of the stimulable cortex. There is also evidence for some variation in function under different conditions of facilitation and inhibition. Brown and Sherrington (2) found that a point which on one stimulation gave contraction might later give extension of the same muscle group. Such a reversal of movement might result after repeated stimulation of the point, after stimulation of an antagonistic point, after epileptoid discharge, or after stimulation of the affer-

[1] EDITORS' NOTE: From *Amer. J. Physiol.*, 1923, **65**, 585–602. Reproduced by permission of the American Physiological Society. From department of psychology, University of Minnesota.

ent nerve of the contralateral limb. They mention one case of seeming spontaneous reversal of effect when a point was reexamined twenty-eight hours after a first test. Their study was restricted to pairs of antagonistic muscles and hence offered little chance of discovering more extensive alterations in the movements elicited from the points studied.

In a series of papers (1) Brown has extended this work and has done much to clear up the mutual relations of points within the central convolutions.

Leyton and Sherrington (5) described a number of cases where successive stimulations of a cortical point resulted in dissimilar movements, after intervening stimulation of other areas. Some of these "deviations of response" involved changes as great as that from finger to shoulder movements and even overlapping of the face and arm areas. The authors regard these deviations as temporary and ascribe them to facilitation from other areas stimulated during the course of the experiment, acting either upon the cortical or subcortical centers.

This conception seems to imply the belief that there is a primary movement typical of each cortical point, stable over long periods of time, which may be modified by facilitation but will return spontaneously to its primary condition when the effects of facilitation have worn off. In several experiments the authors stimulated the same area at intervals of from a few days to several months. They report that the same movements were obtained in the different tests. These reports are fragmentary, however, and do not include any systematic exploration of extensive areas with a view to determining temporal variation. It is possible that, within the limits of deviation found in the experiments, no one movement or pattern of movements is more characteristic of a given cortical point than another and that the movements elicited at any given time are dependent upon the previous condition of activity of the cortex, rather than upon any innate primary function of that point.

Such studies indicate that the functional localization of the motor cortex is capable of wide variations under the influence of the activity of other parts of the cerebrum. They leave the question of precise anatomical localization undecided, however. It is possible that each cortical point is capable of calling out a primary reaction which is relatively stable although capable of temporary modification; it is possible that the reaction elicited from each motor point is wholly dependent upon previous conditions of stimulations and that apparent anatomical localization within the motor area arises only through the relative constancy of dynamic conditions within the time limits of the experiment; or the truth may lie somewhere between these extremes as a given anatomical localization within which the finer movements are determined by transient physiological conditions.

The question may be answered in part by exploring and mapping the same stimulable area at different times, allowing a sufficient interval for a change in the "set" of the organism between successive tests.[2]

Stability of cortical points under such conditions would argue for a definite anatomical basis of function. Great variation in localization on the contrary would indicate that unstable physiological conditions underlie a merely transitory localization. The present paper is a report of a series of tests of localization in the gyrus precentralis made at intervals of from one to fifteen days to test the extent of temporal variation.

Methods

Under deep chloroform-ether anesthesia the skull of a small rhesus monkey was trephined and the opening enlarged with bone forceps until the greater part of the right precentral gyrus was exposed. The dura was trimmed away,

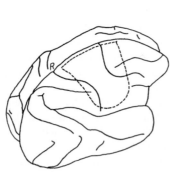

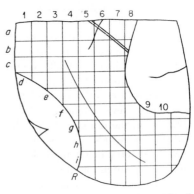

Fig. 10.1. Camera outline of brain from right dorso-lateral aspect. The extent of the area mapped is shown by the broken line.

Fig. 10.2. Diagram of points stimulated on the right precentral gyrus. R, fissure of Rolando. Points outside of the cross-ruled area were inexcitable.

the other meninges left intact. The distances separating the chief visible landmarks on the exposed surface were measured and a map, enlarged to twice the size, was laid off with proportional dividers. The area exposed is indicated by the dotted line in Fig. 10.1. This is a camera drawing of the brain, after hardening in 10 per cent formalin, upon which the original map was projected. The inner margin of the area first exposed paralleled the longitudinal fissure at a distance of 5 mm. Its lateral margin passed 6 mm. from the fissure of Sylvius. Caudad it included a part of the postcentral gyrus. The area was explored and the excitable points indicated on the map. After exploration, which was performed under aseptic conditions, the exposed area was covered with a thin

[2] The desirability of extending studies of variation in the motor cortex to its temporal aspects was pointed out to me some years ago by Dr. S. I. Franz, to whom I wish to acknowledge my indebtedness for the suggestion.

flexible sheet of mica to prevent adhesions, the skin flaps closed with interrupted sutures and securely bandaged. The exploration was repeated in four consecutive tests at intervals of from one to fifteen days.

Stimulation was given by the bipolar method, the points of the electrodes separated by 1 mm. At the beginning of each experiment the threshold was determined for the point *b4* (Fig. 10.2) and current intensity was maintained just above this limen except where areas proved relatively inexcitable. When such areas were encountered the current intensity was increased until responses appeared or until there was indication of spread of current to involve neighboring areas. The electrodes were applied at each stimulation for less than one second so that in most cases only the primary movements of the point were elicited.

The points stimulated were located by reference to visible landmarks on the surface of the cortex and by measurements with proportional dividers, particularly from the two median angles of the skull opening. The points tested were separated by approximately 2½ mm. The method of measurement assures, I believe, the identification of the points in successive trials. It is possible that adjacent points were sometimes confused in different tests, but the possibility of such a defect in technique is inadequate to account for the wide variation found in many cases.

In order to avoid differences in facilitation or deviation in the sense of Leyton and Sherrington the same order of stimulation was followed in successive tests. Exploration was begun at the postero-median corner of the field . . . [and continued in regular order].[3] After systematic exploration in this manner, the chief points from which distinct movements had been obtained were again stimulated in irregular order to verify the first findings and to test the possible influence of the sequence of stimulation upon the character of the movements obtained. In general these check stimulations consistently verified the findings of the systematic exploration. In a few cases deviations of response were noted which were clearly the result of the stimulation of the face area at the end of the systematic exploration, but the major differences in the findings of successive tests were verified in each case and proved stable for the duration of each test.

During the tests the cortex was kept moist with sponges wrung out from warm physiological saline. The electrodes were applied by the experimenter who also recorded the position of the points stimulated upon the enlarged map. Movements were observed and recorded by an assistant.[4]

An effort was made to obtain the same degree of narcosis in the different tests, but this was scarcely possible, owing to marked differences in the resistance of the animal to the anesthetic at different times.

Conditions of the Different Tests

Test I. The first exploration was made on March 27. . . . The field seemed to include a considerable portion of the leg area, and points for all segments of the arm. The lateral margin of the field, later giving movements of the face, was

---

[3] EDITORS' NOTE: A table giving the order of points stimulated and protocols of the movements obtained has not been reproduced.

[4] I am indebted to Mr. Lester Wiley and to Mr. Carney Landis for assistance in this work.

inexcitable to any strength of current. The postcentral gyrus remained inexcitable in all the tests. After exploration the wound was closed and the animal returned to his cage. On recovery from the anesthetic he showed no symptoms of motor disturbance.

Test II. Twenty-four hours later, March 28, the animal was again anesthetized, the cortex exposed and mapped as before. . . . The threshold was slightly higher (one-half division on the Porter inductorium) but epileptoid contractions were occasionally elicited on very slight stimulation. The opening was again closed and the animal kept under observation for 16 days. During this time there was no indication of any motor disturbance and healing of the wound progressed rapidly.

Test III. On April 13 the cortex was again exposed. It appeared perfectly normal, without adhesions, and it was mapped as before. The threshold was approximately that of the first test. The movements obtained . . . [were recorded]. The wound was closed and the animal kept under observation. No motor disturbances were noted until April 25. On April 23 the animal tore off his bandage and infected the wound. Two days later a very slight paresis of the left arm developed. It was detectable only in an occasional extension of the arm when the animal was at rest. In feeding and locomotion the arm was used in normal manner. I had intended to test the effects of disuse, but the infection made it necesary to terminate the experiment. The following test of fatigue was therefore undertaken.

Test IV. Effects of fatigue. April 25, the monkey was driven about the animal room as rapidly as possible and kept in active motion for twenty minutes. At the end of this time he seemed completely exhausted, lay prone on the floor and submitted to every indignity without making an effort to rise. He was then quickly anesthetized and the wound opened. Since the last test a thin membrane had developed over the surface of the exposed cortex. Removal of this entailed superficial injuries to the gyrus, especially over the points *a*, *b*, *c*, 6, 7, and 8, in Fig. 10.2. . . . The threshold was found to be slightly higher than in any previous test. This may have been due to the fatigue, to the infection, or to the injuries to the cortex. Had the experiment shown decreased activity, the infection would have rendered it meaningless, but the variety of movements elicited seems significant in spite of the defects of technique.

At the end of this test the wound was again closed. On the following day the animal showed a well-developed paresis of the left limbs. Examination of the wound showed an inflammation of the exposed cortex and a slight hernia. The area was wholly inexcitable to faradic stimulation although stimulation of the white fibers still induced movements. Enlargement of the skull opening and exploration of the surrounding area was begun. Movements of the leg were obtained from the area mediad to the opening, but with further enlargement of the opening there was a sudden disappearance of all excitability, involving both the cortex and the underlying fibers. This depression persisted for half an hour at the end of which the experiment had to be terminated. During this time the other hemisphere remained normally excitable. It was thus impossible to map the area surrounding the first operative field.

Analysis of Results

The points stimulated are indicated in Fig. 10.2. Each lay within one of the squares marked off by the ordinates and abscissa on the map. . . .

The majority of the reactions obtained from the exposed area were of the arm segment. A relatively large area giving facial movements was exposed but these movements lacked variety and were sometimes completely absent. In the first test an extensive leg area seemed included in the field, but in later tests movements of this segment were rarely obtained.

Comparisons of the results obtained in different tests seem to justify the following generalizations.

1. *In each test the movements obtained were quite constant.*[5] After the systematic exploration, which reviewed the points . . . [in regular order] two or three points in each row were again stimulated and in each test the movements obtained in the systematic exploration again appeared. These check stimulations were given in irregular sequence so that it seems probable that facilitation and deviation played little part in determining the reactions. . . .

2. *In the tests on different days there was almost no constancy of reaction from day to day.*

a. *In the different tests stimulation of the same point usually gave rise to different movements.* Fifty-seven points were examined. Among these the following proportions of duplicate and diverse movements were obtained:

Number of points which gave a different primary movement at every test	22
Number of points which gave the same movement in 2 trials only	26
Number of points which gave the same movement in 3 tests	6
Number of points which gave the same movement in 4 tests	0

Three points were silent throughout the tests. In the above figures only movements were considered. In some cases (*a6–8: c6: e6:*) the areas were silent in two tests and gave diverse movement in the others. These five cases are included in the group of twenty-two above.

The twenty-six points from which the same movement was obtained in two trials include ten cases of duplicate movements of the lips. The mouth area is very extensive and gives little variety of movement so that this duplication receives undue weight when considered in this way. Disregarding the lip movements and silent areas, 50 per cent of the points examined failed to give duplicate movements in any two tests.

[5] EDITORS' NOTE: Italics here and elsewhere in this article are Lashley's.

To determine whether mere reversal of movement as described by
Brown and Sherrington (2) is responsible for the apparent variation of
function or whether the variation is more extreme, we may compare the
movements elicited from the same point at different times.

*b. The results show that not only does reversal of function occur but
the same area may show, as primary movements, flexions or extensions
of different joints or even body segments.* Movements elicited from the
arm area are frequently restricted to a single joint or segment of the arm.
Rarely more than two such segments are involved in the reaction. Of the
fifty-seven points tested twenty-nine gave movements restricted to different joints at different times, as point *b*7 which gave movements of wrist,

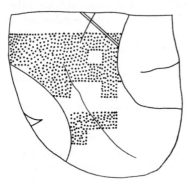

Fig. 10.3. Areas giving movement of
different segments of the arm in different tests. (×2)

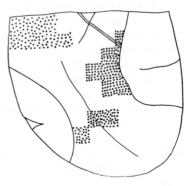

Fig. 10.4. Areas giving movement of
different bodily segments in different tests. (×2)

forearm and shoulder only in three different tests. Figure 10.3 shows in
stippling the points which gave exclusive movements of different segments
of the arm in different tests, with no duplication of movements in at least
two tests.

Further, the variations of function extend even to different bodily segments. Five points gave only movements of the leg in one test and only
movements of the arm in the others; five gave neck and eyes in one test
and only arm in others; three gave face only and arm only in different
tests. The location of these areas is given in Fig. 10.4.

*c. There is apparently no functional relation between the movements
elicited from the same point at different times.* Point *d*7, for example,
gave adduction to the upper arm, rotation of the same segment, shrug-
ging of the shoulder and turning of the eyes with pricking up of the ear in
different tests. There is no reason to suppose that such diverse movements
represent either parts of a coordinated pattern or of antergic patterns.

3. *At different times identical or nearly identical movements may be elicited only from quite widely separated areas.* It is difficult to describe movements in such terms that absolute identity can be determined in successive trials. My general impression is that exactly the same pattern of movement is rarely if ever elicited in tests on different days. But movements of the same segment in the same general direction are recognizable and these were frequently elicited from quite distinct areas at different times. Figures 10.5 to 10.12 inclusive show for typical movements areas from which the same movements were elicited in different trials. In all these figures the same symbols for the test are used. Test I, ☰; test II, ||||; test III, ⟍⟍ ; test IV, /// .

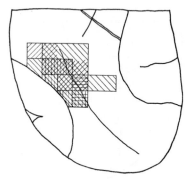

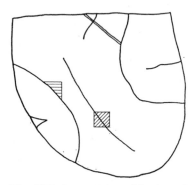

Fig 10.5. Areas which gave flexion of fingers in different tests. For significance of crosshatching see text. (×2)

Fig. 10.6. Areas giving adduction of the thumb. (×2)

The area for closure of the hand (Fig. 10.5) remained fairly constant in all the tests. Separate adduction of the thumb, obtained in two tests, was, on the contrary, elicited only from widely separated points (g6 and e3, Fig. 10.6). Dorsal flexion of the wrist (Fig. 10.7), flexion of the elbow (Fig. 10.8) and rotation of the forearm (Fig. 10.9), and rotation of the upper arm (Fig. 10.10) all showed wide variations in different trials. Abduction (Fig. 10.11) and adduction (Fig. 10.12) of the arm showed a greater tendency to restriction to one part of the field.

In some of these cases there is overlapping of points in two or more trials, but, except for the flexion of the fingers, the distinct areas greatly exceed in extent the overlapping ones. In some cases, as those of rotation of the forearm, abduction and adduction of the upper arm, it might be argued that only one stimulable area is involved and that differences in facilitation or deviation account for the different limits noted. The wide divergence of the areas in Figs. 10.6, 10.7, and 10.10 makes such a general interpretation impossible, however.

4. There is a tendency toward stability in the grouping of excitable points for the same body or limb segment in the same general area, although the details of movement do not show consistent localization. Movements involving the leg were never obtained except from the median portion of the field, movements of the face only from the lateral portion. It thus seems possible to distinguish leg, arm, and face areas, although with shifting and unstable boundaries. Within the arm area movements of the upper segments tend to be restricted to the median portion of the field, movements of the wrist and hand to the posterior edge of the gyrus, but the amount of variation obtained makes it questionable whether the uniformities encountered are not largely a matter of chance.

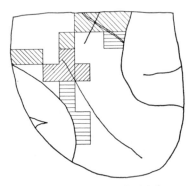 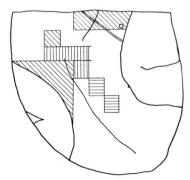

Fig. 10.7. Areas giving dorsal flexion of wrist. ($\times 2$)

Fig. 10.8. Areas giving flexion of elbow. ($\times 2$)

The Effects of Fatigue

The attempt to induce fatigue seemed to bring the animal to the end of his ability to make voluntary movements. He had been unusually wild from the first and always struggled violently to avoid handling. After twenty minutes of continued running he ceased to make any effort to escape and could not be induced to make further attempts at flight by any stimuli that I could apply. It is difficult to determine how much of his inaction was due to actual fatigue and how much to the passivity which the wildest rhesus frequently shows when finally cornered or held. His last movements, however, were weak and lagging and suggested extreme fatigue. Some recurrence of activity appeared as he was being placed on the operating table, but such a possibility of a final spurt seems to characterize any degree of fatigue, if the incentive can be sufficiently increased. The evidence indicates a rather extreme degree of fatigue, although it can not be characterized as absolute.

The movements elicited from the precentral gyrus in this condition give no evidence that the fatigue had any influence upon the activity of this area, but rather indicate that the functioning of the area is scarcely affected in fatigue of voluntary movement. After fatigue, 11 diverse movements were elicited by stimulating the exposed area. The average for the three preceding tests is 11.3 distinct movements. The elevation of threshold, although apparently consistent, was not greater than the difference which is frequently found in the same test between adjacent areas.

The last movements elicited in fatiguing were turning the head and eyes to watch the experimenter. The appearance of these movements for the first time in this test might be ascribed to a persistence of a "set" to

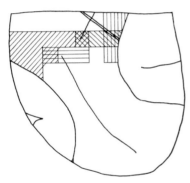 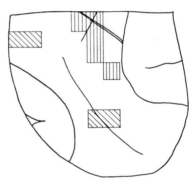

Fig. 10.9. Areas giving inward rotation of forearm. (×2)

Fig. 10.10. Areas giving inward rotation of upper arm. (×2)

this type of response, but similar movements are usually dominant in stimulation experiments just before the animal is anesthetized, so that the assumption of a special relationship in this case does not seem justified.

Even allowing for defects of technique, the experiment points to the conclusion that the incidence of fatigue of voluntary movement is at some point other than at the so-called motor cortex or lower motor neurons. This is in line with the results of many investigations which indicate that the motor end of the reflex arc is relatively unfatigable.

Possible Causes of Temporal Variation

The tests reported show a variation in the functions of the same precentral area from time to time, as great as the diversities found by Franz in the brains of different animals. Is this due to some defect in the experimental technique or to a true variation in functional localization? If the latter, what is the significance of the variation for theories of the organization of the cortico-spinal conduction systems?

The particular methods employed do not seem adequate to account for the variations found. Errors of measurement may have resulted in displacement of points from test to test, but while this might account for variation of adjacent points, it will not explain results such as are shown in Figs. 10.6 to 10.12. Differences in depth of narcosis appeared in different tests, but within a single test approximately the same localization may be demonstrated from the deepest narcosis to the point where avoiding reactions begin to appear and no such wide range was involved in these experiments. Threshold of excitability may be influenced by depth of narcosis, but not localization within any single test. Irritation of the cortex through successive operations and stimulations may likewise be expected

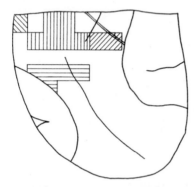

Fig. 10.11. Areas giving abduction of upper arm. (×2)

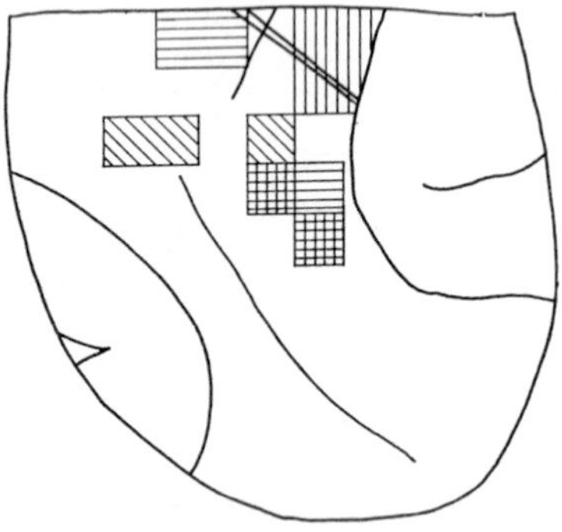

Fig. 10.12. Areas giving adduction of upper arm. (×2)

to produce changes in excitability, but to ascribe the variation in function to this is to admit a multiplicity of functional representation which practically abandons the conception of strict and limited localization.

Finally, deviation of response as a result of the cortical stimulation might be urged as the cause of the apparent variation. But the sequence of stimulation was in every case the same during the systematic exploration, and consequently should have produced similar deviating effects. Further, check stimulations were given after the systematic exploration, usually with an intervening rest period. The conception of deviation involves the spontaneous recovery from the effects of deviating influences. Very few changes in function following periods of rest were noted, and these were not of a character to justify the assumption that they represented a reversion of points to some primary norm of reaction.

It seems clear then that temporal variation must be considered as characteristic of the function of the cortex itself and not as due to the particular technique of this experiment. The experiment is inadequate to test the absolute range of variation either in the localization of specific movements or in the movements which may be elicited from a single point. The areas for different bodily segments remained fairly distinct throughout the tests. This indicates some morphological basis for the differentiation of function in the larger segmental divisions of the gyrus.

Within the same segment, however, the same points at different times elicited diverse responses and the same response was elicited from widely separated and shifting areas. Within this area there is no justification for ascribing a specific function to individual points or for holding that, within rather wide limits, one movement is more typical than another. The variations were in some cases so extensive as to suggest that, had a greater number of tests been given, an equipotentiality of function of all parts within the arm segments would have appeared. This distinction between segmental areas and the lack of differentiation within the segmental area is in accord with the findings in the paralyses. Monoplegias of cortical origin are fairly common, but cortical paralyses of lesser extent are rare, and in experimental work recovery from them is exceedingly rapid.

Such results can be harmonized with the view which implies a point for point correspondence between the Betz cells and specific patterns of ventral horn cells only by assuming that scattered cells in all parts of a segmental area have duplicated anatomical relationships with spinal mechanisms and that the variations found are due to variations in the threshold of these equivalent cells. The continuity of the pyramidal fibers to different levels of the cords seems to favor this view as far as the distinction between segmental areas and the variations in demarcation between these areas is concerned. But within the segmental area it is equally possible that the character of the response obtained at any given time is determined by the total neural equilibrium, in the sense of Herrick (4, pp. 327 ff.). This view would abandon the conception of strict anatomical localization and consider every reaction the algebraic sum of the activities of numberless cells. The present evidence does not permit of a choice between these hypotheses, but does seem to justify the conclusion that within a segmental area the responses obtained on electrical stimulation are due to the temporary physiological condition and do not give evidence for a corresponding structural differentiation.

Summary

A portion of the precentral gyrus of a rhesus monkey was mapped by electrical stimulation in four tests extending over a period of eighteen days.

1. In each test, lasting about half an hour, the reactions were almost constant, subject to slight deviations resulting from the order of stimulation.

2. In the different tests the general fields from which movements of the face, arm, and leg segments were elicited tended to remain constant although the borders of the fields were inconstant.

3. Within the arm area, stimulation of the same point in different tests resulted in widely different movements and at different times the same movement was obtained from widely separated and shifting areas.

4. The results suggest that within the segmental areas the various parts of the cortex may be equipotential for the production of all the movements of that area, and that the particular movements elicited in any test depend upon the temporary physiological organization of the area rather than upon any point-for-point correspondence between pyramidal and spinal cells.

5. Fatigue of voluntary movements produced no significant effect upon the excitability of the precentral gyrus or upon the character of the movements elicited from it.

REFERENCES

1. Brown. *J. Physiol.,* 1915, 9, 81, 101, 117, 131; 1916, **10,** 97, 103.
2. Brown and Sherrington. *Proc. roy. Soc.,* 1912, **85B,** 250.
3. Franz. *Psychol. Rev.* (Monogr. Suppl.), 1915, **19,** 80.
4. Herrick. *Introduction to neurology.* Philadelphia: 1918.
5. Leyton and Sherrington. *Quart. J. exp. Physiol.,* 1917, **11,** 153.
6. Stout. *Psychobiology,* 1917, **1,** 177.

11. THE SURVIVAL OF THE MAZE HABIT AFTER CEREBELLAR INJURIES [1]

The close anatomical relation of the cerebellum to the proprioceptive systems and the importance of the latter for the maze habit suggest that, if the cerebellum is ever concerned in learning or retention, this function will be revealed by a study of the effects of cerebellar lesions upon the activities of animals in the maze. The supposed relations of the cerebellum to the vestibular reflex paths suggest further that the cerebellum may be involved, not only in postural adjustments to gravity, but also in the more remote orientation of the body in space, as in the maintenance of the sense of direction. Although the clinical literature on man lends little support either to the mnemonic or orienting function of the cerebellum, systematic observations on these points are not numerous, and it has seemed worth while to test their possibility by an acute experiment with the maze. An immediate necessity for such tests arose also in work by the senior author on cerebral localization of the maze habit, in which the effects of possible slight lesions to the cerebellum could not be disregarded.

Methods

Rats were trained in a rectangular maze, having eight culs de sac, for five trials per day until ten consecutive errorless trials were obtained. After ten days without practice retention was tested by retraining until ten successive errorless trials were again obtained (preliminary retention tests). The cerebellum was then destroyed more or less completely by cauterization through a small median trephine opening just back of the parieto-occipital suture. Ten days after operation, or longer, in case the animals were still unable to walk at the end of this time, retention was again tested (postoperative retention tests) by the same method as before operation. The data given on time and trials in learning and retention tests include the ten errorless trials. With the completion of these tests the ani-

[1] EDITORS' NOTE: K. S. Lashley and Dorothea A. McCarthy, authors. From *J. comp. Psychol.*, 1926, **6**, 423–433. Reproduced by permission of the Williams and Wilkins Co. From department of psychology, University of Minnesota.

mals were brought to necropsy and serial sagittal sections of the cerebellum and brain stem were prepared with a general cell stain. From these, reconstructions of the lesions were made by the graphic method.

Anatomy of the Cerebellum of the Rat

Figure 11.1 shows a median sagittal section of the cerebellum. It is divided, according to Bradley's embryological studies (1) into five chief lobes, lettered *a* to *e* in his descriptions. These are separated by the principal fissures I to IV. Of these, fissure II corresponds to the Sulcus primarius, III to Fissura secunda, and IV to the Sulcus uvulo-nodularis of Bolk. Lobes *a* and *b* correspond to Bolk's Lobus anterior, the anterior

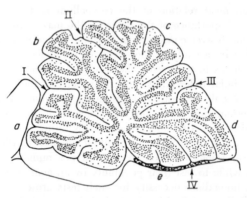

Fig. 11.1. Median sagittal section of the cerebellum. Bradley's nomenclature of lobes and fissures is indicated.

half of *c* to his Lobus simplex. The caudal half of lobe *c* together with lobes *d* and *e* make up his Lobus medianus posterior. On the dorsal surface (Fig. 11.2) only the fissures II and III are visible. The vermis is not well marked off from the hemispheres. The ansiform and paramedian lobes may be distinguished as separated from it by slight longitudinal depressions. Flocculus and paraflocculus are distinguishable and there appears to be also a small pars petrosus.

The dentate nuclei lie rather far laterad beneath the ansiform lobes. We have not attempted to distinguish the various roof nuclei, since all remained intact except in one case, in which all were destroyed.

Graphic Methods

For representation of the lesions the following method was devised. Sagittal sections at equal distances throughout the cerebellum were sketched under the camera lucida. All gyri were identified throughout the series and the surface width of each was measured for each section. These dimensions were then plotted on coordinate paper from a curved base line drawn to represent the Sulcus primarius. Connecting the points so determined gave the diagram shown in Fig. 11.3. Since only sagittal sections were used the diagram is foreshortened laterally and fails to represent the full area of the ansiform lobes. Flocculus and paraflocculus are not represented. Their condition in the operated cases is stated in the protocols.

In Fig. 11.3 the parts are lettered to correspond with Bradley's nomenclature, for identification with the actual visual appearance shown in Fig. 11.2. In making the reconstructions of the lesions sagittal sections of the operated brains were compared with the camera sketches of the normal sections from which the diagram had been prepared, the gyri remaining intact identified and the lesions then blocked out on the diagrams. In addition to the diagram a camera sketch of a median sagittal section of each operated brain is given (Fig. 11.4). Comparison of these with Fig. 11.1 may serve to give a clearer notion of the extent of the injury.

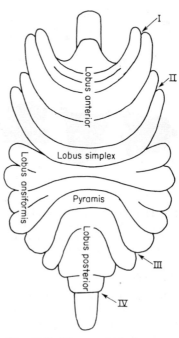

Fig. 11.3. Diagram including ventral and dorsal surfaces of the cerebellum. The lettering of fissures corresponds to that in Fig. 11.1.

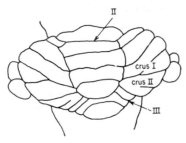

Fig. 11.2. Dorsal view of cerebellum.

Sensory Controls

Watson (4) has shown conclusively that vision, olfaction, and other forms of exterostimulation are, singly, not essential to accurate running of the maze. It has not been shown, however, that, in case of disturbance of the kinesthetic mechanism, they may not supply substitute cues for the normal interal ones. Without some control of exteroceptive stimuli the survival of the maze habit after cerebellar destruction cannot be interpreted, since it might be due either to the normal failure of the cerebellum to participate in the habit or to the use of other sensorimotor integrations when the cerebellar mechanisms are rendered nonfunctional. The maze employed in these experiments offered practically no possibility of differential tactile or olfactory cues which could guide the animal over the true path. Vision was ruled out in two animals (numbers 6 and 7) by enucleation of the eyes after training but before lesion to the cerebellum.

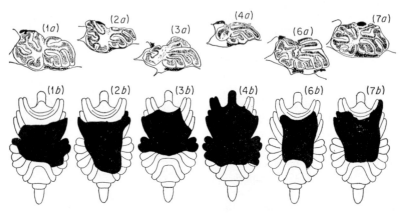

Fig. 11.4. Reconstructions of the lesions described in the protocols. The numbering of the figures corresponds to the numbers assigned to the animals in the text. (*a*) Camera outlines of median sagittal sections; (*b*) diagrams showing the total extent of lesions.

Protocols

Number 1. Adult Female. Inactive and very erratic during training, making frequent errorless trials after the fourteenth of practice but tending to reexplore the maze after brief periods of correct running. Her learning record was: Time, 27,918 seconds. Errors, 139. Trials, 106. Preliminary retention tests were not given.

After operation the only clear motor symptoms were tremor and spasticity of the hind legs, which cleared up completely within ten days. In the postoperative retention tests the animal showed the same erratic behavior as in initial learning. The following is a record of the errors in the first trials of these tests:

Trial	1	2	3	4	5	6	7	8	9	10	11	12	13	14	15
Errors	1	1	0	0	0	3	0	0	0	0	3	1	0	0	0

This gives clear evidence of the animal's retention of the habit as well as of her previous reaction tendencies in the maze situation.

Lesion. The extent of destruction is shown in [Figs. 11.4a and 11.4b]. The lesion embraces the greater part of lobes B and C but leaves their lateral portions (Crus secundum, Bolk) intact. The dentate and roof nuclei are uninjured.

Number 2. Adult Female. The initial learning record was: Time, 1,338 seconds. Errors, 81. Trials, 29. Preliminary retention tests gave the following records: Time, 169 seconds. Errors, 4. Trials, 11.

After operation the animal showed slight action tremors and spasticity of the hind legs, which cleared up within six days. In postoperative retention tests she gave from the first clear evidence of retention of the habit, making an errorless record on the second trial and again on the fourth. The requirements for complete relearning were the following: Time, 657 seconds. Errors, 14. Trials, 19.

Lesion. The extent of destruction is shown in Fig. 11.4, 2a and 2b. It is very similar to that in number 1, but extends into the dorsal margin of lobe D and leaves the greater part of the ansiform lobes intact. The flocculus, paraflocculus and cerebellar nuclei are uninjured.

Number 3. Adult Female. She was very inactive and somewhat erratic during training. Her learning records were: Time, 11,132 seconds. Errors, 60. Trials, 61. Only one error was made in the first five trials of the preliminary retention tests but the record thereafter was irregular: Time, 434 seconds. Errors, 7. Trials, 19. After operation the animal showed gross tremors of the whole body, particularly marked in the hind limbs which were extended laterally and spastic. There was a tendency to rotate to the left and frequent backward somersaulting. This condition persisted for four or five days. After ten days there was great improvement; rapid progression in spite of gross tremors and staggering gait. Retention tests gave the following results: Time, 1,403 seconds. Errors, 9. Trials, 15. There is clear evidence of retention from the first, with some unsteadiness of performance which marked the preliminary tests.

Lesion. The extent of destruction is shown in Fig. 11.4, 3a and 3b. The dorsal half of lobe A together with lobes B and C are almost entirely destroyed. The anterior half of the ansiform lobes is involved. Both dentate nuclei are partially destroyed. Flocculi and paraflocculi are intact.

Number 4. Adult Female. The performance in initial learning was: Time, 2,388 seconds. Errors, 33. Trials, 35. Preliminary retention tests gave errors in only the first two trials: Time, 229 seconds. Errors, 7. Trials, 12. After operation there was extreme contraction of the left hind leg and extension of the right. In walking there was rotation to the left and frequent backward somersaulting. When picked up the animal clutched wildly at anything within reach and gave indications of vertigo. For the first four days she was force-fed, then began to eat spontaneously but showed little improvement in motor symptoms. Thirty days after operation the motor symptoms were still pronounced. She walked as if drawing a heavy weight, with fore and hind legs extended forward and dragging her along in a series of lunges. At this time she was tested in the maze and made a perfect retention record: Time, 801 seconds. Errors, 0. Trials, 10.

Lesion. The extent of destruction is shown in Fig. 11.4, 4*a* and 4*b*. Practically all of lobes A, B, and C, the flocculi and paraflocculi and both dentate nuclei are destroyed. Lobes D and E and the roof nuclei remain intact.

Number 5. Adult Female. The training record follows: Time, 1,179 seconds. Errors, 43. Trials, 48. In preliminary retention tests the animal was erratic and slow, although giving clear evidence of retention: Time, 2,464 seconds. Errors, 52. Trials, 48. For the first five days after operation the animal showed only a slight general tremor, then gave signs of collapse with stupor. This improved but the animal was unable to walk during the succeeding twenty days. On the twenty-fifth day after the operation she was able to progress slowly but still showed marked incoordination and tremor. Retraining was begun at this time. Thirteen days later additional symptoms developed involving rapid rolling to the left on any attempt to walk. Two days later this phase had passed and retraining was resumed. Training was completed three days later with 10 consecutive errorless trials. The record for the postoperative tests was: Time, 5,337 seconds. Errors, 97. Trials, 78. This gives no evidence of retention of the habit but clear proof of ability to reacquire it.

Lesion. At necropsy the position of the cerebellum was found to be occupied by a large cyst. On the removal of this, no trace of the cerebellum could be discovered. The dorsal surface of the medulla was exposed, the medulla was much compressed and the peduncles were completely atrophied.

The animal presents a case of normal orientation in the maze in the complete absence of the cerebellum. The apparent loss of the habit subsequent to operation cannot be ascribed directly to the cerebellar destruction, for we have records of equal deterioration of the maze habit in animals in which infection was limited to the scalp.

Number 6. Adult Male. Initial training in the maze required: Time, 2,846 seconds. Errors, 30. Trials, 33. Preliminary retention tests required: Time, 340 seconds. Errors, 7. Trials, 20. The eye balls were then enucleated, with retention tests two days later: Time, 107 seconds. Errors, 1. Trials, 11. The cerebellum was next partially destroyed. Recovery was rapid and at the end of ten days there remained only a slight action tremor. Retention was tested at this time and found to be perfect: Time, 188 seconds. Errors, 0. Trials, 10.

Lesion. The extent of destruction is shown in Fig. 11.4, 6*a* and 6*b*. All of the dorsal convexity of lobes B and C is destroyed. The lesion extends deep into the substantia alba so that probably large areas in addition are rendered nonfunctional. The cerebellar nuclei seem intact.

Number 7. Adult Male. Initial training gave the following record: Time, 560 seconds. Errors, 12. Trials, 20. Preliminary retention tests: Time, 356 seconds. Errors, 5. Trials, 14. The eyes were enucleated with retention tests two days later: Time, 129 seconds. Errors, 0. Trials, 10. The cerebellum was then partially destroyed. Postoperative symptoms were slight and cleared up entirely in ten days. Postoperative tests showed perfect retention: Time, 182 seconds. Errors, 0. Trials, 10.

Lesion. The extent of the injury is shown in Fig. 11.4, 7*a* and 7*b*. The lesion is very similar to that in number 6 but extends farther laterad in lobe B and invades the white matter to a lesser extent. Basal nuclei are intact.

Discussion

The records of the animals reported individually above are summarized in Table 11.1. Exclusive of number 5, which suffered from infection, the average constants for learning and retention before and after operation are:

	Time, sec.	Errors	Trials
Initial learning	7,697	59.2	47.3
Preliminary retention tests	178	3.8	12.4
Postoperative retention tests	608	6.3	16.5

The averages for the postoperative tests are not significantly higher than those of the preliminary tests. The fact that the animal with the most extensive operative destruction (number 4) made no errors after operation indicates that the slight decrease in efficiency of the others in these tests was not due to any mnemonic disturbance directly resultant from cerebellar lesion. The averages of these cases and the record of number 5, with complete absence of the cerebellum, show that this structure is not necessary for the learning or retention of the maze habit.

Table 11.1. Summary of Training and Retention Tests for All Cases Described in the Text

Number	Learning Time, sec.	Errors	Trials	Preliminary retention tests Time, sec.	Errors	Trials	Postoperative retention tests Time, sec.	Errors	Trials
1	27,918	139	106				417	15	35
2	1,338	81	29	169	4	11	657	14	19
3	11,132	60	61	434	7	19	1,403	9	15
4	2,388	33	35	229	7	11	801	0	10
5	1,179	43	45	2,464	52	48	5,337	97	78
6	2,846	30	33	107°	1°	11°	188	0	10
7	560	12	20	129°	0°	0°	182	0	10

° After enucleation of eye balls.

The results with numbers 6 and 7, in which the cerebellar lesion was preceded by enucleation of the eyes, together with the control of olfaction and differential tactile stimuli provided by the maze itself show that after cerebellar lesions the animals did not fall back upon exteroceptive cues but continued to react on the basis either of kinesthetic stimuli, or of some centrally organized mechanism. Their behavior in the absence of the differential exteroceptive stimuli was not essentially different from that found by Watson with normal rats.

In number 5 the entire cerebellum including the basal nuclei was absent when the animal was running the maze without error. This demonstrates beyond question that the cerebellum is not necessary for the acquisition of the maze habit. The case was complicated by infection, so that the loss of the habit following operation cannot be interpreted. In the other animals not all of the cerebellum was destroyed, yet there seems no reason to believe that the parts remaining intact are any more likely to contain mechanisms functional in orientation than are those destroyed. In number 4, which showed perfect retention of the habit after operation, only lobes D and E (Lobus medianus posterior) escaped destruction. Van Rynberk (3) obtained no symptoms from destruction of this area alone and only an exaggeration of the symptoms following destruction of the Crura prima when the area was destroyed along with the latter. Such meager data on the function of the area are scarcely helpful for the present problem. But previous extirpation experiments indicate rather clearly that, although gross localization of function exists within the cerebellum, there is so great an overlapping and interdependence in the functions of its parts that the restriction of mnemonic or orienting functions to so small an area is virtually ruled out. Moreover, the parts remaining intact belong almost altogether to the primitive cerebellar system (2) in which there is the least likelihood of the localization of these more complex functions.

In view of such considerations the conclusion seems justified that the cerebellum of the rat plays no significant part in the habit systems involved in maze running.

Summary

The cerebellum was severely injured in a number of animals previously trained in the maze. In both seeing and blind animals perfect retention of the maze habit was demonstrated after the operations. One animal with the cerebellum completely destroyed learned to run the maze without error. There is no evidence that the cerebellum plays any part in the performance of the maze habit.

REFERENCES

1. Bradley, O. O. On the development and homology of the mammalian cerebellar fissures, *J. Anat. Physiol.*, 1913, **37**, 112–120, 221–240.

2. Edinger, L. Ueber die Einteilung des Cerebellums, *Anat. Anz.*, 1910, **35**, 319–322.

3. Van Rynberk, G. Das Lokalisationsproblem im Kleinhirn, *Ergebn. Physiol.*, 1908, **7**, 653–698.

4. Watson, J. B. Kinaesthetic and organic sensations: their role in the reactions of the white rat to the maze, *Psychol. Rev.* (Monogr. Suppl.), 1907, **8** (2), pp. vi + 100.

12. SPINAL CONDUCTION AND KINESTHETIC SENSITIVITY IN THE MAZE HABIT [1]

The importance of kinesthetic and organic sensations has been much emphasized in recent psychological speculation, both behavioristic and otherwise. Our most widely taught theory of the emotions is based upon a doctrine of sensory reverberations from visceral activity; the doctrine of "current control" of the speed and accuracy of movement still has many adherents, and the theory of implicit movements as the organic basis of thinking extends the same concepts to the psychology of thinking. In general, these developments represent a tendency, fostered by recent studies of nerve conduction, to seek the immediate completion of the conditioned-reflex circuit in motor activity and to substitute the conception of chain reflexes for that of continued intraneural activity.

Toward the development of this point of view the analysis of the sensory control of the maze habit has contributed no small part. Watson (28) successively and simultaneously eliminated all of the important distance receptors of the rat without serious interference with the animal's ability to learn and execute accurately the maze habit. This seemingly left kinesthetic and organic sensitivity as the sole remaining basis for the habit. As Watson pointed out, these first studies, by the method of sensory elimination, gave only negative evidence without indication of the nature of the intraorganic processes which control the maze running.

In their study of behavior in a maze with alleys adjustable in length, Carr and Watson (3) obtained further evidence that the movement series is internally conditioned and that after distraction the animal regained orientation from the kinesthetic pattern aroused by running some segment of the maze. They then clearly enunciated the theory that "the 'movement to come' is released at the proper time by the afferent (kinesthetic) impulses aroused by the movement which has just been made," and this

[1] EDITORS' NOTE: K. S. Lashley and Josephine Ball, authors. From *J. comp. Psychol.*, 1929, 9, 71–105. Reproduced by permission of the Williams and Wilkins Co. From the Institute for Juvenile Research, Chicago.

interpretation has been followed in almost all succeeding discussions of the maze habit. One of the most definite recent statements of this chain-reflex hypothesis is that of Washburn. "When one is playing a piece of music for the first or second time, each movement has to have the stimulus of the notes on the page; when a piece has been long practiced, each movement sets up the next one 'automatically.' This really means that, as one movement is performed, the sensory processes occasioned by the contraction of the muscles involved excite the motor paths for the next movement. The stimulus for one movement is the kinesthetic excitations received from the preceding movement."

Vincent's later work (27) showed the occasional importance of visual, olfactory and tactile cues, but did not question the essential conclusions from Watson's studies.

We were first led to doubt the validity of this interpretation of the maze habit by observations on the maze running of rats after cerebellar injuries (13). Marked changes in the motor pattern were seen to have no effect upon accuracy of orientation in the maze, even in blind animals under conditions where other than supposedly kinesthetic cues seemed to be eliminated. This raised the question as to whether the habit is controlled by kinesthetic sensitivity or by some wholly intraneural mechanism, once orientation has been obtained. Are automatized sequences of movement the result of a mechanism by which each movement arouses sensory cues to initiate the next, or of some mechanism in which a central organization, once aroused, discharges successive motor impulses constituting the series, with comparative independence of the sensory consequences of the movements?

The experiments with lesions to the cerebellum are inconclusive because we know neither the important components of the movement system nor the afferent impulses which may be essential to the habit. Perhaps the only crucial experiment for the question would be one with animals having section of all the somatic sensory fibers. This seems technically impossible and the question may therefore be one which can be answered only in terms of relative probabilities deduced from indirect evidence. Loss of ability to run the maze after partial destruction of kinesthetic sensitivity might serve to establish the chain-reflex theory. Survival of the habit after even severe disturbance of kinesthetic sensitivity may always be interpreted as due to failure to eliminate the significant afferent impulses. Nevertheless, the probability of the chain-reflex hypothesis is reduced in proportion to the extent of anesthesia and the absence of effects of anesthesia upon the performance of the habit.

With these limitations, it seemed to us that some significant data might still be obtained by a study of the effects of the extensive destruction of the spinal afferent tracts upon the accuracy of maze running. We have, therefore, carried out a series of experiments in which animals trained in the maze were subjected to spinal lesions and subsequently tested for retention of the habit. The senior author alone is responsible for the surgical and histological part of the work. The training and tests of performance have been carried out by both of us independently on different sets of animals, with essentially similar results.

METHODS

Training. The animals were trained with food as incentive and five trials per day in a maze with 8 culs de sac (Fig. 12.1) until 10 consecutive runs without error were made. This maze had been constructed to record errors automatically so that animals could be tested in it in total darkness. The recording platforms were arranged symmetrically on each side of the openings from alley to alley so that they gave no directive tactile cues. Two groups of rats were trained with somewhat different subsequent procedures. The first consisted of young

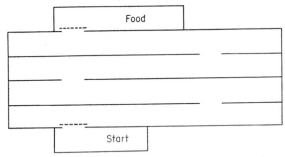

Fig. 12.1. Ground-plan of maze. *Start,* starting compartment; *food,* food compartment. The broken lines represent swinging doors serving to prevent back-tracking from the maze and food compartments.

rats purchased from a local dealer. They were rested for seven days after training, were then retrained until 10 consecutive errorless trials were obtained (preliminary retention tests) and subjected to operation. Seven days after operation they were again retrained to 10 successive errorless trials (postoperative retention tests). During all the work with them these animals were very unstable, easily distracted during the period in the maze and rarely eager for food. They are numbers 1, 2, 3, and 6 of the protocols. Their records were difficult to interpret because of their erratic behavior, so the experiment was repeated with another group.

These were older animals, reared in the laboratory. They were given 50 trials of overtraining after reaching the criterion of 10 errorless trials. They were then rested for ten days, given preliminary retention tests, and also ten trials with the maze in darkness. (This was accomplished by covering the maze with black cloth and several layers of heavy paper. Observation through a peephole failed to reveal light leakage after thirty seconds adaptation for our eyes.) The animals were then operated upon and from six to ten days later, depending upon the rate of recovery, were given postoperative retention tests.

Surgical. Under ether anesthesia the third cervical neural arch was removed and the cord exposed by a transverse incision of the dura. The point of a thin-bladed iridectomy knife was passed through the cord at the depth to which we

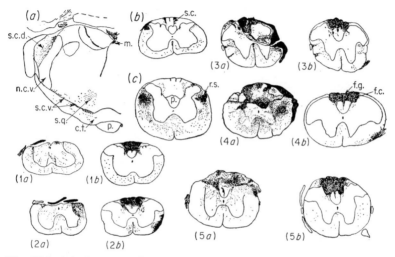

Fig. 12.2. (*a*) Composite diagram showing degeneration at the level of the trapezoid body after section of the lateral and ventral funiculi; (*b*) descending degeneration after section of the dorsal funiculus; (*c*) descending degeneration after section of both lateral funiculi. c.t., trapezoid body; f.c., fasciculus cuneatus; f.g., fasciculus gracilis; m., median longitudinal bundle; n.c.v., nucleus of fifth nerve; p., cortico-spinal tract; r.s., rubro-spinal tract; s.c.d., dorsal spino-cerebellar tract; s.c.v., ventral spino-cerebellar tract; s.q., spino-quadrigeminal system (?); s.c., Schultze's comma. (1) to (5) Cases with lesions in the dorsal funiculus. The numbered figures marked (*a*) represent sections through the level of maximum extent of the lesion (third cervical); numbered figures marked (*b*), sections at about the first cervical level. The numbers correspond to the numbers of the animals in the text. The stippling represents degenerated fibers, solid black unabsorbed clots.

wished the lesion to penetrate and the overlying fibers then cut through with the edge. This ensured that all fibers peripheral to the line of penetration of the knife were cut and not merely pushed aside. The injuries involved either section of the dorsal funiculus, section of both lateral funiculi, or section of the ventral funiculus. The last injury involved lifting the cord from the canal with conse-quent compression and shock and only one animal, and that with a partial lesion, survived. After the injury to the cord the muscles and skin were united above the cord by interrupted sutures and the wound dressed with collodion.

Histological. At necropsy the brain and the cord were removed and prepared in serial sections by the Marchi method. For most cases complete serial sections were preserved from below the level of the lesions to the superior colliculi. The figures [numbered 12.2 and 12.3] are made from camera outlines. Solid lines are used to represent general regions and contours; stippling in all cases represents degenerated fibers; solid black areas represent unabsorbed clots. For the [figures] one section was sketched at the level of maximum injury (a) and one (b) at a sufficiently higher level to avoid the degeneration of the shorter ground bundles and present only tracts which could be traced into the medulla.

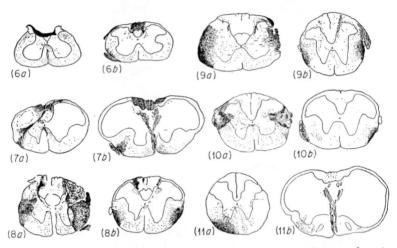

Fig. 12.3. (6) to (11) Sections from cases bearing corresponding numbers in the text; (a) level of a maximum lesion; (b) first cervical level or level of decussation of the pyramids.

There are few data available on the spinal tracts of the rat so we have been compelled to work out their position as well as possible from our material. A certain fallacy may arise here since our knowledge of the tracts is limited to what we have destroyed and our estimates of the character of the lesions are based upon that knowledge. However, the lesions cover every part of the cord except the median ventral columns so we may be sure that in one or another animal we have severed every organized tract in the cord and that the demonstration of the tracts is limited only by the level of the lesions and the defects of the Marchi technique as a method for the rat.

THE SPINAL TRACTS OF THE RAT

The conduction paths of the spinal cord of the rat have not been described in detail. Interest has centered chiefly in the pyramidal tracts because of their deviation from the usual lateral position. They have been described and figured by Lenhossek (14), Bechterew (1), Goldstein (4), Van Der Vloet (26), King (8), Ranson (21), and Linowecki (15). Ranson (22) has described the position of Clarke's column and the tract of Lissauer. The rubro-spinal tract has been traced by Held (6) and by Papez (19), but briefly and without figures so that its exact position in the cord is not clear. We have not found descriptions of other tracts.

The series of cases studied in the present experiment has involved the interruption of all the tracts of the cord in one or another animal and we have been able to trace these in so far as they are revealed by the Marchi technique. The pyramidal tract does not stain readily by the Marchi method, as Ranson and others have pointed out, because of the thinness of its medullation. The same seems true of other long descending tracts, for in only a few of our specimens have we been able to trace degeneration below the lesion. In contrast, many ascending tracts show clearly, with defined limits.

Descending Tracts

Cortico-spinal. The descending fibers from the cortex occupy the median ventral position in the dorsal funiculus [Fig. 12.2c]. Decussation of the pyramidal tracts to this position seems to be complete and Ranson (21, 22) reported no other descending degeneration after hemidecerebration.

Rubro-spinal. This has been described in a preliminary note by Papez (19). He does not figure it and states its position in the cord only as corresponding to that in other mammals. We find a large clearly limited bundle ventro-lateral to the dorsal horns [Fig. 12.2b and c] which is probably the rubro-spinal tract.

Schultz's Comma. After section of the dorsal funiculus the comma appears as a small, well-defined descending bundle lying between the fasciculus gracilis and fasciculus cuneatus on each side [Fig. 12.2b].

No other clearly defined descending tracts are visible in our preparations. After lesions to the lateral and ventral funiculi many degenerated fibers may be traced caudad in these regions, but they appear rather uniformly scattered and as our preparations do not include lesions above the cervical cord it is impossible to distinguish the source of the various scattered fibers.

Ascending Tracts

Fasciculus Gracilis. In degeneration of the dorsal funiculus this tract appears as a clearly defined bundle which can be traced to its complete termination in the nucleus gracilis [Fig. 12.2, 4b].

Fasciculus Cuneatus. This bundle lies lateral to the fasciculus gracilis [Fig. 12.2, 4b]. It gives off fibers to the gray matter throughout its length and receives additions from the dorsal cervical roots [Fig. 12.3, 6b].

After destruction of the lateral funiculus, degeneration appears throughout an extensive zone in the ventro-lateral region of the cord [Fig. 12.3, 8 and 9b]. Traced into the medulla these ascending fibers are seen to break up into four principal groups [Fig. 12.2a]. It has not been possible to determine with certainty the origin of these bundles in the cord, but their most probable positions in the cervical cord, judged by tracing downward from the medulla, are indicated below.

Fasciculus Spino-cerebellaris Dorsalis. The fibers lying in the more dorsal portions of the lateral funiculus may be traced forward to the medulla where they are separated from the remainder of the degenerated mass to pass laterad to the posterior cerebellar peduncles [Fig. 12.2a, s.c.d.].

Fasciculus Spino-cerebellaris Ventralis. The more central fibers of the lateral funiculus may be distinguished in the medulla as a broad band of fibers which ultimately turn laterad to reach the anterior cerebellar peduncle [Fig. 12.2a, s.c.v.].

Spino-quadrigeminal System (?). After destruction of the lateral funiculus a large number of degenerated fibers appear scattered in the ventral region of the reticulated substance of the medulla [Fig. 12.2a, s.q.]. Traced forward they ascend and are lost, in our material, in the region of the inferior colliculi. Traced caudad, they could be followed to the most ventral portions of the lateral funiculus and to scattered fibers of the ventral funiculus.

Fibers to the Median Longitudinal Bundle. After lesions to the ventral portion of the lateral funiculus or to the ventral funiculus a few degenerated fibers appeared in the fasciculus longitudinalis medialis of the medulla [Fig. 12.2a]. These could not be traced to their termination because of defective fixation of our material. They seemed to be derived chiefly from the scattered fibers of the ventral funiculus. Some of the fibers of this and the preceding systems may reach the thalamus.

In our preparations, which included section of every part of the cord, no other definite degenerated tracts could be detected. There is no assurance that other important ascending tracts may not have remained unstained owing to conditions of medullation similar to that of the pyramidal tract. This is, however, of little importance for our experiments since, whether stained or not, there is no question but that they were cut in some of our animals.

In general, the tracts of the rat's cord present no fundamental differences from those of higher mammals, to which we can ascribe the results obtained in our studies of behavior. The ascending tracts of the dorsal funiculus and the spino-cerebellar tracts are large and sharply defined. The pyramidal tract is restricted to a definite area and this seems true also of the rubro-spinal. On anatomical grounds there seems no more reason to predict a diffuseness of function in the cord of the rat than in that of the monkey or man.

The path of the proprioceptive impulses is perhaps not yet certainly established, but the weight of evidence from clinical material indicates that sensitivity to movements and bodily posture is disturbed only by lesions within the posterior columns. Head (5) states that ". . . the impulses associated with passive position and movement and with tactile discrimination do not, within the limits of the spinal cord, reach the point where they are recombined, but continue uncrossed to pass along the fibers of primary afferent systems in the posterior columns. It is not until they reach the posterior column nuclei (nucleus gracilis and nucleus cuneatus) that they pass from a primary to a secondary sensory system" (5, p. 401), and again, "We therefore find, that the only definite consequence of destruction of the posterior columns is to produce loss of tactile discrimination (compass test) and of the sense of passive position and movement on the same side as the lesion" (5, p. 402).

GENERAL EFFECTS OF LESIONS

For each of the regions of the cord involved in the experimental destructions the animals showed definite syndromes. The picture after section of the dorsal funiculi seemed primarily one of reduced sensitivity to bodily position. In walking the animals had a sprawling gait, with feet rather widespread. They tended to walk on the dorsal surface of the forefeet, less frequently of the hind feet. There was occasional incoordination, especially a lack of synchronization of the fore and hind legs. In rapid walking or running, the hind legs tended to drag in recovery from the backward step, and in turning to one side the opposite foreleg was often dragged stiffly behind. In running rapidly in the maze all legs were recovered too slowly from the backward step so that the animals seemed to run ahead of their feet and fall forward. When tested at the edge of a table with one leg unsupported this leg was often allowed to hang flaccid until movements of progression were initiated (a condition noted in many animals after section of the dorsal roots of a limb). When the animals were placed on a board which was tipped at various angles their posture in maintaining balance seemed practically normal. Only crude tests for cutaneous sensitivity could be used. They gave no indication of abnormality, but were unreliable for any but the grossest changes.

Section of the lateral funiculi gave a picture suggestive of cerebellar ataxia. The gait was staggering with exaggerated balancing movements of the tail. The animals frequently fell to one side, especially in making the turns of the maze. Tested at the edge of the table, the unsupporting limbs were recovered as promptly as by a normal animal. On a tipping board adjustments to change of position were sometimes slow or defective, but often normal in all animals. There were suggestions of disturbances of cutaneous sensitivity, a slight analgesia and a tendency to bite at the forefeet during the first few days after operation.

In one case with lesion in the ventral funiculus the behavior was almost normal, with perhaps a slight hyperextension of the legs for the first few days after operation.

PROTOCOLS

Destruction of Fasciculi Gracilis and Cuneatus and of the Pyramidal Tract

Number 1. Young Male. Somewhat unstable during training. Training record: Time, 1,463 seconds; errors, 67; trials, 45. Preliminary retention tests: Trials, 10; time, 53 seconds; errors, 0.

Dorsal funiculus sectioned at third cervical segment. On the following days there was some incoordination in walking, with a tendency to walk on the dorsum of the forefeet. The hind limbs were dragged occasionally in walking and in turning toward either side the foreleg of the other side was dragged. There seemed to be some analgesia. Retention was tested ten days after operation. The record for fifteen trials was the following:

Time	Errors	Time	Errors
18	0	8	0
34	0	10	0
83	3	10	0
92	3	22	1
43	0	10	0
9	0	9	0
7	0	8	0
6	0		

Locomotion was slowed considerably in the maze, owing largely to the motor incoordination, but the first two trials were made without error and the total record gave clear evidence that the maze pattern was retained.

Lesion. Section through the site of injury showed that practically all the cord above the level of the central canal had been destroyed [Fig. 12.2, 1a]. The f. gracilis, cuneatus, and the pyramidal tract together with the dorsal horns of the gray matter were destroyed. Section at the level of the first cervical segment showed complete degeneration of the f. gracilis and cuneatus except for the lateral areas representing the fibers of the first and second cervical nerves [Fig. 12.2, 1b]. Scattered degenerate fibers in the lateral and ventral funiculi probably originate from injury to the third pair of nerves and to the dorsal horns of the gray matter.

Number 2. Young Male. Training marked by periods of refusal to run the maze. Training record: Time, 5,409 seconds; errors, 153; trials, 20. Preliminary retention tests: Time, 63 seconds; errors, 0; trials, 10.

On the first day of preliminary retention tests he would not run in the maze and did not eat when placed in the food compartment.

Dorsal funiculi sectioned at third cervical segment. On the following days he tended to drag his legs and walk on the dorsum of the feet, like number 1. Retention was tested ten days later after operation. On the first day he showed little evidence of hunger and behaved much as on the first day of the preliminary retention tests, making the following record:

Time	Errors
330	8
360	8
142	4
63	1

He was not fed after these tests and on the next day made the following record:

Time	Errors	Time	Errors
21	0	17	0
10	0	15	0
17	0	15	0
27	0	9	0
13	0	6	0
14	0		

The record does not show perfect retention but is far better than that for initial learning. In view of his earlier records, we are justified in concluding that this case does not give conclusive evidence for loss of the habit after spinal lesion.

Lesion. Section at the third cervical segment [Fig. 12.2, 2a] shows destruction of the greater part of the cord above the level of the central canal. The f. gracilis, cuneatus, and practically all of the pyramidal tract were interrupted. A section below the first cervical roots [Fig. 12.2, 2b] shows complete degeneration of the f. gracilis and cuneatus, except for the portions supplied by the second cervical nerve, and extensive degeneration in the right spino-cerebellar tracts corresponding to the degeneration in the right lateral funiculus, shown at the level of injury.

Number 3. Young Male. Behavior normal during initial training. Training record: Time, 1,669 seconds; errors, 97; trials, 20. No preliminary retention tests were given.

The dorsal funiculus was sectioned deeply. On the following days there was marked incoordination in walking. The forefeet were usually flexed with the dorsum on the ground. Hind feet were frequently dragged in walking and were not drawn up when placed over the edge of a support. When making coordinated steps the feet were widespread, so that the belly touched the ground. There was probably some positive disturbance of sensitivity as on the eighth day he amputated his left forepaw. Retention was tested fourteen days after operation. On the first day he would not eat in the maze and his behavior was erratic. The record for the first day was the following:

Time	Errors
24	2
46	4
38	2
689	20

He was not fed on the next day made the following record:

Time	Errors	Time	Errors
17	0	27	0
60	0	26	4
14	2	9	0
7	0	8	0
8	1	7	0
7	1	8	0
8	0	12	1

The behavior on the first day did not resemble that of an untrained animal and there was indifference to food. On the following day, when the incentive to run was increased, errorless trials were obtained from the first. Like the record of number 2, this is somewhat ambiguous. It indicates some retention, but is impossible to interpret.

Lesion. At the third cervical level the position of the lesion was clearly marked by scar tissue and clots [Fig. 12.2, 3a]. It involved all of the dorsal funiculus, the greater part of the gray matter on the right, and the dorsal third of the lateral funiculus, including the rubro-spinal tract. At the second cervical segment [Fig. 12.2, 3b] there was complete degeneration of the f. gracilis and cuneatus and considerable degeneration in both the lateral columns.

Number 4. Large Adult Male. Given 50 trials overtraining. Training record: Time, 1,676 seconds; errors, 49; trials, 29. Overtraining: Time, 279 seconds; errors, 1; trials, 50. Preliminary retention tests: Time, 106 seconds; errors, 3; trials, 16.

The dorsal funiculus was deeply incised at the third cervical segment. On the following days he walked with a sprawling gait falling occasionally in making turns and frequently stepping on the dorsum of the feet. Retention was tested five days after operation. The record was the following:

Time	Errors	Time	Errors
7	0	6	0
6	0	8	0
12	0	6	0
7	0	8	0
5	0	8	0

The record shows perfect retention and a speed in traversing the maze only slightly inferior to the preoperative record. The maze was covered and performance tested in darkness. The record was the following:

Time	Errors	Time	Errors
28	2	7	0
22	0	7	0
8	0	8	0
8	0	6	0
10	0	8	0

After the exploration of the covered top of the maze in the first trial no further errors were made when moving in total darkness.

Lesion. Section at the third cervical level showed complete interruption of the dorsal funiculus, destruction of the posterior horns and a considerable amount of degeneration in the right lateral funiculus [Fig. 12.2, 4a]. Section above the first cervical level [Fig. 12.2, 4b] showed complete degeneration of the f. gracilis and cuneatus with considerable degeneration in the region of the dorsal spino-cerebellar tract.

These four cases all show complete interruption of the fasciculus gracilis, fasciculus cuneatus and pyramidal tracts, with more or less degeneration in the regions of the rubro-spinal tracts and of the dorsal spino-cerebellar bundles. Two cases, numbers 2 and 3, showed somewhat erratic behavior in preoperative tests and similar behavior after operation so that their records are not clear cut. They do, however, show some indication of retention. The other two, with equally extensive destruction give unequivocal evidence for perfect retention of the maze habit. Destruction of the dorsal funiculus did not in the least affect their ability to make the correct turns of the maze.

Destruction of Fasciculus Gracilis and Fasciculus Cuneatus without Extensive Injury to the Pyramidal Tracts

Number 5. Large Male. More than usually stable. Initial training: Time, 957 seconds; errors, 32; trials, 14. Preliminary retention tests: Time, 35 seconds; errors, 0; trials, 10. Overtraining: Time, 182 seconds; errors, 1; trials, 50.

Ten trials with the maze darkened were given before operation.

Time	Errors	Time	Errors
25	2	4	0
18	3	7	0
5	0	6	0
4	0	5	0
4	0	4	0

The dorsal funiculus was sectioned at the third cervical segment. For the first few days the animal tended to circle to the right in walking. This condition cleared up quickly, leaving the usual picture of reduced sensitivity to posture. Retention was tested eight days after operation, with the following record.

Time	Errors	Time	Errors
8	0	13	0
5	0	4	0
16	0	8	1
10	0	6	0
7	0	12	0

On the following day, with the maze darkened, he made the following record:

Time	Errors	Time	Errors
38	2	8	0
36	2	7	0
10	0	6	0
8	0	6	0
18	1	12	0

The postoperative tests show some slowing in locomotion but no loss of ability to traverse the maze correctly. With vision eliminated the record was as good as that made under similar conditions before the spinal lesion.

Lesion. Section above the third cervical level showed complete destruction of the f. gracilis and f. cuneatus with little if any involvement of the pyramidal tracts [Fig. 12.2, 5a]. Section at the first cervical level showed degeneration restricted almost entirely to the two ascending fasciculi [Fig. 12.2, 5b].

Number 6. Young Male. Very unstable throughout the experiment. Initial training: Time, 710 seconds; errors, 53; trials, 50. Preliminary retention tests were not given.

The dorsal funiculus was transected at the third cervical segment. On the following days little abnormality of behavior was noted beyond a tendency to walk on the dorsum of the paws and drag them slightly. Retention was tested seven days after operation, with the following record, made in three consecutive days:

Time	Errors	Time	Errors	Time	Errors
322	12	23	2	8	0
201	11	15	0	13	2
80	3	15	0	12	0
33	1	10	0	7	0
34	1	8	0	11	1
16	1	8	0	8	0
9	0	11	1	5	0
12	1	11	0	5	0
7	0	22	2	6	0
15	2	92	6	5	0

This record is not significantly better than the initial training record. The behavior during retention tests was characterized throughout by prolonged periods of quiescence in the starting compartment and by failure to eat after the food had been reached.

Lesion. There was active infection of the wound, inflammation of the cord with necrosis of the dorsal horns at the third cervical level [Fig. 12.3, 6a]. Section at a higher level showed extensive degeneration of the f. gracilis and cuneatus with some degenerated fibers in the spino-cerebellar tracts, chiefly on the left [Fig. 12.3, 6b].

Of these two cases the first alone can be considered. The infection rules out the negative evidence of the second and leaves only as significant the fact that, in spite of the infection and destruction of tissue, he was able ultimately to traverse the maze without error. Number [5], with greater actual destruction, showed perfect retention of the maze habit and ability to traverse the maze in darkness as well after as before the spinal injury.

Partial Destruction of the Dorsal and of One Lateral Funiculus

Number 7. Large Male. About 200 days old. Initial training: Time, 1,077 seconds; errors, 38; trials, 21. Overtraining: Time, 247 seconds; errors, 0; trials, 50. Preliminary retention tests: Time, 41 seconds; errors, 0; trials, 10.

Preliminary tests with the maze darkened gave the following:

Time	Errors	Time	Errors
85	5	7	1
8	1	4	0
5	0	4	0
5	0	5	0
7	1	5	0

An attempt was made to divide the dorsal funiculus, but the knife was driven deeply into the left side of the cord. General behavior after operation was not markedly different from that of animals with only the dorsal funiculus cut, except that adjustments to tipping the substratum were made rather slowly and inaccurately. Retention was tested six days after operation with the following record.

Time	Errors	Time	Errors
11	0	10	0
22	1	10	0
11	0	7	0
12	0	8	0
10	0	8	0

Tests with the maze darkened gave the following record:

Time	Errors	Time	Errors
35	0	33	0
25	0	14	0
38	0	27	0
55	0	43	0
22	0	30	0

The prolonged time in these tests is due to the fact that the animal was disturbed by the cover of the maze and repeatedly stopped during every trial to push against it with his nose.

Lesion. The cut extended diagonally from the outer margin of the right f. cuneatus through the left dorsal horn to the lower margin of the left spinocerebellar tract, interrupting all the fibers above this line [Fig. 12.3, 7a]. Section at a higher level shows almost complete degeneration of the f. gracilis and cuneatus of both sides, degeneration of the left spino-cerebellar tracts and many degenerate fibers in the region of the spino-tectile bundles [Fig. 12.3, 7b].

This case, with nearly complete section of the f. gracilis and cuneatus and interruption of the spino-cerebellar tracts of one side gave clear evidence of ability to run the maze even in darkness.

Section of the Lateral Funiculi

Number 8. Large Male. About 200 days old. Initial learning: Time, 5,861 seconds; errors, 83; trials, 20. Overtraining: Time, 431 seconds; errors, 0; trials, 50. Preliminary retention tests: Time, 55 seconds; errors, 0; trials, 10.

Preliminary tests with the maze darkened gave the following results:

Time	Errors	Time	Errors
125	9	7	0
16	1	5	0
15	1	3	0
8	0	4	0
10	0	3	0

The lateral funiculus was divided on each side at the level of the third cervical segment. On the following days he showed tremor and hyperextension of the legs, staggering gait with a tendency to fall to the side, especially in turning, and constant balancing movements of the tail. There was some difficulty in adapting to inclination of the substratum. Retention was tested ten days after operation with the following record:

Time	Errors	Time	Errors
10	0	10	0
11	0	12	0
8	0	11	0
11	0	8	0
11	0	7	0

With the maze darkened, the record was the following:

Time	Errors	Time	Errors
115	4	22	0
46	1	18	0
15	0	20	0
15	0	100	2
18	1	13	0

The record is somewhat inferior to the preoperative one, but gives conclusive evidence of ability to traverse the maze in darkness.

Lesion. At the third cervical level the lesions of the two sides were separated longitudinally by about one millimeter, that on the right being the more cephalad [Fig. 12.3, 8]. On the left the knife had passed through the fasciculus cuneatus and diagonally downward to interrupt the entire lateral funiculus, involving the dorsal horn of the gray matter as well. On the right the lesion extended vertically from the lateral margin of the fasciculus cuneatus through the dorsal and ventral horns and involved the entire lateral funiculus [Fig. 12.3, 8].

Number 9. Large Male. About 200 days old. Initial training: Time, 1,297 seconds; errors, 57; trials, 18. Overtraining: Time, 338 seconds; errors, 0; trials, 50. Preliminary retention tests: Time, 47 seconds; errors, 0; trials, 10.

Preliminary tests with the maze darkened gave the following record:

Time	Errors	Time	Errors
175	11	5	0
6	0	4	0
5	0	5	0
5	0	5	0
5	0	5	0

The lateral funiculi of both sides were cut at the third cervical level. The subsequent behavior of the animal was much like that of number 8, but with a less steady gait and some indication of analgesia. In retention tests he fell almost every time in making a turn in the maze. Retention tests were given six days after operation, with the following record:

Time	Errors	Time	Errors
34	1	8	0
10	0	9	0
8	0	10	0
10	0	9	0
8	0	9	0

Tests with the maze darkened gave the following:

Time	Errors	Time	Errors
37	2	9	0
27	1	24	1
13	0	11	0
12	0	9	0
9	0	10	0

Lesion. Section at the level of the injury showed total destruction of both lateral funiculi with little or no injury to the dorsal or ventral funiculi. Section at the first cervical roots showed degeneration of the spino-cerebellar tracts of both sides and ascending degeneration of fibers from the third dorsal root in the right f. cuneatus. [Fig. 12.3, 9a and 9b].

Number 10. Male. About 200 days old. Initial training: Time, 2,022 seconds; errors, 80; trials, 45. Overtraining: Time, 322 seconds; errors, 3; trials, 50. Preliminary retention tests: Time, 85 seconds; errors, 1; trials, 14.

The lateral funiculus of each side was divided at the third cervical segment. On the following days he showed hyperextension of the legs, staggering gait with tendency to fall to the side, constant balancing movements of the tail and some tremor of the legs.

Retention was tested five days after operation with the following record:

Time	Errors	Time	Errors
14	0	8	0
12	0	10	0
45	2	29	0
12	0	10	0
9	0	8	0

Tests with the maze darkened gave the following:

Time	Errors	Time	Errors
56	1	18	0
82	2	11	0
29	0	17	0
52	1	10	0
20	0	10	0

In these tests the additional time was consumed in pushing at the cover of the maze.

Lesion. Section at the third cervical level showed lesions restricted to the dorsal halves of the lateral funiculi without invasion of the gray matter [Fig. 12.3, 10*a*]. At the first cervical level there was partial degeneration of the dorsal spino-cerebellar tract of each side with no other involvement.

These three cases, involving interruption of all the paths of the lateral funiculi and considerable motor disturbance, resembling a cerebellar ataxia, showed perfect retention of the maze habit with ability to traverse the maze in the absence of visual cues.

Injury to the Ventral Funiculus

Number 11. Large Male. About 200 days old. Initial training: Time, 2,491 seconds; errors, 71; trials, 23. Overtaining: Time, 647 seconds; errors, 7; trials, 50. Preliminary retention tests: Time, 83 seconds; errors, 1; trials, 11.

Preliminary tests with the maze darkened gave the following:

Time	Errors	Time	Errors
86	8	16	1
18	1	6	0
11	1	15	1
10	0	7	0
8	0	6	1

The cord was exposed, raised, and the knife passed through the ventral columns. Following the operation there was little disturbance of behavior beyond a slight tendency to drag the hind feet in walking. Retention tests were given six days after operation:

Time	Errors	Time	Errors
9	0	13	0
15	0	25	0
15	0	14	0
13	0	12	0
10	0	11	0
58	1		

Tests with the maze darkened gave the following:

Time	Errors	Time	Errors
54	4	28	0
17	0	18	0
20	0	13	0
15	0	35	1
14	0	28	0

Lesion. In dividing the cord for fixation the segment containing the lesion was destroyed. A section immediately above the lesion shows extensive degeneration throughout the ventro-lateral column of the left side with little involvement of the right. It seems certain that the knife passed diagonally downward to destroy all of the funiculus below the ventral horn on the left side, without serious injury to the right [Fig. 12.3, 11a]. Ascending the cord the degenerated fibers disappear rapidly into the gray matter so that only a few are left at the level of the decussation of the pyramids [Fig. 12.3, 11b]. These lie chiefly in the ventral spino-cerebellar bundle and in the spino-tectile bundles.

This case, with extensive destruction in the ventral funiculus, showed quite undisturbed ability to traverse the maze.

RESULTS OF THE EXPERIMENTS

The records of the animals in the various tests are summarized in Table 12.1. The animals of the first group tested are marked with a dagger. Their records in postoperative retention tests are much worse than those of the others. This is unquestionably due largely to the fact that they were not rendered sufficiently hungry on the first day of retention tests. Number 6 alone showed retardation sufficient to produce anything like a normal learning curve in postoperative tests and he showed evidence of infection in the cord. Numbers 2 and 3 made errors only on the first day of retention tests and on later days, when eager for food, made no errors. Number 1 gave evidence of retention from the first. All these cases ran the maze without error sometime after operation so that they at least show the possibility of acquisition of the habit after section of the dorsal funiculi. However, we are justified in discounting completely their failures after operation in view of the records of the second group.

Number 4 with interruption of the entire dorsal funiculus including the pyramidal tract and number 5 with section of the f. gracilis and cuneatus only made no errors in postoperative tests under the conditions of training. In tests with the darkened maze they made fewer errors after operation than the average for all animals under the same conditions before operation. From them we may conclude that accuracy in running the maze is not disturbed by complete destruction of the afferent and efferent paths of the dorsal funiculus. Number 7 showed a similar ability to traverse the maze after almost complete destruction of the f. gracilis and cuneatus and partial destruction of one lateral funiculus.

Table 12.1. Summary of Results from Protocols

Number	Errors learning °	Errors prelimi- nary retention °	Errors prelimi- nary darkness °	Errors post- operative °	Errors post- operative darkness °	Lesion
1 †	67	0		7		Entire dorsal funiculus
2 †	153	0		21		Entire dorsal f.
3 †	97			37		Entire dorsal f.
4	49	3		0	2	Entire dorsal f.
5	32	0	5	0	5	Dorsal f.
6 †	53			44		Dorsal f.
7	38	0	8	1	0	Dorsal and lateral f.
8	83	0	11	0	8	Lateral f.
9	57	0	11	1	4	Lateral f.
10	80	1		2	4	Lateral f.
11	71	1	12	1	5	Ventral f.

° The errors made in the various tests are given as probably the most reliable of the three criteria.
† Animals in the first group tested.

Numbers 8, 9, 10 made practically perfect records in postoperative tests after section of the lateral funiculi. Their motor incoordination was severe, they fell at almost every turn in the maze yet recovered and turned correctly without getting into the culs de sac. The lesion in number 8 certainly involved all of the tracts of the lateral funiculus with a considerable part of the left f. cuneatus as well. The records of these cases show that none of the tracts of the lateral funiculus is essential for maze running, either under ordinary conditions or in darkness.

Number 11, with severe lesion on the left in the ventral funiculus, gave no evidence of disturbance of the maze habit. The lesion did not involve that portion of the funiculus lying between the ventral horns but shows that the other parts of the funiculus are not essential.

The only significant difference between the preliminary and postoperative tests is in the time required for traversing the maze. The average time per trial for trials without error in the preliminary retention tests (cases 4, 5, 7, 8, 9, 10, and 11) is 5.4 seconds. The corresponding average for the postoperative tests is 9.8 seconds. However, animals with lesions in each region occasionally traversed the maze as quickly after as before operation so that this retardation can not be taken as evidence for a necessity to "feel their way" with greater care than before operation. As a matter of fact all the animals showed ample motor disturbance to account for all the excess time of the postoperative tests and their behavior gave not the slightest indication of an increased dependence upon tactile or olfactory cues.

MOTOR CONTROL OF THE MAZE HABIT

The most surprising result of these experiments was the capacity of the animals to orient in the maze after section of the descending tracts. The inclusion of these tracts in the lesions was inadvertent and the lack of effects wholly confounding. After the first few days the motor capacities of the animals seemed but little disturbed. Their incoordinations of movement resembled the syndromes of sensory disturbances in man rather than any direct paralytic symptoms. Coordinations between sensory and motor systems on opposite sides of the lesions appeared in all cases shortly after the operations. These included such activities as postural coordinations of the head and trunk in sitting erect, turning the head toward the locus of protopathic stimulation on the limbs and trunk, and washing the face with the forepaws, as well as orientation in walking.

The lack of specific symptoms following section of the pyramidal tract is to be expected from the similar absence of motor disturbances following ablation of the entire stimulable cortex. Possibly some of the disturbances of gait after section of the lateral funiculi are referable to the destruction of the rubro-spinal paths rather than of the spino-cerebellar, but there would be little reason to assign the control of habitual movements to these paths. This leaves only the less definite thalamico-spinal, ponto-spinal and similar fibers as potential conductors of the orienting movements and since, in one case or another, the lesions interrupted practically all of the cross-sectional areas of the cord, we are forced to the conclusion that the motor impulses essential to the performance of the acts described above are not restricted to any of the definite tracts, but descend, either diffusely or over alternative paths in the different funiculi.

Similar conditions in the motor functions of the cord have been described by other investigators. Porter's work (20) on the path of the respiratory impulses is well known. Weiss (31) found after hemisection of the cord in dogs a rapid restitution of motor functions and Mott (18) reported a similar recovery in the monkey. Osawa and Borgherini (see 24) found that a double hemisection, when the lesions were separated by six or seven spinal segments, might be followed by restoration of motility of the hind legs in the dog. All of these observations point to a great plasticity or diffuseness of motor conduction in the cord.

In contrast to this condition of the motor paths, the sensory paths seem much more definite and less plastic. All of these investigators report a much slower recovery of sensory functions after spinal lesion with never a complete restitution. Why this difference between afferent and efferent conduction should exist is still wholly obscure, but the difference seems to be clearly established, both by earlier and by our own observations and is of considerable importance for the interpretation of our data.

SENSORY COMPONENTS OF THE HABIT

The lesions to the dorsal funiculi produced serious sensory disturbances if we may judge from the defects of posture shown by the animals. Lesions to other parts of the cord, although followed by a few signs of sensory defect, were complete enough to ensure that all ascending paths were interrupted. It is clear that the ability of the animals to traverse the maze was unimpaired by the observed sensory defects and further, that no particular afferent path of the cervical cord is essential for the performance of the maze habit. There seem to be four possible alternative interpretations of the data.

1. The kinesthetic impulses were eliminated by the lesions and the animals shifted to other sensory cues for direction in the maze. The following controls of such sensory cues seem to rule out this interpretation.

Olfaction. With the older group at the termination of the preliminary retention tests the maze was rinsed out and allowed to stand open and unused for six days before the postoperative retention tests. There is no evidence to indicate that under such conditions directive odors would remain. Moreover, the rat which is following an olfactory trail shows an unmistakable pattern of movements (27) and none of the animals in our experiments showed any significant sniffing at the critical points in the maze during the postoperative tests.

Audition. In passing from one alley of the maze to the next the animal is confronted by two passages of unequal length and must always turn towards the longer. It is conceivable that differences in echoes from the two ends of the passage might give directive cues, but evidence which we have of the enormous difficulty of such a discrimination of localization of sounds for the rat makes such a speculation preposterous. Differences in air pressure in the two passages are positively excluded by the fact that the alleys were covered only by coarse netting.

Vision. The maze was covered in a way as to exclude light. The animals were disturbed by the presence of the cover and spent much time in pushing against it through the wire netting but their behavior in this respect did not differ before and after operation and their accuracy after operation was in general better than before.

Cutaneous. The sides of the maze and the angles of the doorways between the alley offer tactile stimuli. The form of the maze requires that the animal pass through each doorway as he reaches it. Traversing the alleys and turning the doors may therefore be controlled by tactile stimuli. But as the animal passes through each doorway he is confronted by the alternatives of a right or left turn with identical tactile situations at each side. These are the critical points in the maze, the most difficult for the normal animal to learn (7) and they offer no differential cutaneous cues.

2. The important proprioceptive systems for the maze habit are the vestibule and muscles of the neck, whose innervation through the first and second cervical nerves was spared in the cases studied. The great importance of these systems in postural adjustment has been shown by Magnus and Leeuwen (17) but our observations on the behavior of the rats in the maze do not bear out the assumption of especial importance of these systems for the maze habit. The tests in darkness seem especially significant here. When placed in a covered maze all the animals were markedly disturbed. They pushed against the cover, sniffed at the cloth, moved forward a few inches and repeated the exploration. In the first trials in the darkened maze the progress of all the animals could be traced by their continuous pushing at the flexible cover. This behavior does not indicate a disturbance of orientation, for it may be induced by placing a strip of cloth across the top of the maze without significantly modifying visibility of the path. It is an expression, rather, of the tendency of the rat to explore thoroughly any changed conditions in a familiar situation. The lack of real disturbances in orientation is illustrated by the record of number 7 who required thirty-five to fifty-five seconds for each of the first four trials in the darkened maze, yet without a single entry into a cul de sac. On the other hand, these exploratory movements of the head involve a continuous alteration of the pattern of stimulation from the vestibules and neck muscles which does not provide an adequate pattern for a proprioceptive motor chain. For, even if some of the original elements of the chain are retained, such as stereotyped movements of the head at the critical turns of the maze, there is required some mechanism by which these significant movements may be distinguished from the others with which they make up a continuous series. To say that the habit is carried out by utilization of these movements seems thus to beg the whole question since the significant movements can be elicited and effective for subsequent behavior only in case the animal is already oriented and this orientation can not be ascribed to the previous series of irregular movements of the head.

3. The proprioceptive paths of the cord are scattered in such a way

that a sufficient number of afferent impulses to control orientation may ascend through any part of the cord which happens to remain intact. It may be argued that, if the motor impulses can pass caudad over any intact area of the cord, the sensory impulses may likewise pass cephalad. Opposed to this interpretation are the very obvious disturbances in sensitivity to posture after section of the dorsal funiculus and the ataxic symptoms after section of the lateral funiculi; facts which suggest as definite a localization of afferent paths in the rat's cord as in that of higher forms. Evidence from the dog and monkey [see above] also suggests that sensory conduction in the cord is more definitely restricted than motor. Finally we have seen that, anatomically, the tracts are perfectly definite and the corresponding appearance of functional disturbances suggests as distinct a localization of afferent conduction paths as occurs in higher forms.

Thus, none of these three hypotheses seems admitted by the conditions of our experiments. The theory of chain-reflex arcs demands a continuity of adequate stimuli and a constancy of motor response which do not correspond to the observed facts. Marked reduction of proprioceptive sensitivity does not reduce accuracy of maze running although it results in motor disturbances sufficient to alter completely the pattern of motor activity. The hypothesis most in harmony with the facts seems to be one assuming that the successive activities of the maze habit are largely determined by central nervous activities. We are completely ignorant of the details of the mechanism implied here but may hazard some such guess as the following.

4. The engram of the maze habit consists of some central organization in which the general direction and succession of turns are so recorded that, once the series is initiated, the essential sequence of movements may be performed in the absence of sensory control and with considerable variation in the actual movements produced. This is, of course, a very vague statement and implies conceptions of plasticity in nervous functioning which run counter to the whole doctrine of conditioned reflexes, yet the problem seems at present to admit of no greater simplification.

The maze habit presents many complexities. There is clear evidence that the animals acquire some general orientation in addition to the habits of making particular turns and at present this orientation can only be described as an abstraction of a general direction from the diverse directions of the successive alleys. The variations which may occur in the motor pattern in traversing the maze, best illustrated by the disturbances following cerebellar lesions, point to a functional equivalence of motor activities similar to the transfer of motor habits to an unpracticed limb reported earlier (11, 12). It is not within the scope of the present paper to enter into a discusion of the problems suggested here. It must suffice that the maze habit involves intricacies which are not accounted for by any of the theories hitherto proposed, that it has common elements with the problems of rational learning and purposive acts, and that its analysis must await a better understanding of such complexities of behavior. Our present experiments serve only to emphasize the inadequacy of the chain-reflex theory of maze learning. Earlier work has shown the difficulty of interpreting the habit as a succession of reactions to exteroceptive cues. Our data indicate an exactly similar difficulty in basing the habit on proprioceptive ones.

DEFECTS OF THE GENERAL THEORY OF CHAIN REFLEXES

Attempts to explain behavior in terms of simple reflexes elaborated only by combination in chain-reflex arcs have proved of little value for an understanding of the more intricate problems of psychology and, where they have been tested by experiment, have received little factual support. Perhaps the simplest phase of the problem is that involved in the control of accuracy of movement. Are movements of definite extent or duration limited by the sensory components of the movements or by some preliminary central set which determines the limit of movement independently of sensory processes? In many cases the sensory processes obviously play a role in the control of accuracy, but it seems certain that such "current control" is not essential to accurate movement. Observations of Bowditch and Southard (2) on the comparative accuracy of visual and kinesthetic control, of Loeb (16) on the bilateral symmetry of movement, and of Woodworth (32) on the relation of speed to accuracy all indicate a relative independence of sensory control. Lashley (10) has shown that complete anesthesia to movement after lesion to the dorsal roots or spinal funiculus may not result in any disturbance in the accuracy of extent or duration of movements which are not opposed by external resistance.

The results of these studies seem explicable only on the assumption that the speed and extent of movement (intensity and duration of muscular innervation) may be determined in the initial set before any overt movement has actually occurred, and that "current control" enters in only when there is some departure from the conditions for which the initial adjustment was made.

Many swift sequences of movement, such as the execution of rapid musical passages, demand the same sort of explanation of control through the initial set. In sight reading of music it is often impossible to take in the individual notes and the player must learn to respond to groups of notes as does the reader to groups of letters or words. The effective stimulus is momentary yet determines the release of a series of movements in definite order and at such a rate that the initiation of each cannot be ascribed to the completion of the preceding.

The theory of maintenance of emotional status by proprioceptive excitations is not in better case. In the large number of studies of bodily changes in emotion there is not one established invariable correlation between muscular pattern and emotional state. On the contrary, the picture of motor changes during emotion is highly variable, in contrast to the relatively stable motivating effects of the emotions and there is at least as much reason to interpret facial and bodily expression in emotion as an actual "expression," determined in part as a social gesture and in part by chance irradiation of intense neural excitation (9) as to accept the hypotheses of James and Lange.

Finally, such experimental evidence as we have on the question of implicit movements in thinking (25) directly opposes the chain-reflex theory and suggests that, when implicit movements do occur, it is as a result of irradiation and not a part of the normal process of thinking.

The chief attractiveness of the chain-reflex theories lay in their promise that psychology might progress by simple objective methods and escape the need for indirect inference concerning neural complexities which could not be directly observed. The accumulation of evidence against the existence of the observable muscular contractions which can serve as a basis for the chain reflex forces us either to seek the completion of the reflex in action currents without observable muscular contraction (30), or to turn to the central nervous system for explanation of maintenance as well as coordination of activity. There is no direct evidence supporting the excitatory effects of such action currents and it will not be less difficult to disentangle the complex electrical phenomena of tonus and subliminal movement than to measure cerebral changes directly, so that the advantage of greater objectivity can not be claimed for the motor theory.

On the other hand, for the two simplest types of activity where the theory of chain reflexes might be expected to apply, the current control of movement and maze running, the evidence seems definitely to oppose the motor theory and to favor the existence of some wholly central mechanism as the determiner of the motor sequences.

Summary

Rats were trained in a maze with eight culs de sac and subjected to partial section of the spinal cord in the upper cervical region. A series of cases with complete interruption of the dorsal or lateral funiculus were obtained. The ability of the animals to traverse the maze was then tested. In spite of serious sensory disturbances, some animals with each type of lesion traversed the maze without significant errors after each type of lesion. Control experiments indicated that they did not fall back upon exteroceptive cues for orientation and that the persistence of the habit can not be referred to the remaining proprioceptive sensitivity. From this it is argued that the maze habit can not be interpreted as a series of kinesthetic-motor reflexes but must be referred to some intraneural mechanism capable of producing an integrated sequence of movements in the absence of directive sensory cues.

REFERENCES

1. Bechterew, W. v. Ueber die verschiedenen Lagen und Dimensionen der Pyramidenbahnen, usw., *Neurol. Zbl.*, 1890, 738–741.

2. Bowditch, H. P., and Southard, W. F. A comparison of sight and touch, *J. Physiol.*, 1881, **3**, 232–254.

3. Carr, H., and Watson, J. B. Orientation in the white rat, *J. comp. Neurol.*, 1908, **18**, 27–44.

4. Goldstein, K. Zur vergleichenden Anatomie der Pyramidenbahn, *Anat. Anz.*, 1904, **24**, 451–454.

5. Head, H. *Studies in neurology.* London: 1920.

6. Held, H. Der Ursprung des tiefen Markes der Vierhügelregion, *Neurol. Zbl.*, 1890, **9**, 481–483.

7. Hubbert, H. B., and Lashley, K. S. Retroactive association and the elimination of errors in the maze, *J. Anim. Behav.*, 1917, **7**, 130–138.

8. King, J. L. The cortico-spinal tract of the rat, *Anat. Rec.*, 1910, **4**, 245–252.

9. Landis, C. Studies of emotional reactions: II. General behavior and facial expression, *J. comp. Psychol.*, 1924, **4**, 447–511.

10. Lashley, K. S. The accuracy of movement in the absence of excitation from the moving organ, *Amer. J. Physiol.*, 1917, **43**, 169–194.

11. Lashley, K. S. Studies of cerebral function in learning: V. The retention of motor habits after the destruction of the so-called motor areas in primates, *Arch. Neurol. Psychiat.*, Chicago, 1924, **12**, 249–276.

12. Lashley, K. S. Studies of cerebral function in learning: VI. The theory that synaptic resistance is reduced by the passage of the nerve impulse, *Psychol. Rev.*, 1924, **31**, 369–375.

13. Lashley, K. S., and McCarthy, D. A. The survival of the maze habit after cerebellar injuries, *J. comp. Psychol.*, 1926, **6**, 423–433.

14. Lenhossek, M. von. Ueber die Pyramidenbahnen im Rückenmarke einiger Säugetiere, *Anat. Anz.*, 1889, **4**, 208–219.

15. Linowecki, A. J. The comparative anatomy of the pyramidal tract, *J. comp. Neurol.*, 1914, **24**, 509–530.

16. Loeb, J. Untersuchungen über den Fühlraum der Hand, *Arch. ges. Physiol.*, 1897, **41**, 107–127.

17. Magnus, R., and Leeuwen, W. S. v. Die akuten und die dauernden Folgen des Ausfalles der tonischen Hals- und Labyrinthreflexe, *Arch. ges. Physiol.*, 1914, **159**, 157–217, 224–249.

18. Mott, F. W. Results of hemisecting the spinal cord in monkeys, *Philos. Trans. roy. Soc.*, London, 1892, **183B**, 1–59.

19. Papez, J. W. The rubro-spinal tract, Marchi method, *Anat. Rec.*, 1923, **25**, 147.

20. Porter, W. T. The path of the respiratory impulse from the bulb to the phrenic nuclei, *J. Physiol.*, 1895, 17, 455–485.

21. Ranson, S. W. The fasciculus cerebrospinalis in the albino rat, *Amer. J. Anat.*, 1913, 14, 411–424.

22. Ranson, S. W. The tract of Lissauer and the substantia gelatinosa rolandi, *Amer. J. Anat.*, 1914, 16, 97–126.

23. Ranson, S. W. A note on the degeneration of the fasciculus cerebrospinalis in the albino rat, *J. comp. Neurol.*, 1914, 24, 503–507.

24. Sherrington, C. S. The spinal cord. In Schäfer's *Text-book of physiology*. London: 1898–1900. Vol. II. Pp. 783–883.

25. Thorson, A. M. The relation of tongue movements to internal speech, *J. exp. Psychol.*, 1925, 8, 1–32.

26. Van Der Vloet. Ueber den Verlauf der Pyramidenbahn bei niederen Säugetieren, *Anat. Anz.*, 1906, 29, 113–132.

27. Vincent, S. B. The white rat and the maze problem, *J. Anim. Behav.*, 1915, 5, 1–24, 140–157, 175–184, 367–374.

28. Watson, J. B. Kinaesthetic and organic sensations: their role in the reactions of the white rat to the maze, *Psychol. Rev.* (Monogr. Suppl.), 1907, 8, 1–100.

29. Watson, J. B. The place of kinaesthetic, visceral and laryngeal organization in thinking, *Psychol. Rev.*, 1924, 31, 339–348.

30. Watson, J. B. *Behaviorism*. New York: 1924–25.

31. Weiss, N. Untersuchungen über die Leitungsbahnen im Rückenmarke des Hundes, *Sitzungs. Akad. Wiss.*, Wien, 1879, 80 (Abt. 3), 340–356.

32. Woodworth, R. S. The accuracy of voluntary movement, *Psychol. Rev.* (Monogr. Suppl.), 1889, 3 (13), 1–114.

13. BASIC NEURAL MECHANISMS IN BEHAVIOR [1]

Among the systems and points of view which comprise our efforts to formulate a science of psychology, the proposition upon which there seems to be most nearly a general agreement is that the final explanation of behavior or of mental processes is to be sought in the physiological activity of the body and, in particular, in the properties of the nervous system. The tendency to seek all causal relations of behavior in brain processes is characteristic of the recent development of psychology in America. Most of our textbooks begin with an exposition of the structure of the brain and imply that this lays a foundation for a later understanding of behavior. It is rare that a discussion of any psychological problem avoids some reference to the neural substratum, and the development of elaborate neurological theories to "explain" the phenomena in every field of psychology is becoming increasingly fashionable.

In reading this literature I have been impressed chiefly by its futility. The chapter on the nervous system seems to provide an excuse for pictures in an otherwise dry and monotonous text. That it has any other function is not clear; there may be cursory references to it in later chapters on instinct and habit, but where the problems of psychology become complex and interesting, the nervous system is dispensed with. In more technical treatises the neurological explanations are made up mostly of assumptions concerning the properties of the nerve cell which have no counterpart in physiological experiment. Thus we find the superiority of distributed over concentrated practice seriously "explained" by the "fact" that successive passage of neural impulses over a synapse reduces its resistance least when the impulses come in quick succession.

There is no direct evidence for any function of the anatomical synapse: there is no evidence that synapses vary in resistance, or that, if they do, the resistance is altered by the passage of the nerve impulse. If the ex-

[1] EDITORS' NOTE: From *Psychol. Rev.*, 1930, 37, 1–24. Reproduced by permission of the American Psychological Association. From Behavior Research Fund, Chicago. Address of the President of the American Psychological Association before the Ninth International Congress of Psychology at New Haven, Conn., September 4, 1929.

planation is to be given in terms of established facts, as it must be, then it is limited to the following form: the superiority of distributed practice is due to the discontinuity of the neurons, the polarity of conduction, the fact of learning, and the superiority of distributed practice.

This is a typical case of the neurological explanations to be found in our psychological literature. With such conditions prevailing, it seems time to examine critically the relations between psychology and neurology and to attempt an evaluation of current notions concerning the mechanisms of the brain.

INADEQUACY OF CURRENT THEORIES

The starting point for our attempts to account for behavior in terms of nervous processes has been either the cerebral localization of functions or the theory that all nervous integration is patterned after the spinal reflex. I need scarcely point out the difficulties encountered by the older doctrine of cerebral localization. It expresses the fact that destruction of definite areas results in definite symptoms and the probable inference that these different parts have diverse functions, but it has given us no insight into the manner in which the areas or centers exercise their functions or the way in which they influence one another. It is only by applying psychological conceptions like that of association, or by turning to the theory of reflexes that the doctrine of localization is made to express the dynamic relations of behavior.

The extension of the theory of reflex conduction, first derived from studies of the spinal cord, to problems of cerebral function provided a welcome addition to the psychophysical doctrine of localization. It gave clear interpretation of localized areas as relay points or centers along the course of the reflex arc and seemed to explain the functional relations of the areas. However, the theory has not worked well in application to the details of behavior. To understand the difficulties we should have clearly in mind the form and limitations of the theory. It states that the mechanism of cerebral function is essentially the same as that of the spinal reflexes, involving the conduction of nerve impulses from the sense organs over definite, restricted paths to the effectors. The performance of a habit, whether of speech or of manipulative movement, is determined by the existence of definite connections between a limited number of nerve cells, which are always functional in that habit. The model for the theory is a telephone system. Just as two instruments can be connected only by certain wires, so the sense organs and muscles concerned in any act are connected by nerve fibers specialized for that act.

Perhaps few neurologists would agree to such a bare statement. They point to the incalculable number of nerve cells, the interplay of inhibition and facilitation, and suggest that in so complex a system there are limitless possibilities. But the fact remains that the essential feature of the reflex theory is the assumption that individual neurons are specialized for particular functions. The explanatory value of the theory rests upon this point alone, and no amount of hypothetical elaboration of connections alters the basic assumption.

Both the doctrines of localization and of conditioned reflexes imply the correspondence of structural and functional units—the specialization of minute areas or of single cells for definite limited functions. Recent experimental and clinical evidence seems to show that there is no such correspondence, and thus to present fatal difficulties to both theories. I shall sketch the main lines of this evidence, then turn to a consideration of other possible mechanisms.

Analysis of the Adequate Stimulus

The notion of the reflex arc was developed in studies of spinal preparations in which protopathic stimuli or muscle tensions are the chief sources of excitation. Under these simple conditions something like a point for point correspondence between receptor cells and muscle groups could be demonstrated, as in the case of the scratch reflex.

We first attempted the extension of this conception to instinctive behavior, on the assumption that the adequate stimulus to nursing, to the recognition of the mate or young, to the recognition of the nest site, to sexual excitement might be expressed in terms of the excitation of such and such receptor cells. This proved to be a vain hope. The adequate stimulus in such cases may be described in terms of a pattern having definite proportions but always, within wide limits, it is a matter of indifference to what receptor cells this pattern is applied.

A survey of various types of behavior shows that this is an almost universal attribute of the adequate stimuli (6). It is most obvious in pattern vision and can be demonstrated in animals with a rather primitive cortex. I have recently improved the technique for study of vision in the rat so that habits of pattern vision may be established in twenty or thirty trials. It is thus easy to test the equivalence of stimuli under conditions where previous associations are ruled out. Not only do we find transposition as Köhler has described it for chimpanzees, but even more striking equivalencies. An animal trained to discriminate patterns of solid white on a black ground is undisturbed by reversal of the brightness relations, by substitution of outlines for the solid figures, or even by partial outlines which retain some of the proportions of the original figures.

In many cases it is clear that the equivalent stimuli involve none of the retinal elements which were activated during learning. Here we have a situation where a habit is formed by the activation of one set of receptors and executed immediately upon stimulation of an entirely different and unpracticed group. The equivalence of stimuli is not due to the excitation of common nervous elements. The equivalent patterns have in common only ratios of intensity or of proportion in the spacial distribution of excited points. I might multiply examples of this sort indefinitely, but the studies of the Gestalt psychologists leave little doubt that such a condition is the rule for all stimuli with which we deal in the study of behavior.

Analysis of Reactions

Turning to motor activity, we are confronted by an identical problem. If we train an animal in a maze and observe carefully his subsequent errorless running, we find little identity of movement in successive trials. He gallops through in one trial, in another shuffles along, sniffing at the cover of the box. If we injure his cerebellum, he may roll through the maze. He follows the correct path with every variety of twist and posture, so that we cannot identify a single movement as characteristic of the habit (14).

I have earlier reported cases of the direct adaptive use in the performance of motor habits of limbs which were paralyzed throughout training and whose motor paths consequently could not have been exercised during training (11). It is not helpful to say that previously formed general habits are utilized in such performances, for the preexisting habits have not been associated with the new situation and the problem of the spontaneous association of the new patterns remains unsolved.

The problem of equivalence of motor responses has been less studied than that of equivalence of stimuli, but the phenomenon seems to be equally common. Activities ranging from the building of characteristic nests by birds to the so-called purposive activities of man show the absence of stereotyped movements in the attainment of a predetermined goal. The most familiar and most striking example is that of grammatical form in speech. Once we learn a new word, we use it in correct grammatical relations in limitless combinations with other words, without having to form new associations for each new setting.

It is only in certain acts of skill that stereotyped movements are recognizable and the uniformity of these is a result of long practice. We seem forced to conclude that the same motor elements are not necessarily used in the learning and performance of motor habits and that motor elements can be utilized directly when no specific associations have been formed with them.

Plasticity in Central Organization

Studies of the central nervous system give a similar picture. The functions are relatively independent of the structural elements. I can only cite a few of the lines of evidence, but sufficient, I believe, to establish the point.

First with respect to the specificity of conduction paths. The final motor neurons have been studied by Weiss (20). He grafted additional limbs on salamanders, cutting the nerve which supplied the original limb so that the regenerating fibers came to innervate both the original and the new limb. The two limbs innervated by the same nerve showed synchronization of movements in corresponding muscle groups. Histological examination showed that the axons of the original nerve had branched so that the muscles of the two limbs were supplied by fibers from the same axons. There is no selective outgrowth of regenerating fibers and the branches of the same axon do not necessarily go to corresponding muscles. It seems, then, that the coordination of the two limbs is not a function of the particular fibers which innervate each muscle, but is due to some property of the nerve impulse such that the same fiber can selectively elicit either of two antagonistic movements. These experiments are still the subject of controversy, but the objections raised against the results are not particularly impressive and, though they may raise some doubt of this conclusion, they certainly do not establish the specificity of the axon. The results of Weiss are in harmony with many facts revealed by the study of the central nervous system.

In work with injuries to the spinal cord Miss Ball and I (13) have found that orientation of the rat in the maze is undisturbed by interruption in the cervical cord of either the pyramidal, rubrospinal, or any other of the long descending tracts. The impulses controlling turning and threading the maze somehow get down the cord after the destruction of any half of the descending fibers. I have more recently been working with double hemisections of the cord. In these preparations one half of the cord is divided in the upper cervical region, the other half below the nucleus of the phrenic nerve, so that all the long fibers are interrupted above the motor centers for the limbs. After three months such preparations show coordinated movements in walking and are able to control the limbs for orientation in response to stimuli applied to the head. The control is established in spite of the permanent interruption of all the long spinal paths.

We have also been accumulating evidence upon the functions of the projection and association tracts of the cerebrum in the rat. The data are not yet complete, but it seems fairly certain that the interruption of the projection fibers to a part of a functional area produces far less pronounced symptoms than destruction of the cortical area supplied by those fibers. We have now a large number of cases in which linear lesions sever the connections between the different anatomical areas of the cortex or divide the association fibers within single areas. It is rare that any symptoms can be detected in such cases, unless there is involved a considerable destruction of cortical tissue. The most capable animal that I have studied was one in which the cortex and underlying association fibers had been divided throughout the length of each hemisphere. His IQ, based on ten tests, was 309.

In higher forms there is evidence for a somewhat greater specificity of long tracts in the central nervous system, but even in man the evidence is unequivocal only for the pyramidal system, which we have reason to believe is a part of the postural system and not especially concerned in the higher integrative functions of the brain, and for sensory paths of the cord. Although I would not venture the opinion that the association tracts of the cerebrum are a skeletal structure, there is certainly no direct evidence for the existence in them of any sharply defined reflex paths whose interruption results in the loss of isolated elementary functions.

What is the evidence that the cortex itself contains the definite specialized synapses which are demanded by the reflex theory? The data from extirpation experiments are somewhat ambiguous but, taken as a whole, fairly conclusive. Small lesions either produce no symptoms or very transient ones, so that it is clear that the mechanisms for habits are not closely grouped within small areas. When larger areas are involved, there are usually amnesias for many activities. Some of our experiments show that the degree of amnesia is proportional to the extent of injury and, within wide limits, independent of the location of the injury. This may mean that the cells differentiated for the habits are widely and uniformly scattered, or that there are no especially differentiated cells. After injuries to the brain, the rate of formation of some habits is directly proportional to the extent of injury and independent of the position within any part of the cortex. This shows that the rate of learning is not dependent upon the properties of individual cells, but is somehow a function of the total mass of tissue. Rate of change in individual synapses does not express the facts of learning unless we postulate some means by which the capacity for change in any cell is modified by the activity of all other cells of the cortex. Finally, when such habits have been formed after brain injury, their retention correlates with the amount of functional tissue. This can be interpreted only as evidence that memory is not a function of individual cells, but is a property of the total mass of tissue (12).

The reflex theory is not helpful for an understanding of such facts, nor do they seem consistent with it. If we consider the whole reaction, from sense organ to effector, the impossibility of a theory of specialized intercellular connections becomes apparent. Let us analyze a visual reaction, for here the anatomical localization of paths seems best established. The observations of Marie and Chatelin (15), and of Holmes and Lister (8) suggest a detailed projection of the retina upon the cortex, the macula represented in the posterior calcarine region, and successive radial zones along the borders of the fissure. (I am not sure that this interpretation is correct.) Poppelreuter (17), has pointed out that the forms of scotoma are not as varied as the manifold shapes of lesion should lead us to expect, and that all the forms of scotoma can be interpreted as radiating or converging disturbances of the functional balance within the entire area. (I have observations of a migraine scotoma in which the blind area retained a characteristic shape but drifted from the macula to the periphery of the visual field in the course of half an hour.) But granting a cortical retina, the problem of integration is only moved back a step. I have cited evidence to show that the retinal cells used in the formation of a habit need not be excited in order to reinstate the habitual response. This must be equally true, then, for the cortical retina. The same cells may not be twice called upon to perform the same function. They may be in a fixed anatomical relation to the retina, but the functional organization plays over them just as the pattern of letters plays over the bank of lamps in an electric sign.

We find then at the point of projection on the cortex a variable pattern shifting over a fixed anatomical substratum. How can this elicit a response from a definite set of motor cells? It can not do so by excitation over definite association paths, for there is evidence against the existence of such paths and, besides, there are no fixed points of origin for them. Nor is it certain that there are any fixed motor points. We have found in studies of the motor cortex that a point which will elicit a primary movement of the fingers on one day may, a week later, produce a movement of the shoulder and at another time even movements of the face (10). And the motor cortex, with its somewhat definite localization, is probably not concerned in habitual activity, anyway.

There does not seem to be a possibility of a constant anatomical localization at any point from receptor surface to effectors. Somehow the motor system must be sensitized to respond to the sensory patterns, but the phenomena cannot be expressed in terms of definite anatomical connections. This is the fundamental problem of neural integration and must serve as the starting point for any adequate theory of cerebral function.

The Doctrine of Circular Reflexes

An essential element of the reflex theory as applied to psychological problems is the doctrine that all the effects of stimulation are immediately observable in the motor systems. The James-Lange theory of emotion, the idea that mental attitudes are an expression of bodily postures or "sets," the theory that instincts and serial habits are chains of sensory-motor activity, the doctrine that implicit speech or gesture forms the basis of thinking: these are all expressions of the belief that the nervous system serves merely for the rapid switching and conduction of impulses from receptor to effector, without long-continued intraneural sequences of activity. This notion has been attractive, as offering a possibility of direct objective study of mental activity, but attempts to verify it experimentally have given disappointingly negative results.

The problem of emotion is still in such confusion that one can draw no conclusions with confidence, but the accumulation of evidence upon the variability of expressive reactions and the repeated failure to find any consistent correlations between bodily changes and either exciting situations or reported subjective states lends little support to the visceral theory.

On the question of maintained attitude or set we have some recent evidence which seems significant. Studying the influence of bodily posture upon the movements elicited by stimulation of the motor cortex Dr. Jacobsen and I mapped the motor area and selected for study a point giving extension of the fingers. We changed the posture of the limbs, head, and body of the preparation, stimulated muscles and nerve points electrically and in other ways sought to alter the conditions of peripheral stimulation. The excitability of the point was unaltered by this treatment and the same movement was elicited at five-minute intervals for two hours. We then altered the excitability of the point by stimulation of another distant point, changing the primary movement from extension to flexion. This new primary movement persisted for fifty-five minutes in spite of repeated changes in the posture of the animal, then reverted spontaneously to the original movement of extension. The experiment suggests that the pattern of organization of the motor cortex can be altered by central excitation and that the altered condition can be maintained for long periods without reinforcement from peripheral organs. It seems to fulfill the conditions for demonstration of a centrally maintained attitude.

Miss Ball and I have tested the effects on serial habits of sectioning the afferent paths of the cord, together with removal of all external directive clues after the animal is oriented in the starting box. Under these conditions the habits are run off without disturbance. With external and internal sensory cues eliminated it seems that the series of acts must be controlled by some wholly central mechanism.

The work of Thorson on tongue movements (19) and unpublished observations on eye movements during thinking, together with reports of the recovery of speech with use of an artificial larynx, oppose the doctrine of the completed reflex and point to some continued intraneural process as the basis of thinking. The weight of evidence, I believe, favors the view that in emotion, in all persistence of attitudes, in all serial activity there are continuously maintained central processes which, if they become intense, may irradiate to motor centers and produce expressive movements, implicit speech, and the like. The pattern of irradiation varies from subject to subject according to chance variations in the excitability of the motor or vegetative nervous systems, and peripheral activities are not an essential condition for the maintenance of the central processes.

I have devoted so much time to criticism of the reflex theory of behavior because it seems to be deeply rooted in our thinking and to have had an important influence in the development of almost every phase of psychology. It has been valuable in counteracting certain trends toward vitalism and mysticism, but I believe that it is now becoming an obstacle rather than a help to progress. In the youth of a science there is virtue in simplifying the problems so that some sort of decisive experiments may be formulated, but there is a danger that oversimplification will later blind us to important problems. In the study of cerebral functions we seem to have reached a point where the reflex theory is no longer profitable either for the formulation of problems or for an understanding of the phenomena of integration. And if it is not serviceable here, it can scarcely be of greater value for an understanding of the phenomena of behavior.

THE ALTERNATIVE TO THE REFLEX THEORY

What is the alternative to the doctrine of the specialization of nervous elements for definite reactions? It is possible that the modes of organization in the brain are not less numerous and diverse than the types of behavior to which they give rise. We have little direct evidence as to the nature of these central processes, but can deduce some laws from the effects of cerebral injury which may point the way to the significant investigations of the future.

Dynamic Aspects of Localization

Specialization of functions in the cerebral cortex is an indisputable fact, but we have yet to find an adequate interpretation of it. We have asked, Where are psychological functions localized in the brain? and have gained a meaningless answer. We should ask, How do specialized areas produce the details of behavior with which they are associated: what are the functional relationships between the different parts and how are they maintained?

Variable Degrees of Localization. If we survey the disturbances produced by brain injuries in a wide range of activities we are forced to the conclusion that the accuracy of localization or the degree of specialization varies greatly. Definitely limited defects appear in the visual and tactile and to a lesser extent in the motor fields after limited lesions to the calcarine, postcentral, and precentral gyri. In other sensory spheres and in all the more elaborate organizations of behavior, there is little evidence for an equal fineness of differentiation. The visual cortex probably represents the maximum of specialization of small units. In the somesthetic field there is also a cortical projection, but less finely differentiated. In other functions we find every degree of specialization up to the limit where all parts of the cortex participate equally in the same function. The latter is apparently the condition for the maze habit in the rat. Destruction of any part of the cortex produces a partial loss of the habit and equal amounts of destruction produce equal amounts of loss, regardless of locus within the cortex.

An area which is highly specialized for one function may play a more generalized role in another. The habit of brightness discrimination in the rat is abolished by injury to the area striata, and by injury to no other part of the cortex. Here is a clear case of specialization. But the maze habit is abolished by destruction of this same area or of any other of equal size. Is it because the maze habit is dependent on vision? No, for blinding trained animals does not affect the habit, whereas destruction of the area striata abolishes the habit in animals which were blind during training. The deterioration does not differ in any observable way from that following lesions to other parts of the brain.

Except in projection areas there is no evidence for anatomical specialization within the general areas of localization. Thus in the aphasias showing predominantly a loss of naming ability or of memory for words there is not a selective effect upon memories for specific words, but a general difficulty of recall which embraces all words of a functional group.

The evidence on localization suggests that where the relations of stimuli in space are of importance for behavior, there exists in the cortex a spacial distribution of points corresponding to the sensory surfaces, but that for all other functions a similar spacial arrangement is lacking. In terms of the reflex theory such a spacial arrangement has little meaning, but in terms of the hypothesis to which I am leading it is of prime importance.

Functional Levels of Organization. Turning to the dynamics of localization, we find that loss or partial loss of functions may find expression in various ways. In some cases it seems that the fundamental organization for a function has been very little disturbed but that the ease of arousal is markedly altered. Thus in monkeys and probably in man, the severity of cerebral paralysis varies somewhat with the current emotional state, and during great excitement the power of voluntary movement may be temporarily restored. The paralysis seems to consist of a greater or lesser difficulty in initiating movements, whose organization is undisturbed (16). The emotional facilitation can restore the capacity for movement. It clearly does not supply the specific integrations but only makes the final common paths more excitable or increases the intensity of activity in the integrating mechanisms. Here we have the energy for activity supplied, as it were, from an outside source. Some of the symptoms of cerebellar ataxia and the conditions described as pure motor aphasia present the same sort of picture. I have used the term energy here with reluctance, for the notion of nervous energy has led to many extravagant speculations, yet it seems impossible to deal with such phenomena except in terms of some general factor which may influence the ease of functioning of a system of activities without changing the specific integrations.

In another type of quantitative reduction in efficiency, the integrative mechanism itself seems affected, but without disintegration into elementary functions. In the rat, destruction of the occipital cortex abolishes the habit of brightness discrimination in the Yerkes box. Brightness vision is actually undisturbed, as can be demonstrated by other methods, but the association with the specific activities of the training box is disturbed. The amount of practice necessary to reestablish the association is closely proportional to the extent of lesion. Here we are dealing with some function akin to the memory trace of Ebbinghaus. Just as the memory trace grows weaker with the passage of time, so it is weakened by cerebral injury. Recall may be impossible, yet a persisting trace of the former training may be demonstrated by the "savings method." The strength of the trace is determined by the quantity of tissue. The efficiency of performance is determined by the summated action of all parts of the area.

We cannot here use the accepted theories of summation or reinforcement, for these theories are based upon the phase relations of nerve impulses and we seem to be dealing with a continuous summation. It seems impossible to express the facts in other terms than simple variation in energy.

The Relative Fragility of Functions. I have pointed out that the same area may be involved in quite diverse functions. These may be differently affected by lesions. Thus the habit of threading a complex maze is seriously disturbed by destruction of any part of the cortex, provided the lesion involves more than 15 per cent. The habit of a simpler maze is unaffected by lesions involving as much as 50 per cent of the cortex. We do not have an extensive series of tests with different mazes, but a comparison of Cameron's cases (1) with my own indicates that there is a definite relationship between the complexity of the maze habit and the minimal lesion which will produce a measurable disturbance of it.

Dr. Jacobsen has similar evidence from experiments with monkeys.[2] Animals were trained to open a series of simple puzzle boxes and also a box in which the latches of the simple boxes were combined. After destruction of the frontal or parietal lobes, the ability to open the simple boxes was retained, but the same latches in combination could not be opened.

[2] To be reported in *J. comp. Neurol.* [1931, **52**, 271–340.]

We have similar results on the limits of training for both the rat and monkey. Simple problems may be learned at almost normal rate after brain injuries; complex problems are learned slowly, if at all. Further, the greater the brain injury, the greater is the disproportion between the learning of simple and complex habits. In such cases the brain injuries seem to limit the complexity of organization which may be acquired, without disturbing the capacity for the simple acts which are mediated by the same areas.

The clinical literature presents many comparable cases. The aphasic patient may be able to understand and execute simple commands and yet be unable to grasp the same instructions when several are given at the same time. Head cites numerous instances of this limitation in complexity of organization (7). In pattern vision, the stages through which the patient passes during recovery from cortical blindness form a series with respect to complexity. It seems probable that the great fragility of color vision and of the perception of depth is due to the high degree of organization required for these functions, rather than to their separate localization in the cortex.

Both the animal experiments and the clinical material point to the conclusion that a given area may function at different levels of complexity, and lesions may limit the complex functions without disturbing the simpler ones. Further, we cannot ascribe this limitation to the loss of some necessary elementary functions or to disturbances of nutrition or to shock, for it has been shown in some cases to be solely a function of the quantity of tissue. In this respect the limitation of complexity seems to accord with Spearman's view (18) that intelligence is a function of some undifferentiated nervous energy.

The Relational Framework in Cerebral Function

Let us turn now to another important aspect of cerebral function. A review of symptoms suggests that no logically derived element of behavior can be shown to have a definite localization; no single sensation, memory, or skilled movement is destroyed alone by any lesion. On the contrary the various parts of the functional areas seem equipotential for such elements, and either a whole constellation of them is affected by the lesion, or none at all. In these constellations of activities the grouping is determined, not by associative bonds, but by similarities of organization. Let me illustrate this point. In an hysterical amnesia we may find a loss of memory for all events associated with some emotional experience. The constellation is here determined by the grouping of habits. In organic amnesias the grouping is quite different. The speech most commonly retained in aphasia is that related to emotional expression, as was pointed out by Hughlings Jackson. Ejaculations, words of affirmation or negation, profanity, and words having a deep personal significance make up the residual vocabulary. The determining factor here seems to be the relation to emotional facilitation. Head's work shows other groupings, the loss of words involving the object-name relation, or of those concerned with the relations of space, time, and logical order (7). The defects can in every case be related to ways of thinking about things, but not to loss of specific associations.

Many disturbances of vision show the same characteristics. An apparent word-blindness, for example, may be due, not to a loss of visual memory for the words, but to an inability to see the letters in a definite spacial arrangement.

Even in experiments with animals there are suggestions of similar conditions. We find rather frequently a picture which suggests loss of the general sense of direction, with retention of associations with the specific turns in the maze.

I have not time to multiply examples, but I believe that there is ample evidence to show that the units of cerebral functions are not single reactions, or conditioned reflexes as we have used the term in America, but are modes of organization. The cortex seems to provide a sort of generalized framework to which single reactions conform spontaneously, as the words fall into the grammatical form of a language.

The Mutual Influence of Cerebral Activities

Every statement concerning independence of functions must be made with certain reservations. The early students of aphasia, using the crudest of examining methods, were able to identify a great variety of types involving entirely different defects in the use of language. More careful study of the aphasias with finer methods of examination has failed to reveal such clear-cut distinctions, and today we have no accepted classification of the aphasias. Marie concluded that all types are the result of a common intellectual defect. Head denies that the intellectual defect is primary but admits that in all cases intellect suffers to the extent that it employs symbolism in thinking. All investigators seem now agreed that the disturbance of speech is only one symptom of a disorder which can be traced through the whole fabric of thought.

This is typical of recent developments in the clinical field. With improvement in methods of examination, the complete isolation of functions becomes more and more questionable, until it seems as though disturbance in any function implies lesser, but recognizable, changes in every other.

This interdependence is not merely an expression of the subtraction of elementary functions by brain injuries. It seems to involve a genuine fusion of different processes, such as is shown in the observations of

Poppelreuter (17) on the "totalizing function" of the visual area, and those of Gelb on the mutual influence of normal and hemiamblyopic areas. Poppelreuter reports the completion of simple figures in the cortically blind field, much like the normal filling in of the blind spot. Gelb (5) describes a case in which objects were judged smaller when seen in one half of the visual field than when seen in the other. When exposed so as to include both fields they were judged intermediate in size. Evidently in such cases as this there is fusion rather than summation of elements.

Self-regulation in Neural Function

This unity of action seems to be more deeply rooted than even the structural organization. In working with animals and with human patients I have been more and more impressed by the absence of the chaotic behavior which we might expect from the extent and irregular form of the lesions. There may be great losses of sensory or of motor capacities, amnesias, emotional deterioriation, dementia—but the residual behavior is still carried out in an orderly fashion. It may be grotesque, a caricature of normal behavior, but it is not unorganized. There are certain apparent exceptions to this rule, such as the loss of control of laughter in certain thalamic and lenticular cases, jargon in aphasia, the loss of spacial organization in some cases of visual agnosia, but even here the disturbances are not chaotic. Even dementia is not wholly unintelligent. It involves reduction in the range of comprehension, in the complexity of the relations which may be perceived, but what falls within the patient's range is still dealt with in an orderly and intelligible fashion.

There seems always to be a certain spontaneous compensation or adaptive reorganization. The most definite example of this sort is the observations of Fuchs (4) on pseudofovea. He finds that in cases of complete hemianopsia there is a shift of the center of fixation from the anatomical fovea to a variable point in the peripheral retina which acquires a greater visual acuity than can be demonstrated in the anatomical macula.

Such phenomena suggest that the nervous system is capable of a self-regulation which gives a coherent logical character to its functioning, no matter how its anatomical constituents may be disturbed. If we could slice off the cerebral cortex, turn it about, and replace it hind side before, getting a random connection of the severed fibers, what would be the consequences for behavior? From current theories we could predict only chaos. From the point of view which I am suggesting we might expect to find very little disturbance of behavior. Our subject might have to be reeducated, perhaps not even this, for we do not know the locus or character of habit organization—but in the course of his reeducation he might well show a normal capacity for apprehending relationships and for the rational manipulation of his world of experience.

This may sound like a plunge into mysticism, but an example from another field will show that such self-regulation is a normal property of living things. Wilson and later Child (3) have crushed the tissues of sponges and hydroids, sifted the cells through sieves of bolting cloth and observed their later behavior. The cells are at first suspended independently in the water, but may be brought into aggregates by settling or centrifuging. Starting as flat sheets, they round up into spherical masses and begin differentiation. Embryonic stages may be simulated and eventually adult individuals with characteristic structures, mouth, hypostome, tentacles, and stalk in normal relative positions are produced. In spite of the abnormal conditions to which it is subjected, the formless mass of cells assumes the structure characteristic of the species. Of course many abnormal forms appear, but even these follow the characteristic scheme of organization.

Many lines of evidence show a close parallelism between the facts of morphogenesis and those of the organization of the nervous system. In both we have given as the fundamental fact an organization which is relatively independent of the particular units of structure and dependent upon the relationships among the parts. In both there is a capacity for spontaneous readjustment after injury, so that the main lines of organization are restored; in both there is evidence that every part may influence every other; in both there is a possibility of dissociation and independent activity of some parts.

The Mechanisms of Organization

This brings us to the question of the mechanisms by which organization of behavior is brought about. There is, I think, nothing mysterious about the problem. There is no need to assume an emergence of new properties, a transcendent influence of the whole upon the parts, a subordination of substance to form, or the like; there is certainly no need to look for nonphysical agencies. We are dealing with a complex system in which there is an influence of every part upon every other, with all degrees of intimacy in the relations and various degrees of dominance and subordination. Our problem is to discover the means by which these influences are exerted.

We have seen that the notion of isolated reflex paths, exerting mutual inhibition and facilitation and conducting nervous impulses over pathways determined by the specific resistance of synapses, is not only inadequate to account for the simplest facts of behavior, but is also opposed by direct neurological evidence. The greatest progress in neurophysiology within the past decade has been made in the study of conduction in peripheral nerves, but the results have as yet little bearing upon the problems of central organization. At most they offer a basis for speculation concerning the behavior of nerve impulses at intercellular junctions, and recent negative results upon conduction with decrement throw some doubt upon the value of these speculations. Students of nerve conduction have taken for granted the doctrine of anatomical specialization, and their work has not been developed, in the direction of our problems. Lapicque (9) has recently pointed out some of the difficulties of the anatomical hypothesis and has suggested the substitution of temporal for spacial factors in organization, but the study of chronaxie is not far enough advanced for application to the problems of psychology. The laws of conduction in nerve fibers thus far revealed are not alone sufficient for an understanding of integration. The nervous unit of organization in behavior is not the reflex arc, but the mechanism, whatever be its nature, by which a reaction to a ratio of excitations is brought about. We have as yet no direct evidence upon this problem, but the similarities of the problems of nervous function and of growth should direct our interest toward the processes which have been found important in the control of structural development.

The work of many students of experimental embryology has shown the importance of the restriction of gaseous interchange, of gradients in chemical diffusion, metabolic activity or rate of growth, the influences of chemical and electrical polarization and of the flow of action currents in determining the course of development. During its first differentiation the nervous system is subject to the same influences as any other developing tissue and the mechanisms of diffusion and of polarization play an important role in the determination of its structures and inherent organization. It would be strange if, with the completion of growth, these factors should no longer be important in the life of the cells. Rather, we should expect the neurons to be continuously modified by the same influences. The structure of the nervous system is such as to allow of this. The interconnections of distant parts are well insulated, where correlated functions without influence of intermediate parts is required, but within the gray matter the cell bodies and processes are not so protected. They are directly exposed in a liquid medium capable of conducting diffuse chemical and electrical changes which may readily influence the excitability of the neurons. The arrangement of the gray matter in thin sheets and the projection of the receptor and motor surfaces upon these sheets may have a real functional significance. Child (2) has shown that distance of separation favors the development of independently polarized systems, and the arrangement of cell bodies in the gray matter offers the optimal condition for this and for the development of systems in which the spacial arrangement of stresses can be effective. Although the distant intercommunications of cells may be solely through the conduction of nerve impulses, the more immediate coordinations within the gray matter may depend upon relative amounts of excitation, the spacial arrangement of excited points, stress patterns resulting from the total mass of excitation, which may be more important for behavior than the connections of individual cells. It is here, I believe, that we must look for the next significant development in our knowledge of the functions of the brain.

Cerebral organization can be described only in terms of relative masses and spacial arrangements of gross parts, of equilibrium among the parts, of direction and steepness of gradients, and of the sensitization of final common paths to patterns of excitation. And the organization must be conceived as a sort of relational framework into which all sorts of specific reactions may fit spontaneously, as the cells of the polyp fit into the general scheme of development.

Such notions are speculative and vague, but we seem to have no choice but to be vague or to be wrong, and I believe that a confession of ignorance is more hopeful for progress than a false assumption of knowledge.

Conclusion

I have devoted my time tonight to problems which are not strictly psychological, yet I believe that these problems are of real significance for the progress of psychology. Certainly the development of the science up to the present has been strongly influenced by neurological theory. The frantic search for sources of motivation and of emotion in visceral activity, though initiated by introspective analysis, has been supported by the faith that the nervous system is only a conductor having no sources of energy within itself. Our preoccupation with analysis of learning by trial and error, the denial of association by similarity, the belief that transfer of training can occur only through the training of common synapses—these are a result of the belief that learning is simply a linking together of elementary reflexes. The doctrine that the intelligent solution of problems results only through random activity and selection, and that intelligence itself is an algebraic sum of multitudinous capacities, is largely a deduction from the reflex theory.

I shall not pretend to evaluate such doctrines from the standpoint of psychological evidence. They may or may not be true, but their truth must be demonstrated by experiment and cannot be assumed on a background of questionable neurology. Psychology is today a more fundamental science than neurophysiology. By this I mean that the latter offers few principles from which we may predict or define the normal organization of behavior, whereas the study of psychological processes furnishes

208 THE NEUROPSYCHOLOGY OF LASHLEY

a mass of factual material to which the laws of nervous action in behavior must conform.

The facts of both psychology and neurology show a degree of plasticity, of organization, and of adaptation in behavior which is far beyond any present possibility of explanation. For immediate progress it is not very important that we should have a correct theory of brain activity, but it is essential that we shall not be handicapped by a false one.

The value of theories in science today depends chiefly upon their adequacy as a classification of unsolved problems, or rather as a grouping of phenomena which present similar problems. Behaviorism has offered one such classification, emphasizing the similarity of psychological and biological problems. Gestalt psychology has stressed a different aspect and reached a different grouping; purposive psychology still another. The facts of cerebral physiology are so varied, so diverse, as to suggest that for some of them each theory is true, for all of them every theory is false.

REFERENCES

1. Cameron, N. Cerebral destruction in its relation to maze learning, Psychol. Monogr., 1928, 39 (1), 1–68.
2. Child, C. M. Studies on the axial gradients in Corymorpha palma: III. Biol. Generalis, 1926, 2, 771–798.
3. Child, C. M. Axial development in aggregates of dissociated cells from Corymorpha palma, Physiol. Zool., 1928, 1, 419–461.
4. Fuchs, W. Untersuchungen über das Sehen der Hemianopiker und Hemiamblyopiker. In Gelb and Goldstein (5).
5. Gelb, A., and Goldstein, K. Psychologische Analysen hirnpathologischer Fälle. Leipzig: Barth, 1920.
6. Goldstein, K. Die Topik der Grosshirnrinde in ihrer klinischen Bedeutung, Dtsch. Z. Nervenheilk., 1923, 77, 7–124.
7. Head, H. Aphasia and kindred disorders of speech. New York: 1926.
8. Holmes, G., and Lister, W. T. Disturbances of vision from cerebral lesions with special reference to the macula, Brain, 1916, 39, 34–73.
9. Lapicque, L. The chronaxic switching in the nervous system, Science, 1929, 70, 151–154.
10. Lashley, K. S. Temporal variation in the function of the gyrus precentralis in primates, Amer. J. Physiol., 1923, 65, 585–602.
11. Lashley, K. S. The theory that synaptic resistance is reduced by the passage of the nerve impulse, Psychol. Rev., 1924, 31, 369–375.
12. Lashley, K. S. Brain mechanisms and intelligence. Chicago: Univ. of Chicago Press, 1929.
13. Lashley, K. S., and Ball, J. Spinal conduction and kinesthetic sensitivity in the maze habit, J. comp. Psychol., 1929, 9, 70–106.
14. Lashley, K. S., and McCarthy, D. A. The survival of the maze habit after cerebellar injuries, J. comp. Psychol., 1926, 6, 423–433.
15. Marie, P., and Chatelin, C. Les troubles visuels dus aux lésions des voies

optiques intracérébrales et de la sphère visuelle corticale dans les blessures du crâne par coup de feu, *Rev. neurol.*, 1914–15, **28**, 882–925.

16. Minkowski, H. Etude physiologique des circonvolutions rolandiques et pariétales, *Arch. Suisse neurol. psychiat.*, 1917, **1**, 389–459.

17. Poppelreuter, W. *Die psychischen Schädigungen durch Kopfschuss.* Leipzig: 1917.

18. Spearman, C. *The abilities of man.* New York: 1927.

19. Thorson, A. M. The relation of tongue movements to internal speech, *J. exp. Psychol.*, 1925, **8**, 1–32.

20. Weiss, P. Die Funktion transplantierter Amphibienextremitäten, *Arch. mik. Anat.*, 1924, **52**, 645–672.

14. THE MECHANISM OF VISION.

I. A Method for Rapid Analysis of Pattern-vision in the Rat [1]

Our knowledge of the character of vision in mammals below the primates is fragmentary and uncertain. Experimental studies have been limited to the carnivora and rodentia and the results which they have given, especially in the studies of pattern-vision, are at variance both with the popular notion of vision in these animals and with what we should expect from the high degree of differentiation of the optic systems.

The existing studies give little evidence that the rodents are sensitive to visual patterns. Yerkes (8) and Waugh (7) were unable to establish a differential reaction in mice to visual patterns. Lashley (3) succeeded in training rats to distinguish between horizontal and vertical lines, but failed to get discrimination of other patterns. Fields (1, 2) obtained discrimination of an upright and inverted triangle in the rat, but the significance of this as evidence of pattern-vision has been questioned by Munn (5), who found that Fields' apparatus presented differences in size of the stimulus objects and who could not demonstrate discrimination when this element was controlled. During the past ten years I have trained six groups of rats for pattern-vision with various modifications of the discrimination box, continuing training for five hundred or more trials, but always with negative results.

All of this work has been done with some form of the discrimination box and Fields has raised the question whether the failure to gain evidence of pattern-vision may not have been due to a defect in the method rather than visual defects of the animals. During the past summer I hit upon a method for testing vision in the rat which confirms Fields' criticisms and reveals a capacity of the rat to discriminate visual patterns which is little inferior to that of primates. The results of the method call for a revision of our ideas of vision in lower mammals and offer possibilities for the study of many problems in the physiology of vision.

[1] EDITORS' NOTE: From *J. genet. Psychol.*, 1930, **37**, 453–460. Reproduced by permission of The Journal Press. Studies from the Institute for Juvenile Research, ser. B, no. 157, Chicago. Herman M. Adler, M.D., director.

The essential feature of the method is that it requires the animal to jump against the stimulus patterns from a distance, instead of to run past them, as in the discrimination box. A form of apparatus which has proved satisfactory is shown in Fig. 14.1. It consists of a screen of three-ply pine, 3 by 5 feet, having two square holes 5.5 inches (L and R) cut at a convenient height. The openings are at the same level and spaced two inches apart. Attached to the back of the screen, ¼ inch below the lower edges of the openings, is a platform FP 12 inches wide which serves as a landing platform when the rat jumps through one of the openings. A circular stand S is placed with the nearest edge 25 cm.[2] in front of the middle of the screen, and the animals are trained to jump from the stand through the holes to the platform FP where food is placed. A projecting sheet of metal M serves to deflect the rat through the openings in case he jumps too high and a net N catches him in case of a fall. The screen is painted black.

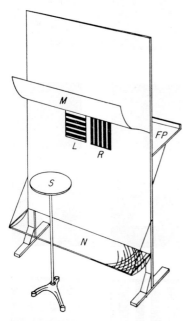

The openings are closed with squares of heavy cardboard upon which the patterns to be discriminated are drawn or pasted. The cards are 6 inches square and stiff enough to resist the impact of a heavy animal. They are held in place against the back of the screen by inserting the lower edge in a shallow groove in the food-platform and fixing the top either by a rigid turn-button or by a light spring. In training, one card, bearing the negative stimulus, is fixed rigidly; the other is held by the spring so that when the rat jumps against it the card falls back and allows him to reach the platform.

Fig. 14.1. Apparatus used for testing discrimination of visual patterns. For explanation see text.

[2] The eye of the rat, both albino and wild, is, contrary to Vincent's statements (6), very myopic. The most distant adaptation is about 8 cm. and occasionally a still more near-sighted individual has been observed. Nevertheless, the depth of focus is great and the eye forms fairly distinct images even of distant objects. The evidence for these statements will be presented in a later study of the structure and resolving power of the eye. Since the longer jump seems more effective for the formation of habits of discrimination, it has been adopted for the majority of tests. For questions like the relation of visual acuity to retinal structure, distances within the focal range have been used.

I have usually trained the animals by placing the stand against the screen and allowing the animals to step through the open holes to the platform, then gradually withdrawing the stand until, in ten to fifteen trials, the distance of 25 cm. is reached. Cards are then placed in position and training in discrimination begun.

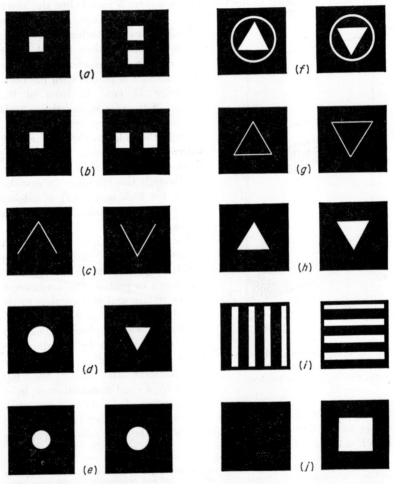

Fig. 14.2. Pairs of patterns between which rats have been trained to discriminate. The cards bearing the patterns are 6 inches square. The patterns are drawn to scale.

Efficiency of the Method

Errorless discrimination of each of the pairs of patterns represented in Fig. 14.2 has been obtained with relatively little practice, using pigmented animals. In comparison with results of training by the discrimination box, the method is extremely rapid. Table 14.1 compares the rates for learning

Table 14.1. Comparison of the Efficiency of the Method of Jumping with the Discrimination Box in the Establishment of the Same Habits in the Rat

Stimuli	Author	Discrimination box °		Jumping †		No. cases
		Trials	Errors	Trials	Errors	
Black vs. white	Lashley (4)	128	42	4.3	0.7	33
Horizontal vs. vertical lines	Lashley (3)	260	98	27.0	6.0	10
Size of circles	Lashley (3)	350–700		37.5	6.5	4
Triangles (H, Fig. 14.2)	Fields (1,2)	600+		28.6	7.8	6

° Figures represent practice to establish a record of 85 per cent correct choices.
† [Figures represent] a record of 100 per cent correct.

of different visual problems which have been tested with both the discrimination box and the jumping method. With the discrimination box a consistent errorless record for pattern discrimination has never been obtained. The figures given, except for black-white discrimination, represent the practice required to reach an accuracy of 80 to 85 per cent, which is actually little better than chance. The records for the jumping method represent practice preceding thirty or more successive errorless trials, which under most conditions is predictive of permanent accuracy.

The variety of discriminations which the rat can make seems almost unlimited, and the directness of adaptation is surprising. Almost all normal animals jump for the single white square (Fig. 14.2*j*) without training and several have chosen the horizontal lines in preference to the vertical (Fig. 14.2*i*) with no error. Direct transfer, as from (*h*) to (*c*) or (*g*), is the rule for similar patterns. Of the patterns tested, (*f*), (*b*), and (*d*) seem to present the greatest difficulties for the animals.

Validity of the Method

The marked difference in results attained by this and by previous methods calls for a careful analysis of the method for possible nonvisual cues. The apparatus itself seems to provide against the common sources of error. The screen framing the patterns is fixed and offers no cues as to the right or left position of the fixed card. The cards fit closely against the back of the screen, the room behind is dimly lighted, and the screen is observed by reflected light, so that leakage of light, so difficult to control in the discrimination box, is ruled out.

Most of the cards bearing the pairs of patterns are interchangeable by rotation, so that either card may be used to present the positive or negative pattern. Neither this change nor the substitution of new cards has ever disturbed discrimination. The animal must choose between the cards while at least 20 cm. from them. Thus tactile and olfactory cues are effectually ruled out.

There remains only the possibility of cues from the behavior of the experimenter. In training series, the experimenter sets the cards while the rat eats, then tosses it around the right side of the screen to the stand, and steps back behind the screen where he remains, ignorant of the animal's actions, until it leaps against the screen. I have varied this procedure in many ways but have not succeeded in disturbing the accuracy of discrimination. The following formal tests of the validity of the method have been made.

1. Two rats which had served in a long series of tests, each making more than a thousand correct discriminations of various patterns, were blinded by enucleation of the eyes. Before the operation their average time for jumping after return to the stand was less than two seconds. After blinding, neither could be induced to jump. If the stand were placed near the screen they would step through the openings, so long as these were in reach of vibrissae and not closed by cards. With the cards in place the edges of the openings seemed not to be identified. With the stand beyond reach of the screen the animals reached out in every direction but were completely disoriented with respect to the position of the screen. They were tested at frequent intervals for a month after operation. During this time one of them jumped once, after much urging, and missed the screen entirely.

2. The openings were closed with fresh white cards, held only by the springs. The room was darkened and patterns (h) and (i) of Fig. 14.2 projected on the cards from a lantern placed above and behind the stand. Four animals previously trained with these patterns painted on the cards were tested. Each made no error in twenty trials.

3. Two animals trained on triangles (h) were tested by an assistant who did not know which of the patterns had been positive during training and who set both cards with the spring. No errors were made in these tests.

4. Animals trained with lines (i) were returned to the home cage during each setting of the cards and the experimenter hastened from the

room after tossing them to the stand. No errors were made in these tests. . . .

In general, no change in the routine of training or in the nonvisual elements of the situations has produced any disturbance in the accuracy of discrimination. On the other hand, any change in the visual pattern results in long hesitation, or inaccurate responses, and only chance scores are obtained with cards bearing identical patterns.

Finally, the most conclusive evidence that the discriminations are based upon visual pattern is the consistent character of the results obtained in tests for thresholds and for central nervous functions. All pigmented animals trained with striations of variable width (Fig. 14.2i) fail to discriminate when the lines are reduced to a width subtending about 57' of arc at 25 cm. With a shorter jumping distance these same lines are discriminated. With finer lines training to 300 trials does not improve the score above chance. Animals with destruction of the lateral geniculate bodies will not jump. Those with extensive lesions in the area striata jump but do not discriminate patterns. Albinos have a lesser acuity than pigmented animals, as measured by reactions to patterns, and acuity corresponds closely to the resolving power of the eye, measured directly.

It will now be profitable to discuss the nature of the rat's vision for patterns. The roles of distribution of masses of light, of acuity for isolated elements, of the relation of figure and ground, of direction and movement, of configuration, of generalizing relations in the perception of objects are largely unknown even in human vision. I have accumulated a considerable amount of material which still serves only to emphasize the complexity of the problem. However, the method seems rapid and accurate enough to permit of a profitable attack upon questions of the organization of the visual field and of an analysis of the function of central nervous structures in various types of visual response.

Summary

Apparatus requiring the rat to jump from a distance upon the stimulus patterns induces a rapid formation of habits of reacting to the visual elements of the patterns. Controls show that the discrimination cannot be ascribed to nonvisual cues.

REFERENCES

1. Fields, P. E. Form discrimination in the white rat, *J. comp. Psychol.*, 1928, **8**, 143–158.

2. Fields, P. E. The white rat's use of visual stimuli in the discrimination of geometrical figures, *J. comp. Psychol.*, 1929, **9**, 107–122.

3. Lashley, K. S. Visual discrimination of size and form in the albino rat, *J. Anim. Behav.*, 1912, **2**, 310–331.

4. Lashley, K. S. Studies of cerebral function in learning: VII. The relation

between cerebral mass, learning, and retention, *J. comp. Neurol.*, 1926, **41**, 1–58.

5. Munn, N. L. Concerning visual form discrimination in the white rat, *J. genet. Psychol.*, 1929, **36**, 291–300.

6. Vincent, S. B. The mammalian eye, *J. Anim. Behav.*, 1912, **2**, 249–255.

7. Waugh, K. The role of vision in the mental life of the mouse, *J. comp. Neurol. Psychol.*, 1910, **20**, 549–599.

8. Yerkes, R. M. *The dancing mouse.* New York: Macmillan, 1907.

15. INTEGRATIVE FUNCTIONS OF THE CEREBRAL CORTEX [1]

Bubnoff and Heidenhain (15) formulated the general principle that in investigations of the physiology of the nervous system every conscious process must be ruled from consideration unless it can be translated into objective terms. Pavlov (131) adopted the same view and has consistently maintained that "there is no need for the physiologist to have recourse to psychology." From the standpoint of explanatory formulations, the validity of this principle cannot be seriously questioned. Psychological studies have resulted in the formulation of many generalizations, but attempts to build up systems based on "psychic causality" have not provided a satisfactory basis for a science. It is now increasingly, if not universally, admitted that the causal relations underlying these generalizations are to be sought in the activities of the brain. There are, however, many facts concerning the behavior of the organism which at present are expressed only in psychological terms and which must nevertheless be considered in any attempt to describe the activities of the brain or to understand the general principles of its organization.

Physiological theories of cerebral function have been derived in large part by inference from studies of nerve-muscle or of spinal preparations, lacking those very traits of behavior (learning and intelligent adaptation) which characterize the animal with intact nervous system and which are of primary importance in all its normal behavior. For all studies of nervous integration the correlation of excitation and reaction has been the most valuable research tool available. Direct measurements of electrical changes and the like have revealed something of the nature of the propagated disturbance, but even the concept of the reflex is based upon the stimulus-response relations within isolated segments, rather than upon any direct observations of what goes on within the integrating system (155). A large part of the data of psychology is based upon attempts at exactly the same sort of analysis of stimulus-response relationships. The chief method of physiological investigation of the nervous system is therefore not logically

[1] EDITORS' NOTE: From *Physiol. Rev.*, 1933, 13, 1–42. Reproduced by permission of the American Physiological Society. From department of psychology, University of Chicago.

prior to that of a behavioristic psychology. The greater scientific importance of the physiological studies lies rather in the simplicity of the conditions imposed and the consequent greater probability of a correct analysis
of the data.

This very simplicity of the situations studied may result in a failure to
consider problems which are fundamental for the behavior of the intact
organism. Psychological studies reveal many instances of behavior which
seem to involve principles of integration not thus far established for the
activities of the decerebrate preparation and which seem out of harmony
with concepts of neural integration derived from studies of lower centers.
Boring (13) has stated the problem clearly.

> The physiologist holds to the faith that the brain, being made up of neurons,
> is capable only of that excitation which is the sum of the excitations of many
> neurons, and that these central neurons obey the same laws and are excited
> under the same limitations as apply to the peripheral neurons which have been
> experimentally studied. To this article of faith the psychologist sometimes
> opposes another belief, that the organization of cerebral excitation corresponds
> to the organization of phenomenal experience.

That there is any essential contradiction between the established facts
of nerve conduction and the phenomena of complex behavior cannot be
maintained by anyone interested in the progress of natural science, but
the extent to which the concepts of cerebral function derived from studies
of lower centers are adequate to account for the facts of behavior can
be determined only by a more complete study of the problems of behavior
and by direct experimental tests of the explanatory concepts.

Clinical observations and experimental studies with animals provide the
two principal sources of more direct data upon the activities of the cerebral hemispheres. The clinical facts are exceedingly complex and the
possibilities of anatomical correlations distinctly limited. With animals
the anatomical control may be far more perfect, but in the earlier work
this advantage was counterbalanced by the difficulties of interpreting
behavior. The past thirty years have seen marked development in the
methods for studying animal behavior, of which little advantage has as
yet been taken for neurological studies.

The object of the present review is to formulate some of the significant
problems on the border line between psychology and neurology which
may be attacked by experimental methods now available for study of
animal behavior, and to summarize experimental data which bear most
directly upon these problems. The subject of cerebral localization has
been very adequately treated by Hines (63) and by Graham Brown
(52) and will be touched upon here only where it bears upon the problems of cerebral integration. Klüver's review of the literature on visual

disturbances (76) and Goldstein's discussions of aphasia (46, 47) deal with clinical aspects of many of the problems discussed here.

Limitations and Possibilities of Method

The development of techniques for the study of animal behavior since the first quantitative work of Thorndike in 1898 has opened many possibilities for correlated studies of behavior and neurology. Methods are available for the measurement of activity (141, 142, 156, 166), for a comparison of the effectiveness of incentives (125, 178), for estimation of individual differences in certain reactions termed emotional (163, 182), for determining sensory capacities by the conditioned-reflex method of Pavlov (131) and the discrimination method of Yerkes and Watson (184), for measuring the rate of acquisition of many varieties of habits, with a number of standardized tests worked out chiefly for the rat and monkey, and for direct adjustment to many situations, comparable to problems requiring reasoning and understanding of relations by man (179, 183, 81, 70, 79).

The chief difficulties in the studies of behavior arise from uncertainty as to the validity of the tests, a handicap shared almost equally by animal and human studies. The development of quantitative psychological tests for various activities is bringing about a change in the fundamental conceptions of the organization of psychological traits which is the most significant phase of current work. In attempts to measure individual differences, it has been a general experience that the activities or traits which were grouped together in the classical and popular categories of psychology (perseverance, emotionality, intellect, and the like) often show a degree of independence which is inconsistent with the assumption that they are products of a common causal agent. Groups of activities do show a high degree of intercorrelation, indicative of a common determining factor, but these groupings are so far from coinciding with the older classification of traits that it has seemed better to investigators to designate them by letters, than to attempt to fit them into the older classification. Thus we have Intellect CAVD (169), traits g, c, w, etc. (157), instead of the familiar terms. A test may correlate with g, which in turn correlates with ability in handling school subjects, but such ability may be independent of ability in handling mechanical problems and both independent of ability to make an intelligent adjustment to social situations.

This means that the validity of the tests used must be established before their results justify any generalizations: that is, the functions which they are intended to measure must be defined and it must be demonstrated that the tests actually do measure the functions. Bianchi (10) and others who have reported intellectual defects after frontal lobe injury have stressed silly behavior, Witselsucht, which is perhaps an inadequacy of social adjustment, whereas Feuchtwanger (27) and others who report normal intelligence have used tests which probably correlate with the group termed g. The controversy has arisen at least in large measure from a failure to recognize the probable diversity of the functions included under the popular term "intellect" and the inadequacy of the tests to measure all of these functions.

In experimental studies with animals the validity of the tests comes still more in question, so that it is scarcely safe to say that a test measures anything more than performance in the test itself. There is a high correlation in performance in certain tests, such as the learning of different mazes (107, 108, 164, 174), which justifies some generalization concerning maze-learning ability, but even here we do not know whether we are measuring fixation in memory (the ekphorie of Semon, 153), or some process akin to the solving of puzzles (insight, Köhler, 82).

On the physiological side, the methods for direct study of cerebral function present equal difficulties of another character. We are still largely restricted to methods available to the workers of the nineteenth century. The direct measurement of electrical changes in the cortex with the development of amplifying and recording instruments may revolutionize cerebral studies, but thus far has not given indication of differentiae which are useful for interpreting cerebral mechanisms (2, 171). Whether this is due to inadequacies of technique or to some fundamental property of the cortex remains to be determined, but leaves us still with stimulation and extirpation methods as the chief means available for direct study of cortical function.

Stimulation of the cortex in animals permits the designation of some areas which seem to be more intimately concerned with movements than are other areas, and in the hands of Sherrington and his co-workers has revealed something of the patterns of organization elaborated at different levels and of the mutual facilitation and inhibition of different areas. Stimulation of conscious human subjects further reveals cortical fields within which sensory elaboration occurs. The strychninization method of Dusser de Barenne (23) has given some similar data for animals. These methods, however, seem limited to revealing rather isolated functions, and extirpation remains the principal method available for gathering data upon the rôle of the cortex in the more complex adaptive reactions of the animal to its environment.

The interpretation of results obtained by the extirpation method presents peculiar difficulties. Following operations, symptoms may arise not only as a result of the simple absence of functional tissue, but also from derangement of the functions of the remaining tissue as in shock, general circulatory and nutritive changes, physical or chemical effects of necrotic or scar tissue, and the indirect depression of diaschisis. As Monakow (123), Pavlov (131), and many others have pointed out, the immediate symptoms are an unreliable index of the functions of the area destroyed. Upon the just ascription of symptoms to these various agencies depend important points in the interpretation of cerebral functions. Surgical shock, circulatory changes, and irritation may be controlled with considerable certainty by following changes in symptoms over a sufficiently long time, while precluding the possibility of relearning or of normal forgetting. The control of diaschisis is more difficult since the concept is not very clearly defined.

Diaschisis and Reeducation. Von Monakow's theory of diaschisis puts serious difficulties in the way of any attempt at experimental analysis of cerebral mechanisms. Briefly, the theory embodies the following points: (a) Destruction of a cortical area may result in symptoms which are due to the withdrawal of facilitation from some other area and the resultant inadequacy of functioning of that facilitated area. (b) Areas subject to such diaschisis effects recover their functions spontaneously, but no limit can be set to the time required for such recovery. (c) Only such functions as are permanently impaired can be ascribed to a destroyed area.

This theory casts doubt upon the validity of any experiment involving reeducation unless it can be shown that the functions studied do not recover spontaneously but do recover under the influence of training. Adequate controls of spontaneous recovery have been reported in few cases. Oden and Franz (127) destroyed the precentral gyrus in three rhesus monkeys, left one untreated, gave the second passive massage, and the third compulsory use of the hemiplegic arm, repeating the experiment with the second motor area after recovery from the effects of the first operation. They found scarcely any spontaneous recovery, whereas compulsory use was followed by nearly complete recovery within a few weeks. Lashley (93) varied the interval subsequent to destruction of the area striata at which retraining in the habit of reacting to light versus darkness was begun. One group, started on the seventh day after operation, had practically reacquired the habit by the fourteenth day. A second group, started on the fourteenth day, began at the level of efficiency shown by the first group on the seventh day. As in the study of Oden and Franz, retraining produced recovery which did not occur spontaneously in the absence of special training. A number of experiments, such as those of Trendelenberg (172), reveal recoveries ensuing promptly upon the forced use of paralyzed organs, after long periods in which no improvement was observed. A good bit of material in human reeducation indicates the same dependence of recovery upon training, but lacks rigid controls (Franz, 30; Graham Brown and Stewart, 55). The evidence seems conclusive that some functions lost through cerebral injury may be recovered as a result of special training and that these functions are not recovered spontaneously in the absence of training. Two questions at once follow this fact: by what neural changes is such recovery brought about and what are the limits of recovery for any function?

The Mechanism of Recovery through Reeducation. The manner in which the retraining is effective offers in each case a special problem. There seem to be at least three possibilities which must be tested: (*a*) Learning to get along without the lost functions. (*b*) Vicarious assumption of the functions by neural structures not previously utilized in the functions. (*c*) A reorganization within the system of which part has been destroyed, such that there is compensation for the loss.

The first of these possibilities is illustrated by the recovery from circus movements reported by Luciani (112) after cerebellar unilateral lesions. The dogs learned to walk in a straight line by altering the postures of the fore- and hind legs as might an animal with a mechanically imposed spinal curvature. Maze running of rats with extensive cerebellar destruction (104) in which animals practically rolled through the maze is a similar instance. Bethe (7) has reported studies of reorganization of gait following amputation of one or more limbs in invertebrates and in mammals. He holds that with the removal of the limbs there is an immediate reorganization of the sensory-motor system such that adequate walking movements, which have no counterpart in the integration of the normal animal, are made. In his cases, substitute activities are obvious; the problem is to determine whether they are learned, or acquired by some spontaneous central reorganization.

In studies of less objective or overt behavior it is more difficult to detect substitute activities or to rule them out as a factor in recovery of functions. The question has been raised (48) whether injury to the nervous system is ever followed by a genuine restitution of functions or whether all cases of recovery under reeducation do not represent the adoption of some roundabout method of achieving the same end, such as in Bethe's studies or in the development of pseudofovea. It is very difficult to obtain conclusive evidence upon the question, for the answer in any specific case depends upon opinion as to the exact nature of the defect. Recovery from cerebral paralyses with acquisition of the use of specific muscles seems to constitute the best evidence for genuine restitution, but even this is not crucial, if the initial loss of use is ascribed in part to sensory defect. Loss of habits resulting from cerebral injury and their subsequent formation at a rate and with objective performance identical with their preoperative formation argue for a restitution rather than a substitution of functions. Formation of motor habits has been reported by Graham Brown (51), Trendelenberg (172), and Lashley (91) after destruction of the motor cortex. Lashley (89) found that after the complete destruction of the area striata, habits based on the discrimination of light and darkness were abolished but could be reformed at exactly the same rate as the original formation in normal animals, and seemed to be performed in the same way.

The clinical literature includes many cases of recovery from amnesias with retraining (34, 35, 57) and of improvement in other functions (55), which can be understood only in terms of some genuine restitution of functions.

The Problem of Vicarious Functioning. It has generally been assumed that the recovery of functions lost after destruction of cerebral areas is due to the assumption of the functions by other cerebral areas which did not originally mediate the activities. Fritsch and Hitzig (38) first suggested this hypothesis as a possible explanation of the recovery of motor control in the dog after extirpation of the stimulable cortex of one hemisphere, assuming that the motor cortex of the other hemisphere assumed the lost functions. They put the hypothesis to experimental test, removing the remaining motor cortex in a second operation, and obtained the usual crossed paralysis with no recurrence of symptoms on the side of the second operation. This negative result has been confirmed by a number of investigators both for the dog (20) and for primates (172, 127, 109, 91). In no case has a recurrence of the motor symptoms produced by the first lesion been reported to follow the destruction of the corresponding area of the opposite hemisphere.

A few tests have dealt with the assumption of functions by adjacent parts of the same hemisphere. Franz (31) reported loss of latch-box habits after destruction of the frontal pole in the cat with relearning and a second loss following destruction of an area just back of the first lesion. He did not control these results by lesions in other parts of the cerebrum and recent work suggests that loss of such habits may follow lesions anywhere within the hemispheres, so these experiments cannot be accepted as demonstrating vicarious function of an adjacent area. All other similar experiments have given negative results. Leyton and Sherrington (109) destroyed small areas in the precentral gyrus of chimpanzees and after recovery from the local paralyses extirpated surrounding regions and portions of the postcentral gyrus. In no case did they get significant recurrence of the original paralysis. Lashley (89) destroyed the area striata in fourteen rats. This lesion invariably causes loss of preexisting habits based on the discrimination of light and darkness. He next trained the animals until accurate discrimination of light and dark was obtained and then destroyed one-third of the remaining cortex in each animal, covering all parts of the cortex in different animals of the series. Nearly perfect retention of the habit followed lesions in all parts of the remaining cortex. No limited part of the remaining cortex assumed the function of the lost striate area.

Arguing from the embryology of the motor cortex that the caudate nucleus might have a related function and be capable of vicarious substitution for the motor cortex, Lashley (91) removed the precentral gyrus in a cebus monkey and after improvement in the consequent paralysis destroyed the greater part of the caudate and the head of the lenticular nucleus. A typical lenticular syndrome resulted but without recurrence of the hemiplegic symptoms.

In several experiments with nerve suturing, the motor nerves have been transferred from one side of the body to the other (6, 129, 74). On later stimulation of the motor cortex, Bethe obtained coordinated movements of all the joints of the limb although different segments of the limb were innervated from different sides of the cord. In other investigations stimulation of the motor cortex after nerve crossing has given evidence only of the connection of the crossed nerves with the originally contralateral motor area. These experiments have been cited as evidence for vicarious functioning, but the reorganization of coordinations in such cases does not necessarily involve anything more than such changes in function as underlie all learning. In fact, the experiments do not even demonstrate a change in the functions of the motor area, since we do not know its normal function in the movements of progression. A reorganization of some portion of the motor system is implied but this presents a somewhat different problem from that of vicarious assumption of functions by centers which have not previously been concerned in the functions.

In every case where a localized area functioning vicariously has been sought, the experiments have given only negative results. The number and variety of such experiments is not great enough to justify a denial of the principle of vicarious functioning, but does point to the necessity for further experimenting before the use of the principle as an explanation of recovery can be accepted.

The alternative to vicarious functioning is a reorganization within a dynamic system of which only a part has been destroyed. Such an hypothesis has been proposed as a substitute for the doctrine of specific centers in spinal integration. Bethe (8), citing his own work and that of Buddenbrock (16) on spontaneous reorganization after amputation of limbs in arthropods, assumes that coordination in walking is not due to specifically localized centers but is the product of relative intensities of excitation, aroused by muscle tensions, within a relatively undifferentiated system. Change in coordination follows spontaneously upon any change in relative masses of excitation within different parts of the system. Direct evidence in support of such a theory is lacking.

The Limits of Recovery. Some improvement in function seems possible after any injury in the central nervous system provided adequate means of retraining are used, but the limits to improvement set by lesions of various sorts have rarely been tested, and few generalizations are possible. There are marked interspecies differences, as in severity of paralysis (143), so that generalization from one form to another is unsafe.

In interruption of spinal tracts, the residual sensory defects seem always more severe than the motor, at least in forms below man, although there are always some residual motor symptoms. With cerebral lesions, sensory defects also present the least possibility of improvement. Scotomas from extensive lesions to the primary visual areas are permanent in many species (rat, Lashley, 100; dog, Minkowski, 121), and such improvement as appears is due to substitution of function (48). Defects in other less highly differentiated areas or in areas with bilateral representation of the receptors, as the somesthetic, show a greater capacity of improvement (28). Pronounced improvement after destruction of the motor cortex is reported for all forms from the rat to man, but even in the rat there are permanent residual symptoms such as determination of the preferential use of one fore paw, after unilateral lesion (133).

For functions further removed from the sensory-motor level the possibilities of recovery are greater. Limits of improvement seem to be set by the extent of injury and by the complexity or psychological difficulty of the problem (Lashley, 94, rat; Jacobsen, 70, monkey; von Monakow, 123, man). The meager data on reeducation do not permit any wide generalizations. The difficulties of interpreting the results of extirpation experiments and the more essential controls of disturbing factors are illustrated by the foregoing discussion. Few investigators have attempted any systematic study of such factors and the great body of work upon cerebral localization is consequently inconclusive. The conclusions drawn in the following sections must be regarded as tentative, pending further analysis of the rôle of diaschisis and of general circulatory and nutritive disturbances in the production of postoperative symptoms.

Cerebral Function in Instinctive Behavior

The majority of problems of cerebral function center around activities which are known to have been acquired through some learning process and the opinion has been expressed that the cerebrum is not essential for the performance of any unlearned or instinctive activity (124). Very few studies have dealt with the rôle of the cortex in instinctive behavior and the problem is greatly complicated by the difficulty of ruling out an element of learning in the acquisition of all activities (see, for example, the analysis of the pecking reaction of chicks by Breed, 14, and Bird, 11).

Many of the reactions which are judged to be instinctive persist in the decorticate animal. Rogers (144) finds that the activities of mating and rearing the young by pigeons are carried out in a nearly normal manner after decerebration. Shaklee (154) reports that decerebration abolishes the drinking reaction of chicks but leaves pecking undisturbed. He interprets this in terms of later phylogenetic acquisition of drinking. In decerebrate mammals the range of activity is less than in birds. All writers (24, 50, 146, 185) have reported loss of feeding reactions (taking food into the mouth and passing it back to the pharynx) after decerebration, with later recovery in most animals.

Mating reactions, at least in male dogs, seem to be permanently abolished (148). Instinctive reactions other than sexual have scarcely been studied in mammals. Patterns of movement and visceral reactions corresponding to emotional behavior of the intact animal have been reported in decerebrate cats (1) and dogs (148). Sleep is normal except for lack of diurnal rhythm (75).

The sex activities of the rat are the only mammalian instincts which have been subjected to careful analysis from the standpoint of origin, adequate stimulus, and other determining conditions (159). Stone has found that destruction of large areas of the cortex in the rabbit produces no disturbance in mating behavior (162). I have observed that nearly complete decerebration in the male rat abolishes the reactions to the female in heat. Lack of recognition of the adequate stimulus seems to be the primary factor in the loss, but it is also possible that the poor physical condition of the animals suppresses the sexual drive (160, 161).

Unpublished observations by Stone and the writer indicate that the more complicated activities involved in rearing the young (nest building, collecting and cleaning the young, nursing, etc.) are interfered with by cerebral lesions and that the behavior is progressively simplified with increasing size of lesion.

The evidence seems quite conclusive that such complex integrations as those involved in recognition of the female in heat and the selection of nest material develop independently of individual experience and there are indications that in mammals they cannot be performed in the absence of large portions of the cerebral hemispheres. This implies that some instincts, which seem to be those requiring accurate differentiation of stimuli, are dependent upon cortical mechanisms. Whether this dependence implies that the necessary integrations are carried out within the cortex, or only that severe diaschisis of subcortical centers after decerebration persists indefinitely, remains uncertain.

Cerebral Function in Learning

The importance of the cerebral hemispheres for the learning process is obvious from a large number of experiments, but little has been revealed concerning the nature of its activities in learning. The demonstration of the formation of complex habits in arthropods (175, 37, 152), molluscs (54), and perhaps still lower invertebrates shows that typical cerebral structures are not necessary for learning. Nor is there any evidence that the rate of acquisition of the simplest associations increases with the development of the vertebrate nervous system. On the other hand, the range of activities and the complexity of relations which can be combined in habits increase pari passu with development of the cerebral hemispheres (95).

Burnett (17) attempted to train decerebrate frogs in a simple maze which was easily learned by normal animals. His results were entirely negative. His operations may have involved injury to the optic lobes. In birds, several investigators report the acquisition of simple habits after removal of the cerebral hemispheres, if the striate nuclei are retained. Treves and Aggazzotti (173) trained a decerebrate pigeon to find its way back to its perch and found that the habit was retained for several weeks without practice. Rogers (144) observed the combination of isolated sexual reactions into the mating cycle in decerebrate pigeons and failed to get the integration after injury to the hypostriatum. Gemelli and Pastori (41, 42) trained fowls in color discrimination and report a partial survival of the habit after decerebration with further improvement under practice and a subsequent, unexplained deterioration.

With decerebrate mammals the results have been for the most part negative or difficult to interpret. Improvement with practice in a number of simple activities has been reported, but with these it is difficult to determine whether the improvement represents learning or the spontaneous recovery of reflexes. Goltz (50) found that following operation food must be placed in the pharynx to induce swallowing but that gradually the dog came to pass food back from the jaws and ultimately to seize it when placed in contact with the lips. Rothmann (146) has reported similar observations. He also described an experiment in which the forefeet of his dog were placed on a chair and the chair drawn along the floor. At first the animal made no effort to follow. With practice he "learned" to step with his hind feet, following the movements of the chair. In later experiments his dogs came to leap over a hurdle, and sit up when supported against a wall (148). The observations of Buddenbrock (16) and of Bethe (7) suggest that this sort of adaptation may be due to changes in postural tonus which are not comparable to learning. These experiments, involving merely restitution of primitive functions, are of doubtful value as evidence of learning by lower centers, for, as Rothmann pointed out, the improvement may represent only the recovery of reflex mechanisms from a depression following the operation, with no involvement of associative mechanisms. On the other hand, they may be instances of genuine learning.

Head and Riddoch (58) report an apparent conditioning of the bladder reflex in patients with complete section of the spinal cord, but the same objection applies to this evidence as to restitution of functions in decerebrate animals.

Ingebritsen (69) attempted to establish conditioned reflexes in the hind legs of rats with spinal sections. He used animals with complete section in the thoracic region and others with two hemisections separated by about four spinal segments, attempting to associate an avoiding reaction of the foot with light contact on the thigh. No indication of conditioning appeared in animals with complete transection. Unstable and irregular reactions appeared in animals with double hemisection, which indicated an increased excitability to tactile stimuli after protopathic stimulation.

Few systematic attempts to establish more complex habits in decerebrate mammals have been made. Goltz (50) tried to train his dog to back out of a stall, but gave up training after a few unsuccessful trials. Kleitman and Camille (75) interpret the irregular periods of activity in decerebrate dogs to a failure to form habits of diurnal activity. In a series of papers Zeliony (185) reported negative results in attempts to establish conditioned reflexes in decerebrate dogs, but more recently Poltyrew and Zeliony (138, 139) have succeeded in establishing a conditioned motor reaction to the sound of a whistle and also a differential reaction to another sound, and in two cases a further response to the lighting of an electric lamp. Necropsies of the animals have not been reported, but the descriptions of operations indicate that at most only small basal portions of the temporal lobe remain intact. The authors find that very strong stimuli are required to establish the conditioned reaction.

From the results with decerebrate animals we can infer little as to the modifiability of subcortical mechanisms in the intact animal. It may be that the removal of the cortex decreases the plasticity of lower centers by withdrawing some nonspecific facilitation, which under normal conditions permits learning without actually contributing to the specific integrations. Such a view is supported by the results of Ingebritsen (69) on learning after double hemisection of the cord, and by the observations of Lashley (93, 94) that the formation of some habits is closely dependent upon the mass of cortical tissue available, irrespective of its specialized character. Crucial experiments are lacking.

The Reduction of Automatized Habits to Subcortical Levels. There is a widespread belief (124, 31) that continued practice results in the formation of subcortical associative connections such that habits which originally involved the cortex are carried out wholly by lower centers.

The belief is based by Morgan on the following argument: all cerebral activities are conscious; long-practiced habits become unconscious or automatic; therefore they are no longer executed by cerebral mechanisms. The major premise is questionable or meaningless and the argument is not valid. The clinical evidence sometimes advanced in support of the claim that old habits survive injuries which abolish more recent ones is not conclusive because the activities compared differ in many other respects than recency of acquisition. Lashley (87) has attempted to test the question experimentally. He gave rats 1200 trials of overtraining in a simple habit of reacting to light. With this amount of training the behavior of the animals indicated automatization. Removal of the striate area of the cortex resulted in a recoverable loss of the habit precisely as in animals without overtraining. This is the only direct evidence bearing upon the question and opposes the doctrine of reduction of automatized habits to subcortical levels.

The Conduction Pathway in Habit. On the assumption that the habit mechanism consists of definite and anatomically localized reflex pathways from receptor to effector, a few attempts have been made to trace such paths through the nervous system. Lang and Olmstead (83) established an association between an auditory stimulus and an avoiding reaction in the left hind leg in dogs. After section of the right half of the cord, the reaction did not reappear on recovery of motor control of the hind legs, but could be reestablished by retraining. The authors conclude that cutting of the sensory path for pain abolishes the reaction to auditory stimulation, and speculate concerning the necessity that the entire unconditioned reflex arc remain intact in order that the habit be maintained. They did not, however, control the normal loss of such reactions through lapse of time, or allow sufficient time without retraining to eliminate a general depression from the operation as possible causes of the loss of function. The fact that the conditional respiratory reflex persisted suggests that depression of motor centers below the lesion was an important factor in their results. Lashley and Ball (102) found survival of orienting control of the limbs required for maze running after cervical section of the entire dorsal or of both lateral funiculi of the cord, and Ingebritsen (69) obtained similar accurate orientation after a double hemisection of the cord at the second and fifth cervical levels, in which no more than a small portion of the tracts of the ventral funiculus remained uninterrupted.

Our most complete experimental data upon the afferent paths in learning and maintenance of habits are derived from studies of vision in the rat (86, 89, 92, 93, 94, 96, 100, 36, 106). The principal findings are briefly the following:

1. The habit of entering an illuminated and avoiding a darkened alley

in the Yerkes discrimination box is formed with equal rapidity by normal animals and by animals lacking the striate area, or any other part (up to at least 60 per cent) of the cerebral cortex.

	Trials	Errors
Average of 98 normals	131	43.8
Average for 113 animals with extensive to complete destruction of area striata	123	40.6

2. Destruction of the striate areas in animals previously trained produces complete amnesia which does not recover spontaneously. Destruction of other parts of the cortex, even adjacent to the striate areas, does not disturb the function.

3. Animals with postoperative loss relearn the habit as rapidly as do normal animals.

4. The amount of training required is closely proportional to the amount of tissue destroyed, provided that there is some invasion of the lateral portions of both striate areas (correlation ratio equals 0.84).

5. Partial interruption of the optic radiations does not produce a proportionate loss of the habit.

6. When the habit is formed in the absence of the striate areas, subsequent destruction of any third of the remaining cortex does not seriously disturb the habit.

7. Animals trained in this habit with one eye blindfolded discriminate correctly when the blindfold is transferred to the other eye. This transfer takes place as readily in the absence of the striate areas.

8. Injuries to the superior colliculi retard the formation of this habit, somewhat in proportion to the extent of injury.

9. The formation of habits based upon pattern vision is not retarded by destruction of the colliculi.

10. Complication of the habit by requiring the discrimination of two lights approaching threshold difference results in a marked slowing of initial learning in animals lacking the area striata, although their threshold for brightness *may* be as low as that of normal animals.

11. Destruction of the striate areas in animals previously trained in this habit results in complete amnesia. Partial destruction of the areas sometimes seems to abolish the discrimination of two lights without markedly reducing accuracy in reacting to one light alone.

12. The degree of disturbance in learning involving two lights is somewhat proportional to the extent of destruction of the area striata, as shown by the following correlations:

Correlation with
extent of lesion

Errors in learning reactions to two lights	0.58 ± 0.10
Difference threshold	0.49 ± 0.09
Postoperative retention	0.65 ± 0.10

13. Interruption of the optic radiations as they enter the external capsule from the lateral geniculate bodies permanently abolishes all reactions to discrete visual objects, but does not interfere with the formation of the reaction to light versus darkness.

14. Destruction of the lateral portion of both striate areas permanently abolishes all pattern discrimination.

15. Destruction of the median portions of the striate area or of any other cortical fields does not interfere with the formation of habits based on discrimination of patterns.

16. Lesions in the median portion of the striate areas produce an amnesia for habits based on pattern discrimination, which may be reacquired by training. Lesions to other cortical fields do not produce such an amnesia (unpublished data).

17. Animals trained on visual patterns react on the basis of the relative attributes of the stimuli, reacting at once to similarities when there is no identity of retinal elements stimulated.

These results embody data upon both defects of vision and disturbances of memory, and, as has proved true for clinical material also, it is difficult to disentangle these two aspects of the problem. The habit based on the discrimination of light and darkness shows least dependence upon the cortex. It is formed at normal rate in the absence of the striate area or of any other portion of the cortex (tested to 60 per cent), or even after a probably complete interruption of the optic radiations which abolishes all capacity to differentiate the position of objects within the visual field. This fact, taken together with the retardation from injuries to the superior colliculi and the formation of such habits in decerebrate dogs (139), indicates that the associative mechanism for the habit lies in the subcortical structures. When the habit is formed in normal animals injury to the striate areas results in its loss, with the rate of relearning proportionate to the extent of injury. This loss is not due to general shock, since equal injuries in other parts of the cortex do not disturb the habit. It cannot be ascribed to localized visual defects such as scotoma, since there is no evidence that these in man necessarily involve amnesia or that the capacity to make discriminations of light and darkness is abolished in those parts of the visual field which are not included in the scotomatous area. It cannot be ascribed to a change in the criteria of discrimination (as from reaction to a definite visual form to reaction to simple luminosity), for under the conditions of this experiment it is practically impossible to establish a visual discrimination of pattern in normal animals and the formation of a habit based on the simplest spatial attribute of the stimulus lights, relative size, requires from five to ten times as long training as to obtain a habit to relative brightness. The regularity of effect of extent of lesion indicated by a correlation coefficient of 0.84 indicates that the various parts of the area striata have an equal function in preserving the residual traces of the habit mechanism which contribute to the shortening of retraining [see below]. These results have been interpreted as indicating one of two alternatives: either that in the learning of this habit in normal animals the cortex participates by the development of some nonspecific facilitative effects upon the lower centers, and that the specific integrations between receptors and the motor systems used in orientation are not contained in the cortex itself; or that the integrations of the habit involve a reorganization of the entire visual system without the local development of specific integrative connections.

The data upon discrimination of two lights cannot be interpreted because we have no evidence concerning the effects of interruption of the optic radiations or of destructions in the anterior portions of the cortex upon this function.

For pattern vision it seems clear that the discrimination of the gross visual characters of objects requires some cortical connections, but can be mediated by the frontal portions of the cortex. This part of the system can mediate reactions to the relative position of discrete objects within the visual field but fails to distinguish between surface area and luminosity. The clear differentiation of spatial attributes of the stimulus is dependent upon the striate areas. There is no indication that any other portions of the cortex than the striate areas are concerned in the performance of habits based on pattern discrimination. Data on postoperative amnesias for this type of habit are as yet incomplete, but from results so far obtained it seems clear that the habits are disturbed only by lesions within the striate area and there are indications that the habits may survive the destruction of any part of the visual cortex up to at least 50 per cent in both hemispheres.

Such data are by no means adequate to solve the problem of the mutual relations of cortex and lower structures in learning, but they suggest that there may be both general facilitative effects and specific integrative relations involved. They show that the concept of simple conduction pathways from receptor to the cortex, with the establishment there of an integrative pattern of neuron connections, is a quite inadequate picture of the afferent mechanism.

Attempts to trace the path of associative reactions within the cortex have been largely confined to the motor cortex as the most plausible point of exit. Wagner, Bechterew (5), and Gierlich (53) have maintained that formation of motor habits is impossible after destruction of the motor cortex. Pike and Chappel (136) have more recently reported failure in attempts to train animals (cats) in a motor habit after small injuries in one motor area. Failure in these cases may have been due to the fact that the lesions were unilateral, since Trendelenberg (172) and Oden and Franz (127) have shown that recovery of one paralyzed limb is unlikely so long as the animal has free use of the other.

Isolation of the motor cortex from surrounding areas has given conflicting results. Marique (116) and Exner and Paneth (26) reported symptoms after circumsection of the area identical with those following excision. Schäfer (150) found normal control of movement in one case, which was not controlled histologically.

Starlinger (158) trained a dog to give his paw after interruption of both pyramidal tracts. Rothmann (147) and Graham Brown (51) report formation of motor habits after destruction of motor areas or pyramidal tracts. Trendelenberg (172) taught a dog to give his right paw after total extirpation of the left cerebral hemisphere. Pavlov (131) reports the establishment of conditioned reflexes after removal of all of the motor areas in dogs. These authors, dealing with learning after extirpation, have been inclined to regard the motor cortex as the chief normal source of motor impulses for habitual acts and to ascribe their results to vicarious functioning of efferent paths from other cortical areas.

Lashley and Franz (103) have reported the survival of maze running and Lashley (88) of visual habits after complete removal of the motor areas in the rat. Lashley and Ball (102) and Ingebritsen (69) report the survival of more complex maze habits after interruption of the pyramidal paths. Lashley (91) found that manipulative habits and habits involving visual discrimination survived the destruction of the precentral gyri in monkeys. From these experiments he has argued that the motor areas are not normally involved in the specific integrations of habits, but are to be regarded as part of the system controlling postural reflexes. Herrick (60) has criticized this conclusion on the grounds that the experiments are not crucial, but the postulation of a vicarious functioning of some other cerebral mechanism after removal of the precentral gyrus leaves unexplained the immediate production of the complicated patterns of movement which appeared without retraining after the lesions. Lashley (94) has found that the habit of traversing a complex maze is disturbed by injuries to any part of the cortex and that equal injuries in different areas have about equal effects. This indicates either a reduplication of specialized paths from lower centers to and from each part of the cortex, without significant transcortical connections, or some reorganization of transcortical activity which involves all parts of the system.

Thus far the attempts to trace conduction pathways involved in habits through the central nervous system have done little more than reveal the difficulty of obtaining evidence either for or against the existence of specifically differentiated conduction paths for learned actions. Most, perhaps all, of the results can be interpreted in terms of reduplication of paths through different parts of the functional areas. On the other hand, the data are equally compatible with an interpretation which denies the existence of pathways specifically differentiated for the habits through the different functional areas, and this latter interpretation seems more in harmony with the facts of sensory and motor equivalence which will be presented in a later section. . . . The evidence does not seem conclusive that the efferent connections of the cortex which control learned or voluntary activity descend directly from the sensory or associative areas without the intervention of the so-called motor cortex.

The Mechanism of Formation of Associations. A survey of recent studies of the conditions under which associations are formed shows that most of the supposed laws of learning from which the nature of the nervous changes involved has been inferred are seriously questioned. Practically all neurological theories of the learning process are based on the belief that the mere repetition of an act tends to fix it as a habit, or that the repeated occurrence together of two stimuli serves to associate them in memory. The older theories have been reviewed by Matthaei (118) and more recent ones by Lashley (95). Starting with the importance of repetition, the theories have postulated the repeated passage of nerve impulses over connecting pathways and a consequent increase in conductivity in these paths brought about by cell growth, changes in intercellular connections, membranes, or the like. Recently Cason (21) has pointed out that supposed repetition rarely if ever involves an exact or even approximate repetition of the same act. Peterson (134), Dunlap (22), and Thorndike (170) on experimental grounds have denied that repetition in itself is effective in producing learning. Lashley (95) has stressed the fact that sensory and motor paths which were not activated during learning may mediate the performance of the habit without additional training.

Such data seem to rule out the formation of associations by the repeated passage of nerve impulses over specific paths, with the concomitant doctrines of local change in synaptic resistance and the like. Alternative psychological conceptions of the learning process are still very vague. Goldstein (45) and Köhler (82) have stressed the importance of the organization or Gestaltung of the material and Thorndike (170) has formulated a similar concept of "togetherness," but so far it is possible to define the effective organization only by the fact of learning, and there seem to be clear exceptions to the rule (77). The positive inferences concerning possible neurological bases of learning which can be drawn from recent studies are still too vague to permit any experimental evaluation (95).

The Significance of Cerebral Localization

The association of diverse cytoarchitectural areas with different functions is well established, but the fact has been emphasized until it obscures the really fundamental problems of cerebral physiology. The production of specific symptoms by restricted cortical lesions furnishes a valuable clue to the nature of cerebral organization but, considered alone, provides no adequate picture of the processes which determine integration. We cannot accept an interactionist theory which localizes psychic entities in the cortical fields and then appeals to psychological laws to explain adaptive behavior. The facts of cerebral localization leave unanswered the question of how the specialized areas carry out their functions and of how their functions are interrelated.

Integration within Specialized Cortical Areas. The character of organization within different cortical fields seems to differ fundamentally. The highest degree of subordinate specialization within single fields has been demonstrated for the stimulable cortex and for the visual area. Especially in primates, stimulation of the precentral gyrus reveals a great number of points whose excitation results in different coordinated movements of the skeletal muscles. These have been interpreted by investigators since Fritsch and Hitzig as a mosaic of points directly and more or less exclusively connected with specific motor cells of the cord. Comparison of the position and extent of excitable areas in different animals of the same species and in the two hemispheres of the same animal (33, 165, 109) have shown a marked variation which has no obvious counterpart in the behavior of the animals. Lashley (90) mapped the arm area in the right hemisphere repeatedly at intervals of 1 to 14 days. He found that, although the excitable points remained constant in function (except for the familiar phenomena of facilitation and deviation) during any one period of exploration, there was little correspondence from day to day and the same point might elicit as primary movements entirely different patterns of activity, even movements in different segments of the body. The segmental areas (arm, leg, face) tended to retain a constant position, though with widely varying boundaries, but within each segmental area there was no consistency of primary reactions. From this he concluded that the apparent specificity of excitable points within the secondary areas (head, arm, leg) may be a matter of temporary physiological organization of the area, rather than of stable anatomical connection. Talbert (167) and Leyton and Sherrington (109) also report some variability in the effects of stimulation at different times, but less than that found by Lashley.

Experimental studies of differentiation within the visual cortex of animals give far less certain results than clinical studies of man, owing to our lack of any adequate means of mapping scotomas. The older experiments of Munk (126), Hitzig (64), and Loeb (110) seem largely to have missed the projection area and to have interrupted projection fibers or induced temporary trophic disturbances. The experiments of Minkowski (121) on the visual cortex of the dog are the most decisive available. He finds that the projection areas lie on the posterior and mesial surfaces of the occipital lobe, rather than at Munk's area A. Complete destruction of the posterior half of the field results in permanent homonymous hemianopia in the superior quadrant, of the anterior half, a like effect in the inferior quadrant. Any lesser lesions are followed by complete recovery. He interprets the results as showing that each retinal point is projected, not to a single point, but to an extensive area of the cortex, so that only extensive lesions result in the complete destruction of the representation of any point.

Experimental studies of primates have little bearing upon the problem. Munk (126), Schäfer and Brown (151), and Panici (130) found complete blindness only after destructions involving almost the posterior half of the cortex. The recoveries of vision reported by these investigators and by Vitzou (177) and Franz (32) did not include the estimation of scotomatous areas and only a limited analysis of visual functions. Recent anatomical studies (137) indicate that the projection area for the macula in the rhesus monkey, which has been chiefly used in experimental studies, is far more extensive than earlier experimenters have assumed, so that it is probable that considerable portions of the macular area were uninjured in all cases where recovery was observed.

Except for the limited differentiation indicated by Minkowski's studies, experimental work with animals gives no significant evidence concerning the differentiation of function within the visual cortex. We must turn, therefore, to the clinical literature for evidence of functional differentiation within the primary visual cortex. The studies of Marie and Chatelin (115), Holmes and Lister (66), Holmes (65), and Sänger (149) establish a correspondence between retinal zones and projection fields. The fineness of this differentiation is still in dispute and there is no clear evidence by which we can judge whether there is a distinct point within the area for each ganglion cell of the retina (59), a pattern of overlapping zones (121), or merely a gross polar arrangement with maximal macular effect at the pole and maximal peripheral effect at the anterior boundary of the area, as suggested by Poppelreuter (140, pp. 68ff.).

For the somesthetic area the stimulation experiments of Graham Brown (51) and of Leyton and Sherrington (109) and the strychnine methods of de Barenne (23) show differentiation in accord with the receptor surfaces, but details are not established either by the experimental or by the clinical literature.

In no other cortical area is there any clear evidence of a spatial sub-division with which elementary sensory or psychological units can be correlated. Larionow (85) and Eliason (131) have reported temporary loss of sensitivity to high or low tones following injuries to the auditory areas, but such results have been interpreted by Börnstein (12) as the result of a general lowering of the level of functional activity and crucial experiments are lacking.

It seems unquestionably established that within some cortical areas, as defined by anatomical methods, there is a subordinate differentiation of function constituting a sort of mosaic. It seems very probable that this mosaic differentiation is not in any case as fine as the peripheral functional units. For other areas it seems equally certain that there is no subordinate spatial representation of functions and that any injury to the area reduces efficiency in a number of activities which are independent in behavior.

It seems significant that the functions for which mosaic specialization within centers is established are just the ones which involve reaction of the organism to the spatial attributes of its environment.

The Mechanism of Integration within the Spatially Differentiated Centers. In the cortical fields where there is a projection of sensory surfaces, how do the points or foci corresponding to the sensory units function to produce differential reactions? Two opposing views have been advocated, the specialization of each point for a specific reaction and the functional equivalence of the system. Beyond the tacit assumption that the integration within centers is due to associative connections between neurons, little effort has been made to formulate and to test experimentally hypotheses concerning the functions of a cortical mosaic. Pavlov (131) has developed a definite theory, making use of the conception of mosaic organization in explaining discrimination of tactile stimuli and of differences in pitch. A conditioned salivary reflex was established to contact on the shoulder and conditioned inhibition to contact on the thigh. Progressive stimulation from shoulder to thigh then resulted in a gradual diminution of secretion with distance from the shoulder, an indifferent region between the points, and gradually increasing inhibitory effect as the point on the hip was approached. Points in front of the shoulder or on the hind foot produced reactions like but weaker than the trained points. Pavlov interprets this as evidence that separate but adjacent inhibitory and excitatory centers are established in the cutaneous projection area of the cortex from which facilitation or inhibition irradiate so that, as the projected excitation moves across the cortex with change in the locus of cutaneous excitation, the cortical effect shifts from excitation to inhibition. The same hypothesis is applied to discrimination of pitch.

The hypothesis is adequate only for the relatively simplified conditions of his experiments. In the visual discrimination of size we may find a parallel condition. If an animal is trained to choose a white circle of 6 cm. diameter and to avoid one of 4 cm., and is then confronted with a 5-cm. circle there is hesitation, vacillation, with sometimes negative, sometimes positive reactions (131, neutral zone, p. 227). A 2-cm. circle and a 10-cm. circle produce some uncertainty of reaction but are definitely negative and positive respectively. The experimental data exactly parallel those of cutaneous or of auditory discrimination. But in this case the circles are fixated successively on the same general regions of the retina and consequently the excitation is projected to the same general areas of the cortex. Further, if the animal is confronted with a 6-cm. and a 10-cm. circle, after successive inspection he chooses the 10-cm. and avoids the 6-cm. circle. When seen in conjunction with a larger, the previously excitatory stimulus at once becomes inhibitory.

The assumptions concerning a mosaic of inhibitory and excitatory centers is entirely inapplicable to the above data. If we assume a central inhibitory zone surrounded by a circular excitatory zone, the negative reaction to a previously positive stimulus remains unexplained. Further, in unpublished experiments I have found that the animal, trained to choose the largest of three circles, may immediately react positively to the widest lines when confronted with three fields with different widths of stripes. There is here no possibility of conformity to preexisting inhibitory or excitatory areas. From what we know of transposition (82) in audition and discrimination of weights, the mosaic theory is equally inapplicable for these sensory fields, and if it fails here, we must be skeptical of it as applied to the special case of tactile discrimination.

Theory of Functional Equivalence. Opposed to the mosaic theory of the the functional activity of specialized fields is the concept that within the special area all parts are, in certain respects and for certain functions, equivalent. This view has been expressed by Goltz (49) with reference to intelligence and the entire cortex, by Lashley (94, 95) as the equipotentiality of parts, by Bethe (8, 9) in the theory of "sliding coupling," by Börnstein (12) and Matthaei (119) and seems implicit in the systems of Bianchi (10) and of von Monakow (123), at least as applied to restricted fields. Three principal lines of evidence have been presented in favor of the theory: the functional equivalence of receptor surfaces, the spontaneous reorganization of motor reactions, and the survival of functions after destruction of any part of nervous centers whose total destruction abolishes them.

The data upon visual discrimination of size presented above are typical of experimental analyses of the sensory determinants in behavior. Becher (3) formulated the problem clearly in relation to nervous integration. The work of Stone (159, instincts in rats), Herter (62), Perkins and Wheeler (132, visual reactions of fishes), Klüver (78, 79, visual, auditory, and kinesthetic sensitivity of monkeys), Köhler (82, chapter 5, human vision), and Leeper and Leeper (108) may be cited as examples of such analysis for different orders of vertebrates. The work shows that, within very wide limits, the absolute properties of the stimulus are relatively unimportant for behavior and the reactions are determined by ratios of excitation which are equally effective when applied to any group of receptor cells within the system (92). The significance of these data for interpretation of integration within cortical sensory fields has been discussed by Köhler (82) and Lashley (97).

Experimental studies of spontaneous motor reorganization have been reported by Buddenbrock (16), Bethe (8), Lashley (91, 92), Lashley and McCarthy (104), Lashley and Ball (102). In general the results indicate that when habitually used motor organs are rendered nonfunctional by removal or paralysis, there is an immediate spontaneous use of other motor systems which had not previously been associated with or used in the performance of the activity. In normal human activities an unlimited number of similar instances of transfer can be cited. The shift from writing with finger movements to movements of the arm or even with a pencil held in the teeth still preserves the characteristics of individual chirography. Of course there are limits to such transfer which are set by the fineness and accuracy of the movements involved, but the essential patterns may be imposed upon the muscles of any limb.

Direct experimental evidence on the equivalence of parts of cerebral fields has been presented by Franz (31), Franz and Lashley (103), Lashley (86, 93, 94), Loucks (111), Maier (113, 114), and clinical evidence has been given by Fuchs (40), Poppelreuter (140), and Börnstein (12) among others. The experimental work deals with the formation or postoperative retention of specific habits after the partial destruction of cortical fields. Franz (31) found that motor habits survived the destruction of the frontal pole of either hemisphere but were abolished by destruction of both. Bianchi (10) draws a somewhat similar conclusion from his studies with monkeys. Lashley and Franz (103) found loss of a latch-box habit after complete destruction of the frontal pole in rats, with more or less complete survival of the habit with lesser lesions. In this work there was no adequate control of shock or diaschisis effects. Lashley (93) found that lesions in the area striata result in a partial loss of habits based on discrimination of light and darkness, which is not qualitatively different for different parts of the area, in experiments where shock was controlled by showing that the loss persisted for at least two weeks whereas animals could relearn the habit within the second week after operation. Loucks (111) found partial loss of the "delayed-alternation habit" after partial destruction of the motor and somesthetic areas which was complete only after very extensive destructions. The significant point in these observations is that a limited lesion does not abolish any identifiable parts of the function, leaving others intact, but lessens efficiency in all aspects of the function.

The same type of result appears after extirpation of parts of the motor cortex of monkeys. Destruction of small areas in general produces only temporary focal disturbances and large amounts must be destroyed in order to produce lasting defects (15, 109).

These three lines of evidence indicate that certain coordinated activities, known to be dependent upon definite cortical areas, can be carried out by any part (within undefined limits) of the whole area. Such a condition might arise from the presence of many duplicate reflex pathways through the areas and such an explanation will perhaps account for all of the reported cases of survival of functions after partial destruction of their special areas, but it is inadequate for the facts of sensory and motor equivalence. These facts establish the principle that, once an associated reaction has been established (e.g., a positive reaction to a visual pattern), the same reaction will be elicited by the excitation of sensory cells which were never stimulated in that way during the course of training. Similarly, motor acts (e.g., opening a latch box), once acquired, may be executed immediately with motor organs which were not associated with the act during training. Bethe (8) has generalized similar facts under the principle of "sliding coupling" and, following Buddenbrock (16), has proposed an explanation for motor equivalence based on the assumption that the excitation of a motor center depends upon its tonic state, which in turn is determined by excitations aroused by the state of tension in the motor organs supplied by it. The theory is adequate for the cases of direct adaptation of limb-coordination with which he deals, but seems inadequate for the adaptive reactions described by Lashley (92).

Quantitative Results in the Study of Cerebral Functions

Goltz (49) first suggested a relationship between the extent of cerebral destruction and the consequent degree of deterioration in more complex adaptive behavior. He interpreted the effect as due to a lowering of attention, implying that the latter is a function of the total energy of nervous activity available. Clinicians have occasionally emphasized the importance of the extent of cerebral involvement in production of general deterioration (123, 10, 57) but have not presented systematic evidence.

Lashley and Franz raised the question as an experimental problem in

1917 and a number of statistical studies have since been reported. They are summarized in Table 15.1. The use of the correlation coefficient is justified in these studies only as a crude indication of the existence of a relationship. The relationship is probably not rectilinear. Lashley (93) computed the correlation ratio for lesions in the visual cortex and obtained a value of 0.84 ± 0.03 as compared with a coefficient of 0.72 ± 0.05. From data on 127 cases Lashley and Wiley (105) find that the retardation is best described as a logarithmic function of the extent of destruction. Beyond establishing that the retardation is disproportionately more severe after large than after small lesions and that the function is a continuous one, the mathematical expression of the relationship has little significance.

The distribution in magnitudes of the coefficients summarized in the table confirms the genuineness of the relationship. Only three of the values available fall between 0.10 and 0.50, whereas five are approximately zero and fourteen above 0.60. This indicates that the functions fall definitely into two types, either completely independent of extent of lesion (within the limits of the tests) or closely dependent. It is not possible from the data to formulate any generalizations concerning the activities which fall into these two classes. Apparently the simplest sensory habits and the simplest maze habits show the least relationship to cortical lesion, but the absence of correlation for initial formation of the latch box and delayed alternation habits do not fit this interpretation on the sole basis of simplicity.

From limited data Lashley (95) concluded that in maze learning the deterioration was relatively greater for mazes with many culs de sac. Lashley and Wiley have failed to confirm this, finding that the relative ease of learning simple and complex mazes is the same for normal and for operated animals. In these latter experiments only reduplication of elements in the tests was involved. Where qualitative differences in the tasks are concerned there are indications that small lesions markedly retard some functions such as are involved in the experiments of Cameron (19), Maier (113, 114), and Buytendijk (18), and leave others relatively undisturbed. Jacobsen (70) found that, after lesions to the frontal lobes in monkeys, the opening of problem boxes with several latches was greatly interfered with although each of the latches alone was opened without difficulty.

The question of what determines relative difficulty of tasks for normal animals and for animals with brain injuries is complicated by many factors. Sensory defects and motor handicaps unquestionably play a part in retarding the operated animals but in addition to this there are other factors, more clearly indicated in clinical and psychological studies than in the results of physiological experiments. Such conditions as the suitability of the task to the instinctive equipment of the organism, the

Table 15.1. Relation between Extent of Lesion and Efficiency of Performance in Statistical Studies of the Effects of Cerebral Injury [*]

Task	Locus of lesion	Coefficient of correlation	Reference
Postoperative retention of simple maze	Frontal areas	Zero	Lashley and Franz (103)
Learning double platform box	Frontal areas	0.24 ± 0.15	Lashley (86)
Learning double platform box corrected for motor disorders	Frontal areas	Zero	Lashley (86)
Initial learning, delayed alternation	Frontal areas	−0.02 ± 0.19	Loucks (111)
Delayed alternation, postoperative relearning	Frontal areas	0.54 ± 0.12	Loucks (111)
Postoperative maze learning, 8 culs de sac	Frontal areas	0.64 ± 0.08	Maier (113)
Reasoning, postoperative records	Frontal areas	0.54 ± 0.09	Maier (113)
Light-darkness discrimination, postoperative learning	Visual cortex	0.08 ± 0.14	Lashley (93)
Light-darkness discrimination, postoperative relearning	Visual cortex	0.72 ± 0.05	Lashley (93)
Light-darkness discrimination, postoperative relearning, corrected for critical area	Visual cortex	0.73 ± 0.08	Lashley (101)
Light-darkness discrimination, postoperative relearning	Visual cortex	0.64 ± 0.10	Lashley (96)
Postoperative learning discrimination two lights	Visual cortex	0.58 ± 0.10	Lashley (96)
Postoperative relearning discrimination two lights	Visual cortex	0.65 ± 0.10	Lashley (96)
Difference threshold discrimination two lights	Visual cortex	0.49 ± 0.09	Lashley (96)

number of elements which must be dealt with simultaneously in integration, and previous familiarity with these elements, are obviously significant. A number of clinical and psychological studies suggest a still more fundamental factor which cannot as yet be described in terms of the properties of the test situations but only in terms of effects on behavior integration. This is illustrated by the completion of simple figures in the hemianopic field (39, 140), by the disturbances of verbal organization in agrammatic aphasia, and in normal psychology by the relative obscurity of different logical relations. Such variations in the difficulty of qualita-

Table 15.1. Relation between Extent of Lesion and Efficiency of Performance in Statistical Studies of the Effects of Cerebral Injury * (*Continued*)

Task	Locus of Lesion	Coefficient of correlation	Reference
Visual acuity and pattern vision	Visual cortex	All-or-nothing effect	Lashley (100)
Reasoning, postoperative records	Visual cortex	0.75 ± 0.05	Maier (114)
Postoperative retention reaction to noise	Auditory cortex	0.61 ± 0.11	Wiley (180)
Postoperative maze learning, 8 culs de sac	All parts	0.86 ± 0.03	Lashley (94)
Postoperative maze learning, 3 culs de sac	All parts	0.65 ± 0.07	Lashley (94)
Postoperative maze learning, 1 cul de sac	All parts	0.30 ± 0.16	Lashley (94)
Postoperative maze retention, 8 culs de sac	All parts	0.51 ± 0.11	Lashley (94)
Postoperative maze retention, 1 cul de sac	All parts	0.00 ± 0.13	Lashley (94)
Postoperative maze retention, 4 culs de sac	All parts	0.80 ± 0.05	Lashley and Wiley (105)
Postoperative maze retention, 8 culs de sac	All parts	0.80 ± 0.05	Lashley and Wiley (105)
Postoperative maze retention, 12 culs de sac	All parts	0.70 ± 0.07	Lashley and Wiley (105)
Postoperative maze retention, 16 culs de sac	All parts	0.60 ± 0.08	Lashley and Wiley (105)
Postoperative maze retention, 8 culs de sac reversed	All parts	0.64 ± 0.04	Lashley and Wiley (105)

* The constants are for error scores where these are available, otherwise trials required for learning, or postoperative relearning.

tively different tasks and indications of specific organizing tendencies in nervous function suggest that the nervous mechanisms tend innately to certain types of integration and that the relative difficulty of tasks is in large measure dependent upon the extent to which they fit this pre-existing schema of organization. The available evidence upon the relation between extent of lesion and difficulty of task is at least suggestive that further investigations may reveal significant correlations.

The fact of a relationship between amount of tissue destroyed and severity of deterioration for certain activities seems firmly established by the data of Table 15.1. Interpretation of the fact still remains in question. Four possible explanations have been suggested, and in part experimentally tested.

1. General shock or metabolic disturbance proportional to the severity of injury. In tests of this it has been shown that some functions which certainly involve the cortex (initial formation of latch-box and light-darkness discrimination habits) are not affected by lesions which produce severe deterioration in other functions (maze learning, "reasoning," various postoperative amnesias). The formation of habits based on light-darkness discrimination is not retarded by destruction of the area striata although injuries in this area markedly reduce performance in Maier's experiments in peripherally blinded animals (114). Lesions invading the area striata without destruction of its lateral portions do not interfere with formation of habits based on discrimination of visual patterns, but do retard maze learning.

2. Deterioration arises from sensory defects due to destruction of the sensory projection areas. To test this Lashley (94, 98) has compared the effects on maze performance of destruction of sense organs or sensory tracts with the effects of lesions in the corresponding cortical projection areas. In all cases the deterioration from cortical lesions, which do not completely abolish the sensory functions, is far more severe than that following complete peripheral destruction of sensitivity. Maier has shown that blindness reduces efficiency in his tests but that in blind animals lesions in the visual cortex produce a still greater loss of efficiency.

3. Reduplication of functionally equivalent conducting paths through different parts of the cortex, with deterioration proportional to the number of paths destroyed. This explanation seems applicable to all results on postoperative amnesia except those for the visual area. Lashley (93) found that linear lesions which interrupted a large part of the optic radiations produced a disturbance only proportionate to the amount of cortical tissue destroyed and not to the extent of interruption of fibers.

It is difficult to see how the hypothesis of reduplicated arcs can be applied to the limitations in learning capacity revealed for mazes and the "reasoning problem." Here we should have to assume that the rate of learning is proportional to the total number of potential pathways available. After destruction of the area striata, or of the posterior half of the cortex, by which the great majority of potential visual pathways have certainly been destroyed the formation of the habit based upon light-darkness discrimination proceeds at normal rate and must therefore be independent of the number of potential cortical pathways. Lashley (94) has presented some evidence that retentiveness for habits formed after cerebral injury is reduced and interprets this as meaning that the capacity to retain alterations imposed by learning upon some parts of the nervous system is reduced by the absence of other parts, under conditions where shock or diaschisis is improbable. If this interpretation is correct, it is difficult to harmonize with the maintenance of habits by local alterations of structure. Melton (120) has suggested that the apparent reduction of retentiveness may have resulted from retroactive inhibition, but this interpretation does not avoid the difficulty for the theory of specific paths.

4. The deterioration is due in part to reduction of some cerebral activity which is not related to specific sensory or motor functions, but is essentially the same for all parts of the cortex. Lashley (94) has shown that the loss of the maze habit after destruction of the visual cortex is not dependent upon the sensory function of this area, since the loss is the same in animals which were blinded by enucleation of the eyes before training in the maze. He also presented some evidence that with lesions restricted to any single cortical area the retardation in maze learning is proportional to the amount of destruction within that area, and that when equal amounts of destruction within different areas are compared, the degree of retardation is equal. Maier (113, 114) obtained similar results in comparison of the frontal and occipital regions for a different activity. The data of Lashley and Wiley (105) are less consistent on this point, but support it at least for certain areas.

These facts imply that the activities of any part of the cortex in the acquisition, retention, and performance of more complex integrative functions are conditioned by the activities of all other parts. How this influence is exerted and what its relation to the specific integrative functions of the different areas may be, remains obscure.

Nonspecific Facilitation in Cerebral Activity

Munk (126) first reported the loss of motility in a limb after section of its dorsal roots with temporary recovery of use during excitement or with restraint of the normal contralateral limb. This type of evidence points to some general facilitative effect of the afferent impulses from the limb, as well as specific reflex integrations. There is a considerable amount of unsystematic evidence that this principle of nonspecific facilitation plays an important part in all nervous activity. The postural system of the cord and medulla, the cerebellum, and the striate complex are generally regarded as not participating directly in the specific integrations of learned activities, but as providing a background of posture and tonus upon which the specific influences of the associative mechanisms are superimposed (181, 67).

The condition of animals in cerebral paralysis suggests a similar function of the motor areas. Peterson (133) found that a small injury in the motor area of the forefoot normally used in feeding usually resulted in a shift to the use of the other foot. Injury to the motor area of that foot then resulted in a return to the preferential use of the first. The prompt use of the paralyzed limb in monkeys after amputation of the sound one (172) and the partial recovery under emotional excitement noted by Minkowski (122) and Franz suggest that the paralysis is in part due to inadequate facilitation of lower motor centers.

It is uncertain what part such nonspecific facilitative effects may play in cerebral activity. Several lines of evidence suggest fluctuations in some general dynamic condition as important in the production of symptoms. Franz has pointed out that the cerebral paralyses in man consist in an enormous difficulty rather than an impossibility of making movements. In the milder amnesic forms of aphasia also there is difficulty in recalling rather than impossibility of recalling verbal material and Head (57) has noted some of the ways in which the speech mechanism may be facilitated.

A parallel problem appears in the relearning time for habits lost after cerebral lesions. On the first day or two of retraining in light-darkness discrimination the animal with injury to the striate areas makes a purely chance score, irrespective of whether the injury is large or small, or whether the tests follow soon or later after the operation. But with continued training a difference appears. After ten to twenty trials the animal with a small lesion begins to make better than chance scores and the proportion of right reactions increases rapidly. The animal with larger lesions continues for a longer time to make chance scores and increases the percentage of right responses more slowly than the other. This corresponds closely to the results of Ebbinghaus (25) and later psychologists on the strength of the memory trace. In this work it was found that a certain minimal number of repetitions of verbal material are necessary to obtain a correct recall. After a lapse of time recall is impossible but fewer repetitions are necessary to reinstate it. If more repetitions are given than necessary to get recall in the first learning period, fewer will be required for relearning. The longer the intervening time, the more repetitions are necessary to obtain a correct reproduction. This led to the concept of varying strength of associative connections and to the theory that a residual association may exist which is too weak to cause reproduction, but which is effective in reducing the amount of retraining necessary for reproduction. These facts suggest that associations may exist at different energy levels and this seems best expressed in terms of mutual facilitation of the associative mechanisms within the total system of integrations constituting the engram.

The assumption of general dynamic action of the cerebral cortex is common in neurological literature. Upon it depend theories of the release of lower centers from inhibition in explanations of contracture, of hyperesthesias, increased emotional excitability and the like, as well as such general concepts as "vigilance" (56), "affective regulation" (135), and the conception of "dominance" of Orton (128). The need for critical investigation in this field is obvious.

Summary

The evidence reviewed here can scarcely be regarded as crucial upon any question of the cerebral mechanism of integration, but the picture which it gives us of cerebral activities lacks the precision which was anticipated by earlier workers. There is evidence of mutual dependence of parts in which the specialization of structures seems less important than the mere mass of functional tissue. There are indications that within the entire cortex, for certain functions, and within specialized areas, for others, the subordinate parts are all equally capable of performing the functions of the whole. Even where the highest degree of specialization exists, as in the visual and motor areas, the facts of equivalence of stimuli or equivalence of motor responses preclude any narrowly localized specialization of intercellular connections.

Herrick (61) has expressed the significance of such data as follows: there is "first, a known localization of stable structural elements whose functions are also known, and, second, a localization of fields within which various recurring patterns of performance or schemata are known to be fabricated and within which inhibition, modification, or conditioning of these patterns takes place." The evidence seems most consistent with the view that these schemata are dependent upon some dynamic patterns of organization such as that proposed by Bethe (8) for spinal coordination.

REFERENCES

1. Bard, P. A diencephalic mechanism for the expression of rage with special reference to the sympathetic nervous system, *Amer. J. Physiol.*, 1928, **84**, 490.

2. Bartley, S. H., and Newman, E. B. Studies of the dog's cortex: I. The sensori-motor areas, *Amer. J. Physiol.*, 1931, **99**, 1.

3. Becher, E. *Gehirn und Seele.* Heidelberg: 1911.

4. Bechterew, W. v. *Die Funktionen der Nervencentra.* Jena: 1911.

5. Bechterew, W. v. La localization des psychoréflexes dans l'écorce cérébrale, *Scientia*, 1916, **20**, 444.

6. Bethe, A. Ueber Nervenverheilung und polare Wachstumserscheinungen am Nerven, *Münch. Med. Wschr.*, 1905, **52**, 1228.

7. Bethe, A. Studien über die Plastizität des Nervensystems, *Pflüg. Arch. ges. Physiol.*, 1930, **224**, 793.

8. Bethe, A. Plastizität und Zentrenlehre, *Handb. norm. path. Physiol.*, 1931, **15** (II), 1175.

9. Bethe, A., and Fischer, E. Die Anpassungsfähigkeit (Plastizität) des Nervensystems, *Handb. norm. path. Physiol.*, 1931, **15** (II), 1045.

10. Bianchi, L. *The mechanism of the brain and the function of the frontal lobes.* Edinburgh: 1922.

11. Bird, C. The effect of maturation upon the pecking instinct of chicks, *Ped. Sem.*, 1926, **33**, 212.

12. Börnstein, W. Teilfunktionen oder Einheitsfunktion im kortikalen Hörzentrum? *Mschr. Psychiat. Neurol.*, 1932, **81**, 353.

13. Boring, E. G. The physiology of consciousness, *Science*, 1932, **75**, 32.

14. Breed, F. S. The development of certain instincts and habits in chicks, *J. Anim. Behav.* (Monogr. Suppl.), 1911, **1**, 1.

15. Bubnoff, N., and Heidenhain, R. Über Erregungs- und Hemmungsvorgänge innerhalb der motorischen Hirncentren, *Pflüg. Arch. ges. Physiol.*, 1881, **26**, 137.

16. Buddenbrock, W. v. Der Rhythmus der Schreitbewegungen der Stabheuschrecke Dyxippus, *Biol. Zbl.*, 1921, **41**, 41.

17. Burnett, T. C. Some observations on decerebrate frogs with especial reference to the formation of association, *Amer. J. Physiol.*, 1912, **30**, 80.

18. Buytendijk, F. J. J. Le cerveau et l'intelligence, *J. Psychol.*, 1931, **28**, 345.

19. Cameron, N. Cerebral destruction in its relation to maze learning, *Psychol. Monogr.*, 1926, **39** (1), 1.

20. Carville, C., and Duret, H. Sur les fonctions des hémisphères cérébraux, *Arch. Physiol.*, 1875, **7**, 352.

21. Cason, H. The physical basis of the conditioned response, *Amer. J. Psychol.*, 1925, **36**, 371.

22. Dunlap, K. A revision of the fundamental laws of habit formation, *Science*, 1928, **68**, 360.

23. Dusser de Barenne, J. G. Experimental researches on sensory localization in the cerebral cortex, *Quart. J. exp. Physiol.*, 1916, **9**, 355.

24. Dusser de Barenne, J. G. Recherches expérimentales sur les fonctions du système nerveux central, factes en particulier sur deux chats dont le néopallium avait été enlevé, *Arch. neur. physiol. Homme Anim.*, 1919, **4**, 31.

25. Ebbinghaus, H. *Memory: a contribution to experimental psychology.* Transl. by H. A. Ruger. New York: 1913.

26. Exner, S., and Paneth, J. Versuche über die Folgen der Durchschneidung von Assoziationsfasern im Hunden, *Pflüg. Arch. ges. Physiol.*, 1889, **44**, 544.

27. Feuchtwanger, E. Die Funktionen des Stirnhirns, ihre Pathologie und Psychologie, *Monogr. Ges. Neurol. Psychiat.*, 1923, **38**, 194.

28. Foerster, O. I. Restitution der Motilität: II. Restitution der Sensibilität, *Dtsch. Z. Nervenheilk.*, 1930, **115**, 248.

29. Franz, S. I. On the functions of the cerebrum: the frontal lobes in relation to the production and retention of simple sensory-motor habits, *Amer. J. Physiol.*, 1902, **8**, 1.

30. Franz, S. I. The re-education of an aphasiac, *J. Phil. Psychol. sci. Meth.*, 1905, **2**, 589.

31. Franz, S. I. On the functions of the cerebrum: the frontal lobes, *Arch. Psychol.*, 1907 (2), 1.

32. Franz, S. I. On the functions of the cerebrum: the occipital lobes, *Psychol. Rev. Monogr.*, 1911, **13** (4), 1.

33. Franz, S. I. Variations in the distribution of motor centers, *Psychol. Rev. Monogr.*, 1915, **19** (1), 80.

34. Franz, S. I. *Nervous and mental re-education.* New York: 1923.

35. Franz, S. I. Studies in re-education: the aphasias, *J. comp. Psychol.*, 1924, **4**, 349.

36. Freeman, G. L., and Papez, J. W. The effects of subcortical lesions on the visual discrimination of rats, *J. comp. Psychol.*, 1930, **11**, 185.

37. Frisch, K. v. Der Farbensinn u. Formensinn der Biene, *Zool. Jb.* (*Physiol.*), 1914, **35**, 1.

38. Fritsch, G., and Hitzig, E. Über die elektrische Erregbarkeit des Gross-hirns, *Arch. Anat. Physiol., Lpz.*, 1870, 300.

39. Fuchs, W. Untersuchungen über das Sehen der Hemianopiker und Hemiamblyopiker. II. Die totalisierende Gestaltauffassung, *Z. Psychol.*, 1920, **86**, 1.

40. Fuchs, W. Eine Pseudofovea bei Hemianopkern, *Psychol. Forsch.*, 1921, **1**, 157.

41. Gemelli, A., and Pastori, G. Sulla rieducabilita di animali scerebrati, *Boll. Soc. ital. Biol. sper.*, 1930, **5**, 1076.

42. Gemelli, A., and Pastori, G. Recherches sur la rééducabilité des animaux décérébrés, *Arch. ital. Biol.*, 1931, **85**, 165.

43. Gierlich, N. *Über Symptomatologie, Wesen, und Therapie der hemi-plegischen Lähmung.* Wiesbaden: 1913.

44. Goldsmith, M. Quelques réactions sensorielles chez le poulpe, *C. R. Acad. Sci.*, Paris, 1917, **164**, 448.

45. Goldstein, K. Merkfähigkeit, Gedächtnis und Assoziation, *Z. Psychol.*, 1906, **41**, 38, 117.

46. Goldstein, K. Die Topik der Grosshirnrinde in ihren klinischen Be-deutung, *Dtsch. Z. Nervenheilk.*, 1923, **77**, 7.

47. Goldstein, K. Das Wesen der amnestischen Aphasie, *Schweiz. Arch. Neurol. Psychiat.*, 1924, **15**, 163.

48. Goldstein, K. Über die Plastizität des Organismus auf Grund von Erfah-rungen am nervenkrank Menschen, *Handb. norm. path. Physiol.*, 1931, **15** (II), 1131.

49. Goltz, F. *Über die Verrichtungen des Grosshirns.* Bonn: 1881.

50. Goltz, F. Der Hund ohne Grosshirn, *Pflüg. Arch. ges. Physiol.*, 1892, **51**, 570.

51. Graham Brown, T. Studies in the physiology of the nervous system: XXVII. 6. The motor activation of parts of the cerebral cortex other than those included in the so-called "motor areas" in monkeys, *Quart. J. exp. Physiol.*, 1916, **10**, 103.

52. Graham Brown, T. Die Grosshirnhemisphären, *Handb. norm. path. Physiol.*, 1927, **10**, 418.

53. Graham Brown, T., and Sherrington, C. S. On the instability of a cortical point, *Proc. roy. Soc.,* 1912, **85B,** 250.

54. Graham Brown, T., and Sherrington, C. S. Note on the functions of the cortex cerebri, *J. Physiol.,* 1913, **46,** 22.

55. Graham Brown, T., and Stewart, R. M. On the disturbances of the localization and discrimination of sensations in cases of cerebral lesions and on the possibility of the recovery of these functions after a process of training, *Brain,* 1916, **39,** 348.

56. Head, H. The conception of nervous and mental energy, *Brit. J. Psychol.* (Gen. Sec.), 1923, **14,** 126.

57. Head, H. *Aphasia and kindred disorders of speech.* New York: 1926.

58. Head, H., and Riddoch, G. The automatic bladder, excessive sweating and some other reflex conditions in gross injuries to the spinal cord, *Brain,* 1917, **40,** 188.

59. Henschen, S. E. Über das Sehzentrum, *Neurol. Zbl.,* 1917, **36,** 946.

60. Herrick, C. J. *Brains of rats and men.* Chicago: 1926.

61. Herrick, C. J. Localization of function in the nervous system. *Proc. nat. Acad. Sci., Wash.,* 1930, **16,** 643.

62. Herter, K. Dressurversuche an Fischen, *Z. vergl. Physiol.,* 1929, **10,** 688.

63. Hines, M. On cerebral localization, *Physiol. Rev.,* 1929, **9,** 462.

64. Hitzig, E. Alte und neue Untersuchungen über das Gehirn, *Arch. Psychiat. Nervenkr.,* 1903, **37,** 277.

65. Holmes, G. Disturbances of vision by cerebral lesions, *Brit. J. Ophthal.,* 1918, **2,** 352.

66. Holmes, G., and Lister, W. T. Disturbances of vision from cerebral lesions with special reference to the macula, *Brain,* 1916, **39,** 34.

67. Hunt, J. R. Static and kinetic systems of motility, *Arch. Neurol. Psychiat., Chicago,* 1920, **4,** 353.

68. Hunter, W. S. A consideration of Lashley's theory of the equipotentiality of cerebral action, *J. gen. Psychol.,* 1930, **3,** 455.

69. Ingebritsen, O. C. Co-ordinating mechanisms of the spinal cord, *Comp. Psychol. Monogr.,* 1932.

70. Jacobsen, C. F. A study of cerebral function in learning: the frontal lobes, *J. comp. Neurol.,* 1931, **52,** 271.

71. Karplus, J., and Kreidl, A. Über Totalextirpation einer und beider Grosshirnhemisphären an Affen, *Arch. Anat. Physiol., Physiol. Abt.,* 1914, 155.

72. Kelly, T. L. *Crossroads in the mind of man.* Stanford, Calif.: Stanford Univ. Press, 1928.

73. Kennedy, R. On the restoration of co-ordinated movements after nerve crossing, *Trans. Roy. Soc., Lond.,* 1901, **194B,** 127.

74. Kennedy, R. Experiments on the restoration of paralyzed muscles by means of nerve anastomosis: Part II. Anastomosis of the nerves supplying limb muscles, *Proc. roy. Soc.,* 1913, **87B,** 331.

75. Kleitman, N., and Camille, N. The role of the cerebral cortex in diurnal sleep in dogs, *Amer. J. Physiol.,* 1931, **97,** 537.

76. Klüver, H. Visual disturbances after cerebral lesions, *Psychol. Bull.,* 1927, **24,** 316.

77. Klüver, H. Fragmentary eidetic imagery, *Psychol. Rev.*, 1930, **37**, 441.

78. Klüver, H. Zur Psychologie der Veränderungsfassung bei niederen Affen, *Z. angew. Psychol.*, 1931, **59**, 132.

79. Klüver, H. The equivalence of stimuli in the behavior of monkeys, *J. genet. Psychol.*, 1931, **39**, 3.

80. Köhler, W. *Die physichen Gestalten in Ruhe und im stationären Zustand.* Erlangen: Weltkreisverlag, 1920.

81. Köhler, W. *Intelligenzprufungen an Menschenaffen.* Berlin: 1921.

82. Köhler, W. *Gestalt psychology.* New York: 1929.

83. Lang, J. M., and Olmstead, J. M. D. Conditioned reflexes and pathways in the spinal cord, *Amer. J. Physiol.*, 1923, **65**, 603.

84. Lapique, L. The chronaxic switching in the nervous system, *Science*, 1929, **70**, 151.

85. Larionow, W. Über kortikale Gehörcentra bei Hunden, *Neurol. Zbl.*, 1898, **17**, 137.

86. Lashley, K. S. Studies of cerebral function in learning, *Psychobiology*, 1920, **2**, 55.

87. Lashley, K. S. Studies of cerebral function in learning: II. The effects of long-continued practice upon cerebral localization, *J. comp. Psychol.*, 1921, **1**, 453.

88. Lashley, K. S. Studies of cerebral function in learning: III. The motor areas, *Brain*, 1921, **44**, 255.

89. Lashley, K. S. Studies of cerebral function in learning: IV. Vicarious function after destruction of the visual areas, *Amer. J. Physiol.*, 1922, **59**, 44.

90. Lashley, K. S. Temporal variation in the function of the gyrus precentralis in primates, *Amer. J. Physiol.*, 1923, **65**, 585.

91. Lashley, K. S. Studies of cerebral function in learning: V. The retention of motor habits after destruction of the so-called motor areas in primates, *Arch. Neurol. Psychiat., Chicago*, 1924, **12**, 249.

92. Lashley, K. S. Studies of cerebral function in learning: VI. The theory that synaptic resistance is reduced by the passage of the nerve impulse, *Psychol. Rev.*, 1924, **31**, 369.

93. Lashley, K. S. Studies of cerebral function in learning: VII. The relation between cerebral mass, learning, and retention, *J. comp. Neurol.*, 1926, **41**, 1.

94. Lashley, K. S. *Brain mechanisms and intelligence.* Chicago: 1929.

95. Lashley, K. S. Learning: I. Nervous mechanisms in learning. In *Foundations of experimental psychology.* Worcester: 1929. Pp. 524–563.

96. Lashley, K. S. The mechanism of vision: II. The influence of cerebral lesions upon the threshold of discrimination for brightness in the rat, *J. genet. Psychol.*, 1930, **37**, 461.

97. Lashley, K. S. Basic neural mechanisms in behavior, *Psychol. Rev.*, 1930, **37**, 1.

98. Lashley, K. S. Cerebral control versus reflexology, *J. genet. Psychol.*, 1931, **5**, 3.

99. Lashley, K. S. Mass action in cerebral function, *Science*, 1931, **73**, 245.

100. Lashley, K. S. The mechanism of vision: IV. The cerebral areas necessary for pattern vision in the rat, *J. comp. Neurol.*, 1931, 53, 419.

101. Lashley, K. S. Studies of cerebral function in learning: VIII. A reanalysis of data on mass action in the visual cortex, *J. comp. Neurol.*, 1932, 54, 77.

102. Lashley, K. S., and Ball, J. Spinal conduction and kinesthetic sensitivity in the maze habit, *J. comp. Psychol.*, 1929, 9, 71.

103. Lashley, K. S., and Franz, S. I. The effects of cerebral destruction upon habit-formation and retention in the albino rat, *Psychobiology*, 1917, 1, 71.

104. Lashley, K. S., and McCarthy, D. A. The survival of the maze habit after cerebellar injuries, *J. comp. Psychol.*, 1926, 6, 423.

105. Lashley, K. S., and Wiley, L. E. Studies of cerebral function in learning: IX. Mass action in relation to the number of elements in the problem to be learned, *J. comp. Neurol.*, 1933, 57, 3–56.

106. Layman, J. D. *The function of the superior colliculi in vision.* Master's thesis, Univ. Chicago, 1931.

107. Leeper, R. The reliability and validity of maze experiments with white rats, *Genet. Psychol. Monogr.*, 1932, 11, 137.

108. Leeper, R., and Leeper, D. O. An experimental study of equivalent stimulation in human learning, *J. gen. Psychol.*, 1932, 6, 344.

109. Leyton, A. S. F., and Sherrington, C. S. Observations on the excitable cortex of the chimpanzee, orang-outan, and gorilla, *Quart. J. exp. Physiol.*, 1917, 11, 135.

110. Loeb, J. Sehstörungen nach Verletzungen der Grosshirnrinde, *Pflüg. Arch. ges. Physiol.*, 1884, 34, 67.

111. Loucks, R. B. Efficacy of the rat's motor cortex in delayed alternation, *J. comp. Neurol.*, 1931, 53, 511.

112. Luciani, L. *Physiologie des Menschen*, Bd. 3. Jena: 1907.

113. Maier, N. R. F. The effect of cerebral destruction on reasoning and learning in rats, *J. comp. Neurol.*, 1932, 54, 45.

114. Maier, N. R. F. Cortical destruction in the posterior part of the brain and its effect on reasoning in rats, *J. comp. Neurol.*, 1932, 56, 179–214.

115. Marie, P., and Chatelin, C. Les troubles visuels dus aux lésions des voies optiques intracérébrales et de la sphère visuelle corticale dans les blessures du crâne par coup de feu, *Rev. neurol.*, 1914–15, 28, 882.

116. Marique, J. M. L. Recherches expérimentales sur le mechanisme des centres psychomoteurs du cerveau, *Brain*, 1885, 8, 536.

117. Martin, E. G., and Rich, W. H. The activity of decerebrate and decerebellate chicks, *Amer. J. Physiol.*, 1918, 46, 396.

118. Matthaei, R. Von den Theorien über eine allgemein-physiologische Grundlage des Gedächtnisses, *Z. allg. Physiol.*, 1921, 18, Sammelref. 1.

119. Matthaei, R. Über die Funktionsgestaltung im Zentralnervensystem bei experimentellen Eingriffen am Organismus, *Dtsch. Z. Nervenheilk.*, 1930, 115, 232.

120. Melton, A. W. A note on the relation between brain injury and retentiveness, *Psychol. Bull.*, 1931, 28, 175.

121. Minkowski, M. Zur Physiologie der Sehsphäre, *Pflüg. Arch. ges. Physiol.*, 1911, 141, 171.

122. Minkowski, M. Étude physiologique des circonvolutions rolandiques et pariétales, *Arch. suisse Neurol. Psychiat.*, 1917, **1**, 389.

123. Monakow, C. v. *Die Lokalisation im Grosshirn.* Wiesbaden: 1914.

124. Morgan, L. *Instinct and intelligence.* London: 1912.

125. Moss, F. A. Study of animal drives, *J. exp. Psychol.*, 1924, **7**, 165.

126. Munk. H. *Über die Funktionen von Hirn und Rückenmark.* Berlin: 1909.

127. Oden, R., and Franz, S. I. On cerebral motor control: the recovery from experimentally produced hemiplegia, *Psychobiology*, 1917, **1**, 33.

128. Orton, S. T. "Word-blindness" in school children, *Arch. Neurol. Psychiat., Chicago*, 1925, **14**, 581.

129. Osborne, W. A., and Klivingston, B. Central nervous response to peripheral nervous distortion, *Brain*, 1911, **33**, 260.

130. Panici, L. Sulla sede del centro psichico della visione nelle scimmie, *Arch. scienze med.*, 1903, **27**, 141.

131. Pavlov, I. P. *Conditioned reflexes.* Oxford: 1927.

132. Perkins, F. T., and Wheeler, R. H. Configurational learning in the goldfish, *Comp. Psychol. Monogr.*, 1930, **7**, 1.

133. Peterson, G. M. A preliminary report on right and left handedness in the rat, *J. comp. Psychol.*, 1931, **12**, 243.

134. Peterson, J. Learning where frequency and recency factors are negative, *J. exp. Psychol.*, 1922, **5**, 270.

135. Piéron, H. *Le cerveau et la pensée.* Paris: 1923.

136. Pike, F. H., and Chappell, M. L. On the recovery following lesions in the cerebral cortex, *Science*, 1930, **71**, 76.

137. Poljak, S. *The main afferent fiber systems of the cerebral cortex in primates.* Berkeley: 1932.

138. Poltyrew, S. S., and Zeliony, G. P. Der Hund ohne Grosshirn, *Amer. J. Physiol.*, 1929, **90**, 475.

139. Poltyrew, S. S., and Zeliony, G. P. Grosshirnrinde und Assoziationsfunktion, *Z. Biol.*, 1930, **90**, 157.

140. Poppelreuter, W. *Die psychischen Schädungen durch Kopfschuss.* Leipzig: 1917.

141. Richter, C. P. A behavioristic study of the activity of the rat, *Comp. Psychol. Monogr.*, 1922, **1**, 1.

142. Richter, C. P. Animal behavior and internal drives, *Quart. Rev. Biol.*, 1927, **2**, 307.

143. Rizzolo, A. Motor disturbances consequent upon experimental lesions of the cerebral cortex, *Amer. J. Physiol.*, 1930, **95**, 584.

144. Rogers, F. T. Studies of the brain stem: VI. An experimental study of the corpus striatum of the pigeon as related to various instinctive types of behavior, *J. comp. Neurol.*, 1922, **35**, 21.

145. Rothmann, M. Über die Ergebnisse der Hörprüfung an dressierten Hunden, *Arch. Anat. Physiol., Physiol. Abt.*, 1908, 103.

146. Rothmann, M. Demonstration des Hundes ohne Grosshirn, *Ber. V. Kongress exp. Psychol., Lpz.*, 1912, 256.

147. Rothmann, M. Über die physiologische Wertung der cortico-spina-

len (Pyramiden) Bahn, *Arch. Anat. Physiol., Physiol. Abt., Lpz.,* 1917, 217.

148. Rothmann, M. Zusammenfassender Bericht über den Rothmannschen grosshirnlosen Hund nach klinischer und anatomischer Untersuchungen, *Z. ges. Neurol.,* 1923, **87,** 247.

149. Sänger, A. Ueber die durch die Kriegsverletzungen bedingten Veränderungen im optischen Zentralapparat, *Deutsch. Z. Nervenheilk.,* 1918, **59,** 192.

150. Schäfer, E. A. Note on the results of circumsection of the motor cortex, *J. Physiol.,* 1901, **26,** 28.

151. Schäfer, E. A., and Brown, S. An investigation into the functions of the occipital lobes and temporal lobes of the monkey's brain, *Philos. Trans. roy. Soc.,* 1888, **179B,** 303.

152. Schneirla, T. C. Learning and orientation in ants, *Comp. Psychol. Monogr.,* 1929, **6,** 1.

153. Semon, R. *Die Mneme.* Leipzig: 1908.

154. Shaklee, A. O. The relative heights of the eating and drinking areas in the pigeon's brain and brain evolution, *Amer. J. Physiol.,* 1921, **55,** 65.

155. Skinner, B. F. The concept of the reflex in the description of behavior, *J. gen. Psychol.,* 1931, **5,** 427.

156. Slonaker, J. R. Description of an apparatus for recording the activity of small mammals, *Anat. Rec.,* 1908, **2,** 116.

157. Spearman, C. E. *The abilities of man.* London: 1927.

158. Starlinger, J. Die Durchschneidung beider Pyramiden beim Hunde, *Neurol. Zbl.,* 1895, **14,** 390.

159. Stone, C. P. The congenital sexual behavior of the young male albino rat, *J. comp. Psychol.,* 1922, **2,** 95.

160. Stone, C. P. Delay in the awakening of copulatory ability in the male albino rat incurred by defective diets: I. Quantitative deficiency, *J. comp. Psychol.,* 1924, **4,** 195.

161. Stone, C. P. Delay in the awakening of copulatory ability in the male albino rat incurred by defective diets: II. Qualitative deficiency, *J. comp. Psychol.,* 1925, **5,** 195.

162. Stone, C. P. The effects of cerebral destruction on the sexual behavior of rabbits: II. The frontal and parietal regions, *Amer. J. Physiol.,* 1925, **72,** 372.

163. Stone, C. P. Wildness and savageness in rats of different strains. In *Studies in dynamic psychology.* Chicago: Univ. Chicago Press, 1932.

164. Stone, C. P., and Nyswander, D. The reliability of rat learning scores from the multiple-T maze, as determined by four different methods, *Ped. Sem.,* 1927, **34,** 497.

165. Stout, J. D. On the motor functions of the cerebral cortex of the cat, *Psychobiology,* 1917, **1,** 177.

166. Szymanski, J. S. Aktivität und Ruhe bei Tieren und Menschen, *Z. allg. Physiol.,* 1920, **18,** 105.

167. Talbert, G. A. Über Rindenreizung am freilaufenden Hunden nach J. R. Ewald, *Arch. Anat. Physiol., Physiol. Abt., Lpz.,* 1900, 195.

168. Talmud, J. L. Bedingter Reflex und Allergie, *Nervenarzt.,* 1930, **3,** 467.

169. Thorndike, E. L., et al. *The measurement of intelligence.* New York: 1926.

170. Thorndike, E. L. *Human learning.* New York: 1931.

171. Travis, L. E., and Herren, R. Y. The relation of electrical changes in the brain to reflex activity, *J. comp. Psychol.*, 1931, **12**, 23.

172. Trendelenberg, W. Untersuchungen über den Ausgleich der Bewegungsstörungen nach Rindausschaltung am Affen, *Z. Biol.*, 1915, **65**, 103.

173. Treves, Z., and Aggazzotti, A. Essai d'éducation du pigeon privé des hémisphères cérébraux, *Arch. ital. biol.*, 1901, **36**, 189.

174. Tryon, R. C. Studies in individual differences in maze ability: V. Luminosity and visual acuity as systemative causes of individual differences and an hypothesis of maze ability, *J. comp. Psychol.*, 1931, **12**, 401.

175. Turner, C. H. Behavior of the common roach (Periplaneta orientalis L.) on an open maze, *Biol. Bull.*, 1913, **25**, 348.

176. Van Rynberk, G. Das Lokalisationsproblem im Kleinhirn, *Ergebn. Physiol.*, 1908, **7**, 653.

177. Vitzou, A. N. Récuperation de la vue perdue à la suite d'une première ablation totale des lobes occipitaux chez les singes, *J. Physiol.* (Suppl.), 1898, **23**, 57.

178. Warden, C. J. *Animal motivation.* New York: 1931.

179. Warner, L. H., and Warden, C. J. The development of a standardized animal maze, *Arch. Psychol.*, 1927 (93), 1.

180. Wiley, L. E. The function of the brain in audition, *J. comp. Neurol.*, 1932, **54**, 109.

181. Wilson, S. A. K. An experimental research into the anatomy and physiology of the corpus striatum, *Brain*, 1913, **36**, 427.

182. Yerkes, R. M. The heredity of wildness and savageness in rats, *J. Anim. Behav.*, 1913, **3**, 286.

183. Yerkes, R. M., and Coburn, C. A. A study of the behavior of the pig (Sus scrofa) by the multiple choice method, *J. Anim. Behav.*, 1915, **5**, 185.

184. Yerkes, R. M., and Watson, J. B. Methods of studying vision in animals, *Behav. Monogr.*, 1911, **1**, iv + 90.

185. Zeliony, G. P. Observations sur des chiens auxquels on a enlevé les hémisphères cérébraux, *C. R. Soc. Biol.*, Paris, 1913, **74**, 707.

16. THE MECHANISM OF VISION.

VIII. The Projection of the Retina
upon the Cerebral Cortex
of the Rat [1]

In a previous paper (14) the anatomical projection of the retinal quadrants upon the primary optic centers of the rat was described. The present study is an attempt at further tracing of the projection of the retina from the lateral geniculate nucleus to the cerebral cortex. Putnam and Putnam (21) have described the connections of the lateral geniculate nucleus and area striata in the rabbit and their methods have been followed in this work. In the rabbit the binocular field is projected to the anterior end of the area striata. Behind this, the remainder of the temporal quadrants is represented, and the nasal quadrants are projected to the posterior third of the area. The inferior quadrants are represented laterad to the superior (Fig. 16.1). The topographical relations in the rat are significantly different from this, so that the data from the rabbit cannot safely be used as a basis for experimental work on the rat.

Materials and Methods

The animals used were from a fully pigmented strain derived from a cross of Wistar albino stock with local wild rats. Under ether anesthesia parts of the cerebral cortex in the occipital region were destroyed and after intervals of from three to twenty-four weeks the animals were killed and the brains were fixed, sectioned, stained with thionin, and mounted. The lateral geniculate nuclei were searched for evidence of retrograde degeneration. Camera lucida sketches of sections showing degeneration were made and from these the extent of the degeneration was plotted upon a standard series of drawings of sections at equal intervals through the nucleus. The portions of the area striata remaining intact were identified by their cytoarchitecture and mapped on a standard diagram of the

[1] EDITORS' NOTE: From *J. comp. Neurol.*, 1934, **60**, 57–79. Reproduced by permission of The Wistar Institute. From department of psychology, University of Chicago. This study was aided by a grant from the Otho S. A. Sprague Memorial Institute.

cortex by the graphic method previously described (8). The extent of lesion was mapped in the same way.

Two types of lesions were used: (*a*) small injuries made by undercutting the cortex with a fine knife without damage to the underlying fibers; (*b*) large lesions made with thermocautery, destroying the greater part of the area striata with the underlying fibers and leaving only small parts intact. After small injuries it is often difficult to discover any degeneration in the lateral geniculate nucleus. After extensive lesions the small areas of normal cells in the nucleus are easily identified, but the method is limited by the difficulty of destroying the lateral parts of the

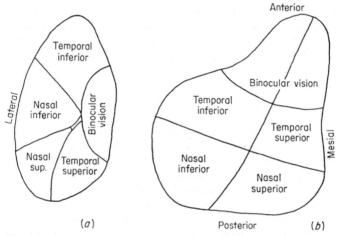

Fig. 16.1. Projection of the retinal quadrants upon the lateral geniculate nucleus and area striata of the rabbit. Modified after Putnam and Putnam (21). (*a*) Transverse section of the left lateral geniculate nucleus, pars dorsalis; (*b*) left area striata.

striate area without interrupting the fibers to the more mesial areas. The combination of the two methods gave best results for a complete survey of the area.

The material available for the study included seventy-four cases with complete serial sections through the lateral geniculate nucleus and striate area and 144 cases from a previous study in which sections at intervals of 0.25 mm. had been preserved. This material was inspected and fifty-two cases were selected for complete reconstruction.

When the reconstructions were completed the diagrams of the cortical lesions were superimposed and the areas of destruction common to different lesions and those unique for each lesion were determined. Similarly the diagrams of the lateral geniculate nuclei were superimposed and corresponding areas plotted. This gave a basis for correlation of small cortical and nuclear regions. . . .

The Character of Retrograde Degeneration in the Nucleus

In the lateral geniculate nucleus,[2] pars dorsalis, of the rat only one type of ganglion cell is demonstrable with the thionin stain. These cells are triangular in section and of quite uniform size, averaging 17 by 25 μ, with a variation in length from 20 to 35 μ. Their large nuclei average 12 μ in diameter. In the normal nucleus they are somewhat scattered, the mean number determined from twenty counts being 22 per 0.001 cu. mm. . . .

Two types of glia cells occur in the nucleus. Of these, one type has spherical nuclei, 4 to 6 μ in diameter, and is about as numerous as the ganglion cells, averaging 18.5 per 0.001 cu. mm. The second type has thin rod-like nuclei, 2 by 10 μ, and is less frequent, averaging 5 per 0.001 cu. mm. The cytoplasm of both is unstained.

After total destruction of the striate area of the cerebral cortex or interruption of the optic radiation, there seems to be ultimately a complete degeneration of all of the ganglion cells in the pars dorsalis of the lateral geniculate nucleus. In two such cases studied carefully, with brains fixed three months after operation, not a single normal ganglion cell could be identified in the nucleus. The cells are reduced in number, counts giving 9 or fewer per 0.001 cu. mm., and those which remain are reduced to less than half of their normal dimensions. Their nuclei are shriveled and neither nucleus nor cytoplasm stains sharply. . . . The number of glia cells is much increased, those with spherical nuclei averaging 63, those with rod nuclei 24 per 0.001 cu. mm.

When only a part of the area striata is destroyed, a limited zone of degeneration appears in the nucleus. The outlines of such zones are quite sharp. Within the degenerated zone no normal ganglion cells are found, and the number of glia cells is more than doubled. Outside of the zone the ganglion cells appear quite normal. Along the borders of the zone for a depth of about 0.2 mm. degenerated and normal cells may appear intermingled. There sometimes appears to be an increase in number of glia cells throughout the nucleus.

Limits of the Cerebral Visual Field

The limits of the total distribution of the optic radiation to the cerebral cortex have not been determined for lower mammals. Poljak (20), using Marchi methods after lesions in the lateral geniculate nucleus of monkeys,

---

[2] EDITORS' NOTE: A series of photomicrographs showing degeneration in the lateral geniculate body, as well as one related diagrammatic figure and accompanying description in the text, have been omitted.

was able to establish the fact that the termination of the optic radiation is entirely confined to the area striata.

The area striata in the rat has been described by Fortuyn (3), Sugita (23) and Volkmann (24). More detailed studies of the area in the mouse have been made by Isenschmid (6) and Rose (22). These investigators differ with respect to the cytoarchitectural criteria by which the area is identified and the extent of the area as shown on their maps, although they agree in locating it upon the dorsal convexity of the occipital pole.

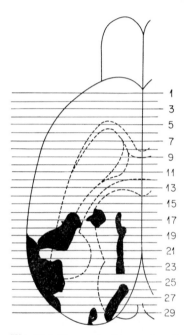

The criterion upon which there is the closest agreement is the character of the layer IV as "strikingly thick, with small closely packed granular elements" (22). In the rat this layer is clearly recognizable on the dorsal convexity of the occipital pole. Its mesial and caudal limits are sharply defined and anteriorly it adjoins a typical motor field containing the largest pyramidal cells of the entire cortex. Its lateral and anterolateral margins, however, blend gradually with the auditory and somesthetic cortex, so that exact determination of its limits in these directions seems impossible. In our reconstructions of the area striata the lateral margin was arbitrarily set at the point where layer IV was no longer visible as a distinctly darker stripe under low magnification.

Fig. 16.2. Composite diagram based upon eight cases with lesions bordering upon the area striata without discoverable degeneration in the lateral geniculate nucleus.

Our material includes a number of cases with lesions bordering upon but not invading the area striata. Figure 16.2 is a composite showing in eight cases the extent of lesions outside of the striate area after which no trace of degeneration in the nucleus was found. Almost the entire perimeter of the area has been explored in this way without evidence of degeneration in the nucleus.

The nucleus has also been examined in cases with extensive lesions in the frontal and temporal regions and no trace of degeneration detected. On the other hand, any invasion of the area distinguished by the characteristic fourth layer is attended by degeneration in the nucleus. It seems certain therefore that the striate area delimited by cytoarchitectural methods represents quite accurately the visual projection area and that no large number of visual fibers from the lateral geniculate goes to any other area.

Degeneration in the Lateral Geniculate Nucleus after Lesions in the Area Striata

The structural relations between the cortex and lateral geniculate nucleus are complicated and the number of cases upon which our detailed analysis is based is too great for complete presentation. For brevity of

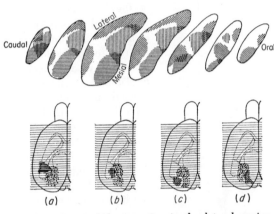

Fig. 16.3. Zones of degeneration in the lateral geniculate nucleus after the lesions within the area striata shown in the lower figures. Seven coronal sections at equal intervals through the left nucleus are shown, arranged as if viewed from the caudal pole. Below are reconstructions of the cortical lesions in four cases in which the lesions were confined to the cortex and did not involve the external capsule. The extent of the area striata is indicated by stippling. The four lesions and corresponding zones of degeneration in the nucleus are distinguished by the direction of hatching. The degeneration in these four cases corresponds quite closely to the projection of the four retinal quadrants. (a) Superior temporal; (b) inferior temporal; (c) inferior nasal; (d) superior nasal.

exposition a few clear cases presenting the general principles of arrangement will first be described.

As found by Putnam and Putnam (21) in the rabbit, there is no degeneration in the pars ventralis of the lateral geniculate nucleus after any lesion to the striate cortex. Further description and discussion of the lateral geniculate nucleus will therefore be limited to the pars dorsalis. Figure 16.3 is a composite of four cases with lesions confined to distinct parts of the area striata with only a little overlapping of the lesions and with relatively slight overlapping of the zones of degeneration in the lateral geniculate nucleus. Seven transverse sections at equal intervals throughout the length of the lateral geniculate nucleus, pars dorsalis, are shown.

The figure brings out several features of the relations of cortex and nucleus which are characteristic of all the cases studied. (a) Lesions in separate cortical areas are followed by degeneration in distinct zones of the nucleus. The extent of overlapping of the degenerated zones of the nucleus does not seem to exceed the overlap of the corresponding lesions. (b) Irrespective of the locus of the lesion within the area striata, the zone of degeneration extends throughout the entire length of the nucleus, with the following qualification: (c) The boundaries of the zones do not conform to the long axis of the nucleus, but intersect this at a sharp angle, so that each zone of degeneration passes from the anteromesial to the posterolateral region of the nucleus. This is not an artifact due to chance form of the lesions, but appears in all of the cases reconstructed. An identical arrangement of zones appeared in the projection of the retina within the nucleus (14). The arrangement is such that only the posterior half of the area striata is represented in the anterior pole of the nucleus and only the anterior half in the posterior pole. Since the data are more complete for the projection of the angular than of the concentric dimensions of the retina these two projections will be considered separately.

Projection of the Angular Dimensions of the Retina upon the Area Striata

In the analysis of the projection of the retina upon the lateral geniculate nucleus a close correspondence was found between adjacent sectors of the retina and adjacent sectors around the longitudinal axis of the lateral geniculate nucleus. The horizontal mid-plane of the nucleus corresponds to the horizontal meridian of the retina, the vertical mid-plane to the vertical meridian of the retina, inverted, and intervening sectors of the retina are represented at corresponding angles.

This angular differentiation is equally accurately represented in the projection of the lateral geniculate nucleus upon the cortex. The four cases shown in Fig. 16.3 were selected as involving degeneration in almost exactly the four zones of the lateral geniculate nucleus representing the four retinal quadrants: (a) inferior temporal; (b) superior temporal; (c) superior nasal; and (d) inferior nasal. The overlapping areas in Fig. 16.3 serve to define more limited points of correspondence of nucleus and cortex than any of the lesions alone. Similar overlapping areas of the cortex and zones of the nucleus were determined for all of the cases reconstructed. From these a number of cases were selected to give a series of restricted areas continuous around the perimeter of the area striata. These areas with the corresponding zones of degeneration in the nucleus are shown in Fig. 16.4. The figure represents a surface view of the left area striata (b) and a coronal section through the middle of the pars dorsalis

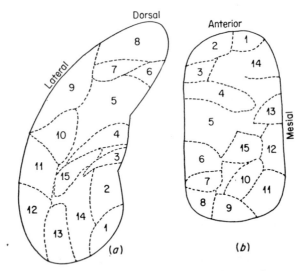

Fig. 16.4. Detailed projection of the lateral geniculate nucleus upon the area striata, determined by plotting the overlap of lesions and of zones of degeneration in the area and nucleus. (a) Lateral geniculate nucleus; (b) area striata, in surface view. For simplicity, only one coronal section at the area of maximal thickness of the nucleus is shown. Each of the areas marked represents a section of a zone passing diagonally through the length of the nucleus. Corresponding areas bear the same number in the two figures.

of the nucleus (a). For simplicity of presentation only one section is shown. Each of the degenerated areas represented in Fig. 16.4a could be traced throughout the length of the nucleus. A comparison of Figs. 16.3 and 16.4 should make this point clear. Thus the zone marked 6 in Fig. 16.4 was determined from the overlap of the lesions in b and c of Fig. 16.3 and the corresponding overlapping of the zones of degeneration in the nucleus can be traced through the caudal 5 of the sections shown in that figure.

Most of the areas shown in the figure were verified in at least two cases.

When smaller areas of overlap than those shown were dealt with, some irregularities appeared as apparent reversals in the order of arrangement around the perimeter of the area, but this never involved displacement from the consistent position on the map of more than 10 or 15 degrees and was almost certainly due to inaccuracies in reconstruction or to individual differences in the shape of the striate area.

It is evident that there is a fine differentiation of the area striata corresponding to limited regions of the lateral geniculate nucleus and that this in turn corresponds closely to the angular dimensions of the retina. The anterior border of the area corresponds to the superior temporal quadrant. Passing caudad along the lateral margin of the area, the points correspond to successive sectors around the inferior temporal retina, reaching the ventral mid-line at the caudal end of the area and so on around its margin through the nasal quadrants to the starting point.

The Projection of the Concentric Zones of the Retina

In his study of the projection of the retina upon the lateral geniculate nucleus of the rabbit Overbosch (19) concluded that the peripheral regions of the retina are projected to the surfaces of the nucleus and that the nearer the disc the fibers originate, the deeper is their termination in the nucleus. In the rat the projection of the concentric retinal zones upon the nucleus is difficult to establish from Marchi material, but seems to be like that in the rabbit (14).

In the projection of the lateral geniculate nucleus upon the area striata there is clearly a correspondence between the central portion of the nucleus and the middle of the striate area. Thus, in Fig. 16.4*b* the areas numbered 4, 7, 10, and 15 are regions where the overlap of two lesions was confined chiefly to the central part of the striate area and in the nucleus the corresponding degenerated zones are largely confined to the interior of the nucleus and in the same relative positions. Although the number of areas identified in this way is not large, it seems adequate to establish the correspondence of concentric nuclear zones and concentric areas within the visual cortex.

The Fineness of Anatomical Localization

From his physiological studies of the dog, Minkowski (17) concluded that each retinal point is projected to a relatively large cortical area and that the cortical fields for adjacent retinal points overlap. Anatomical evidence upon the fineness of differentiation in the retinal projection has been somewhat uncertain, but has favored the view that there is a good bit of overlap between the zones representing separate retinal points. The present study has brought out a finer degree of differentiation than has been demonstrated in any previous anatomical study. Small cortical lesions are followed by degeneration within small, sharply delimited zones of the nucleus; with diverse cortical lesions the order of arrangement of the degenerated zones in the nucleus corresponds accurately to the order of arrangement of lesions and this is true also for diverse lesions in the retina. Although far from showing a cell to cell correspondence the evidence seems clear that the degree of differentiation and anatomical correspondence is finer than any anatomical units which can be dealt with by operative procedures. Moreover, in order to give the correspondence found in size of overlap for lesions and degeneration, no small point in the cortex can be connected with any large area in the lateral geniculate nucleus. Conversely, no small zone of the nucleus can be projected to a large cortical field, for this would result in partial, diffuse degeneration after small cortical lesions instead of complete degeneration of clean-cut areas as found. The precision and consistency of the data can be accounted for only upon the assumption that the units separately represented are exceedingly small.

The Projection of the Field of Acute Vision

In studies of the rat's retina I have found a greater concentration of ganglion cells in the inner half of the upper temporal region than in other parts of the retina. This region corresponds at least roughly to the retinal areas in the line of fixation in binocular vision. There is some evidence that accurate discrimination of visual patterns does not occur unless they are fixated with a rather limited part of this binocular field (12). The projection of this area within the lateral geniculate nucleus is to approximately the regions numbered 2, 3, 4, and 5 in Fig. 16.4a. The corresponding regions of the area striata occupy the anterolateral fourth of the area.

Experimental evidence also points to the greater importance of this than of other parts of the striate area for pattern vision. In a study of the effects of destruction of the striate area upon the rat's capacity to form habits based upon visual pattern discrimination I found that the only area common to all lesions which abolished pattern vision was this anterolateral portion of the striate area (9). A later study (15) showed that the region is not essential for discrimination of simple patterns, but its relatively greater importance for detail vision than the remaining parts of the striate area seems clear.

Absence of Degeneration in the Other Optic Centers

Fibers from the optic nerve have been described as terminating in the lateral nucleus, pars posterior, of the thalamus, in the pretectile nucleus, and in the large-celled nucleus of Clark. It is still uncertain whether the fibers observed actually terminate in any of these nuclei or merely pass through them on the way to the superior colliculus (14).

In our material several good series are available with complete destruction of the area striata and degeneration throughout the lateral geniculate nucleus, pars dorsalis. The so-called optic thalamus of these cases has been examined for traces of degeneration. In all of the nuclei enumerated above, the cells appear normal and there is no suggestion of reduction in their number or of the multiplication of glia cells so characteristic of degeneration in the lateral geniculate nucleus. The same is true of the pars ventralis of the lateral geniculate nucleus in which no trace of degeneration could be detected.

The Probable Forms of Scotoma in the Rat

In interpreting the effects of cerebral lesions upon visually determined reactions of animals it is difficult to distinguish between a limitation of the visual field by scotoma and an amnesia or agnosia for visual objects. Thus the controversy between Loeb (16) and Munk (18) concerning the existence of "psychic blindness" hinged upon the possible extent of scotoma, Loeb holding that the dog's inability to recognize objects after the destruction of area A was a purely sensory defect due to a restriction of the visual field and not, as Munk thought, a limitation of the perceptual process.

No method has been devised for accurate mapping of scotomas in animals and even the rough determination of hemianopsia possible with the dog cannot be made with the rat. For the present we must therefore fall back upon anatomic data to gain any notion of the form of the restricted visual field after cortical lesions.

In our experimental work the majority of lesions which destroy the cortex also pierce the underlying layers of fibers. As a result there is involvement not only of the cortex actually destroyed, but also of projection fibers to regions more remote from the lower centers. Penetrating lesions in the area striata are generally followed by a characteristic pattern of degeneration in the lateral geniculate nucleus. . . . The zone of degeneration extends diagonally downward across the nucleus from the mesial to the ventral surface. For practically all penetrating lesions the boundaries of degeneration are parallel to those shown. This means that all the fibers of the optic radiation enter the anterior and lateral margins of the area striata and follow a parallel course diagonally mediad and caudad to their termination in the cortex.

In Fig. 16.5 I have attempted to translate these relations into terms of limitation of the visual field. A small penetrating lesion in the anterolateral part of the area striata (Fig. 16.5e) should produce a scotoma in the lower inner margin of the half field and lesions progressively farther caudad should eliminate vision through a series of zones parelleling those indicated in the figure.

The condition here is seemingly quite different from the definite

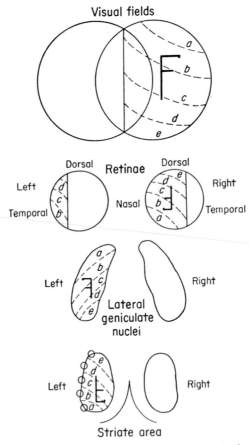

Fig. 16.5. The probable form of scotomas in the rat after penetrating lesions in the lateral margin of the area striata. Below is shown a surface view of the left area striata with five lesions indicated by circles and the zones of projection fibers interrupted by them suggested by broken lines. Next above is shown a coronal section through the middle of the lateral geniculate nucleus with the corresponding zones of degeneration. These in turn are projected upon the crossed and uncrossed retinae, as viewed from behind, and finally the projection upon the visual fields is indicated. The asymmetrical letter *F* is inserted to indicate the inversions which occur during projection to the cortex.

quadrantic defects in human scotoma. There is, however, a certain resemblance to the forms of scotoma reported by Hitzig (5) after partial interruption of the optic radiation in the dog. The edges of the scotomas described by Hitzig rarely correspond to the horizontal axis of the eye, but pass diagonally across the field. The difference in direction of these lines from that predicted for the rat is what might be expected from the shift of the striate area to the posteromesial surface of the cortex in the dog, which would give the fibers of the radiation a course more cephalad through the area.

Discussion

This study and the preceding one in the series give a fairly detailed picture of the projection of different parts of the retina upon the cerebral cortex of the rat. The results clearly establish a "cortical retina," as conceived by Munk. Not only do the retinal quadrants have separate representation, but the fineness of localization must approach a point-to-point correspondence to give such consistent results with the crude anatomical methods available. In the projection the spacial arrangement of elements is consistently maintained, so that the cortical field presents not only a specific representation of different parts of the retina, but also maintains essentially the same relative positions of the parts represented.

The demonstration of such a point-to-point correspondence in the topographic arrangement of the visual system (reported also by Poljak for the monkey) still leaves the question of the functional significance of the correspondence unsettled. It is conceivable that the maintenance of the spacial relations of the retinal elements in their projection to the cortex might be no more than an accident of growth due to the fact that growing nerve fibers within a tract tend to parallel each other rather than cross. In such a case no functional significance could be attached to the orderly arrangement of corresponding points in the peripheral and central structures. But such an interpretation is precluded by the complex reassortment of fibers which occurs upon emergence from the chiasma and again within the optic radiation. In the rat the orderly arrangement of optic fibers seems wholly lost in the optic nerve (14), the fibers cross each other complexly in the optic tracts and finally resume their original relative positions, but now inverted and projected in a third dimension in the lateral geniculate nucleus. Again within the optic radiation the projection fibers are complexly crossed [3] yet emerge in the cortex after a second inversion to reproduce the topographic arrangement of the retina, once more in two dimensions.

[3] Lesions which damage the optic radiation at some distance in front of the anterior margin of the area striata are followed by a partial degeneration of the lateral geniculate nucleus characterized by the presence of a few normal nerve cells scattered uniformly throughout the nucleus. This can only mean that the topographic relations of the fibers are not maintained in the radiation.

Such facts are incomprehensible except on the assumption that not only is the conduction of excitations from separate retinal ganglion cells over separate isolated paths to the cortex important for integration, but that the establishment in the cortex of a pattern of excitation corresponding in its spacial properties to the spacial pattern of excitation on the retina is also essential for integration. This in turn has clear implications concerning further stages of integration in the system. The reflexological theories of cerebral integration assume that the conditioned-reflex mechanisms consist of chains of neurons with limited intercellular connections, differentiated by reduction of synaptic resistances or neurobiotactic growth of fibers. If this were true for the entire conditioned-reflex circuit, there would be no more reason for the preservation of the topographic relations of the sensory surface in the cortex than for the reproduction of the geographic distribution of the instruments of a telephone system upon the switchboard of the central exchange.

The spacial reproduction of sensory surfaces upon the cortex becomes intelligible only upon the assumption that it forms the basis for some "field organization" in which the pattern of excitation in definite spacial relations is a determining factor in the arousal of the final motor response. Bethe (1) has applied this conception to the spinal reflex centers and has formulated a theory to account for the coordinations of walking based upon the relative excitation of different centers rather than upon specific neuron connections. I have suggested other possible types of "field organization" (11) which conform both to the anatomical facts of localization and restricted conduction and to experimental data on plasticity and equivalence of function of parts within the system.

A number of recent writers have expressed the view that the brain of the rat is relatively undifferentiated in localization of functions and that experimental results upon cerebral function in this animal cannot therefore be generalized to higher forms in which the principle of localization is more fully expressed. The results of the present study make this position rather untenable. The visual system of the rat is clearly as highly differentiated with respect to anatomic localization, within the limits of the animal's visual acuity, as is that of primates yet this specialized system shows precisely those field properties of plasticity, equipotentiality and mass action (7, 9, 10, 11, 13) which the principle of localization is supposed to preclude.

I have elsewhere summarized the experimental data upon the functions of the rat's visual system (10, 13). After complete destruction of the striate areas the animals still retain some capacity to distinguish separate objects in the visual field and even after complete interruption of the optic radiations the capacity to form habits based upon the discrimination of different degrees of luminosity is little, if at all, impaired.

Since after such lesions the lateral geniculate nucleus seems to undergo complete degeneration, these functions can scarcely be ascribed to it as I have formerly done.

My finding that some discrimination of separate visual objects is possible after destruction of the striate cortex but not after interruption of the optic radiations (9) was interpreted as evidence for scattered geniculo-cortical fibers to regions outside of the striate area, but the complete degeneration of the lateral geniculate nucleus after destruction of the striate cortex opposes this and seems to require some optic connection to the cortex other than by way of the lateral geniculate nucleus. Only a further refinement of experimental and anatomic methods can settle these questions.

Summary

Retrograde degeneration of the lateral geniculate nucleus, pars dorsalis, of the rat was mapped after a variety of lesions in the cerebral cortex. No degeneration is evident except after lesions within the area striata. The projection of the lateral geniculate nucleus upon the cortex shows a high degree of localization which must approach a point-to-point correspondence to give the clear differentiation obtained.

The most anteromesial part of the striate area represents the dorsal meridian of the eye. Along the lateral margin of the area successive sectors of the temporal quadrants are represented and the projection of the nasal quadrants continues along the mesial border. Concentric zones of the retina seem to be represented by concentric zones in the area striata. The binocular field is projected to the anterolateral margin of the area. Thus in the rat there seems to be a true cortical retina in which there is not only a separate representation of small retinal areas but a maintenance of the general topographical relations of these areas.

No degeneration in other primary optic centers after lesions to the area striata could be demonstrated.

REFERENCES

1. Bethe, A. Plastizität und Zentrenlehre, *Handb. norm. path. Physiol.*, 1931, **15** (II), 1175–1220.

2. Clark, W. E. Le Gros. The structure and connections of the thalamus, *Brain*, 1932, **55**, 406–470.

3. Fortuyn, A. E. B. D. Cortical cell lamination of the brains of some rodents, *Arch. Neurol. Psychiat.*, Lond., 1914, **4**, 221–354.

4. Gurdjian, E. S. The diencephalon of the albino rat, *J. comp. Neurol.*, 1927, **43**, 1–114.

5. Hitzig, E. Alte und neue Untersuchungen über das Gehirn: IV. Über die Beziehungen der Rinde und der subcorticalen Ganglien zum Sehact des Hundes, *Arch. Psychiat. Nervenheilk.*, 1903, **37**, 277–609.

6. Isenschmid, R. Zur Kenntnis der Grosshirnrinde der Maus, *Abh. königl. preuss. Akad. Wiss., phys.-math. Classe*, 1911, 1–78.

7. Lashley, K. S. Studies of cerebral function in learning: VII. The relation between cerebral mass, learning and retention, *J. comp. Neurol.*, 1926, **41**, 1–58.

8. Lashley, K. S. *Brain mechanisms and intelligence.* Chicago: 1929.

9. Lashley, K. S. The mechanism of vision: IV. The cerebral areas necessary for pattern vision in the rat, *J. comp. Neurol.*, 1931, **53**, 419–478.

10. Lashley, K. S. Cerebral control versus reflexology, *J. genet. Psychol.*, 1931, **5**, 3–20.

11. Lashley, K. S. Mass action in cerebral function, *Science*, 1931, **73**, 245–254.

12. Lashley, K. S. The mechanism of vision: V. The structure and image-forming power of the rat's eye, *J. comp. Psychol.*, 1932, **13**, 173–200.

13. Lashley, K. S. Integrative functions of the cerebral cortex, *Physiol. Rev.*, 1933, **13**, 1–42.

14. Lashley, K. S. The mechanism of vision: VII. The projection of the retina upon the primary optic centers of the rat, *J. comp. Neurol.*, 1934, **59**, 341–373.

15. Lashley, K. S., and Frank, Margaret. The mechanism of vision: VI. The lateral portion of the area striata in the rat: a correction, *J. comp. Neurol.*, 1932, **55**, 525–529.

16. Loeb, J. Die Sehstörungen nach Verletzungen der Grosshirnrinde, *Arch. ges. Physiol.*, 1884, **34**, 67–172.

17. Minkowski, M. Zur Physiologie der Sehsphäre, *Arch. ges. Physiol.*, 1911, **141**, 171–327.

18. Munk, H. *Über die Funktionen der Grosshirnrinde.* Berlin: 1890. Pp. 1–320.

19. Overbosch, J. F. A. *Experimenteel-anatomische onderzoekingen over de projectie der retina in het centrale zenuwstelsel.* Amsterdam: 1928. Pp. 1–88.

20. Poljak, S. The main afferent fiber systems of the cerebral cortex in primates, *Univ. Calif. Publ. Anat*, 1932, **2**, xiv + 370.

21. Putnam, T. J., and Putnam, I. K. Studies on the central visual system: I. The anatomic projection of the retinal quadrants on the striate cortex of the rabbit, *Arch. Neurol. Psychiat., Chicago*, 1926, **16**, 1–20.

22. Rose, M. Cytoarchitecktonischer Atlas der Grosshirnrinde der Maus, *J. Psychol. Neur., Lpz.*, 1929, **40**, 1–51.

23. Sugita, N. Comparative studies on the growth of the cerebral cortex: II. On the increase in the thickness of the cerebral cortex during the postnatal growth of the brain, *J. comp. Neurol.*, 1917, **28**, 495–591.

24. Volkmann, v. Vergleichende Untersuchungen an der Rinde der 'motorischen' und 'Sehregionen' von Nagetieren, *Anat. Anz., Ergheft*, 1926, **61**, 234–243.

17. THE MECHANISM OF VISION.

XI. A Preliminary Test of
Innate Organization [1]

Observations upon young animals (1, 4, 5) and studies of the recovery of vision in congenitally blind patients operated for cataract (3) suggest that the perception of spacial extent and of depth in the visual field is not dependent upon experience or the building up of a system of motor habits, but is the immediate product of some coordinating mechanism elaborated by growth processes in the absence of visual stimulation adequate for learning. The available material is not well controlled, however, either from the standpoint of the past visual experience of the subjects or of the accuracy of the spacial localization. The experiments reported below were devised to give more adequate data upon the accuracy of reaction to visual distance when there has been no opportunity for the formation of specific associations.

Method

Rats were reared in darkness from birth to 100 days of age and their thresholds for visual distance then determined with a minimum of practice. Females with litters 2 to 3 days old were placed in small cages within a large ventilated dark box in a dark room. Every second day the box was opened in dim light for not more than 10 seconds while food was supplied. These brief exposures to light, amounting to less than 10 minutes in 100 days, may have given opportunity for the formation of some visual habits. They should have been avoided, but we do not regard them as a serious defect in the experiment since, in the first place, the time was too brief for the elaboration of such a system of motor habits as would be required for accurate space perception; second, the maximum dimension of the cages was 25 cm. so that there was not opportunity for formation of motor habits for the range of distances used later in tests; and third, the animals were wild and invariably crouched in the rear of the cages during exposure to light.

For testing the limen for distance in the visual field a modified form of the apparatus previously described by Russell (2) was used. This measures the

[1] EDITORS' NOTE: K. S. Lashley and J. T. Russell, authors. From *J. genet. Psychol.*, 1934, **45**, 136–144. Reproduced by permission of The Journal Press. From the department of psychology, University of Chicago.

force exerted by the animal in attempting to jump through a predetermined distance from one small platform to another. The animal is placed upon the recording-platform, the landing-platform is placed at a measured distance from the first, the animal is induced to jump, and the force exerted is recorded. The apparatus is calibrated to read in grams of force required to displace the pendulum to each scale-reading.

The procedure in the experiment was as follows:

1. The animal was removed from the dark cage to an artificially lighted room and placed on the recording-platform. The landing-platform was placed 5 cm. away and the animal forced to step across the gap to the food on the landing-platform. Five repetitions of this were sufficient to establish spontaneous crossing.

2. The landing-platform was removed to 20 cm. This was the animal's first sight of the landing-platform at a distance too great to span with the vibrissae. Five trials at this distance were given on each of two consecutive days, to establish spontaneous jumping. Between test periods the animals were kept in darkness.

3. After 5 trials at 20 cm. on the second day, the distance between the platforms was increased to 40 cm. Records of 3 jumps at this distance were secured. The distance was again reduced to 20 cm. for 3 jumps, and again increased to 40 cm. for 3 jumps.

4. On the following day the animal was given one jump at each of the distances 24, 26, 28, 30, 32, 34, 36, 38, and 40 cm. in chance order.

Experimental Data

Thirteen animals were put through the tests. For brevity, their individual records are omitted and only averages for the group are given. In general, their records are consistent and for each constant the number of cases failing to conform to the trend of the majority is reported.

Preliminary Training. On the first jump at 20 cm. (the animals' first attempt to jump to any visual object) all but 2 exerted a force in excess of that required to span the distance. Only one fell short of the landing-platform. During the practice trials all the others tended to reduce the force exerted. The averages of the 13 animals for the 10 successive trials were the following:

Trial	1	2	3	4	5	6	7	8	9	10
Average force	13	14	13	10	12	7	7	7	6	7 gms.[2]

[2] The small amount of force exerted in these trials is accounted for by the animal's first method of jumping. From the short distance he usually stands almost erect on his hind feet and tail at the edge of the recording-platform; he stretches forward, overbalances, and as he falls forward gives a slight hop with the hind feet, stretches out the forefeet and catches the edge of the landing-platform. For greater distances the method of jumping is entirely changed. The animal crouches with all four feet on the edge of the recording-platform, tenses and launches himself almost horizontally toward the landing-platform. With a little practice the latter method is adopted for all distances. This fact accounts for the greater force exerted at 20 cm. after the animals had jumped at 40.

First Jump at 40 cm. After the tenth jump at 20 cm. the landing-platform was removed to 40 cm. All the animals were disturbed by the change, hesitating, stretching toward the landing-platform, and swaying from side to side. When they finally jumped, it was in all but 3 cases with significantly greater force than the last jump at 20 cm. The average force exerted by the 13 animals in the last 5 trials of preliminary training at 20 cm. was 6.8 gms. Their average force for the first jump at 40 cm. was 15.4 gms. On this trial all but one of the animals fell short of the landing-platform, but the increase in force above that at 20 cm. is significant.

The ratios between the average force for the last 5 jumps at 20 cm. and the force in the first jump at 40 cm. for each of the 13 animals were the following. Decreased force is indicated by italics.

6.8; 4.1; 1.9; 2.4; 3.0; 4.6; 3.4; 3.9; 5.0; 1.4; *0.9; 0.8; 0.7.*

Ten of the animals showed a significant increase in force and 7 of them increased the force by more than 300 per cent.

Subsequent Tests at 40 and 20 cm. All but one of the animals fell short on the first jump at 40 cm. All were given 2 more trials at this distance. The averages for the 3 trials at 40 cm. were 15.4, 19.7, and 26.2. The averages show a progressive increase and the individual scores of every animal showed a similar increase in force. The force was still inadequate for the distance, and of the 39 jumps only 5 reached the landing-platform.

The distance between the platforms was again decreased to 20 cm. Since all but 3 of the animals had fallen short in the last jump at 40 cm., we should expect a further increase in force, if the change in the visual situation were ineffective. But 10 of the animals immediately reduced the force of their jump, so that the average was reduced from 26.2 to 22. Considerable hesitation and disturbance were exhibited again with the change in distance, which indicates that the first increase in force with the 40 cm. distance was not due merely to an increase in emotional tone.

Two more trials were given at 20 cm., resulting in further decrease in force (22.0, 18.8, 14.7 gms. in the 3 successive trials). The distance was again increased to 40 cm. with an immediate increase of average force from 14.7 to 22.4. Two animals now refused to jump at this distance. Ten of the remaining 11 increased their force. Two more trials at 40 cm. brought the average force up to 31.5 gms.

Liminal Tests. Russell (2) has shown that animals reared under normal daylight conditions are able to distinguish intervals of less than 2 cm. through a range from 26 to 36 cm. His conclusions were based upon the scores of 8 animals with 12 jumps at each distance and the average scores for the group show only one reversal in the force exerted for intervals of 1 cm. throughout this range. We could not employ this method with our animals, since it involves too much practice, but decided to give each animal one trial at each 2 cm. interval through a similar range. The distances were presented in chance order, thus: 28, 38, 34, 24, 32, etc. cm. Four of the animals refused to jump at distances above 30 cm. The average scores are based upon the records of the remaining 9.

The averages of force for each of the 9 intervals were the following:

Distance	24	26	28	30	32	34	36	38	40	cm.
Average force	24.3	26.3	26.9	29.4	27.7	32.1	38.5	36.3	41.1	gms.

The series contains two reversals of order in the force exerted with increasing distance, but the inversion is of only one place and the figures give conclusive evidence that the limen for distance is below 2 cm. throughout most of the range of the test. We cannot compare these data directly with the group scores reported by Russell because his figures are based upon the averages of 12 trials

Table 17.1. A Comparison of the Relation of Force in Jumping to Distance to Be Covered for Animals Reared in Daylight and for Animals Reared in Darkness

Distance	24	25	26	27	28	29	30	31	32
Percentage force:[*] "Light" group			100	103	107	111	115	113	117
"Dark" group		87	100		102		112		105

Distance	33	34	35	36	37	38	39	40
Percentage force:[*] "Light" group	117	121	122	128				
"Dark" group		122		146		138		156

[*] Force is expressed as percentage of that exerted for a jump at 26 cm. The data for animals reared in light are taken from Russell (2) and each figure represents the average of 96 records. The others are based upon a single jump for each of 9 animals.

for each rat at each distance and the larger number of trials should decrease irregularities in the scores, even with animals having no lower limen. The individual scores which he gives (2, Table 6) are based upon 12 jumps for each animal and show an average of 1.8 inversions of order for the distance of 2 cm. Our group scores are based upon an average of 9 jumps and give two inversions of order. On the basis of this comparison we may conclude that the limen for distance for the animals reared in darkness is not significantly inferior to that of animals reared in the light.[3]

We may also compare the two groups with respect to the graduation of force to distance. Russell (2, p. 146) presents these figures as percentage of the force for a distance of 26 cm. His data are given with ours in Table 17.1. The gradation of force is very similar in the two series.

[3] These tests do not, of course, measure the difference limen for distance but merely give a figure below which the limen must lie and measure the accuracy of discrimination for the interval of 2 cm. The significance of the number of inversions may be estimated by a comparison of Russell's data for pigmented and albino animals. The latter required an interval of 4 cm. before they reached an accuracy equal to that of our present series of 2 cm.

Thus, in so far as the data are comparable, the animals reared in darkness do not seem significantly inferior to those reared in light in their ability to graduate the force of their jumps in proportion to the distance to be covered.[4]

Discussion

The results of our experiment are shown graphically in Fig. 17.1. The evidence seems clear that the animals, upon the first experience of a new visual distance, attempted to adjust the force of their jumps to the distance and that, for a series of distances, the force was nearly as accurately graduated as was that of animals reared under normal daylight conditions.

The measurement of depth perception in the animals has required some preliminary training in order to establish the reaction used as an

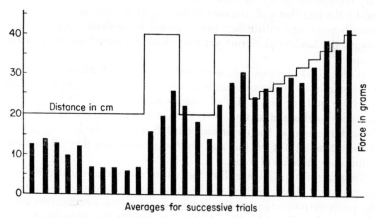

Fig. 17.1. Graphic presentation of the data of these experiments. The vertical bars represent the average force in grams exerted by the rats in their efforts to cover the distance represented by the light line above. Successive jumps are represented in order from left to right, except the last 9, which were given in chance order of distance.

indicator. Are this training and the previous visual experience during introduction of food into the dark box sufficient to account for the discrimination of distance shown by the tests? The following considerations seem to compel a negative answer to this question.

Before the tests the animals had never jumped to a visual object. They had had not more than 10 minutes' exposure to light and not one tenth of this time had been spent in activity which would permit of the association of visual distance with the effort required to cover it by running. The 10

[4] Russell's animals were given a great deal of training in jumping in various tests to determine the role of binocular vision, etc., in perception of distance before the liminal series was run. The ability of the animals reared in darkness is therefore all the more striking in comparison.

trials of preliminary training were with the landing-platform at a constant distance and therefore offered no opportunity for association of different distances with motor activity. Thus before the first test series there was certainly no chance for the formation of a system of motor habits with reference to visual stimuli at different distances.

With the first increase in visual distance (from 20 to 40 cm.) the animals, which had been progressively reducing the force of their jumps during the 10 training tests, immediately increased the force to more than twice that of the last 5 jumps of preliminary training. This must have involved either a direct adjustment to the new visual distance or a greater tension due to emotional disturbance by the new condition without necessary recognition of the *increased* distance. The latter alternative is ruled out by the fact that with the next shortening of the distance to 20 cm. the animals were again disturbed (as indicated by hesitation and stretching toward the landing-platform) yet immediately reduced the force of their jumps.

With a total previous practice of only 13 jumps at 20 cm. and 6 at 40 cm. the animals then in ten trials showed a difference limen for distance nearly or quite as low as that of animals reared in light. Only one of the distances in this test series (40 cm.) had been experienced before and seven of the animals had never succeeded in reaching the landing-platform at this distance. Yet for this and the 8 new distances they all showed a significant gradation of force.

Tests of this type involve three factors for success in reaching the landing-platform: discrimination of the distance, gradation of the force of the jump in proportion to the distance, and motor coordination for an effective take-off and landing. In the last respect the animals reared in darkness are far inferior to those reared in the light. For distances above 20 cm. more than half of their jumps fell short or missed the landing-platform. The actual force expended was as great as that of the animals in Russell's previous series but the accuracy of control was significantly less.

These facts seem to admit of only one interpretation. The discrimination of visual depth and the regulation of the force of the jump in relation to the distance are not dependent upon past experience. The association of the perceptual mechanism for visual depth with motor discharges of graded intensity is an inherent property of the reaction mechanism, independent of learning and therefore presumably a product of the growth processes in the nervous system. The coordinations in jumping, placing the feet, poising and directing the body before jumping, balancing and placing the feet for a landing, and the adjustment of the absolute energy to the absolute distance to be covered are dependent upon specific learning processes. But underlying these acquired reactions there seems also to be an innate mechanism by which the relative force exerted is immediately adjusted to the relative distance.

In the experienced animal the discrimination of distance is a complex affair, involving binocular and monocular parallax, and changes in apparent size and brightness. Which of these enter into the innate discrimination of distance cannot now be determined. The elaborate tests necessary to differentiate the various factors would defeat their purpose by the amount of practice which they require.

Summary

Thirteen rats were reared to 100 days of age with a total exposure to light of not more than 10 minutes. They were then trained to jump across a space of 20 cm. from a platform arranged to record the force exerted in jumping. When the distance to be covered was first increased they showed a significant increase in force. Tests of the regulation of the force exerted to the distance to be covered showed nearly, if not quite, as great accuracy as was previously determined for animals reared in light. From these data it is concluded that the visual perception of distance and gradation of force in jumping to compensate for distance are not acquired by learning, but are the product of some innately organized neural mechanism.

REFERENCES

1. Fletcher, J. M., Cowan, E. A., and Arlitt, A. H. Experiments on the behavior of chicks hatched from alcoholized eggs, *J. Anim. Behav.*, 1916, **6**, 103–137.

2. Russell, J. T. Depth discrimination in the rat, *J. genet. Psychol.*, 1932, **40**, 136–161.

3. Senden, M. v. *Raum- und Gestaltauffassung bei operierten Blindgeborenen vor und nach der Operation.* Leipzig: Barth, 1932.

4. Thorndike, E. L. *Animal intelligence.* New York: Macmillan, 1911.

5. Watson, J. B. *Psychology from the standpoint of a behaviorist.* Philadelphia: Lippincott, 1919.

18. STUDIES OF CEREBRAL FUNCTION IN LEARNING. XI. *The Behavior of the Rat in Latch-box Situations* [1]

Studies of the rate of learning subsequent to lesions in the cerebral cortex of the rat have given diverse results, depending upon the type of problem used in the study. In maze learning (9, 17), "reasoning problems" (19, 20), the discrimination of two lights (10), reaction to sound (30), and the delayed alternation problem (18) animals with cerebral lesions are definitely retarded in learning. In contrast to these results, no retardation has been found in the formation of habits based upon reaction to light in the Yerkes box, even after complete destruction of the striate areas of the cerebrum. The association of motor reactions with visual patterns is also little, if at all, retarded by lesions unless the projection area for binocular vision is almost completely destroyed (13). Most puzzling of the situations in which cerebral lesions produce no retardation has been the double platform box described by Lashley (8). Nineteen animals with cortical lesions ranging from 14 to 50 per cent of the neocortex and ten normal controls were trained on this problem. The operated animals were actually 44.6 per cent superior to the controls with the difference six times its probable error. Segregation of cases with motor disorders showed that the problem favored such animals, but the operated animals without obvious motor symptoms were still somewhat superior to the normal ones. The correlation between extent of lesion and trials for learning was $p = -0.24$. Corrected for cases with paretic symptoms this correlation became $p = -0.07$, which shows that there was no significant relation between extent of lesion and learning.

In striking contrast to these results, more recent studies with mazes and other problems have revealed a marked retardation in learning after cerebral lesions and a significant correlation between extent of lesions and rate of learning. The reason for the discrepancy is by no means clear.

[1] EDITORS' NOTE: From *Comp. Psychol. Monogr.*, 1935, 11 (2), 5–40. Reproduced by permission of the Johns Hopkins Press. From department of psychology, University of Chicago.

Superficially the task set by the double platform box resembles that of the maze. Both seem to require the same sensory-motor activities and both prescribe a definite path from starting to food boxes. The final path for the double platform box is at least as complex as the true path in a maze with three or four culs de sac and the opportunities for departure from it considerably greater. We should therefore expect that the behavior of animals with cerebral lesions should be somewhat similar in the two situations. But animals with an average lesion of 24 per cent of the neopallium gave no evidence of retardation in the double platform box whereas a group with scarcely larger lesions (31 per cent) were retarded by almost 200 per cent in a maze with three culs de sac (9).

In attempting to account for this difference I suggested that the problems set by the discrimination and latch boxes are psychologically simpler than those of the mazes or "reasoning problems," assuming that the maze involves a thorough integration of sensory impressions into a "sense of direction," whereas the latch and discrimination boxes involve only the formation of a few sensory-motor associations. Pavlov (21) has criticized this interpretation. He points out that the practice required by normal animals for learning of latch and discrimination boxes is many times that required for any maze and that, since the difficulty of a problem is the only available criterion of its complexity, my assumptions concerning psychological complexity of different problems were not supported by objective evidence.

The factors which determine the difficulty of a psychological task have not yet been clearly defined. We speak of the complexity of a problem or of a relation to be perceived without any clear notion of what constitutes complexity, using the term almost as synonymous with difficulty. Objectively, the contrast of simple and complex refers to the relative number of items involved in the situation. In many earlier discussions the difficulty of a task for learning has been identified with the number of items involved, as seems implied in Thorndike's hypothesis that the quality of intellect depends upon the quantity of connections available (26, pp. 412–432). Studies of the relation of length of task to rate of learning (27) show that the number of elements is an important factor in determining the difficulty of a learning situation. Wiley and I (17) have found, however, that reduplication of elements in the maze situations does not increase the relative difficulty of the maze for animals with cerebral lesions. This means that the problems which are relatively more difficult for animals with cerebral lesions than for normal ones do not owe this difference to the mere number of elements which they present for association.

As an alternative to such an explanation in terms of number of items associated, there seems to remain only some unknown qualitative difference in the tasks which makes some more difficult for animals with cere-

bral lesions. The evidence is as yet inadequate for any satisfactory definition of these qualitative differences. The purely sensory aspects of the
problems seem of relatively minor importance, since sense privation does
not produce a retardation comparable to that resulting from cerebral
lesions (12, 28) and the double platform box and brightness-discrimina-
tion habits are formed at normal rate in the absence of the cerebral
sensory areas most likely to be involved in the habits.

Krechevsky (7) has presented objective evidence that the behavior of
the rat in the discrimination box consists of a series of systematic reactions each appearing and disappearing as a unit (going to the right, going
to the light, alternating, etc.). Each of these reactions consists of many
sensory-motor activities but in learning serves as a unit which may become
stereotyped in a few successful trials. This confirms my interpretation of
learning in the discrimination box as involving fewer items in association
than does learning of the maze. But in view of the more recent work on
the relation of the number of culs de sac to rate of learning (17) this is
not a satisfactory explanation of the relatively greater difficulty of the
maze than of the double platform box for animals with cerebral lesions.

If neither number of items nor limitation imposed by specific sensory
defects is responsible for the greater difficulty of some problems for animals with cerebral lesions, we are thrown back upon a vague notion of
some qualitative difference in the relations which must be perceived by
the animal under the different conditions. The present experiments were
undertaken in an effort to discover the distinctive features in the rat's
learning of the latch box which exempt this habit from the retarding effects of cerebral lesions so evident in the learning of other problems.
The questions proposed at the beginning of the experiment were the
following:

1. Can the original results with the double platform box be confirmed
in an independent experiment?

2. If so, is the absence of influence of cerebral lesion characteristic of
all learning of latch boxes?

3. If the learning of some latch boxes is retarded by cerebral lesions,
what are the distinguishing features of such boxes?

4. Is the retardation due to simple sensory and motor defects or to some
other effect of the cerebral lesion?

The experiment consisted in the training of three groups of animals
upon five latch boxes requiring diverse sensory-motor adjustments. The
groups were the following: (a) Twenty normal controls; (b) thirty-eight
animals with lesions of diverse magnitudes covering most of the cerebral
cortex; (c) ten animals peripherally blinded, without vibrissae, and with
the dorsal funiculus of the spinal cord cut in the upper cervical region,
as controls for sensory defect.

Training Situations

Five latch boxes were devised for the experiment. Three appeared to require the association of a single homogeneous act (pushing, pulling at a definite object, or gnawing) with getting food, the others a sequence of acts (pulling a latch and holding open the door while shifting posture to get behind it, or the successive pressing of two latches in predetermined order). The latches differed also in other respects: in their conspicuousness and ease of chance operation, in the directness of their relation to the opening of the boxes, and in the motor control required for their manipulation.

The latches used are shown in Fig. 18.1. They were arranged upon interchangeable partitions which could be inserted in a rectangular box, closing off a restraining cage 30 × 45 cm. from a smaller food compartment. A device in the latter provided for automatic stopping of the time clock when the animal reached the food. The latches are described below:

1. **Single Lever.** A metal rod, 3 mm. in diameter, extends horizontally from the right end to the middle of the partition, 2 cm. from the screen and 8 cm. from the floor. The door, sliding in grooves, is at the left end of the partition, 8 cm. from the end of the rod. Pressing down on the rod with a weight of 20 gms. through an arc of 10 degrees releases the door, which is raised by a light spring. Criterion of learning: an average of 3 seconds per trial for 5 consecutive trials. Limit of training: 100 trials.

2. **Paper Strip.** The door, in the middle of the partition, is held shut by a strip of newsprint, 1 cm. broad by 5 cm. long, fastened between two toothed clips attached to the sill and door. The average tensile strength of the strips is 200 gms. The animal must cut or tear the paper strip in two in order to release the door, which is raised by a spring. Criterion of learning: an average of 3 seconds per trial for 5 consecutive trials. Limit of training: 50 trials.

3. **Spring Door.** A light wooden door, hinged to swing to the left, is held closed by a spring with a tension of about 10 gms. per centimeter. A wire handle is attached to the door 1 cm. from the free edge. The edges of the door fit flush in the frame and the door can only be opened by pulling the handle. The animal must pull the door open with teeth or paws, then shift his grip so as to get around the edge of the door while holding it open against the pull of the spring. Two initial trials with the spring detached from the door were given before formal training was begun. Criterion of learning: an average of 3 seconds per trial for 5 consecutive trials. Limit of training: 50 trials.

4. **Pull Chain.** The door is in the middle of the partition. At the right, next to the edge of the door a lever covered by a metal guard projects 10 cm. in front of the partition. A chain, suspended from the end of the lever, reaches to within 3 cm. of the floor. The animal must grasp the chain with teeth or paws and pull down with a force of 20 gms. to release the door, which is raised by a spring. In working the latch many animals climb on the metal guard, get their feet entangled in the chain and release the latch in scrambling back to the floor.

Some of the operated animals never improved on this method, which was too slow to meet the criterion, an average of 3 seconds per trial for 5 consecutive trials. Limit of training: 50 trials.

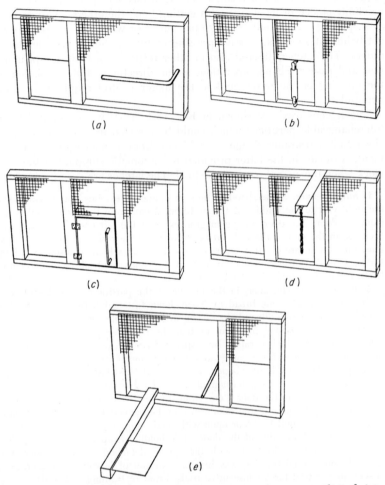

Fig. 18.1. Partitions bearing the latches. In use, these were slipped into grooves between the starting and food boxes. (*a*) Simple lever, (*b*) paper strip, (*c*) spring door, (*d*) pull chain, (*e*) double latch. × 1/6.

5. Double Latch. The door is at the right of the partition. Just to the left of the door a metal rod 3 mm. in diameter and 8 cm. from the floor projects horizontally from the partition. At the left, 30 cm. from the partition, is a metal platform, 6 x 8 cm. and 1 cm. from the floor, attached to a projecting support. To release the door the animal must first depress the metal rod through a distance of 2 cm. with a force of 20 gms. He must then turn away from the door and step on the platform. This sequence of acts releases the door, which is raised by a spring. Criterion of learning: an average of 5 seconds per trial for 5 consecutive trials in three of which the latches must be attacked in the correct order without any departure from the most direct path. Limit of training: 200 trials.

The double latch described above is a modified form of the original double platform box. The modifications were introduced to avoid two defects of the original box. In the latter, the use of two low platforms favored animals with partial motor paralysis, since they tended less than normals to jump over obstructions in their path. With the present box the animal must rise on his hind feet to reach the lever. In the original box the platforms were both located against the walls of the food box so that an animal running in contact with the walls would accidentally trip the latches without any specific reaction to them. In the present box the platform is located almost in the middle of the restraining compartment, so that the animal must give up his usual habit of keeping in contact with the walls and seek out the platform.

Methods of Training

Each animal was trained in the five problems in the order in which they are listed above, beginning with the single lever and ending with the double latch. In training through such a series there are various transfer effects from one problem to the next. Since our interest is primarily in a comparison of normal and operated animals trained under similar conditions, these transfer effects may be disregarded except where the question of the relative ability of the two groups to profit by previous training is concerned.

Hunger was used as incentive and during the experimental period the animals were fed enough to maintain weight. On the first problem the animals were allowed to explore the restraining and food cages with the door open for 30 minutes on each of three days preceding the beginning of formal training. With the other problems they were confronted with the locked door from the first. On the first trial with each box, if the animal failed to operate the latch within 30 minutes, he was fed, returned to the home cage, and the trial continued on the following day. Failing for three such periods, he was left in the box over night with a device which automatically recorded the time at which the door was opened. If he had not operated the latch after three nights, a total of about 40 hours, he was recorded as "failing on the first trial."

For the animals which operated the latches, training was continued until an arbitrary criterion of complete learning was reached. This was an average of 3 to 5 seconds per trial for 5 consecutive trials as indicated in the descriptions of the different latches. With each problem an arbitrary limit was set for training, 100 trials for the single lever, 200 for the double latch, and 50 for the others, at which point training was discontinued. Animals which did not satisfy the criterion within these numbers of trials are referred to in later discussions as having failed to learn, although all showed significant improvement with respect to directness of attack on the latches and in time per trial.

For statistical treatment the animals which failed to reach the criterion were grouped together as having equal scores. The animals which failed on the first trial were included with the others for correlation purposes and ranked as worse than the animals which failed to reach the criterion. Their inclusion in this way is at least partially justified by the fact that, in those problems where they did operate the latches, their scores were among the worst.

Table 18.1. Intercorrelations of Training Scores of Animals with Cerebral Lesions on the Different Problems (Rank Order) [o]

	S.L. Tr.	P.S.T.	P.S. Tr.	S.D.T.	S.D. Tr.	P.C.T.	P.C. Tr.	D.L. T.	D.L. Tr.	Per cent lesion
S.L.T.	0.65	0.15	0.11	0.28	0.36	0.40	0.35	0.33	0.41	0.18
S.L.Tr.		0.40	0.43	0.59	0.55	0.65	0.46	0.58	0.18	0.48
P.S.T.			0.65	0.49	0.56	0.48	0.47	0.13	0.09	0.48
P.S.Tr.				0.66	0.78	0.55	0.65	0.35	0.18	0.51
S.D.T.					0.88	0.70	0.65	0.41	0.35	0.68
S.D.Tr.						0.72	0.71	0.47	0.42	0.61
P.C.T.							0.74	0.42	0.33	0.62
P.C.Tr.								0.26	0.53	0.72
D.L.T.									0.86	0.09
D.L.Tr.										0.12

[o] S.L., simple lever   D.L., double latch
P.S., paper strip   T., time
S.D., spring door   Tr., trials
P.C., pull chain

The probable errors range from 0.03 to 0.12 in inverse proportion to the magnitude of the correlations.

As measures of learning, total time and total trials preceding the five meeting the criterion have been used. Neither is a very satisfactory index. It is impossible to make allowance in the time score for irrelevant activity or periods of inactivity, so that the time score fails to differentiate between the inactive animal which learns with little actual attention to the problem and the active animal which works persistently in nonadaptive ways. The score for trials is dependent upon final speed of performance and may therefore vary with physiological factors which are not related to the processes of the problem solving or fixation of habits. No other objective criterion of performance in the latch boxes is available, however, so we must be content with the time scores, making allowance for their more obvious defects.

Heron (5) has shown that the reliability of latch boxes for the determination of individual differences is very low when the differences represent the range of variation of a group of normal animals. I have computed intercorrelations of the scores on all problems of this experiment for normal animals and for animals with cerebral lesions. For the normal animals the average correlation of scores among the five problems is 0.21 with a range from -0.17 to $+0.53$. This confirms Heron's conclusion that the latch box is not a reliable instrument for measuring individual differences within a normal group.

With the operated cases, however, the correlation of scores on different problems is high. The correlations for trials (rank order) for the animals with cerebral lesions are given in Table 18.1. In general, they show that for the paper-strip, spring-door, and pull-chain problems individual performance is consistent. The single lever and the double latch show the least consistency, giving an average correlation of 0.36 with the other problems, whereas the latter show an average intercorrelation among themselves of 0.60. The low correlations for the first and last problems may indicate that they have a lower reliability than the others. It may, however, be due to the low correlation between performance and extent of lesion for these problems, since the extent of lesion is evidently the common factor in determining the higher correlations for the other three.

Experimental Animals

The animals used were pigmented male rats from a strain derived by interbreeding Wistar, hooded, and trapped wild stock. They were taken at random from the colony when about 150 days old and distributed to the experimental groups. For this type of work the control of individual differences does not seem of great importance, since the effects of the operative procedures are not regarded as significant unless they greatly exceed the range of normal variation of the group. I have never been able to demonstrate any relation between preoperative and postoperative training records in animals tested for the effects of cerebral lesions, so it appears that any individual differences are obscured by the far greater differences induced by the lesions.

Three differentially treated groups were used. Members from all of the groups were trained at the same time, to maintain greater uniformity in handling and in the procedures of training. The groups were the following:

1. Normal controls. Twenty animals were included in this group. . . .

2. Cases with cerebral lesions. Thirty-eight animals are included in this group. . . . They were subjected to operations on the cerebral cortex in which various amounts of tissue were destroyed, the series covering rather completely all of the dorsal and lateral surfaces of the neopallium. In the group were included 7 cases (numbers 19, 25, 27, 29, 36, 37, and 38) which had had some previous training in another problem. These animals were operated by Mr. H. G. Swann for use in tests of olfaction. They showed disturbances of orientation and difficulty in adaptation to his

apparatus which indicated serious general retardation. All ultimately passed his tests for olfactory discrimination, however.

3. Sensory controls. To test the influence of sensory defects upon the learning of the latch boxes a number of animals were prepared as follows: The dorsal funiculus of the spinal cord, including the fasciculus gracilis and f. cuneatus and in most cases the pyramidal tract, was cut through at the level of the second cervical arch. The eyes were enucleated and the vibrissae trimmed close to the skin.

The character of the defects resulting from such spinal lesions is not well established. For the first days following the operation there are marked sensory and motor disturbances which largely disappear in the course of two weeks. The residual defects have been described by Lashley and Ball (16) and seem chiefly postural. The animals occasionally drag the hind feet for a few steps. Cutaneous sensitivity seems unaffected, except that a good many of the animals gnaw their feet. The reason for this is not clear, but is probably an analgesia with, perhaps, referred irritation from the spinal wound. Ten animals of this group remained in good condition throughout the training in the five problems.

The Effects of Cerebral Lesions upon Learning in the Latch Boxes

The primary question in these experiments concerns the existence and degree of retardation shown by animals with cerebral lesions in learning the latch boxes. This involves the comparison of the training records of normal and operated animals in the five problems. . . . The differences between the groups are summarized in Table 18.2. The averages are based upon all cases which met the criterion or which were trained to the arbitrary limit for the problem. Additional animals, as noted in Table 18.2, failed to operate the latches on the first trial and therefore had no training score for inclusion in the averages. In some respects these are the most significant cases in the series.

The average extent of cerebral lesion in operated cases was 26.4 ± 1.6 per cent of the surface area of the neopallium. This average amount of destruction produces a retardation of from 200 to 1000 per cent in experiments with the maze (17). Its effects upon the learning of the latch boxes varied significantly for the different boxes.

The comparison of the normal and operated animals on the first problem (single lever) is somewhat complicated by a difference in wildness at the beginning of the experiment. The operated animals with extensive lesions required hand feeding for some days after operation and consequently were accustomed to handling. The group contained in addition the seven animals which had had previous training in the experiment on olfactory sensitivity. The normal animals had only such adaptation to handling as was gained through three days of feeding in the apparatus. Their greater timidity is indicated by the consumption of

Table 18.2. Comparative Records of Normal and Operated Animals for the Five Problems Studied *

	Single lever		Paper strip		Spring door		Pull chain		Double latch	
	Time	Trials	Time	Trials	Time	Trials	Time	Trials	Time	Trials
Normal group	2390±399	36±2.5	750±129	11±0.79	112± 20	6±0.5	713±151	11±0.8	2986±238	84±6.5
Operated	1803±200	43±2.4	2715±426	16±1.3	785±234	14±1.5	1318±168	28±1.9	2771±295	91±6.1
Difference	587±446	7±3.5	1965±446	5±1.5	673±235	8±1.6	605±226	17±2.0	215±379	7±8.9
Difference, % of the normal	24	19	262	45	600	133	84	154	7	8
Failed criterion (normal)	0		0		0		0		1	
Failed criterion (operated)	1		1		2		10		5	
Failed on 1st trial (normal)	0		0		0		0		0	
Failed on 1st trial (operated)	0		9		7		2		0	

* The averages are based upon the records of 20 normal animals and from 35 to 38 operated ones.

a relatively greater amount of time in the first trials, by a tendency toward increase in time for successive trials in each day's training, and by efforts to escape when handled.

The difference in wildness certainly did not persist beyond the first problem, since the criterion of 3 seconds per trial could not be met by an animal showing the least hesitation or avoidance of the experimenter. It makes the records for the first problem of doubtful value, however, since it probably raised the scores of the normal in comparison to those of the operated animals.

The average scores of the normal and operated animals in the single-lever problem are not reliably different. In time, the operated animals are 24 per cent superior, in trials 19 per cent inferior. Neither difference is twice its probable error. That a real inferiority of the operated animals is obscured by the wildness of the normal ones is indicated by the correlation between extent of lesion and trials for learning ($p = 0.48$) reported for this problem in a following section. From this it follows that the animals with small lesions made better scores than the normals, surely due to the greater timidity of the latter. That the effect of the lesions was not as great for the single lever as for some of the other problems is attested by the facts that none of the operated animals failed to operate the latch and only one failed to meet the criterion of complete learning.

For the other problems the statistical differences may be regarded as significant for the effects of cerebral lesions. With the paper strip, the spring door, and the pull chain the operated animals were markedly inferior to the normals. The percentage retardation ranges from 45 for trials on the paper strip to 600 for time on the spring door. These differences are based upon the scores of the animals which operated the latches. In addition nearly one-fourth of the operated animals failed in the first trial on the paper strip and spring door and one-fourth failed to reach the criterion with the pull chain, whereas there was no failure among the normal animals. The average scores and numbers of animals failing give conclusive evidence that the animals with cerebral lesions are inferior in solving or learning these problems.

In contrast to the results with the three preceding tasks, the double-latch problem reveals no significant difference between the normal and operated animals. The former are 8.3 per cent superior in trials but 7.2 per cent inferior in time and neither difference is greater than its probable error. Five of the operated and only one of the normal animals failed to meet the criterion, but these animals were all making direct solutions of the problem without departure from the most direct path and the greater number of operated cases failing may be largely discounted as indicating only that the movements of the animals with large lesions are somewhat slower than those of normals. The training scores show quite definitely that the cerebral lesions have no effect whatever upon the rate of learning of the double latch box.

The training scores for the five problems thus show a surprising difference in the effects of cerebral injury upon the learning of the different problems. The paper strip, spring door, and pull chain are significantly more difficult for animals with extensive cerebral lesions than for normal ones, as attested both by the greater amount of practice required to reach the criterion of complete learning and also by the number of operated cases which failed to operate the catches in the first trial. The double latch box, on the contrary, does not reveal any significant difference between normal and operated animals. This result is in accord with my earlier study of the double platform box, in which animals with very extensive lesions learned at normal rate.

A verification of these results by another method of treating the data is provided by the analysis of the relation between extent of lesion and the learning scores, which will be presented in a later section. Before this material is presented and the significance of the difference between the problems is considered, it is desirable to consider the effects of lesions in different parts of the cortex, and those of peripheral sense privation.

The Influence of Locus of Lesion

Our knowledge of the projection fields of the rat's cerebral cortex is still very inadequate as a basis for functional analysis. I have found that projection of the lateral geniculate nucleus is definitely restricted to the striate area and that this area is associated with detail vision (15). Wiley's studies (30) show auditory function associated with Fortuyn's field p. I have not yet been able to define accurately the limits of projection of the median geniculate nucleus, but it is much less extensive than field p, leaving a band of cortex without clear subcortical relations which is fully as wide as the striate area between the visual and auditory areas, as described by Cajal (24) from studies with the Golgi method. Bard and Brooks (1) have described a zone on the dorsal convexity of the hemisphere in front of the striate area, injury to which abolishes the "hopping" and "placing" reactions, which are tactile- and kinesthetic-motor. They interpret the area as motor and it lies within the electrostimulable zone, but lesions in the area are followed by extensive degeneration in the lateral thalamic nuclei, so this region also represents the projection field for kinesthetic and tactile impulses and the defects described are more probably due to reduced sensitivity. This interpretation is consistent with Dusser de Barenne's observation (2) that in the cat the tactile and motor fields overlap. The field does not coincide clearly with any well marked cytoarchitectural area. The special functions of the large lateral field designated j by Fortuyn remain obscure. Animals with extensive lesions in this region sometimes show postural abnormalities, of not very pronounced character. The area also contains stimulable points for the movements of the jaws. Lesions within the region are attended by degenerative changes in the ventral anterior and ventrolateral nuclei, according to Waller's recent analysis (29). This would relate the area also to the tactile or kinesthetic system.

The frontal regions are electrostimulable, giving rise to movements of the head and fore paws. Extensive lesions in this region are attended by some paresis, but not enough to interfere with manipulative movements of the head and fore limbs. The clearest evidence of its motor functions is the demonstration by Peterson (22) of the change in preferential use of the fore paws after small unilateral lesions.

The mesial cortical fields and the large masses of the archipallium probably have close connections with the olfactory system, but Swann (25) has been unable to demonstrate any disturbances in olfactory function from large lesions anywhere within the system. The functions of this great mass of primitive cortex remain obscure.

If my observations of the visual and auditory projection fields are confirmed, we shall probably find that the associative fields of the rat's cortex are relatively large, occupying an equal area to that of the projection fields. Their functions in relation to projection fields cannot be stated even for man.

The limited number of cases and irregular distribution of lesions in the present series makes any attempt at detailed analysis of the influence of locus of lesion unprofitable. We may ask, however, whether there is any indication of greater effectiveness of lesions in one than another part of the cortex in producing retardation in the latch-box situations. To test this I have selected cases with the lesions confined to certain groups of functional areas and have computed the average extent of lesion for each group and the average scores for the paper-strip, spring-door, and pull-chain problems in which retardation of learning occurred. Since most of the lesions are larger than the extent of any single cortical field, I have classified the cases in such a way as to give groups involving various combinations of fields, without significant destruction within more than two major fields. For example, there are a few cases with lesions restricted to the striate area, but in the majority of animals with lesions in this field the lesions extend also either into the auditory or into the somesthetic fields. These are divided into two groups: visual (auditory) in which the lesions extend laterad from the striate area, and visual (somesthetic) in which the lesions extend in front of the striate areas. The groups and the cases included in each were the following: Auditory, numbers 1, 2, 3, 4, 5, 6, 13; visual, 8, 9, 11, 15, 20; somesthetic (motor), 7, 10, 27, 29, 32; visual (somesthetic), 16, 18, 21, 24, 25; visual (auditory), 22, 26, 28, 30, 31, 33; motor (somesthetic), 14, 23, 34, 35. The averages are given in Table 18.3. The table reveals a relation between extent of lesion and degree of retardation. With allowance for the difference in extent of lesion, there is no clear indication that any field is more concerned in the formation of the habit than any other. The visual (auditory) and the motor (somesthetic) groups involve little overlap and give an equal amount of retardation in learning. The larger lesions in both groups extend somewhat into the somesthetic field, but the retardation cannot be due to destruction of this common area, for the area was more completely involved in the somesthetic group, with considerably less average retardation.

Table 18.3. Average Training Scores for Animals with Lesions Restricted to Different Areas [*]

Areas invaded	Average lesion	Average trials
Auditory	6.9	9.3
Visual	18.2	16.2
Somesthetic (motor)	26.1	23.3
Visual (somesthetic)	28.8	23.0
Visual (auditory)	29.8	33.2
Motor (somesthetic)	34.6	33.0

[*] The first column gives the locus of lesion, the second the average extent of lesion for the group, the third the average learning score in trials for the three problems noted in the text. Where more than one area is significantly involved, the one more completely destroyed is given first.

The evidence upon the effects of lesions in different loci cannot be regarded as conclusive. It indicates, however, that the formation of the habit is not conditioned by the intactness of any particular part of the cortex and that the retardation cannot be ascribed to the destruction of any particular sensory or motor cortical field. Two alternative interpretations of this result are possible: the retardation from lesions in different areas may be due to the fact that different sensory functions are involved in the problems and that the loss of different cortical sensory fields may produce retardation through sense privation; or the retardation may be due to some more general effect of cerebral lesion such as I have postulated to explain retardation in maze learning (9). To test the possible effects of sense privation, I have carried out the following control experiment.

The Effects of Sense Privation upon Learning of the Latch Boxes

The regions of the cortex included in the lesions of the cases considered above were the motor, tacto-somesthetic, visual, and auditory. The sensory disturbances which we have been able to observe after lesions in any of these fields are limited and, unless the entire sensory field is destroyed, do not interfere seriously with the formation of sensory habits. Thus learning of habits dependent upon detail vision may go on at normal rate if any small part of the projection field for binocular vision is left intact; auditory habits, at least to the presence and absence of sound, are formed nearly normally in the absence of field p (30); habits based on olfactory discrimination are retained after destruction of any part of the olfactory cortex (25). Data on tactile and kinesthetic habits are lacking, but it seems likely from clinical data that such habits are not more dependent upon small cortical areas than are other habits. In general, the sensory defects from cortical lesions are less severe than those produced by destruction of the peripheral apparatus.

In the experiment reported below an attempt was made to produce by peripheral lesions sensory defects which should be at least as severe as any resulting from the maximal cerebral lesions included in this study. To effect this a group of animals was subjected to enucleation of the eyes, removal of the vibrissae, and transection of the dorsal funiculus of the spinal cord in the second or third cervical segment. These animals were certainly blind and lacking in such distance perception as is provided by the vibrissae. In addition they suffered some diminution of tactile and kinesthetic sensitivity, giving symptoms somewhat more severe than I have ever observed after cerebral lesions. Although we cannot be certain, there is good evidence that these animals were as severely handicapped with respect to sensory capacities as any of the cases with cerebral lesions. Exception must be made with respect to the tactile and kinesthetic sensitivity of the head. I have never been able to detect disturbances of this sort in the rat after cerebral lesions and in man sensory disturbances of cerebral origin in the face and head are generally held to be of rare occurrence. Goldstein and Reichmann (3), however, find them quite generally after cerebral lesions which produce hemianesthesia of the trunk. Our methods of testing tactile and organic sensitivity of the rat are unreliable, and anesthesias of the head and neck may well have escaped notice. There seems little reason to believe, however, that the cutaneous sensitivity of the head or postural impulses from the neck can be an important factor in the learning of the latch boxes, since the animals manipulate most of the latches almost entirely with their paws.

These animals were trained with the latch boxes under the same conditions as the normal and cerebral groups. Their training records are . . . summarized in comparison with the records of the other groups in Table 18.4.

Table 18.4. A Comparison of Normal Animals (1), All Animals Having Cerebral Lesions (2), Animals with Peripheral Sensory-motor Defects (3), and Animals with Cerebral Lesions Extensive Enough to Produce Similar Sensory-motor Defects (4), with Respect to Trials for Learning

	Single lever	Paper strip	Spring door	Pull chain	Double latch
(1) Normal	36	11	6	11	83
(2) All cerebral	43	16	14	28	90
(3) Peripheral defects	84	19	12	32	75
(4) Cerebral sensory	54	30	24	45	97

Sketches of the spinal lesions . . . [were prepared]. The lesions in numbers 61 and 68 were very superficial and included not more than the dorsal third of the dorsal funiculus. In numbers 59, 63, and 65 the entire dorsal funiculus, including the corticospinal tract, was completely interrupted. In numbers 60,

64, and 66 practically the whole of the fasciculus gracilis and f. cuneatus of both sides was destroyed with the cerebro-spinal tract left intact. In numbers 62 and 67 parts of the sensory as well as the entire motor path remained intact.

In comparison with the normal group these animals with sense privation are seriously retarded for all problems except the double latch box. The average amount of retardation is slightly greater than that of the animals with cerebral lesions, if the animals which failed on the first trial are not taken into consideration. This result might justify the conclusion that the major factor in the retardation of the cases with cerebral lesion is also their sensory defect. The comparison of averages is, however, misleading since the average for the operated group with cerebral lesions does not include the animals which failed on the first trial and does include a number of cases in which the lesion is such as to have produced no significant sensory or motor defect.

For a pertinent comparison we must select those cases in which the cerebral lesions are such as to make probable a grade of sensory defect comparable to that of the animals with defects of peripheral origin. Only three of the animals with cerebral lesions (numbers 56, 57, and 58) have invasion of the visual, somesthetic, and motor fields likely to produce disorganization of these sensory and motor functions. In addition, numbers 44, 45, 50, 53, 54, and 55 have lesions significantly invading the visual and somesthetic or somesthetic and motor areas. Defect in more than one sensory field cannot be surely ascribed to other animals of the series.

The records of these nine cases with the possibility of severe sensory defect of central origin are also summarized in Table 18.4. Sixty per cent failed on the first trial in the paper-strip and spring-door problems and 20 per cent with the pull chain, in contrast to no such failures among the peripherally operated cases. On these three problems also, the cerebral cases which did get in on the first trial required significantly more trials for learning than did the peripherally operated cases.

The most striking characteristic of the peripherally operated cases was their timidity in the first problem. More than half of the total time consumed by them in training was spent crouching before the open door of the box after releasing the latch. This accounts for their bad records on the first problem (6,000 seconds, 84 trials). No such behavior appeared in the cases with cerebral operations (1,800 seconds, 43 trials).

Thus when we contrast the records of animals with sensory-motor defects of peripheral origin with those of animals in which the cerebral lesions may have produced sensory-motor defects of comparable severity, the latter show significantly poorer learning records, where both groups are inferior to normals. This result is in accord with what I have found in previous studies (9, 12). Where a habit may be formed in terms of diverse sensory cues, limited sense privation of peripheral origin produces less disturbance of learning than the destruction of the corresponding cortical fields. The conclusion is justified that the defects of learning following cerebral lesions are not explicable wholly in terms of the sensory-motor defects produced. In addition to these sensory and motor functions we seem forced to postulate some activity of the areas in question which when abolished decreases learning capacity of sensory-motor mechanisms not directly involved in the lesion.

Relation of the Extent of Lesion to the Degree of Retardation

The surface areas of the lesions were plotted on conventional diagrams and measured by the methods previously reported (9). . . . Correlation coefficients between extent of lesion and the trial and time scores for each of the problems have been computed by the method of rank orders. In computing these, the animals which failed on the first trial were included by assuming that this failure represents a greater deterioration than failure to reach the criterion and so ranking all such cases further from the mean than the worst cases which operated the latches. This procedure is justified by the fact that, in the problems where they did operate the latches, these animals were among the worst of the series.

The coefficients of correlation are presented in Table 18.5. The highest is 0.72 ± 0.06, for trials with the pull chain. For the paper strip, spring door and

Table 18.5 Coefficients of Correlation (Rank Order) between the Extent of Lesion and Training Scores (Time and Trials) for Each of the Five Problems

	Single latch	Paper strip	Spring door	Pull chain	Double latch
Time	0.18 ± 0.11	0.48 ± 0.09	0.68 ± 0.06	0.62 ± 0.07	0.09 ± 0.12
Trials	0.48 ± 0.9	0.51 ± 0.08	0.61 ± 0.07	0.72 ± 0.06	0.12 ± 0.12

pull chain the coefficients are all positive, statistically reliable, and large enough to indicate a significant relationship. In these problems in which the operated animals were inferior to the normals it is also true, as we should expect, that the animals with larger lesions are more retarded than those with smaller.

In contrast to this, the correlations for the double latch box ($p_{time} = 0.09 \pm 0.12$: $p_{trials} = 0.12 \pm 0.12$) are insignificant and unreliable. Thus not only was the average of all operated animals as low as that of normals, but even the animals with extensive lesions did just as well as those with small injuries.

For the simple lever the results are ambiguous with correlations of 0.48 ± 0.07 for trials and 0.18 ± 0.10 for time. This is consistent with the view that the animals were somewhat retarded, but the effects of the lesion were obscured by individual differences in wildness in the initial problem.

The Significance of the Correlations. A possible source of spurious correlation must be considered first. Some of the animals used in this experiment were prepared for anatomical studies of the cerebral projection of the auditory fibers. As a result a disproportionate number of cases with small lesions in the auditory area is included. If these problems do not involve audition, as seems probable, the inclusion of auditory cases with lesions smaller than the average for all cases might give rise to an apparent correlation with extent of lesion, due actually to the ineffectiveness of lesions in the auditory field. To control this possibility I have computed the correlations for trials for the spring door and pull chain, omitting all cases with lesions confined to the auditory fields (numbers 1, 2, 3, 4, 5, 6, and 13). This reduces the correlations from 0.61 to 0.60 and from 0.72 to 0.59. This reduction is no greater than would be expected from the reduction in range of variation effected by omitting the 6 cases with smallest lesions and leaves a significant correlation. . . .

With such a limited number of cases we cannot put much faith in correlations, but the results give a picture which is consistent with the results of earlier studies. Where before I have found no significant difference between the performance of normal and operated animals there has also been no correlation between performance and extent of lesion (double platform box: initial learning of habits based on vision). Where differences have appeared between the averages for normal and operated animals there has generally been a correlation of performance with extent of lesion (14). This is true in these experiments also. Correlations above 0.50 generally appear where the operated animals are on the average inferior to the normals: no correlations where there is no significant difference between the average scores of the normal and operated groups.

The Nature of the Retardation in Latch-box Situations

Significant retardation in learning after cerebral lesions is clearly established by these experiments for the paper-strip, spring-door and pull-chain situations. The character of the defect leading to the retardation is, however, not revealed by the objective records. Since the animals with peripheral sensory defects show a similar slowing of learning, it is probable that cortical anesthesias are an important factor in producing the effect. But the retardation of animals with cerebral lesions capable of producing sensory defects comparable to those of the peripherally operated cases is significantly in excess of that produced by the peripheral operations. We therefore cannot ascribe the whole of the inferiority of animals with cortical lesions to the anesthesia.

The behavior of animals with cerebral lesions in the latch-box situations suggests two more general defects which may have contributed to their poor records. Much of their activity indicates a general reduction in sensitivity. The animals with extensive cerebral lesions, irrespective of locus, wander about the restraining cage without giving specific responses to many items to which the normal animal continuously reacts. The corners and projecting edges of the box, the cover, cracks and irregularities in the floor which call out persistent reactions from the normal animal are ignored or excite only a momentary reaction from the animal with cerebral lesions. His range of exploratory activity seems limited. It is doubtful that this is primarily a function of sensory defect, for the animals with peripheral sense privation show such indifference to stimuli to a much more limited degree. The behavior is characteristic of all animals with fairly extensive lesions (20 per cent or more) irrespective of the cortical field involved.

In a former experiment dealing with the difference limen for brightness (11) after lesions in the area striata, I found it difficult to obtain
consistent performance from the operated animals when the difference in
light intensity approached the limen. The animals would make better than
chance scores but could not be brought to the criterion of errorless performance required in the experiment. One animal with both striate areas
completely destroyed showed a limen as low as that of normal animals,
but the majority were very irregular in performance, suggesting fluctuating
attention rather than a genuine disturbance in vision for brightness.

Such evidence indicates that animals with cerebral lesions suffer from
a general lowering of excitability in addition to the specific defects in
the discrete functions of the cortical fields involved. Goltz (4) so interpreted the defects which he observed in dogs and the clinical literature
abounds with evidence of a reduced attention after extensive lesions in
any part of the cortex. The aphasic patient fails to understand a sentence
until it has been repeated several times: the patient with an amblyopia
has difficulty in locating objects in the visual field although his residual
vision is adequate to perceive them.

A second characteristic of the behavior of rats with cerebral lesions may
best be described as a lack of aggressiveness toward elements of the problem situation. The normal animal in the restraining cage actively attacks
any object which yields to his efforts. A loose wire, an opening in the
mesh of the partition through which he can thrust his nose, an exposed
wooden frame, the loose cover of the box, as well as the latches and doors
are seized, shaken, or gnawed persistently. Animals with peripheral
sensory defects show much the same behavior as normals in this respect.
Animals with large cerebral lesions are much less apt to show this aggressive behavior. They may give clear evidence that they are stimulated by
the objects, exploring and nibbling at the paper strip, for example, but
neither exert sufficient force nor persist long enough to effect an entrance
into the food box. Their reactions to the various objects in the problem
situation lack the variety and adaptive character of the behavior of the
normal animals. The latter, especially after a little experience with latch
boxes, seem actively to seek out possible means of releasing the door or
breaking through the partition. The operated animals spend the greater
part of the time in wandering about the restraining cage or climbing on
the partition. This behavior definitely correlates with failure to operate
the latches on the first trial.

In addition to these differences between normal and cerebral operated
cases a third may be significant. The normal rat rather quickly modifies
his reactions to the latch so that, whereas his original movement in spring-
ing it may have been a random stumbling, his subsequent movements are
directly adapted to operating it with a minimum of effort. Thus the

simple lever is operated on the first trials by most animals by stepping on the lever with a hind foot when climbing on the partition. Within a few trials the normal animal comes to operate the lever by placing one fore paw on it and pushing down sharply. The animal with extensive lesions continues to climb on the lever and his final trials may still consist of climbing on the lever, falling in front of the door and scurrying through within the 3-second limit.

With the pull chain most animals first effect entrance by climbing upon the projecting bar, tangling the hind feet in the chain and releasing the catch by dropping to the floor. The normal animal, often on the second trial, grasps the chain with teeth or paws and pulls. Moreover, pulling with paws or with teeth is likely to be interchangeable with no appearance of learning the two movements by independent trial and error. The various motor activities by which the latch is released seem to be equivalent. The animal with extensive lesions, on the contrary, usually continues to climb to the bar, so that his behavior appears stereotyped and badly adapted to the problem, although it does lead to opening the door. The failure of so large a percentage of the operated animals to reach the criterion within 50 trials was largely due to this persistence in climbing to the bar.

Such behavior suggests that the normal rat, after a little experience with latch-box situations, comes to identify the movable latch as a distinct object connected with the opening of the door and thereafter reacts to the latch with movements which release the catch with a minimum of effort. The situation seems comparable to Köhler's interpretation (6) of the chimpanzee's identification of a stick as a tool. The rat seems to dissociate the latch from other parts of the problem situation and later to react to it as an object to be manipulated in a certain way. Whatever the explanation of behavior of this character, animals with extensive cerebral lesions show a limitation in acquiring it. Their behavior is more stereotyped in that they tend to repeat the movements which were first successful in opening the boxes, instead of modifying them to conform to the actual requirements of the latch.

This brief account of the differences in behavior of normal and operated rats is based upon detailed notes taken during the experiment which abound with examples of the differences illustrated. The observations may be summarized by the statement that the rats with extensive cerebral lesions are less observing, have less initiative, and show less insight into the relations of latch and door than do normal animals. These are functions which few students of cerebral localization have attempted to place in any particular part of the brain, the majority considering them as indices of the general level of functional activity rather than as specific localizable faculties.

In previous discussions of the effects of cerebral lesions I have striven to avoid such psychological interpretations of behavior. They do not give us any understanding of the cerebral mechanisms involved and tend to obscure the issues by presenting a pseudoscientific explanation in terms of empathy. At best they merely serve to classify the behavior with certain categories of human experience, for which we have no physiological explanation. But my efforts to confine discussion to a physiological level seem to have led to serious misunderstandings of my position. Conceptions of nonlocalized undifferentiated functions of the cerebrum have been rejected by writers who use a psychological terminology implying precisely the same thing. I therefore present the above psychological interpretations, not because they have any explanatory value, but in order to make the dynamic concepts of cerebral function sound less strange by identifying them with terms which, though scientifically meaningless, are familiar.

Interpretation of Results with the Double Latch Box

The marked difference in the results of cerebral lesions upon the learning of the double latch and of the other problems is the most striking result of these experiments. It seems clearly established here and by the previous experiments with the double platform box that cerebral lesions even greater than 50 per cent do not disturb the learning of this problem.

A possible simple explanation of this is that the solution of the double latch boxes is a matter of pure chance, even after continued training and that the "learning score" consequently measures nothing significant in the behavior of the animal. A consideration of what happens in the course of training on this problem seems to rule out such a supposition concerning the unreliability of the problem. On the first trials practically all animals show a transfer of the training on the simple lever, going directly to the projecting rod and pushing it down as they had done with the first problem. This failing, they wander about attacking the partition, door, and so on, until they chance to run across the platform. Within a few trials the platform and door are associated, the animal goes directly to the platform, pushes it down and runs to the door. But with the acquisition of this behavior the reaction to the lever drops out. The animal then leaves the platform and attacks the partition in a random manner, only working the lever by chance. Practically every learning curve shows a marked increase in time per trial after the third to tenth trial, corresponding to the point at which direct reaction to the lever was dropped. For the majority of animals the next step is an abandonment of the platform and return to the lever (depression of which produces a slight click at the door); with this appears a circling movement which carries him from the lever past or over the platform. Behavior from this point on is more variable, but the final reaction of the normal animal, which must take not more than 5 seconds, almost invariably involves running directly to the lever, pushing it down with the forefeet, turning about to place the forefeet on the platform with a definite downward push, and a final turn through the door. The final performance is in no sense random, but involves obvious association of definite manipulations of the latches.

The double-latch situation thus surely requires as much of the animal in the way of formation of associations as does any of the other problems and meeting the criterion is a certain assurance that this learning has taken place. We must therefore seek some other reason for the good performance of the operated animals than the unreliability of the measure. A clue to this comes from the methods of operating the latches adopted by animals with extensive lesions. Thus, number 54 early abandoned direct attack on the lever, used it as a step to climb to the top of the partition, fell backward to strike the platform with his shoulder and so released the door. He repeated this performance day after day, with a speed which met the criterion after the 41st trial. Most animals with extensive lesions run to the door, scramble over the lever, circle across the platform and back to the door within the required time, but without any indication that the lever and platform are reacted to otherwise than as obstructions to running.

This behavior, with what I have reported above concerning the failure of the operated animals to dissociate the latches from the general problem situation, seems the most plausible explanation of the records with the double latch box. These latches may be worked by movements which are not specifically modified to suit them. The operated animal learns to traverse a simple path, in following which he incidentally springs the catches. The normal animal follows the same path and acquires a set of definite reactions to the latches as well, but these do not give him any advantage over the operated animal, with respect to time consumed per trial.

The normal records of the animals with extensive cerebral lesions in the double latch box seem thus to be due to the very limited requirements of the "inclined plane" type of problem box. It may be operated without dissociation of the latch from the general situation and without the development of such "skilled movements" as are required by many manipulative problems. It nevertheless requires the development of a limited sequence of movements and this has certain implications for the problem of cerebral function in learning.

The Influence of Cerebral Lesions upon Learning

Learning, as it appears in latch-box, maze, and similar experiments, involves not only the fixation of associations (engraphic action of Semon;

conditioning of reflexes of Pavlov) but also various activities which objectively resemble the human ones in problem solving which are described as systematic attacks on the problem, hypotheses, abstraction, generalization and insight. Various lines of evidence suggest that the associative mechanism is very primitive. There is no evidence that the rate of formation of simple associations has been increased in evolution from the lower metazoa to man (10). Conditioned reflexes may, apparently, be formed in the decerebrate animal (23). Habits involving sensory discrimination in which the terms are so presented as to involve only the relationship of contiguity are formed at normal rate by nearly decerebrate animals.

The results with the double latch box are further evidence in the same direction, with the additional complication that two acts or a sequence of movements must be automatized. Such associations may, evidently, proceed at normal rate in the absence of any part of the cortex, in amounts up to 58 per cent.

It appears therefore that the deterioration following cerebral lesions is due to disorganization of some other function than the fixation of associations or conditioning of reflexes. The nature of these functions is still obscure. I have suggested (9) their relation to the processes involved in intelligent adaptation and the present experiments add to this some evidence that the deterioration involves a limitation in the variety of exploratory activity and the ability to react to parts of the problem situation as isolated units.

Summary

Rats with various cerebral lesions were trained in comparison with normal animals and with animals having severe peripheral sensory deficiency, on five latch boxes of various types.

The rate of learning of the box with two latches to be depressed in predetermined order was unaffected by cerebral lesions as great as 58 per cent, and with this problem there was no significant relation between rate of learning and extent of lesion. This result confirms my earlier study of the double platform box. With other latch boxes the animals with cerebral lesions were seriously retarded. The amount of retardation with these boxes was roughly proportional to the surface extent of lesion, the correlations ranging from 0.48 to 0.72.

Animals lacking vibrissae and eyes and with the dorsal funiculus of the spinal cord divided at the second cervical segment were also retarded in learning these problems, but to a significantly lesser extent than animals with cerebral lesions capable of producing the same grade of anesthesia.

Consideration of the differences in behavior of normal and operated animals and of the diverse requirements of the latch boxes indicates that the major elements in the retardation of the animals with cerebral lesions are limitation in the variety of exploratory acts, failure to develop movements specifically adapted to manipulate the latches, reduction of time spent in exploring separate items in the situation, and sensory deficiency. The first three of these are characteristic of all animals with extensive cerebral lesions, irrespective of the locus of the lesions. The latches which are learned at normal rate by animals with cerebral lesions are those which may be operated by the running and climbing movements of the animal, without the development of adaptive manipulative movements.

The learning of such problems at normal rate indicates that the mechanism of association, as such, is not disturbed by cerebral lesions and that retardation from cerebral lesions is due rather to disturbance of such function as are implied by the terms attention, insight and initiative.

REFERENCES

1. Bard, P., and Brooks, C. M. Localized cortical control of some postural reactions in the cat together with evidence that small cortical remnants may function normally, *Proc. Assoc. Res. nerv. ment. Dis.*, 1934, 107–157.

2. Dusser de Barenne, J. G. Experimental researches on sensory localization in the cerebral cortex, *Quart. J. exp. Physiol.*, 1916, **9**, 355–390.

3. Goldstein, K., and Reichmann, F. Ueber corticale Sensibilitätsstörungen besonderere am Kopfe, *Z. ges. Neurol. Psychiat.*, 1919, **53**, 59–79.

4. Goltz, F. *Über die Verrichtungen des Grosshirns.* Bonn: 1881.

5. Heron, W. T. The reliability of the inclined plane problem box as a method of measuring the learning ability of the rat, *Comp. Psychol. Mongr.*, 1922, **1**, 35.

6. Köhler, W. *Intelligenzprüfungen an Menschenaffen.* Berlin: 1921.

7. Krechevsky, I. "Hypotheses" vs. chance in the pre-solution period in sensory discrimination-learning, *Univ. Calif. Publ. Psychol.*, 1932, **6**, 27–44.

8. Lashley, K. S. Studies of cerebral function in learning, *Psychobiology*, 1920, **2**, 55–135.

9. Lashley, K. S. *Brain mechanisms and intelligence.* Chicago: 1929.

10. Lashley, K. S. Nervous mechanisms in learning. In *Foundations of experimental psychology.* Worcester: 1929. Pp. 524–563.

11. Lashley, K. S. The mechanism of vision: II. The influence of cerebral lesions upon the threshold of discrimination for brightness in the rat. *J. genet. Psychol.*, 1930, **37**, 461–480.

12. Lashley, K. S. Cerebral control versus reflexology, *J. gen. Psychol.*, 1931, **5**, 3–20.

13. Lashley, K. S. The mechanism of vision: IV. The cerebral areas necessary for pattern vision, *J. comp. Neurol.*, 1931, **53**, 419–478.

14. Lashley, K. S. Integrative functions of the cerebral cortex, *Physiol. Rev.*, 1933, **13**, 1–42.

15. Lashley, K. S. The mechanism of vision: VIII. The projection of the retina upon the cerebral cortex of the rat, *J. comp. Neurol.*, 1934, **60**, 57–79.

16. Lashley, K. S., and Ball, J. Spinal conduction and kinaesthetic sensitivity in the maze habit, *J. comp. Psychol.*, 1929, **9**, 71–105.

17. Lashley, K. S., and Wiley, L. E. Studies of cerebral function in learning: IX. Mass action in relation to the number of elements in the problem to be learned, *J. comp. Neurol.*, 1933, **57**, 3–55.

18. Loucks, R. B. Efficacy of the rat's motor cortex in delayed alternation, *J. comp. Neurol.*, 1931, **53**, 511–567.

19. Maier, N. R. F. The effect of cerebral destruction on reasoning and learning in rats, *J. comp. Neurol.*, 1932, **54**, 45–75.

20. Maier, N. R. F. Cortical destruction in the posterior part of the brain and its effect on reasoning in rats, *J. comp. Neurol.*, 1932, **56**, 179–214.

21. Pavlov, I. P. The reply of a physiologist to psychologists, *Psychol. Rev.*, 1932, **39**, 91–127.

22. Peterson, G. M. Mechanisms of handedness in the rat, *Comp. Psychol. Monogr.*, 1934, **9** (46), 67.

23. Poltyrew, S. S., and Zeliony, G. P. Grosshirnrinde und Assoziationsfunktion, *Z. Biol.*, 1930, **90**, 157–161.

24. Ramón y Cajal, S. *Histologie du système nerveux de l'homme et des vertébrés.* Paris: 1911.

25. Swann, H. G. The function of the brain in olfaction: II. The results of destruction of olfactory and other nervous structures upon the discrimination of odors, *J. comp. Neurol.*, 1934, **59**, 175–201.

26. Thorndike, E. L. et al. *The measurement of intelligence.* New York: 1926.

27. Thurstone, L. L. The relation between learning time and length of task, *Psychol. Rev.*, 1930, **37**, 44–53.

28. Tsang, Yü-Chüan. The functions of the visual areas of the cerebral cortex of the rat in the learning and retention of the maze, *Comp. Psychol. Monogr.*, 1934, **10** (50), 1–56.

29. Waller, W. H. Topographical relations of cortical lesions to thalamic nuclei in the albino rat, *J. comp. Neurol.*, 1934, **60**, 237–269.

30. Wiley, L. E. The function of the brain in audition, *J. comp. Neurol.*, 1932, **54**, 109–141.

19. THE MECHANISM OF VISION.

XII. Nervous Structures Concerned in Habits Based on Reactions to Light [1]

The interrelations of the visual cortex, thalamus, and midbrain in various phases of visual function are still obscure. A mass of experimental and clinical evidence establishes the fact that the striate area of the cerebral cortex is essential for detail vision in mammals. Lesions in this area in man produce permanent scotomas. In lower mammals the mapping of scotomas is very uncertain and the evidence concerning their recovery conflicting. Munk (21) believed them permanent in the dog, but Hitzig (6) reported recovery of all types of scotoma. Both these investigators were in error concerning the location of the visual area and actually dealt chiefly with interruption of the optic radiation. Minkowski (20) was unable to obtain lasting visual defects in the dog unless at least half of the visual cortex of one hemisphere was destroyed. He found that complete ablation of the visual cortex produced total blindness which did not recover. Anatomical data (16, 17, 27) indicate that more limited scotomas may occur in lower mammals, but no method of demonstrating them is at present avialable.

Complete destruction of the striate areas permanently abolishes detail vision in the rat, dog,[2] and monkey (Klüver [3]). Such animals cannot be trained to differentiate visual paterns, yet they are not totally blind. With the possible exception of the anthropoids, animals lacking the visual cortex can still form habits based upon the discrimination of light and darkness or the relative intensities of lights (8, 11, 12, 13, 19). In the rat the residual vision after destruction of the striate and peristriate areas still

[1] EDITORS' NOTE: From *Comp. Psychol. Monogr.*, 1935, **11**, 43–79. Reproduced by permission of the Johns Hopkins Press. From department of psychology, University of Chicago.

[2] Pavlov (24) has reported formation of conditioned reflexes to visual patterns in dogs after removal of the posterior half of the cerebrum. No details of the experiment or reports of necropsies are available. I have reported one case of discrimination of horizontal and vertical stripes in the absence of the striate cortex in the rat. These results are so atypical that one suspects some experimental error.

[3] Unpublished experiments.

seems to include not only sensitivity to light but also ability to distinguish differences between two or more masses of light simultaneously presented within the visual field (14, Meroney [4]); a sort of primitive detail vision. No data, beyond demonstration of mere sensitivity to light, are available for other animals with such lesions.

Whether the formation of visual habits in animals lacking the striate areas is carried out wholly at subcortical levels or is in some way dependent upon the remaining "nonvisual" cortex is not settled. I found no evidence of participation by other parts of the cerebrum in the formation of habits based on brightness discrimination in rats trained after destruction of the striate areas (10). Poltyrew and Zeliony (26) have reported the formation of conditioned reflexes to light in an almost completely decerebrate dog. They have not yet reported histological analysis of this case, so that it cannot be accepted as final.

The principal subcortical centers which might be involved in the formation of visual habits are the lateral geniculate nuclei, the optic thalamus, the superior colliculi, and perhaps, the nucleus of the posterior accessory optic tract. In the rat the lateral geniculate nuclei undergo a complete degeneration after destruction of the striate areas (17). Animals in this condition can still distinguish the difference in intensity of two lights (13, 14), so the residual vision cannot be ascribed to the geniculate nuclei.

Papez and Freeman (23) found some retardation in the formation of habits based on reaction to light in rats after injuries to the superior colliculi. I found that such lesions prevent the animal from jumping (14, 18). Layman, repeating these studies, found relatively little retardation in the formation of the brightness habit after severe lesions in the colliculi. He also found a normal discrimination of visual patterns when the animals had finally been trained to jump. These results show that, if the colliculi are involved in brightness vision, they are not necessary for it or for the discrimination of simple patterns.

If the striate areas are injured or totally destroyed before training, the rat will form the habit of reaction to light in the Yerkes box as rapidly as does a normal animal. Data are now available upon 89 normal animals and 113 animals with lesions in the striate areas ranging from small to total destruction. The average training required for learning was:

> Normal (89 cases): 131 trials, 44 errors
> Operated (113 cases): 123 trials, 40 errors

Whatever the role of the striate cortex in the brightness vision of the normal animal, its loss is no handicap for the learning of a simple differential reaction between light and darkness.

4 Unpublished experiments.

When a discrimination between the intensities of two lights is required, animals with lesions in the striate areas are somewhat handicapped. In tests of the difference limen for brightness, animals were first trained as positive to light versus darkness. A second light was then introduced at an intensity of 1/50 of the standard light and, in successive tests, increased in intensity to ratios of 1/25, 1/9, 1/2, and 2/3. The reactions of the normal animals were not disturbed by these changes. They continued to choose the brighter light until the difference approached their threshold. The animals with cerebral lesion, on the contrary, were disturbed at each change in the dimmer light and, in general, had to be retrained for each change in ratio, although the differences were well above their limen. They showed, on the average, a higher limen than the normals, but one animal with complete destruction of both striate areas had as low a limen as any normal animal (13). Marquis (19) has reported some decrease in differential sensitivity in the dog. Klüver has found that the threshold for light of the Java monkey is probably not raised by removal of the striate cortex.[5]

Tests of postoperative amnesia for visual habits after cerebral lesions have given contradictory results. In four studies of postoperative retention of the reaction to light in the Yerkes box I have obtained consistent data (8, 9, 11, 13, 15). In every case, destruction of the striate areas abolished the habit. But the animals were able to learn it again with no more practice than that required for initial learning by a normal animal. Memory was lost, but the capacity to distinguish the light and to form the habit again was not affected. Marquis (19) reports similar results in experiments with dogs. Injuries to other parts of the cortex had no influence on the habit.

In two experiments I sought to test the effect of extent of lesion upon the degree of loss of the habit. In both cases a close relationship appeared between the extent of lesion and amount of practice required to relearn the habit (11, 13). Two explanations of this relationship seemed possible: first, that there is some small cortical area essential to the habit which, by chance, is more often injured by large than by small lesions: second, that the correlations express some dynamic function, perhaps a facilitation of subcortical centers, for which the mere quantity of tissue is important.

Studies of cerebral function in detail vision revealed a small zone along the lateral border of the striate area, destruction of which eliminated pattern vision. Analysis of the data on postoperative retention for brightness habits showed that there is no loss, if this area is not involved in the lesion. But if the area is involved, the degree of loss is proportional to the extent of lesion outside of the area critical for detail vision (15).

[5] Unpublished experiments.

In view of this result and the fact that animals completely lacking the striate areas are not retarded in learning the brightness habit, it seemed impossible to ascribe the quantitative results of postoperative retention tests to the production of scotomas.

Tests of postoperative amnesia for habits based on detail vision (18) gave entirely different results. They did not reveal any loss after lesions in the striate areas which could not be accounted for on the basis of central scotomas. No disturbances of these habits followed injuries in the peristriate areas, in the median halves of the striate areas, or in any other parts of the cerebrum except the anterolateral parts of the striate cortex. No correlation appeared between extent of lesion and practice for relearning in animals which showed some loss of the habit. Destruction of the anterolateral parts of the striate areas resulted in permanent inability to discriminate patterns. These results are so different from what had been found previously in studies with the discrimination box as to reopen the whole question concerning the production of postoperative amnesias for brightness habits and to throw doubt upon the interpretation previously offered for the correlation between extent of lesion and practice for relearning.

Studies of the anatomical projection of the retina upon the cerebral cortex (16, 17) now make it possible, by reconstruction of the degeneration of the lateral geniculate nucleus, to determine exactly what parts of the geniculo-striate system have been destroyed and to map the resultant scotomas with considerable confidence. We may thus determine the extent to which an operation has abolished central vision and can pick out with certainty those cases in which the entire striate areas or optic radiations have been destroyed. With this possibility of more complete anatomic analysis it has seemed desirable to attack the problem of brightness vision again.

Problem and Plan of Experiments

The questions which I sought to answer by experimental analysis are the following: (a) Is the habit based upon reaction to light in the discrimination box dependent upon any particular part of the striate cortex or peristriate areas? In particular, what is its relation to the projection field for binocular vision? (b) Can the correlation previously found between extent of lesion and postoperative practice for relearning be confirmed and, if so, can it be explained in terms of the extent or character of the scotomas produced? (c) What structures may be concerned in relearning the habit after complete destruction of the striate areas? The experiment was not planned to include the third problem, but a number of accidental injuries to subcortical optic centers throw some light on the matter.

The experiment involved training a group of animals in a modified form of the Yerkes discrimination box to choose an illuminated alley and avoid a darkened one. Following the initial training the animals were given tests to determine the amount of loss through a lapse of time equal to that required for recovery from operation (preliminary retention tests). They were then subjected to operation involving destruction of various parts and amounts of the striate cortex and surrounding fields and when recovered were again tested for retention. Except for some modification of the training box, described below, the experiment duplicated previous tests for postoperative loss of the brightness habit.

The important new phase of the experiment is the method of analyzing the lesions and the detailed comparison of the experimental data with the anatomical findings. This included the reconstruction of the lesion and measurement of its area, the identification of the remaining normal striate cortex, and the mapping of the areas of the lateral geniculate nuclei showing retrograde degeneration. Since the interpretation of the data depends upon anatomical details, a brief account of the structure of the visual system in the rat will be given before the experimental data are reported.

Visual Structures Involved in the Experiments

The fibers from the optic nerve, after passing the chiasma, turn upward around the base of the thalamus. Two small bundles, the anterior and posterior accessory optic tracts, are given off to terminate in a nucleus lying along the inner ventral margin of the cerebral peduncle. The great majority of the fibers pass up to the lateral geniculate nucleus. Here they lie on the lateral surface of the thalamus, next to the hippocampus. Some of the fibers pass inward through the pars ventralis of the lateral geniculate nucleus to reach the inner ventral part of the pars dorsalis. The majority pass over the lateral surface of the nucleus, sending collaterals into the pars dorsalis. At the dorsal and caudal margins of the lateral geniculate nucleus the tract turns inward to reach the superior colliculus. Between the nucleus and the colliculus the fibers traverse the "optic thalamus," whose constitution in the rat is doubtful. Fibers are found in the pars posterior of the lateral nucleus, in the pretectile nucleus, in the lateral part of the nucleus of the posterior commissure, and in a group of large cells lying under the lateral margin of the colliculus (Clark's large-celled nucleus?). It is uncertain whether optic fibers terminate in any of these structures. The chief evidence of their termination is the occurrence in these nuclei of uncrossed fibers none of which reach the colliculus. There is no clear evidence that projection fibers go from the optic thalamus to the cortex in the rat. I found no degeneration in the pretectile or posterior nuclei after lesions in the striate and peristriate areas and Waller (28) found no certain evidence of degeneration in this region after any lesion to the cortex. Waller reports degeneration in the posterior part of the lateral nucleus after lesions in the peristriate areas and I am able to confirm this, but doubt that the lateral nucleus receives optic fibers, since in it Marchi granules appear only in bundles with no indication of scattered terminal fibers, after enucleation of the eye.

The anatomic projection of the retina upon the lateral geniculate nucleus, colliculus, and cortex is illustrated in Fig. 19.1. The binocular field, essential for detail vision (at least as tested by the jumping method), occupies the anterior and lateral margins of the striate area. Lesions which leave intact any part of

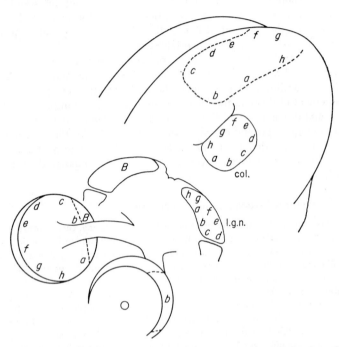

Fig. 19.1. Diagram of the projection of the retina upon the lateral geniculate nucleus (l.g.n.), colliculus (col.), and striate area in the rat. Zones represented by letters around the perimeter of the retina are projected to approximately the positions bearing the corresponding letters in the central nervous system.

the area indicated in Fig. 19.1, *a, b, c,* do not interfere with detail vision, whereas the destruction of this area, with the remainder of the field left intact (Fig. 19.1, *d, e, f, g, h*), permanently abolishes pattern discrimination with the jumping apparatus (18).

Overbosch (22) has reported a projection of the retinal quadrants to separate parts of the superior colliculus in the rabbit and I have confirmed this for the rat. This projection mechanism is inadequate, however, for discrimination of visual patterns.

Methods

The apparatus consisted of a modified form of the Yerkes discrimination box which I first used unsuccessfully in 1926 for tests of detail vision. It differed from the familiar form in that the animal must push aside an illuminated door. The door was of larger area and greater surface brightness than the stimulus patch in the boxes used before in similar experiments. The ground plan of the box is shown in Fig. 19.2. In all features except the arrangement of the light, it was like the boxes previously used and figured (12). The modified design was adopted in order to facilitate the initial training, which it reduces from the average of 125 trials of the old form to 67 trials. The advantage of quicker learning is perhaps offset by the fact that some animals learn so quickly that their preliminary retention scores are inferior to their initial learning. This makes it more difficult to interpret data on postoperative retention.

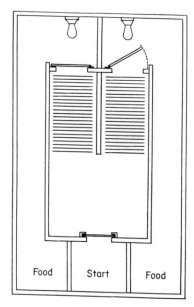

The animals were females from a pigmented strain derived from a cross of trapped wild with Wistar stock. The strain produces numerous individuals with defective eyes, but none was noted in the experimental group. Sixty-eight animals survived the experiment.

Punishment for errors and food were used as incentives, as in previous experiments. The animals were allowed to explore the unlighted box for half an hour on five days before the beginning of training. They were then trained at 10 trials per day with the light irregularly alternated until they reached the criterion of 10 errorless trials on each of two consecutive days (initial learning). They were next allowed 14 days without training and then retrained to the same criterion (preliminary retention tests), as a measure of the loss to be expected

Fig. 19.2. Ground plan of training box. The starting compartment is separated from the discrimination compartment by a clear glass door. The grill in the dark alley is charged with 110 volts A.C. current regulated by a variable high resistance. Swinging doors of flashed glass close the ends of the alleys. The dark one is locked; the illuminated one may be pushed open by the animal.

through lapse of time. After these tests they were operated immediately, allowed 14 days for recovery, and again trained to the criterion (postoperative retention tests) as in previous experiments. Training was discontinued after 200 to 350 trials, in case the animals did not reach the criterion earlier.

Operations were performed under ether anesthesia with thermocautery. At the termination of the experiment the animals were brought to necropsy, and the brain sectioned and stained with thionin. The cortical lesions were mapped and measured as in earlier experiments (12). The remaining parts of the striate areas, wherever identifiable by the internal granular layer, were plotted on the diagrams of the cortex. . . . The cautery usually destroys not only the cortex but also the underlying layer of fibers. The destruction of the fibers is, however, often incomplete and difficult to determine exactly from sections. The most certain evidence of the extent of destruction of the striate cortex comes therefore from the retrograde degeneration in the lateral geniculate nucleus. The nuclei were studied in each case and the zones of degeneration plotted on diagrams of sections. For any lesion to the striate area the degenerated zone extends throughout the length of the nucleus so a single transverse section near the middle of the nucleus represents all parts of the striate area. . . .

An unusually large number of cases with direct injury to the thalamus was produced in this experiment in the effort to ensure complete destruction of the striate areas. These direct lesions were studied in detail. The majority consist of an invasion of the optic tract above the posterior end of the lateral geniculate nucleus and involve parts of the nucleus, optic thalamus and colliculi. In a few cases the nucleus was destroyed and in one the colliculus.

Interpretation of Postoperative Behavior

Possible Reactions to Nonvisual Cues. Before attempting to interpret the reactions of animals after operations involving the visual structures, we must be sure that some other than visual cues are not responsible for their apparent reactions to light in the problem box. In previous experiments of this type I have run systematic controls to test the influence of the experimenter, heat from the lights, sounds in changing the setting of the apparatus, cues from the charged grill (7), and chance order of the trials. No animal has ever been detected in the use of any of these possible cues when making better than chance scores. In the present experiment systematic controls were not introduced, since they are laborious and past experience indicates that they are unnecessary. However, all but cues from the experimenter and heat from the lights are directly controlled in the apparatus. Many of the animals were tested by a second experimenter without disturbance of their accuracy of discrimination. In a series of trials, with the animals running rapidly and the lights shifted quickly from side to side, both stimulus doors are warmed and the flashed glass radiates heat slowly, so that differences in temperature must be inappreciable. Finally, the best possible control is that animals with destruction of the primary optic paths never make better than chance scores.

Validity of the Evidence for Loss of the Habit. The mere occurrence of numerous errors after a cerebral lesion is not in itself evidence of forgetting of the habit. If the power of attention were reduced by the operation, errors might occur with no direct disturbance of the specific integrations constituting the habit. Much of the amnesia reported for clinical material is indeed of this type; the patient is unable to recall material directly yet with sufficient mnemonic aids may finally succeed in recall. The forgetting is not absolute but is rather a reduction in availability of the memories.

If the defect in our animals were of this character, we should expect to find either some evidence of retention from the first or a spontaneous recovery to which the specific training on the problem would contribute little. The retraining scores of the animals with complete destruction of the striate areas have, however, all the characteristics of the initial learning of normal animals: they start at the level of pure chance and from the rate or form of improvement it would be impossible to guess whether or not the animals had ever been trained in the problem. I have shown also (10) that spontaneous recovery does not occur within the time during which the habit may be reestablished by training.

This of course does not prove that the cerebral destruction has wiped out all traces of the previous training or that relearning is identical in nature with original learning. But objectively the two processes are similar and the course of relearning has more in common with the original training than with any other reported process of recovery.

Experimental Results

The records of the animals in initial training, preoperative, and postoperative retention tests are given in Tables 19.1 to 19.4. . . . In the tables the animals are divided into four groups, according to the nature of the lesions, as follows:

Group I. Cases with damage to the striate areas but with some normal cells in one or both lateral geniculate nuclei.

Group II. Cases with complete destruction of both striate areas, as indicated by complete degeneration of both lateral geniculate nuclei.

Group III. Cases with complete destruction of the striate areas and with direct damage to one optic tract.

Group IV. Cases with complete destruction of both striate areas and with invasion of both optic tracts.

Criteria of Postoperative Loss of Memory. Since there is some overlap between the scores for initial learning and preoperative retention, it is necessary to set somewhat arbitrary figures as evidence of loss or retention in postoperative tests. The averages of all animals in initial learning were for trials 67.0, for errors 20.5. This is about half the practice required to reach the same criterion in the old apparatus. The range is from zero trials and errors to 200 trials and 61 errors. The average scores for preoperative retention tests were for trials 15.4, for errors 1.7, with a range from zero trials and errors to 50 trials and 9 errors.

Since no animal made more than 9 errors in preoperative retention tests, we may assume that 10 or more errors in postoperative tests represents some loss of the habit, directly or indirectly caused by the operation. A postoperative score of 20 or more errors represents as much practice in relearning as the average for initial learning, that is, a complete loss of the habit.

Only 3 per cent of the animals made fewer than 5 errors in initial training and only 19 per cent made fewer than 10 errors. A postoperative score of 5 or fewer errors may therefore be accepted as evidence of perfect or nearly perfect retention. Postoperative error scores between 5 and 10 are of somewhat

doubtful significance, indicating some loss not certainly ascribable to the operation. The criteria adopted for evaluation of the data are summarized as follows:

No significant loss: 5 errors or less
Partial loss: more than 10 errors
Complete loss: more than 20 errors
Doubtful: 6 to 9 errors

Retention of the Habit after Partial Destruction of the Striate Cortex. Table
19.1 records the animals in which some part of the geniculo-striate system
remained intact. Of the 38 cases, only 8 gave any evidence of loss of habit
and only 4 made more than 10 errors, which is perhaps the minimum to be
regarded as a sure indication of loss. The animals of this group have been
classified according to the parts of the striate areas involved in the lesion.

   a. Cases with considerable part of one or both binocular fields intact. This
includes numbers 1 to 12, 16, 18, 19, 20, and 25. Their average for errors in
postoperative retention tests was 3.1. Only numbers 19 and 20 showed a significant loss and their behavior cannot be accounted for in terms of the lesions.
Number 20 had a considerable part of both inferior temporal quadrants intact
and the total damage was exceeded in numbers 13, 14, 17, 21, and 27; all of
which showed practically perfect retention. This rat made better than chance
scores from the beginning of postoperative tests but was recorded as timid and
nervous. Number 19 also had less injury to the temporal fields than many
animals which made perfect scores. The records of these two animals are so
atypical that we must ascribe them to some other cause than the cerebral lesion.

   b. Cases with less than one-twelfth of the total temporal fields intact. This
group includes numbers 13, 14, 21, 24, 31, and 34. Their average of errors was
2.6, number 31 only exceeding 5 errors. The data from these two groups justify
the conclusion that retention of the brightness habit is undisturbed, if any part
of the binocular field remains intact.

   c. Cases with no part of the temporal field remaining. This group includes
numbers 17, 27, 33, and 35, with error scores of 2, 0, 8, and 11 respectively.
The condition of the remaining cells in the lateral geniculate nuclei in numbers
33 and 35 is uncertain. They seemed reduced in number, so these cases, the
only ones of the group to show loss, probably belong in the following group.

   d. Cases with irregularly scattered groups of cells in the lateral geniculate
nuclei, due to partial interruption of the radiations or irregular pathological
changes in the cortex: large areas completely degenerated and the cells markedly
reduced in number in the areas where they do appear. In previous studies such
animals have been found to lack detail vision. The group includes numbers 15,
22, 23, 26, 28, 29, 30, 32, 36, 37, and 38. Their average score for errors is 6.5.
The majority of animals of this group made 3 to 5 errors and only two, numbers
15 and 38, gave evidence of significant loss. Both of these animals had only
small areas of scattered cells in the lateral geniculate nuclei.

The results with these cases, in spite of some irregularity, justify the
conclusion that, so long as any part of the geniculo-striate system remains
intact, the reaction to brightness, formed before operation, may remain

Table 19.1. Learning and Retention Scores for Animals in Which the Destruction of the Striate Areas Was Incomplete [*]

Number	Extent of lesion	Initial training		Preoperative retention		Postoperative retention	
		Trials	Errors	Trials	Errors	Trials	Errors
1	2.4	80	31	0	0	10	1
2	2.6	50	17	20	4	10	1
3	2.6	110	33	40	7	0	0
4	3.2	90	23	0	0	0	0
5	3.5	80	27	10	2	10	2
6	3.8	40	11	0	0	40	3
7	5.2	50	24	10	2	0	0
8	5.8	50	21	20	1	0	0
9	6.0	90	20	10	1	0	0
10	8.6	100	28	50	4	30	5
11	9.0	30	18	20	1	0	0
12	9.0	0	0	30	7	0	0
13	9.8	90	49	0	0	0	0
14	10.0	90	30	0	0	40	2
15	10.3	40	8	0	0	60	16
16	11.5	100	39	10	5	10	1
17	12.4	90	29	40	3	10	2
18	13.0	100	33	20	1	10	1
19	13.0	150	45	20	3	30	9
20	13.2	10	3	30	3	80	25
21	13.9	90	25	0	0	30	4
22	15.0	40	15	0	0	30	5
23	16.9	80	35	30	3	10	2
24	16.9	200	41	0	0	20	4
25	17.1	100	61	10	1	10	1
26	18.4	130	45	0	0	60	5
27	19.0	40	10	0	0	0	0
28	19.8	110	36	50	3	30	3
29	21.1	60	16	0	0	20	9
30	21.3	40	6	0	0	30	4
31	21.6	60	23	20	2	40	8
32	21.7	50	7	20	2	30	4
33	21.8	50	11	10	1	20	8
34	22.6	20	9	10	2	10	1
35	22.8	60	13	10	1	70	11
36	23.2	70	21	0	0	10	4
37	24.9	90	29	0	0	10	2
38	27.3	30	7	20	1	80	17

[*] The extent of lesion is expressed as percentage of the surface area of the diagram. The learning scores are those preceding 20 consecutive errorless trials.

undisturbed. In cases where the small remaining areas have undergone partial degeneration, indicated by reduction in the number of cells per unit area in the nuclei, the animals make some errors in retraining tests but, even so, make fewer errors than the average for initial learning. Whatever the function of the geniculate nucleus and cortex in the habits, any small part of the system is capable of carrying it out.

Loss of the Habit after Complete Destruction of Both Striate Areas. Table 19.2 gives the records of animals in which the degeneration of the lateral geniculate nuclei appeared to be complete. In them either the entire striate cortex was destroyed in both hemispheres or the optic radiations were interrupted. The range of errors in postoperative tests for the group is from 10 to 41, with an average of 21.8. This is almost the same as the average score in initial learning for all cases, and 20 per cent above the initial learning score for this group. Compared with the cases having partial destruction of the geniculo-striate system, these animals all show a significant loss of the habit.[6] It seems clear that complete destruction of the geniculo-striate system abolishes the reaction to light formed before the operation. This result is in agreement with all previous experiments, in which animals with complete destruction of the dorsal convexity of the occipital pole have lost the habit of reaction to brightness.

The experiment is also in agreement with earlier ones in showing that, even when the entire striate cortex is destroyed, the animals are capable of relearning the reaction to light with no more average practice than is required for initial learning by a normal animal.

Partial Scotomas and Correlation of Training Scores with Extent of Lesion. In previous experiments of this type I have excluded animals with direct damage to subcortical visual centers, so the cases included in Tables 19.1 and 19.2, combined, are comparable to the groups reported earlier. These earlier studies gave correlations between extent of lesion and practice for postoperative relearning ranging around 0.70. The present data give a similar result. The rank order correlation between scores in postoperative retention tests and percentage lesion for the cases included in Table 19.1 (with partial destruction of the geniculo-striate system) is for errors, $p = 0.55$; for trials, $p = 0.47$. For all cases included in Tables 19.1 and 19.2, a group comparable to those previously studied, the correlations are for errors, $p = 0.67$; for trials, $p = 0.60$. This study, like the other, therefore shows a relationship between extent of lesion and practice for relearning. Can this be explained in terms of direct visual defect without recourse to the conception of a general dynamic factor such as I have postulated before?

Consideration of the groups of cases described above in testing the effect of locus of lesion shows that such an explanation is probably correct. The average

---

[6] It is of course impossible to be absolutely certain that all cells of the nuclei are degenerated. In many cases no nerve cells can be found; the nuclei are shrunken and packed with glia cells. A few apparently normal cells may occur along the margin of the pars ventralis. They probably belong to the latter nucleus, but may have cortical connections. They are sometimes absent, in which case the brightness habit may still be formed.

Table 19.2. Learning and Retention Scores for Animals with
Complete Destruction of Both Striate Areas *

Number	Extent of lesion	Initial training		Preoperative retention		Postoperative retention	
		Trials	Errors	Trials	Errors	Trials	Errors
39	14.1	140	53	90	9	30	10
40	15.2	80	20	50	3	100	15
41	17.1	90	25	30	3	70	15
42	19.4	60	7	10	1	110	29
43	23.7	50	8	50	8	130	41
44	26.0	90	16	10	1	40	14
45	26.2	30	14	0	0	110	36
46	26.9	70	18	50	3	100	21
47	28.1	50	9	0	0	70	18
48	32.6	30	13	20	2	40	20
49	35.6	30	8	0	0	120	21

* Arranged as in Table 19.1.

extent of lesion for all cases in Tables 19.1 and 19.2 is 16.0 per cent of the neocortex. For group *a*, with the greater part of one nuclear zone for the temporal field intact, the average extent of lesion is 7.7 per cent. For group *d*, with extensive degeneration in the nuclei and only scattered cells remaining, the average destruction was 19.9 per cent. For the group with complete degeneration of both nuclei (Table 19.2), the average extent of lesion was 24.1 per cent. Thus it appears that the larger the lesion, the more apt it is to produce a partial degeneration of the portions of the striate cortex not directly invaded, or a partial interruption of fibers from such areas, which must result in an amblyopic condition in the parts of the visual field not totally blind. Still larger lesions are more apt to produce complete destruction of both striate areas, with consequent total loss of the habit.

If the cerebral lesions were the only factor inducing differences in the postoperative retention scores, we should expect to get a trimodal distribution of errors: cases with no loss, cases with slight loss due to amblyopia in the residual visual fields, and cases with total loss. But with the scores influenced by many other chance factors this grouping is partly obscured, so that an appearance of continuous variation, somewhat in proportion to the extent of lesion, is produced.

Thus it appears that the correlation between extent of lesion and postoperative amnesia for the brightness habit is in reality an artifact due only to the obscuring by chance variations of an "all-or-none" function of the entire striate cortex. My previous assumption that the striate area exercises an influence upon subcortical centers to a degree proportional to its area was clearly wrong in the light of the present evidence.

Rate of Learning in the Absence of the Striate Areas. No animal with lesions restricted to the cortex failed to reacquire the habit of reaction to light after the operation. As in previous experiments, the rate of learning for animals lacking the striate areas is not significantly different from the rate of normal animals: 21.8 errors for the operated, 20.5 errors for the normal animals. Thus we still have the paradoxical result that the habit is somehow dependent upon the striate cortex when it is learned by the normal animal and yet is formed just as readily when the striate cortex is absent. "Localization" of the functions appears in a region which is not at all essential for efficient acquisition of the function. What part is played by the striate cortex in this habit and what structures are involved in learning when the striate areas have been destroyed? Some evidence on the second question is now available.

Brightness Vision in the Absence of the Striate Cortex

In addition to the cases with lesions restricted to the cortex there were a number with lesions invading the posterior part of the thalamus. The records of these cases are presented in Tables 19.3 and 19.4. The relearning scores of all these animals are poor and more than half failed to satisfy the criterion within 300 trials. Before these results can be interpreted the

Table 19.3. Learning and Retention Scores for Animals with Complete Destruction of the Striate Areas and Injury to One Optic Tract in Front of the Superior Colliculus [*]

Number	Extent of lesion	Initial training		Preoperative retention		Postoperative retention	
		Trials	Errors	Trials	Errors	Trials	Errors
50	21.8	70	25	10	1	200	53 F
51	25.0	50	10	20	1	110	44
52	26.6	90	20	0	0	30	10
53	27.9	70	25	20	2	40	12
54	28.3	50	16	10	2	100	24
55	30.7	60	22	0	0	30	10
56	30.8	100	11	30	3	200	72 F
57	32.4	40	18	0	0	240	91
58	33.5	70	19	0	0	180	39
59	42.4	80	18	0	0	300	62 F
60	42.6	30	6	0	0	160	42

[*] Arranged as Table 19.1.
F, failed to satisfy the criterion.

structural relation of the visual system must be considered in somewhat greater detail than was presented in our introduction.

Subcortical Visual Structures. The fibers of the optic nerve, after passing the chiasma, turn upward around the cerebral peduncle toward the lateral genicu-

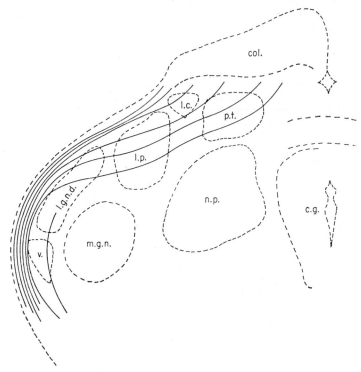

Fig. 19.3. Topographical relations of the optic thalamus in the rat. A section through the caudal tip of the lateral geniculate nucleus and anterior margin of the colliculus is shown. The course of fibers from the optic tract is indicated by solid lines. c.g., central gray; col., colliculus; l.c., large-celled nucleus; l.g.n.d., lateral geniculate nucleus, pars dorsalis; l.p., lateral nucleus, pars posterior; m.g.n., medial geniculate nucleus; n.p., nucleus of the posterior commissure; v., lateral geniculate nucleus, pars ventralis.

late nucleus. A small group of fibers (anterior accessory optic tract) passes mediad to the peduncle to enter a nucleus in the region of the nucleus of the third nerve. The relations from this point are shown in Fig. 19.3. The main bundle of fibers passes to the lateral geniculate nucleus. Below the nucleus the optic tract divides, most of the fibers passing around the lateral surface of the nucleus, but some go through the pars ventralis to reach the inner portions of the pars dorsalis. As the tract passes around the lateral surface of the lateral geniculate nucleus it sends collaterals into the nucleus. Some bundles of fibers also pass through the nucleus and continue through the pars posterior of the lateral nucleus toward the colliculus. The posterior accessory optic tract is given off at the posteroventral margin of the nucleus and passes downward to mix with the fibers of the anterior accessory tract. The main group of fibers passes over the posterior end of the geniculate nucleus, and through or above the lateral nucleus, pars posterior, the pretectile nucleus, and the nucleus of the posterior commissure to the colliculus. Various investigators have reported the termination of optic fibers in the lateral nucleus, pars posterior, in the large-celled nucleus of Clark, in the pretectile nucleus, and in the posterior nucleus. Conclusive evidence for such terminations has not been presented. Marchi granules can be seen throughout the region after enucleation of one eye, but whether these represent terminating fibers or fibers passing through to the colliculus remains uncertain.

The connections of these nuclei with the cerebral cortex are also in doubt. Clark (2) considers the posterior part of the lateral nucleus to be homologous with the pulvinar of primates. Waller (28) reports degeneration in this region after lesions in a cortical area just in front of the striate area and I have been able to confirm this. Neither Waller nor I have been able to establish degeneration in the pretectile or posterior nuclei after cerebral lesions. Clark believes that the pretectile nucleus sends no fibers to the cortex. I have been unable to detect degeneration in large-celled nucleus after lesions in the striate or peristriate areas.

Thus, in this group of nuclei, cortical connections have been established only for the posterior part of the lateral nucleus and it is doubtful that this receives fibers from the optic nerve. The majority of the fibers of the optic tract reach the colliculus. In it they show a topographic distribution corresponding to their origin in the retina, the temporal retina being represented in the anterolateral, the nasal in the posteromedial parts of the colliculus. Only crossed fibers reach the colliculus (16, 22). No ascending fibers from the colliculi to the cortex have been reported.

Cases with Subcortical Lesions. The striate area in the rat extends from the level of the caudal end of the lateral geniculate nucleus to the posterior pole of the hemisphere. It is separated from the thalamus only by the superior edge of the hippocampus, about 1.5 mm. in thickness. In the effort to assure destruction of the entire striate area I injured the thalamus in an unusually large number of cases. In some, the subcortical lesions were confined to one side of the thalamus. The records of these cases are given in Table 19.3 and diagrams of the cerebral lesions . . . [were prepared]. In others the lesions involved both sides of the thalamus. The records of these cases are given in Table 19.4. Brain diagrams have not been prepared for this group. The striate areas were destroyed in every case. The lesions range from complete destruction of the thalamus above the level of the aqueduct to only slight invasions of the optic tract where it passes over the posterior part of the lateral nucleus. The extent

Table 19.4. Learning and Retention Scores for Animals with Destruction of the
Striate Areas and Injury to Both Optic Tracts in Front of the
Superior Colliculi *

Number	Initial training		Preoperative retention		Postoperative retention	
	Trials	Errors	Trials	Errors	Trials	Errors
61	70	16	50	4	300	118 F
62	70	22	0	0	360	163
63	30	12	10	1	300	169 F
64	30	5	40	4	310	115 F
65	40	10	0	0	300	144 F
66	30	17	20	2	300	127 F
67	40	14	0	0	310	67 F
68	60	19	20	3	250	141 F

* Arranged as Table 19.1.
F, failed to satisfy the criterion.

of thalamic injury in all cases is shown in Table 19.5. The 19 animals included in this table fall into 3 classes with respect to their retraining records: those which relearned the reaction to brightness, those which failed to satisfy the criterion of 20 consecutive errorless trials but gave unmistakable evidence of discrimination by making 90 per cent correct reactions for at least 50 consecutive trials, and those which never made better than chance scores in 250 to 300 trials.

In number 54 the ventral half of the right lateral geniculate nucleus appeared normal. In all other cases with thalamic lesions the lateral geniculate nuclei showed complete retrograde degeneration.

Considering first the cases which satisfied the criterion (numbers 51, 52, 53, 54, 55, 57, 58, 60, and 62) we find that all but three (numbers 54, 57, and 62) had the thalamic lesion confined to one side. In the three cases with bilateral injuries, the lesion on one side was confined to the superficial layer of fibers, laterad to the pars posterior of the lateral nucleus (Fig. 19.3). The average practice required for relearning by these animals was 139 trials and 37 errors. The retardation indicated by these figures is 94 per cent of the practice required for initial learning. Thus, in the absence of the striate cortex, relatively slight damage in the optic thalamus may double the practice required for learning the reaction to brightness.

Of the cases which failed to satisfy the criterion but gave evidence of discrimination, all had a destruction of the lateral geniculate nucleus and entire optic thalamus on one side with no injury (numbers 50, 56, and 59) or only slight invasion (number 67) of the tract on the other.

The cases which made only chance scores (numbers 61, 63, 64, 65, 66, and 68) all had either interruption of the tract with destruction of the lateral genicu-

Table 19.5. Description of Lesions to the Thalamus in All Animals in Which They Occurred

Number	Side of thalamus involved	Tract	L.G.N.	L.p.p.	Pret.	Relearning scores Trials	Errors
52	Right	*	*			30	10 L
55	Right	*	*			30	10 L
53	Right	*	▪			40	12 L
54 {	Right	*				100	24 L
	Left	*					
60	Right	*				160	42 L
51	Left	*	?	*	*	110	44 L
58	Left	*	*	*	*	180	89 L
57 {	Right	*				240	91 L
	Left	*					
62 {	Right	*				300	163 L
	Left	*		*	*		
50	Right	*	*	*	*	200	53 FD
59	Left	*	*	*	*	300	62 FD
67 {	Right	*	*	*	*	310	67 FD
	Left	*					
56	Left	*	*	*	*	200	72 FD
61 {	Right	*	*			300	118 F
	Left	*	*	*	*		
63 {	Right	*	*			300	169 F
	Left	*	*				
64 {	Right	*				310	115 F
	Left	*	*	*	*		
65 {	Right	*				300	144 F
	Left	*	*	*	*		
66 {	Right	*	*			300	127 F
	Left	*	*	*	*		
68 {	Right	*	*	*	*	250	141 F
	Left	*	*	*			

* Direct lesion in any structure. The injuries were restricted to one side of the thalamus except where both right and left sides are specified. In number 54 there were a few normal cells in the right lateral geniculate nucleus. In all other cases these nuclei, when not directly destroyed, showed complete retrograde degeneration. Animals which satisfied the criterion are marked "L" after the training scores. Those which failed to satisfy the criterion but made better than 90 per cent correct in 50 trials are marked "FD." Those which made only chance scores are marked "F." Tract, fibers laterad to the lateral nucleus; L.G.N., lateral geniculate nucleus; L.p.p., lateral nucleus, pars posterior; Pret., pretectile nucleus.

late nucleus, or practically complete destruction of the optic thalamus on both sides.

The Structures Involved in Acquisition of the Brightness Habit in the Absence of the Striate Cortex.

The remaining cortex. In seeking an explanation of the formation of habits based on brightness discrimination in the absence of the striate areas, one naturally turns first to other parts of the cortex. The peristriate areas, perhaps homologous to field 19 in primates, should have visual function. Their destruction, however, produces no disturbance of memory based on detail vision (18), nor is there other evidence of their visual function in the rat. In cases numbered 41, 43, 44, 46, 47, 48, and 49 of the present series the peristriate areas or their radiations were destroyed as well as the striate areas and the posterior parts of the lateral nuclei were degenerated, but these animals all relearned the brightness habit.

It is possible that scattered fibers of the visual system go to other parts of the cortex, outside of the recognized visual areas. The existence of such fibers has not been demonstrated nor, in view of the precise and limited projection of the lateral geniculate fibers upon the cortex, does it seem likely. I attempted to test the function of such hypothetical fibers (10) by training animals which lacked the striate areas and then removing parts of the remaining cortex, about one-third in each case and covering all parts of the cerebrum in the series. None of these lesions resulted in a significant loss. In seems clear from this evidence that no secondary visual center in the cortex assumes the function of the striate areas after their destruction.

The lateral geniculate nuclei. In earlier studies I was inclined to ascribe the postoperative relearning to the lateral geniculate nuclei but the evidence now seems conclusive that in the rat these nuclei contain only cells which send their axones to the striate cortex and undergo degeneration after removal of the latter. After destruction of the striate area a few scattered cells may be found in the nucleus, along the margin of the pars inferior or just under the optic tract, but often even these cells are absent in animals which show visual reactions. These cases rule out any significant function of the lateral geniculate nuclei in the relearning of the habit.

Nucleus of the accessory optic tracts. The interruption of the optic tracts, in animals which failed to re-form the habit of reaction to light, was at some distance beyond the point at which the accessory optic tracts leave the main bundle of fibers, in practically all cases. Reaction to light thus seems impossible with only the accessory optic tracts intact.

The optic thalamus and superior colliculus. This leaves the optic thalamus and superior colliculus as possibly concerned in the reacquisition of the habit. Severe injury in the optic thalamus of one side produces a marked retardation in relearning, and when both sides are involved the reaction to light becomes impossible. Superficial injuries to the tracts of both sides, where they pass over the pars posterior of the lateral nucleus, produce some retardation, but do not prevent relearning.

Optic fibers to the colliculus apparently pass not only over the surface of the thalamus but also penetrate deeply into the lateral and pretectile nuclei, as indicated in Fig. 19.3. It is thus impossible to injure the optic thalamus without destroying the optic supply of the colliculus. The distribution of fibers to the colliculus is such that the temporal retina is represented in the anterolateral and the nasal retina in the posteromedial regions. As a result of this, all fibers from the temporal retina cannot be interrupted except by practically complete destruction of the optic thalamus.

In the present experiments it is thus impossible to distinguish the functions of the colliculi from possible functions of the optic thalamus. The fact of retardation from superficial interruption of the tracts might be taken as evidence that the colliculus is chiefly involved, but such lesions also injure the fibers to the large-celled nucleus. We can conclude only that in the absence of the striate cortex the reaction to light is dependent upon some part of the complex of structures included in the optic thalamus and colliculi.

Discussion

By analysis of retrograde degeneration in the lateral geniculate nuclei it has been possible to divide the cases studied for postoperative amnesia into three classes: those with some part of the geniculo-striate system uninjured, those with cells much reduced in number in the parts of the system not completely degenerated, and those with complete destruction of the striate areas and degeneration of the lateral geniculate nuclei. The members of each of these classes have fairly consistent postoperative training records. So long as any part of the geniculo-striate system remains intact, the animal is likely to make a practically perfect score in retention tests. If the residual parts of the system show a marked reduction in number of cells, the animal makes more errors in postoperative than in preoperative retention tests, but still gives evidence of memory. If the entire striate cortex of both hemispheres is destroyed, or the radiations interrupted, the animals require as much practice for relearning as for original learning.

The effect of a lesion in the striate cortex has thus an all-or-nothing character, depending upon the complete destruction of the geniculo-striate system. The coefficients of correlation between extent of lesion and relearning scores based on all cases without subcortical lesions, are between 0.60 and 0.70, virtually as high as those reported in previous similar studies. It follows that the correlations previously found were likewise due to the inclusion of cases with different types of scotoma and that I was wrong in interpreting the amnesia as a continuous function of the extent of lesion.

In an earlier study (11) I reported that linear lesions interrupting the optic radiations produced an effect only proportionate to the surface area of the lesions rather than to the number of projection fibers interrupted, as judged by the corresponding effects of lesions within the striate cortex. This result is understandable in the light of the present evidence. Clean-cut lesions interrupting part of the optic radiation are likely to leave the uncut parts of the radiation normal. Lesions to the striate cortex are more likely to produce diffuse changes in the parts not actually invaded, with consequent amblyopia and poorer retraining records.

The effects of cerebral lesions on brightness habits are thus in harmony with those on detail vision (18). Both show no significant loss unless the whole of the functional area is destroyed. For detail vision, as tested with the jumping apparatus, this critical area is that for the projection of the binocular field; for brightness it is the entire striate cortex.

It is not certain that all of my earlier results in the study of postoperative retention of reactions to light can be explained entirely in terms of this all-or-nothing effect. In previous studies a smaller percentage of animals showed perfect retention of the habit and the relation between extent of lesion and retention scores also seemed more continuous throughout the range than in the present study. In a study of the postoperative retention of habit based on discrimination of two lights of liminal difference I obtained some evidence that the differential reaction to two lights might be disturbed when that to a single light was unaffected. The training box used in the present experiments is of a type which forces the animal's attention to the stimulus plates to a greater extent than does the customary form. The question therefore remains whether or not the forcing of attention in this experiment and in studies with the jumping technique may not have failed to reveal defects of visual attention resulting from slighter lesions which would be effective in prolonging training in the conventional Yerkes box. The clinical literature contains numerous suggestions that the power of visual attention is reduced by lesions which do not abolish the ability to distinguish details, when sufficient effort is expended.

The loss of the habit after destruction of the striate cortex with subsequent relearning at normal rate remains the most puzzling result obtained in studies of brightness vision. All experiments have been consistent on this point. Animals with lesions to the striate cortex produced before training are indistinguishable from normal ones in their rate of learning: animals which have lost the habit from operation after training regain it with no more practice than was required for their initial learning. The experiments of Marquis (19) with the dog confirm the latter result, although they indicate some retardation in initial learning after operation. No clear explanation of the loss and subsequent relearning has been offered. I have tested for diaschisis effects (11) by retraining animals at different time intervals after the operation, and have found that no spontaneous recovery occurs within an interval during which other animals may be retrained to nearly perfect performance. Operative shock or specific depression of other visual centers thus seems ruled out.

It seemed clear that the capacity to form the habit is not dependent upon the cerebral area the destruction of which gives evidence for "localization" of the habit. I suggested that the engram for the habit might consist of an organization of the entire visual system, in which case postoperative amnesia would consist of a disturbance of equilibrium within the system, leaving the parts capable of reorganization. Pavlov (25) has criticized this interpretation and advanced an alternative of his own. . . . .

I have elsewhere (15) discussed the possibility that for the normal animal the form of the object dominates so that the reaction is not to light, but to a specific luminous object. In such a case the light stimulus acting after destruction of the striate areas might not be identified with the original object and a new set of associations would have to be established with the now formless light. The practical impossibility of establishing reactions to specific visual patterns in the Yerkes box, with which most of these experiments were performed, seems strong evidence against this explanation.

Goldstein (5) in discussing the mechanism of recovery after injuries to the nervous system points out that, so long as a given system can function, even at low efficiency, the organism will not shift to the use of another mechanism, although with complete destruction of the first system the shift occurs immediately. This is best illustrated by the data of Fuchs (4) on formation of a pseudofovea. The data on cerebral localization of the brightness habit fit such a description, but it offers no understanding of the mechanism by which the regulation of the activity of different systems is brought about.

None of these explanations is altogether satisfactory. If we assume that learning involves the formation of specific conduction paths, there seems no reason why they should not be formed at subcortical levels in the normal animal and persist after operation. If we assume a disorder of attention, this should be evident in a slower initial learning in animals with cerebral lesions. If we assume, as I have done, that the entire visual system is involved in the habit organization, then we should expect a partial destruction of the striate areas to disturb the habit. If we assume a shift to a different mechanism, as from detail to brightness vision the exact equality of learning records for animals with and without the striate areas could scarcely result.

The anatomical basis for the formation of visual habits in the absence of the striate areas is only partly cleared up by these experiments. Further work, both anatomical and experimental, must be done before the inter-relations of the geniculo-striate system, the optic thalamus, and the superior colliculi become intelligible. Are the subcortical nuclei capable of forming visual associations without participation of the cortex? The present experiments have eliminated those parts of the cortex to which visual fibers are known to be projected, but others may exist. The experiments of Poltyrew and Zeliony (26) show the formation of visual habits after very severe cerebral lesions and the recent work of Culler and Mettler (3) seems to establish the formation of simple associations in the absence of the entire neopallium.

Are the reactions to light, acquired in the absence of the visual cortex, direct associations with optic paths, or mediated by an intervening muscular sensitivity? It is possible that the reflex movements of adaptation give rise to an excitation of intrinsic or extrinsic muscles of the eye which could be conducted to the kinesthetic areas of the cortex and serve as a basis for learning. The sensory areas of the cortex in the rat are very extensive and none of our operations has destroyed them completely.

The available data suggest an equivalence of function for brightness vision between the striate cortex and the superior colliculi. Either system may be destroyed without abolishing the capacity to react to brightness. Before we can accept this equivalence, however, more must be learned concerning the functions of the optic thalamus. This rather than the colliculus may be concerned in brightness vision. Some of Layman's animals, which formed the brightness habit after destruction of the colliculi, had also large lesions in the optic thalamus, but none so extensive as those of the present series. To settle this matter it will be necessary to compare effects of destruction of the colliculi alone and in conjunction with destruction of the optic thalamus.

The survival of the habit after the destruction of any part of the striate areas accords with our previous results on detail vision in showing that the memory trace is not localized anywhere within the visual cortex. Any part of the system which can be excited by impulses from the retina, even though it be only a few scattered cells connected with the nasal retina, is capable of eliciting the appropriate motor response.

Summary

Rats were trained in a modified discrimination box to go to light and avoid darkness. They were then subjected to lesions within the striate areas of the cerebral cortex and tested for retention of the previously formed habit. The lesions were studied with reference to both the cortical areas destroyed and the distribution of retrograde degeneration within the lateral geniculate nuclei.

So long as any small part of the geniculo-striate system remained intact perfect retention of the habit was possible.

When the remaining cells in the lateral geniculate nuclei were few and diffusely scattered, the animals showed some loss of the habit, but re-learned in significantly less than the practice required for initial learning.

With complete destruction of both striate areas and complete degeneration of the lateral geniculate nuclei, the animals required as much practice for relearning as for initial learning before the operation.

The postoperative loss of the habit thus follows an all-or-nothing principle, and occurs only after complete destruction of the striate areas. Computation of correlations between extent of cerebral lesion and postoperative training records gives coefficients of about 0.60, due to the inclusion of cases with and without complete destruction of the striate areas. My earlier conclusion that the loss of the habit is proportional to the amount of tissue destroyed, irrespective of locus within the visual areas, was therefore incorrect.

After complete destruction of the striate cortex and degeneration of the lateral geniculate nuclei, relearning of the brightness habit requires no more practice than does initial learning by normal animals.

Relearning occurs when the peristriate areas as well as the striate areas have been destroyed.

Destruction of the striate areas with severe injury to the optic thalamus on one side results in a marked retardation in relearning. When the optic thalamus is severely injured on both sides relearning becomes impossible. It is uncertain whether this effect is due to the injury to the nuclei of the optic thalamus or to the interruption of the optic fibers to the colliculi.

The accessory optic tracts and nuclei are not adequate for the formation of visual habits.

REFERENCES

1. Bechterew, W. von. *Die Funktionen der Nervencentra.* Jena: 1911.

2. Clark, W. E. Le Gros. An experimental study of thalamic connections in the rat, *Philos. Trans. Roy. Soc., Lond.*, 1932, **222B**, 1–28.

3. Culler, E., and Mettler, F. A. Conditioned behavior in a decorticate dog, *J. comp. Psychol.*, 1934, **18**, 451–454.

4. Fuchs, W. Untersuchungen über das Sehen der Hemianopiker und Hemi-amblyopiker. In *Psychologische Analysen Hirnpathologischer Fälle.* Leipzig: 1920.

5. Goldstein, K. Ueber die Plastizität des Organismus auf Grund von Erfahrungen an nervenkranken Menschen, *Handb. norm. path. Physiol.*, 1931, **15**, 1130–1174.

6. Hitzig, E. Alte und neue Untersuchungen über das Gehirn, *Arch. Psychiat. Neurol.*, 1903, **37**, 277–609.

7. Johnson, H. M. Visual pattern-discrimination in vertebrates: II. Com-

parative visual acuity in the dog, the monkey and the chick, *J. anim. Behav.*, 1914, **4**, 340–361.

8. Lashley, K. S. Studies of cerebral function in learning, *Psychobiology*, 1920, **2**, 55–135.

9. Lashley, K. S. Studies of cerebral function in learning: II. The effects of long-continued practice upon cerebral localization, *J. comp. Psychol.*, 1921, **1**, 453–468.

10. Lashley, K. S. Studies of cerebral function in learning: IV. Vicarious function after destruction of the visual areas, *Amer. J. Physiol.*, 1922, **59**, 44–71.

11. Lashley, K. S. Studies of cerebral function in learning: VII. The relation between cerebral mass, learning, and retention, *J. comp. Neurol.*, 1926, **41**, 1–58.

12. Lashley, K. S. *Brain mechanisms and intelligence.* Chicago: 1929.

13. Lashley, K. S. The mechanism of vision: II. The influence of cerebral lesions upon the threshold of discrimination for brightness, *J. genet. Psychol.*, 1930, **37**, 461–480.

14. Lashley, K. S. The mechanism of vision: IV. The cerebral areas necessary for pattern vision in the rat, *J. comp. Neurol.*, 1931, **53**, 419–478.

15. Lashley, K. S. Studies of cerebral function in learning: VIII. A reanalysis of data on mass action in the visual cortex, *J. comp. Neurol.*, 1932, **54**, 77–84.

16. Lashley, K. S. The mechanism of vision: VII. The projection of the retina upon the primary optic centers of the rat, *J. comp. Neurol.*, 1934, **59**, 341–373.

17. Lashley, K. S. The mechanism of vision: VIII. The projection of the retina upon the cerebral cortex of the rat, *J. comp. Neurol.*, 1934, **60**, 57–79.

18. Lashley, K. S., and Frank, Margaret. The mechanism of vision: X. Postoperative disturbances of habits based on detail vision in the rat after lesions in the cerebral visual areas, *J. comp. Psychol.*, 1934, **17**, 355–380.

19. Marquis, D. G. Effect of removal of the visual cortex in mammals, with observations on the retention of light discrimination in dogs, *Proc. Assoc. Res. nerv. ment. Dis.*, 1934, **13**, 558–592.

20. Minkowski, M. Zur Physiologie der Sehsphäre, *Arch. ges. Physiol.*, 1911, **141**, 171–327.

21. Munk, H. *Über die Funktionen von Hirn und Rückenmark.* Berlin: 1909.

22. Overbosch, J. F. A. *Experimenteel-anatomische onderzoekingen over de projectie der retina in het centrale zenuwstelsel.* Amsterdam: 1928.

23. Papez, J. W., and Freeman, G. L. The effect of subcortical lesions on the visual discrimination of rats, *J. comp. Psychol.*, 1930, **10**, 185–193.

24. Pavlov, I. P. *Conditioned reflexes.* Oxford Press: 1927.

25. Pavlov, I. P. The reply of a physiologist to psychologists, *Psychol. Rev.*, 1932, **39**, 91–127.

26. Poltyrew, S. S., and Zeliony, O. P. Grosshirnrinde und Assoziationsfunktion, *Z. Biol.*, 1930, **90**, 157–161.

27. Putnam, T. J., and Putnam, I. K. Studies on the central visual system: I. The anatomic projection of the retinal quadrants on the striate cortex of the rabbit, *Arch. Neurol. Psychiat., Chicago*, 1926, **16**, 1–20.

28. Waller, W. H. Topographical relations of cortical lesions to thalamic nuclei in the albino rat, *J. comp. Neurol.*, 1934, **60**, 237–269.

20. FUNCTIONAL DETERMINANTS OF CEREBRAL LOCALIZATION [1]

Since the pioneer work of Broca and of Fritsch and Hitzig, there has been a steady accumulation of evidence for the anatomic and functional specialization of different cerebral areas. Diversities of cortical structure revealed by myelino-architectural and cyto-architectural studies have been correlated with differences in subcortical connections and with consistent and characteristic symptoms of defect following local injuries. The principal sensory and motor areas have been delimited, and the problem of cerebral localization has become one of the degree of specialization within cyto-architectural areas, of the nature of the functional disturbances following various types of injury, and of the mechanisms of organization.

Behind these questions of detail and interpretation there remains, however, the problem of the functional significance of all localization. The basis of localization of function within the nervous system is apparently the grouping of cells of similar function within more or less isolated nuclei or fields. The fundamental problem for the student of localization is to discover what functions are served by this grouping and isolation. What activities of the cells are favored by such an arrangement? What functions does it permit that could not be carried out if the cells were uniformly distributed throughout the system? Has localization or gross anatomic differentiation any functional significance whatever?

The answers to these questions are not so self-evident as is often assumed. Neither current theories of the physiology of nervous integration nor the observed phenomena of anatomic and functional specialization provide an obvious reason for the particular functional divisions of the cortex which must be deduced from symptoms of local injury. Increasing knowledge of the facts of cerebral localization has only emphasized ignorance of the real reason for any gross localization whatever.

[1] EDITORS' NOTE: From *Arch. Neurol. Psychiat.*, Chicago, 1937, 38, 371–387. Reproduced by permission of the American Medical Association. From department of psychology, Harvard University. Read before the Boston Society of Psychiatry and Neurology, March 19, 1936.

Mentalistic Interpretations of Localization

For early investigators it was sufficient to regard the separate cerebral areas as the seat of distinct mental functions. Descartes had described the brain as a sort of filing cabinet in which the memories of the soul are stored. Phrenologists followed the facultative psychology of their time and found it natural that a thoroughly compartmentalized mind should have its activities distributed in space in accordance with a logical classification of its functions. Fritsch and Hitzig (4) described the stimulable cortex as the "place of entry of single psychic functions into matter," and many, even recent, authors have followed their lead in mentalistic interpretation. In such dualistic systems localization of functions could be regarded as a necessary consequence of the organization of mind, and the question of the functional value of anatomic specialization scarcely arose.

The error of the phrenologists lay in the assumption that a classification of mental traits, arrived at by logical analysis of behavior, reveals functions which must necessarily have a separate cerebral localization. More recent clinical studies have only in part avoided this fallacy. They have not assumed that all supposed psychologic entities must have separate localization but have sought the reason for localization in mental organization. Wernicke and later students of aphasia, notably Pick (30), have tried to analyze the language function in terms of logical categories which would correspond to the clinical types of aphasia. The explanation of localization implied is still in terms of the products of cerebral activity rather than terms of the nature of the cerebral mechanisms themselves.

Perhaps this is only a methodologic dualism necessary in any pioneer study. Insight into the organization of behavior may be gained by study of its disorganization following organic lesions, and something of the mechanism of cerebral physiologic activity may be inferred from the organization of behavior. Explanations of cerebral activity, however, cannot satisfactorily be cast in mentalistic or behavioral terms. The conclusion that two functions the separate localization of which has been determined clinically have disparate cerebral loci because they are recognizable as distinct functions in behavior is merely a circular argument.

An approach to the problem of localization from the standpoint of psychologic functions leads to a hopeless tangle of contradictions. The projection areas for the various sense modalities are anatomically separate; yet it does not follow that spatial separation is essential for differential sensory reactions, since some of the finest discriminations, such as between odors, are certainly not dependent on gross anatomic separation of receptive centers. The discrimination of qualities or "dimensions" within any sense modality does not seem to involve any processes psychologically different from those in discrimination between modalities, so that one cannot correlate the discriminative process in general with the anatomic separation of the excitations distinguished or appeal to discrimination to account for localization.

Psychologic unity is also not a criterion of localization. The motor processes of "voluntary movement" seem psychologically quite unitary. The various disturbances arising from lesions to the cortical motor and premotor areas, the basal nuclei and the cerebellum indicate, however, that the motor function is a physiologic complex the components of which are unintelligible in terms of psychologic analysis. Thus, a function which from an introspective or a behavioristic standpoint is completely integrated and unanalyzed turns out, when its pathologic aspect is studied, to be controlled by widely scattered loci contributing quite diverse elements to the whole.

Much stress has been laid on the discrete localization of memory traces, but nothing is more evident in the clinical and experimental literature than that individual memories are never destroyed by small lesions. The clinical picture of amnesia is one of a greater or lesser weakening of all memories of a general class from any lesion which is at all effective; the experimental picture is that of the preservation by any part of a functional area of all memory traces with which the whole is concerned (16, 21). The development of conditioned reflex paths or the formation of memory traces is not the basis of observed localizations.

The evidence for the parallel development of intelligence and the "association areas" provides no reason for the anatomic separation of such areas. The single sensory projection area can mediate functions of the same psychologic character as those which are classed as intelligent. Thus, Frank and I (23) have found that the discrimination of visual patterns by the rat is not disturbed by lesions in any cerebral area except the primary visual centers. Such discriminations involve processes of differentiation and organization which are not definably different from the generalizations and abstractions involved in the "higher" intellectual processes. The early controversy concerning the functions of the "associative areas," in which Munk maintained that the interaction of sensory fields is sufficient for the intellectual functions while Hitzig stressed the need for higher correlating centers, at least demonstrated the lack of any a priori reason for expecting the development of separate "intellectual" centers.

These illustrations are typical of what is found in any attempt to relate localization of function to psychologic or behavioral categories. Functions which seem unitary in behavior are broken up by local lesions, and functions which seem markedly diverse are carried out within the same anatomically homogeneous field. Whenever separate localization of two psychologic entities is established, giving an apparently valid reason for spatial separation, a parallel and equally impressive case can be found in which there is not separate localization.

Localization and General Theories of Integration

The reflex or connectionist theories of nervous integration, which assume that activity is determined by the transmission of impulses over relatively isolated neural paths through associative connections built up in learning, would be equally applicable if no gross localization existed. In a telephone system convenience of administration and economy of construction are attained by a system of local exchanges, but the working of the exchanges is not dependent on a geographic arrangement of the switchboards. The extreme connectionist theory, represented by behaviorism, asserts that the formation of new associative connections is independent of any innate structural organization of the cortex and therefore implies the absence of localization except as built up by chance associative connections. At most, therefore, the connectionist theories suggest that economy in length of reflex arcs may be effected by localization, but they give no reason for such detailed topographic arrangements as appear in the striate area or the central gyrus, nor do they give the least hint of a reason for such dissociations of function as are seen in the aphasias or agnosias.

The theory of the development of adjacent excitatory and inhibitory centers, irradiation between which determines balance of activity and the character of integration, as proposed by Pavlov (29), might provide a reason for the spatial separation of functional mechanisms. Clinical and experimental data on localization, however, give no indication that this is the actual basis of structural differentiation. On the contrary, studies of spinal reflexes and of the motor cortex indicate that excitation and inhibition may be originated within the same center. The major anatomic fields of the cortex are clearly not interrelated on any principles of reciprocal innervation, nor did Pavlov himself suggest any such relation.

Other general theories of neural integration, resonance theories, doctrines of cortical dominance and the like are too vague to suggest anything definite concerning the basis of cerebral localization.

Morphogenic Basis of Localization

The aggregation of neurons having similar functions in distinct areas or nuclei does not in itself justify an interpretation of structure in terms of adaptation, any more than does the distribution of pigment on the skin of a piebald animal. Both may be the product of developmental forces, important for the formation of the embryo but without significance in the behavior of the differentiated animal. The function of the cells may be deduced from their position and connections, but their position is not therefore a necessary consequence of their function. Some part of the structural diversity of the nervous system may well be an accidental product of the mechanism of embryonic development. By the general principles of neurobiotaxis, neuroblasts developing simultaneously in a given region are subject to the same developmental forces and will send their axons to a common field. Thus, local groups of cells having similar functional connections will arise; yet the fact of their aggregation and the consequent "localization of function" may be entirely without significance for the integrative processes in which they participate.

For example, the regular arrangement of ascending fibers in the dorsal funiculus of the spinal cord seems to be determined by the time at which developing axons reach a given level, the later arrivals from lower levels displacing laterally those established earlier. Continuation of this arrangement into the nucleus gracilis and nucleus cuneatus would give a definite "localization of function," yet would not justify the conclusion that the physiologic activity of these nuclei is dependent in any way on the spatial arrangement.

How much of the structural differentiation of the nervous system is ascribable to such developmental processes and is irrelevant for behavior cannot be determined from the anatomic facts alone. The common occurrence of vestigial structures in other parts of the body suggests that the arrangement of many of the major divisions of the mammalian nervous system may represent only a recapitulation of their phylogenetic history. The separation of the sensory fields of the cortex may have no further significance than that the neuroblasts in the thalamic nuclei differentiate at different times; the association areas may be distinct from the projection fields only because they represent masses of nerve tissue of later evolutionary origin. Thus, the mere existence of specialized regions in the brain is not conclusive evidence that the specialization is necessary or important for the integrative functions. On anatomic grounds alone there is no assurance that cerebral localization is anything but an accident of growth.

I do not wish to overemphasize this point. The vast majority of structural arrangements in the nervous system, especially among the lower nuclei and tracts, look as if they must have some functional value. But it is important to realize that this functional value is accepted largely as a matter of faith and that there are no certain anatomic or behavioral principles by which the significance of any particular instance of localization may be judged.

Functional Value of Cerebral Localization

The most impressive evidence that the differentiation of cerebral fields is more than a chance product of developmental mechanics comes from cases in which nature seems to be at great pains to restore an order which has been lost at some earlier developmental stage. In the visual system, for example, the orderly arrangement of the fibers from the retinal elements is partly or completely lost in the optic nerve and chiasm, to be reconstituted within the lateral geniculate nuclei, in a three dimensional system (19, 34). Again, between the lateral geniculate nucleus and the area striata the fibers are confused in the optic radiation, and the order is again restored, this time in two dimensions, in the visual cortex (20). The developmental history of the visual system is such that simple principles of displacement, such as apply to the dorsal spinal funiculus, will not account for the distribution of fibers. The cortical retina becomes intelligible only on the assumption that the projection of the retina on the cerebral surface is essential for some phase of visual reaction.

What is the nature of the nervous processes which demand such isolated mechanisms or depend on the topographic reproduction of sensory surfaces in the cerebrum? It has been seen that interpretations in terms of behavioral resultants lead to confusion. The answer must be sought in the nature of the physiologic mechanisms themselves. Recent experimental work presents some clues as to the reasons for physiologic isolation and for the separate localization of such functions as are actually dissociated by lesions. Two types of nervous function stand out conspicuously as characteristic of the activities of different centers and suggest the principle that separate localization of functions is determined by the existence of diverse kinds of integrative mechanism which cannot function in the same nerve field without interference. The assumption of such incompatibility or mutual exclusion of physiologic processes is consistent with many facts of cerebral localization.

Mechanisms Which Regulate Intensity of Response. The studies of Sherrington and his co-workers on the properties of the motoneuron pool defined the activities of a center which is primarily concerned with the regulation of the intensity of response (32, 33). The mechanisms suggested for facilitation, recruitment and inhibition depend on the aggregation of neurons of like function within a homogeneous field, within which there is overlap of axon terminations. Summation within the subliminal fringe (the overlapping fields of different axons) contributes importantly to the gradation of intensity of the discharge from the motoneuron pool.

Such a mechanism is well adapted for gradation in intensity of activity, but it would work imperfectly in maintaining separate representation of very small functional units, such as are involved in foveal vision or in tactile discrimination. The efficiency of the system for gradation of intensities is dependent on the close anatomic grouping of cells with common function and on the extent of the subliminal fringes, and this is incompatible with cell to cell correspondences.

Regulation of Spatial Orientation. If one examines the chief cerebral projection areas with respect to the degree of subordinate localization within them, as indicated by the diversity of symptoms produced by small focal lesions, one finds that the visual, tactile and motor regions have a high degree of internal specificity, whereas there is little or no evidence of subordinate localization within the olfactory and gustatory fields. (The position of the auditory area in this grouping is uncertain. I have found some separate projection of different parts of the medial geniculate nucleus but no such detail of anatomic differentiation as prevails in the visual and tactile systems.) Reactions mediated by the visual and tactile areas are primarily spatial; that is, the reactions are to the relative spatial position of points on the receptive surfaces. The motor region is concerned with the selective spatial distribution of excitations to different muscle groups. There is a striking contrast between these areas which are most directly concerned with spatial reactions and other projection and association areas with respect to the degree of subordinate differentiation within them. This suggests that reproduction of the topography of the sensory surface on the surface of the cortex is somehow important for orienting reactions.

Little is known of the actual mechanisms of such reactions. They consist of the translation of a pattern of sensory excitement into a pattern of movement with reference to bodily posture. Studies of perception, especially in vision, have defined some of the properties of the mechanism. It is clear that no simple connectionist hypothesis will account for the facts of functional equivalence of parts and for the relational character of the adequate stimuli. The system has the characteristics of a field of interacting forces, as illustrated by interacting magnetic fields or overlapping diffusion gradients. Motor reactions are determined by the distribution of excitations within the field, irrespective of the particular neurons excited (17).

When one tries to imagine a mechanism for this type of reaction, it is necessary to postulate two fields of force so related that a pattern of tensions or stresses within one field (a sensory area) will induce a different, but constant, pattern in the other (motor zone) (13). Rashevsky has approached this problem from the standpoint of physical systems and has shown that such patterns of excitation as form or contour have certain simple mathematical properties which differentiate each from every other and that postulated physical correlates of the mathematical properties will exhibit relations corresponding to the phenomena of behavior (31). I have proposed a theory of interference effects of radiated excitations to account for the phenomena of sensory equivalence (18), and the "resonance" hypothesis of Weiss suggests a still different mechanism (37). None of the hypotheses gives a satisfactory solution of the problem at present, but all imply a type of organization between cortical systems different from the organization revealed by studies of the motoneuron pool.

Evidence for the Anatomic Separation of Mechanisms for Spatial Adjustments and Regulation of Intensity. Thus, the little that is known of the mechanisms of spatial orientation and regulation of intensities of reaction suggests that the nervous organizations involved must be different and incapable of unrestricted function within the same anatomic field. The available facts of localization seem consistent with such an assumption. Studies of the visual system have shown a dissociation of functions which seems inexplicable on any other basis. In the rat destruction of the striate areas permanently abolishes detail vision, leaving unimpaired the ability to discriminate differences in the intensity of light. Injury to the superior colliculi alone produces some impairment of brightness vision, without destroying the capacity for detail vision. Destruction of the striate areas, with serious injury to the colliculi and optic thalamus, precludes the formation of any habits based on vision. In animals without the visual cortex, reaction is determined by the total amount of light entering the eye: Difference in the area of luminous surface is equivalent for behavior to difference in surface luminosity (21).

The condition is probably similar in higher mammals. Marquis (27) showed the persistence of brightness vision in the dog after destruction of the visual cortex, and Klüver (11) found normal sensitivity to light in lower monkeys from which the whole of both occipital lobes was removed.

The visual cortex, functioning in the differentiation of small spatial differences of retinal excitation, shows a high degree of internal anatomic and functional differentiation. The available evidence indicates little or no subordinate functional localization within the colliculus, although the quadrants of the retina have separate projections on its surface.

Thus, in spite of the fact that brightness seems psychologically a characteristic of visual form, the two variables position and intensity seem to be integrated at different levels of the nervous system, with no evidence yet as to where the final integration takes place which gives them psychologic unity.

In contrast to the visual cortex, most intimately concerned in the space system, are the olfactory centers and the olfactory cortex. Olfactory experience is lacking in spatial character. In spite of the numerous centers and elaborate structure of the olfactory system, clinical studies and the experimental investigations of Swann (35) have failed to reveal any subordinate localization. Herrick (8) pointed out that the structure of the olfactory bulb and the lower centers is especially adapted to facilitative effects, and the recent studies of Lorente de Nó (26) showed a mechanism for recurrent excitation in the cornu ammonis which seems especially adapted for summation. The absence of subordinate localization in a system adapted to facilitative effects is consistent with my hypothesis.

In motor functions the picture is similar. There are indications that many isolated masses of cells in the central nervous system are concerned with regulation of the general level of excitation and that they contribute little, if anything, to the specific patterning of reaction. The cerebellar system, the corpus striatum and basal cerebral nuclei and, in general, the structures making up Hunt's paleokinetic system (10) seem to be of this character.

Lesions in such systems result in global symptoms of decreased force and steadiness or inaccurate timing of movements, without marked change in the combination of muscles employed in voluntary acts. Within such centers there is generally little evidence of subordinate specialization, either structural or functional.

The motor cortex represents the opposite extreme—an area with highly specialized internal arrangement. For this area there is little evidence of gradation of response with intensity of excitation. With electrical stimulation the responses are generally of an all or nothing character, and an increase in the intensity of stimulation produces longer after-discharge, rhythmic oscillation of movement or irradiation to other muscle groups rather than simple increase in the intensity of reaction.

Thus, in both sensory and motor systems there are indications of the separation of mechanisms having to do with reactions to space and to intensity. This is consistent with my assumption that these functions involve different and incompatible kinds of nervous organization and that the reason for separate localization of the functions is that the same group of nerve cells cannot give graded responses by irradiation and also preserve the spatial relations of sensory excitation. This hypothesis cannot be applied too rigidly. It is possible that such a field as the motor cortex may consist of an aggregation of cell groups, each behaving as an excitable unit in space reactions while organized to give graded responses by irradiation restricted within the individual unit. Likewise, the small amount of detail vision shown by animals lacking the striate areas implies that within the subcortical visual centers which are primarily concerned with intensity of the stimulus there is some focalizing and limited irradiation of excitation.

The evidence for the separation of these two functions is not conclusive, since too little is known of any area to delimit its functions clearly, but the hypothesis suggested makes intelligible some of the facts of localization which are otherwise wholly mysterious.

Orientation in space and regulation of intensity are only two of several or many integrative processes which contribute to the total picture of behavior. If my hypothesis is correct, that separate localization is determined by incompatibility of nervous mechanisms, there should be other fundamental nervous organizations or processes which cannot be combined with these two and which will account for still different types of localized function. One such organization is suggested by the problem of serial order in behavior.

Serial Order in Reactions. The least studied and most obscure problems of nervous organization are presented by the temporal aspects of behavior. Every action above the level of a spinal reflex involves time factors for which there is available no adequate explanation. Control of speed and duration enters into the simplest adaptive movement. Accurate timing of the separate components of an organized movement is as important as the spatial pattern. Most adaptive activities depend on the serial release of a succession of movements in a predetermined order, as in the production of a musical phrase or a grammatical form in speech.

Understanding of these problems has been delayed and confused by the doctrine of chain reflexes, which attempts to account for each act of the series as a reaction to sensory excitations from the preceding act. This doctrine is utterly without foundation. I have shown that the control of speed and accuracy of movement may be unimpaired in a limb totally insensitive to movement (14). The interval between successive movements of a musician in playing rapid scale passages is less than the reaction time to kinesthetic stimulation. Ball and I (22) showed that the serial activities of the animal in maze running may be independent of sensory cues. A large amount of evidence, such as transposition of a musical phrase to any key or the grammatical use of newly acquired words, makes it clear that the order of the series of acts is relatively independent of the particular form of the acts which constitute it and therefore cannot be interpreted as a chain of habits. The doctrine of chain reflexes must be abandoned, and some other explanation of serial acts must be sought.

A clue to the possible mechanism is given by the studies of limb coordination reported by Buddenbrock (2) and Bethe (1). Coordinated movements following the amputation of one or more legs in arthropods and vertebrates were observed, and immediate reorganization adapted to progression was found to occur spontaneously, often with complete reversal of the normal reciprocal relations of the movement of different legs. Without consideration of details, the mechanism of coordination suggested by these studies is somewhat as follows: In the ganglionic chain only limb centers participate in coordination which are in a state of tonic excitation from sensory stimulation of the limb. Dominance or lead in progression is taken by the most anterior functioning center on each side, which may be interpreted in terms of Child's conception of polarization of neuron systems (25). Reciprocal relations of the centers are determined by their relative ipsilateral and contralateral positions with respect to the dominant centers.

Details of the mechanism are, of course, obscure, but it seems probable that in this system spatial position of the center with reference to polarity of the system as a whole and to the excitation of other centers is the determining factor for the serial order of movement. Turning to activities of higher levels, one finds reasons for believing that temporal relations are determined by spatial patterns of excitation. Koffka (12) reached this conclusion from psychologic considerations. His fundamental argument was that the memory trace of a stimulus and the process by which it is identified with a current repetition of the stimulus cannot be identical and therefore cannot be localized in the same neurons—that the temporal aspects of experience must therefore have a spatial basis.

There are indications that the production of an ordered series of acts involves preliminary simultaneous priming or subliminal excitation of many or all of the acts, with subsequent supraliminal excitation in predetermined order. Evidence for this comes from contaminations in speech and other serial acts—anticipations of words which should come later, as in spoonerisms, confusions of alternative words and the like. This also implies a spatial representation of the temporal series.

Such considerations are not conclusive; yet the best guess that can be made from psychologic evidence is that temporal phenomena in behavior are dependent on spatial relations in the nervous system. Is there evidence for separate localization of the mechanisms for serial timing? Clinical symptoms suggest it. In apraxia, in syntactic (transcortical, agrammatical) aphasia and in some cases of sensory aphasia the primary defect seems to be in the temporal ordering of activity. Confusions and contaminations of act or speech become more frequent; the execution of an ordered series of acts becomes impossible, although the isolated acts may still be performed. Recent experimental work on the functions of the frontal lobes suggests that one of the major functions of this region may be the elaboration of such temporal schemata.

If temporal order is determined by space factors in the nervous system, the fields in which this type of organization is dominant cannot also serve in other space systems. There is thus some reason to believe that the utilization of the spatial arrangement of excitations in the timing functions determines an additional group of isolated cerebral areas.

Higher Orders of Integration

The physiologic basis of the more complicated modes of behavior is still a mystery, but it seems probable that the same separate localization of "patterning" and of dynamic processes holds for them as for the simpler sensory and motor activities. Many students of clinical neurology have felt the need for a general conception to cover observed variations in the level of efficiency, such as are described by Head's conception of "vigilance" (6) and which affect the readiness of elicitation of response rather than its form.

There are many indications that the general level of excitability of a center depends on facilitative effects from various sources. Thus, the early work of Munk showed that the deafferented paw of a dog is not ordinarily used to hold a bone in feeding, though it can be so used when the intact paw is restrained. The same condition is apparent in cerebral paralysis in the monkey, when intense excitement will lead to temporary use of the paralyzed limbs (15, 28). In such cases the organized pattern of the movements has not been destroyed, but the excitability of the final common path is greatly reduced, apparently as an affect of diaschisis, since emotional facilitation can still elicit the reaction. Such dynamic deficiencies are apparently responsible for many disturbances of more complex behavior.

Amnesia. In the course of normal forgetting the possibility of recall may be lost; yet traces of the former memory can be demonstrated by the "savings method" of relearning. The amount of practice necessary for relearning is a function of the time elapsed since the original learning. The memory trace may thus exist at different levels of availability for recall, which in physiologic terms are probably represented by levels of excitability. In experiments on postoperative amnesias I found that the amount of practice necessary to reestablish a habit is proportional to the extent of the lesion (18, 24), and Hu (9) showed that the rate of forgetting of habits formed after cerebral operation is also a function of the lesion. These experimental results suggest that the organic amnesia is a weakening of the memory trace, of the same nature as that which normally results from lapse of time.

In mild amnesic aphasia and other organic disorders of memory in man, the condition may be described as difficulty of recall rather than absolute destruction of traces. Recall may be effected by associative aids when spontaneous recall does not occur (7), and affectively toned words are most likely to be preserved (emotional facilitation). Such facts suggest that the pattern of the trace is not destroyed in pure organic amnesia and that the defect is rather a reduction of excitability. The fluctuations in severity of symptoms reported by Franz (3) bear this out.

Agnosia. In contrast to the amnesias, there is another general type of disorder in which the major symptom is disorganization of the integrated patterns. Klüver [2] found that after various cerebral lesions in macaques, the ability to make comparisons of sensory stimuli was lost for a considerable period. Once the trick of comparing was again acquired, all the

[2] Personal communication.

habits based on sensory discrimination—tactile, visual and kinesthetic—immediately reappeared. The defect in these cases was distinctly different from the usual amnesia. It involved a disturbance in the mode of integrating or organizing excitations without reduction in the availability of the associated reactions when this type of organization was again reestablished. Many of the symptoms of apraxia, visual agnosia, agrammatism and semantic aphasia seem to be of this character. Certain modes of relating experience are disturbed, without fundamental amnesia. The disorder may occur at a perceptual level, as in the loss of spatial attributes in the visual field, or at various higher integrative levels.

In amnesia and agnosia there is thus the same contrast of dynamic and patterning mechanisms which appeared in the separation of fields concerned with space and with intensity. There are only vague indications of the interplay of these mechanisms. I have shown that in the rat habits based on the recognition of visual objects are not disturbed by any cerebral lesion which leaves intact any small part of the binocular projection field of the striate area. This indicates that the efficiency of a mechanism concerned in patterning behavior is not greatly reduced by extensive injury and that therefore the dynamic aspects of amnesia are probably not the result of direct injury to the patterning mechanism.

In these experiments on visual memory the lesions were not large enough to produce serious general deterioration. From other sources there is evidence that larger lesions in any part of the cortex produce general lowering of efficiency. Tsang (36) showed that in rats blinded at birth lesions limited to the area striata produce severe retardation in maze learning and, hence, that the primary visual cortex has an important non-visual function. I have shown that the retarding effects of lesions of equal area in different parts of the cortex are practically identical in a variety of types of learning. I have interpreted such results as evidence that, in addition to their specific functions, all parts of the cortex exercise a general facilitative effect on the rest. It is possible that in higher animals cortical areas having more localized facilitative functions may have developed and that some of the specific dynamic disturbances observed clinically may be due to their injury. Whether this is the case or whether the observed dynamic disturbances are really the expression of general lowering of functional efficiency can be determined only by more detailed studies of the range of defect in various types of disorder.

Physiologic Interpretation of Localization

Nearly a century of psychologizing concerning the cerebral cortex has added practically nothing to knowledge of its fundamental activities. The transmission, summation and inhibition of nerve impulses, with such obscure processes as are implied in humoral and electronic conduction, form the real basis of nervous integration and the foundation on which understanding of cerebral function and of the problems of behavior must be built. So far as it is not an accident of development, the separation of functions shown in cerebral localization must be due to some physiologic necessity. The phenomena of behavior and of "mind" present problems to the neurophysiologist and define the physiologic mechanisms in terms of what they can accomplish but give no clue to the nature of the integrative processes.

Knowledge of such processes in the cortex is still too limited to permit of anything but vague speculations concerning their nature largely inferred from the phenomena of behavior. The direction of the speculations, however, is important for the development of further research. It has been assumed that the properties of experience are represented at the level of some simple nervous activity or in single loci: sensations in the sensory areas, volitional patterns in the motor regions or particular forms of intelligent behavior in restricted coordinating centers. Such conceptions of localization are oversimplified and must be abandoned. Nothing is known of the physiologic basis of conscious states, but there is some reason to believe that these states can be correlated only with the summated activity of all centers simultaneously excited. The position of Goldstein, that the functions of every center are dependent on its relations to the rest of the intact nervous system (5), cannot be too strongly emphasized in considering problems of neuropsychology. Conceptions of the organization of mind or of behavior are based on a logical analysis of the activities of the total organism, and the final synthesis of nervous states which constitute these activities must transcend the excitation of any single center.

Thus, one must expect to find fractionings of behavior following organic lesions which cannot be expressed or understood in the current psychologic terminology. Indeed, psychologists are in scarcely better case than neurologists when it comes to interpreting the fundamental variables of behavior. The recently developed technics of factor analysis often reveal variables which are difficult to identify with any psychologic units. The "unit traits" or mathematical abstractions which account for correlations of ability in different tasks often indicate relations which are as unintelligible in terms of the total behavior pattern as are the symptoms of organic lesion of the brain. The technic of factor analysis has been criticized for this failure to reveal expected relationships; yet this very fact may be an argument in its favor. A single physiologic variable may well contribute to activities which are logically unrelated, and the most bizarre results of factor analysis may become quite reasonable when the physiologic variables are understood. The functional units of behavior must be determined by the exigencies of nerve conduction and integration.

The problem of why there is localized specialization of function in the nervous system is far from solved by the hypotheses which I have formulated in this paper. But the hypotheses may serve to point the contrast between the physiologic point of view and the mixed metaphysics of the current mentalistic interpretations of localization. Not the logical sequences of a course in Euclid but the interplay of nerve impulses determines the localization of intellect and the variables which enter into it. There is small chance of understanding either the phenomena of localization or the physiologic basis of logic until they can be cast in terms of elementary nervous activities.

Summary

In the foregoing discussion I have sought to illustrate a physiologic approach to the problem of cerebral localization. Various lines of evidence indicate that the spatial distribution of excitations within a nerve center may form the basis for several types of integration, such as the regulation of intensity of discharge, the establishment of fields of force to determine spatial orientation and the control of the serial timing of activities. Each of these functions implies a different mechanism of organization and, consequently, a spatial separation of the fields in which the different processes operate. Experimental and clinical data indicate that the dissociation of functions resulting from cerebral lesions is in harmony with the assumption that cerebral localization is determined by the separation of such incompatible mechanisms.

REFERENCES

1. Bethe, A. Plastizität und Zentrenlehre, *Handb. norm. path. Physiol.*, 1931, **15**, 1175.

2. Buddenbrock, W. v. Der Rhythmus der Schreitbewegungen der Stabheuschrecke Dyxippus, *Biol. Zbl.*, 1921, **41**, 41–48.

3. Franz, S. I. On certain fluctuations in cerebral function in aphasics, *J. exp. Psychol.*, 1916, **1**, 355–364.

4. Fritsch, G., and Hitzig, E. Ueber die elektrische Erregbarkeit des Grosshirns, *Arch. Anat. Physiol. wiss. Med.*, 1870, 300–332.

5. Goldstein, K. *Der Aufbau des Organismus.* The Hague, Netherlands: Nijhoff, 1934.

6. Head, H. The conception of nervous and mental energy, *Brit. J. Psychol.* (Gen. Sect.), 1923–24, **12**, 126–147.

7. Head, H. *Aphasia and kindred disorders of speech.* London: Macmillan, 1926.

8. Herrick, C. J. *An introduction to neurology.* (5th ed.) Philadelphia: Saunders, 1931.

9 Hu, Chi-Nan. *The effects of brain injury upon retentiveness in the rat.* Unpublished dissertation, Univ. Chicago, 1934.

10. Hunt, J. R. The static and kinetic systems of motility, *Arch. Neurol. Psychiat.*, 1920, **4**, 353–369.

11. Klüver, H. An analysis of the effects of the removal of the occipital lobes in monkeys, *J. Psychol.*, 1935, **2**, 49–61.

12. Koffka, K. *Principles of gestalt psychology.* New York: Harcourt, Brace, 1935.

13. Köhler, W. *Die physischen Gestalten in Ruhe und im stationären Zustand.* Erlangen: Weltkreisverlag, 1920.

14. Lashley, K. S. The accuracy of movement in the absence of excitation from the moving organ, *Amer. J. Physiol.*, 1917, **43**, 169–194.

15. Lashley, K. S. Studies of cerebral function in learning: V. Retention of motor habits after destruction of the so-called motor areas in primates, *Arch. Neurol. Psychiat.*, *Chicago*, 1924, **12**, 249–276.

16. Lashley, K. S. Nervous mechanisms in learning. In Murchison, C. A., *Foundations of experimental psychology.* Worcester, Mass.: Clark Univ. Press, 1929.

17. Lashley, K. S. Basic neural mechanisms in behavior, *Psychol. Rev.*, 1930, **37**, 1-24.

18. Lashley, K. S. Mass action in cerebral function, *Science*, 1931, **73**, 245–254.

19. Lashley, K. S. The mechanism of vision: VII. The projection of the retina upon the primary optic centers in the rat, *J. comp. Neurol.*, 1934, **59**, 341–373.

20. Lashley, K. S. The mechanism of vision: VIII. The projection of the retina upon the cerebral cortex of the rat, *J. comp. Neurol.*, 1934, **60**, 57–79.

21. Lashley, K. S. The mechanism of vision: XII. The nervous structures concerned in the acquisition and retention of habits based on reactions to light, *Comp. Psychol. Monogr.*, 1935, **11** (52), 43–79.

22. Lashley, K. S., and Ball, J. Spinal conduction and kinesthetic sensitivity in the maze habit, *J. comp. Psychol.*, 1929, **9**, 71–105.

23. Lashley, K. S., and Frank, M. The mechanism of vision: X. Postoperative disturbances of habits based on detail vision in rat after lesions in cerebral visual areas, *J. comp. Psychol.*, 1934, **17**, 355–380.

24. Lashley, K. S., and Wiley, L. E. Studies of cerebral function in learning: IX. Mass action in relation to the number of elements in the problem to be learned, *J. comp. Neurol.*, 1933, **57**, 3–55.

25. Lillie, R. S. *Protoplasmic action and nervous action.* Chicago: Univ. Chicago Press, 1923.

26. Lorente de Nó, R. Studies on the structure of the cerebral cortex: II. Continuation of the study of the ammonic system, *J. Psychol. Neurol.*, *Lpz.*, 1934, **46**, 113–177.

27. Marquis, D. G. Effect of removal of the visual cortex in mammals, with observations on the retention of light discrimination in dogs, *Proc. Assoc. Res. nerv. ment. Dis.*, 1934, **13**, 558–592.

28. Munk, H. Ueber die Folgen des Sensibilitätsverlustes der Extremität für deren Motilität, *Sitzungsb. Akad. Wiss. math.-naturw. Cl.*, 1903, 1038–1077.

29. Pavlov, I. P. Die Charakteristik der Rindenmasse der Grosshirnhemi-

sphären, vom Standpunkte der Erregbarkeitsveränderungen ihrer einzelnen Punkte, *Schweiz. Arch. Neurol. Psychiat.*, 1923, **13**, 568–574.

30. Pick, A. *Die agrammatischen Sprachstörungen.* Berlin: Springer, 1913.

31. Rashevsky, N. Physico-mathematical aspects of the gestalt-problem. In Sheen, F. J., *Philosophy of science.* Milwaukee: Bruce, 1934.

32. Sherrington, C. S. Some functional problems attaching to convergence, *Proc. roy. Soc.*, 1929, **105B**, 332–362.

33. Sherrington, C. S. Quantitative management of contraction in lowest level co-ordination, *Brain*, 1931, **54**, 1–28.

34. Sjaff, M., and Zeeman, W. P. C. Ueber den Faserverlauf in der Netzhaut und im Sehnerven beim Kaninchen, *Arch. f. Ophth.*, 1924, **114**, 192–211.

35. Swann, H. G. The functions of the brain in olfaction: II. The results of destruction of olfactory and other nervous structures upon the discrimination of odors, *J. comp. Neurol.*, 1934, **59**, 175–201.

36. Tsang, Yü-Chüan. The functions of the visual areas of the cerebral cortex of the rat in the learning and retention of the maze, *Comp. Psychol. Monogr.*, 1934, **10**(50), 1–56; 1936, **12**(57), 1–41.

37. Weiss, P. Das Resonanzprinzip der Nerventätigkeit, *Arch. ges. Physiol.*, 1931, **226**, 600–658.

21. THE THALAMUS AND EMOTION [1]

For many years some relation between the thalamus [2] and emotions has been suspected. As early as 1822 Fodéra reported that stimulation of a region between the level of the *chiasma* and the *corpora quadrigemina* induced cries and other emotional expressions which could not be elicited by stimulation of the cerebral hemispheres. Bechterew (3, 4, 6) was the first to collect evidence systematically to show that the thalamus is concerned in emotional expression. He described the production of a variety of expressive and visceral responses by stimulation of the thalamus, the expression of major emotions in the decorticate animal, and the appearance of spasmodic laughter and weeping after lesions involving the internal capsule in man (3). His objective system of psychology had no place for a separate category of emotions. He developed the Darwinian concept of the origin and adaptive character of expressive and visceral reactions, but made no effort to relate them to emotional experience (5).

From his work on the sensory pathways, Head (19) was led to postulate a thalamic center concerned with the affective character of somatic sensation. He assumed that damage to the center or to its corticopetal connections produced hypaesthesia and that release of the center from cortical control resulted in intensification of the affective character of the sensations. He was not explicit concerning the mode of action of the thalamic center. He seems to have accepted the James-Lange theory for the emotions, yet to ascribe the affective value of sensations of pain and tickle to direct action on a thalamic center.

Increasing doubt of the James-Lange theory of emotions has led more recently to a search for an alternative physiological hypothesis. Of the various ones which have been proposed, level of central tonus, conflict of reaction tendencies, and the like, an elaboration of Head's theory of thalamic function has excited the widest interest and following. It has been expressed with some variations by Dana (12), Cannon (10), Bard (1, 2), and Harlow and Stagner (18).

[1] EDITORS' NOTE: From *Psychol. Rev.*, 1938, **45**, 42–61. Reproduced by permission of the American Psychological Association. From Harvard University.
[2] In the following discussion I shall use the term thalamus to identify the general region of the diencephalon. This is in accord with frequent usage, and more accurate designation of the various regions of the diencephalon is immaterial to the argument.

The theory of emotion as a function of thalamic activity has been most precisely stated by Cannon (10) in essentially the following form. Afferent impulses initiated by the stimuli capable of arousing emotion are transmitted to the cortex. Within the cortex they are integrated to arouse the appropriate overt behavior. A center in the thalamus is also excited, either directly as the sensory impulses are relayed there, or secondarily by impulses from the cortex. The thalamic center (center for emotion) discharges somewhat explosively, exciting the effectors in patterns which constitute the "expression" of the emotion and also discharging to the cortex, where the impulses from the thalamic center add the "peculiar quality of emotion" to the simple sensation aroused by the direct effects of the exciting stimulus. In addition it is suggested that the flood of impulses from the thalamus constitutes the emotional tension and accounts for the dynamic or motivational character of the emotion.

Harlow and Stagner (18) have assumed that only one type of facilitation, corresponding to a general excitement, is contributed by the thalamus and that differentiation of diverse emotions is the result of cortical discriminative processes depending upon the stimulating situation. Bard (1, pp. 323–324) points out, in criticism of these writers, that the motor patterns elicited from the thalamus are specific for different emotions and consequently imply a difference also in the pattern of corticopetal impulses from the thalamic center. He thus seems to hold that the thalamic center determines the qualitative differences between emotions.

To account for the phenomena in certain pathological cases the theory further assumes that the cortex has both excitatory and inhibitory influences upon the thalamus and that the inhibition is effective both upon the motor and the corticopetal excitations arising in the thalamic center.

The theory has the virtues of clearness and simplicity and of apparent support by a large body of experimental evidence. In these respects it has an advantage over vague theories of nervous tension and over more complicated formulations which seek to deal with the intellectual and motivational aspects of the problem. From the psychological standpoint, however, it is inadequate in several respects. Like the James-Lange theory, which it seeks to displace, the thalamic theory is concerned primarily with the problem of experience. It minimizes, if it does not disregard entirely, the problem of motivation which looms so large with the development of dynamic psychology and psychopathology. Further, a unity and constancy of emotional experience is assumed, which is scarcely justified by introspective findings. It is by no means established that there are any identifiable emotions which have a constant qualitative character, or that the "peculiar quality of emotion" is a genuine phenomenon. The evidence which has been cited for the specificity of different emotions is the constancy of the patterns of bodily reaction (2), yet the proponents of the thalamic theory have denied subjective significance to these very reactions in their attack upon the James-Lange theory.

These criticisms, however, are not serious obstacles to the thalamic theory of the emotions. It could doubtless be elaborated to provide a basis for motivation and it has been modified by Harlow and Stagner to conform to psychological data concerning the importance of intellectual factors in the subject's identification of his emotions.

A far more fundamental issue for the theory is that of the validity of the evidence upon which it is based. The theory ascribes three functions specifically to the thalamic region: action as a higher motor center in the integration of patterns of expressive reaction, the initiation or facilitation of nervous impulses which modify cortical processes to give them an emotional character, and the reinforcement of behavior in the sense of the addition of an emotional drive. In this paper I propose to examine the evidence that the thalamus contains a specific center or centers for these functions.

The Integration of Motor Patterns in the Thalamus

Bechterew (3, 5) compiled evidence of the functions of the thalamus in the elaboration of expressive movement. On electrical stimulation of the thalamus he was able to elicit vocalization, respiratory and circulatory changes, erection of hair and other expressive movements from a variety of animals. T. G. Brown (8) described respiratory movements resembling laughter on stimulation of a region mediad to the red nucleus and sighing on stimulation of the caudal portion of the thalamus of the chimpanzee. Other investigators have added to the number of visceral activities found to be elicitable from this region.

Bechterew (3) also reported that decorticate animals were readily induced to display patterns of expressive movement but that after section behind the thalamus only partial patterns, cries and the like, could be elicited, and these only by strong stimulation. The careful systematic studies of Bard (1, 2) have confirmed these observations on thalamic preparations and have localized the motor center for some of the expressive movements more closely in the caudal part of the hypothalamus.

These studies leave no doubt that there are centers within the thalamus whose excitation elicits organized patterns of emotional expression. Parts of the patterns are integrated at lower levels. Elements of the fear and rage patterns may be elicited from midbrain preparations (3, 33), and stretching, which might be interpreted as a sign of contentment, may occasionally be elicited even from the spinal animal, but for complete integration the caudal portion of the thalamus is essential. The occurrence of spasmodic laughter and weeping in cases of diplegia, together with Graham Brown's observation on the chimpanzee, tend to localize the motor centers for these expressive patterns also in the thalamic region.

In the hierarchy of motor centers we may then recognize the thalamic region, especially the hypothalamus, as the region within which the complex patterns of expressive movement are elaborated. It does not follow from this, however, that the pathological phenomena of hyper-excitability of emotional reactions are due solely to release from cortical inhibition or that the thalamic motor center for expressive movement contributes to the emotional experience.

Excitability of the Motor Centers. All investigators have reported a more ready elicitation of some emotional expressive movements from the decorticate than from the normal animal. In carnivora these have been described as rage and fear. In the anencephalic infant startle, expression of pain, and crying are readily obtained. Comparable data are not available for the human adult, but the spasmodic laughter and weeping of pseudobulbar paralysis and the excitement and euphoria of frontal lobe cases have been interpreted as representing a similar condition. On the basis of Hughlings Jackson's principle that lesions cannot produce a gain in function, the increased reactivity must be ascribed to a decrease in inhibition. Head (19) developed this conception to explain the hyper-algesias resulting from thalamic lesions, assuming that the release of a thalamic affective center from cortical inhibition leads to an increase in affective discharge to the cortex. The theory of thalamic function in emotion has made use of the same concept to account for the increased emotional excitability in organic nervous disorders.

Although we may assume that the increased excitability of the motor centers is a result of withdrawal of inhibition, a survey of the evidence leaves some doubt as to the source of this inhibition in the normal animal. It is by no means certainly established that the disturbances of emotional expression in pseudobulbar palsy are actually due to the interruption of cortico-thalamic paths. Wilson (32) reported spasmodic laughter and weeping in progressive lenticular degeneration, which involves the striatum, but perhaps not important cortico-thalamic tracts. Tilney and Morrison (31) have reviewed the cases of pseudobulbar palsy for which there were anatomical controls. Of these, half which exhibited spasmodic laughter and weeping had no lesions in the striatum or thalamus, and half of the cases with lesions in these structures did not show disturbances of expressive movement. The ascription of the loss of control of emotional expression in such cases to interruption of cortico-thalamic inhibitory fibers is an inference from the thalamic theory and is not based upon conclusive anatomic evidence.

Facile laughing and weeping, especially the latter, appear in a number of other conditions, such as extreme fatigue, debility after infectious disease, depressions of pregnancy and menopause, hysteria, and under the effects of various drugs. Since these conditions seem to form a continuous series with the extreme condition in pseudobulbar palsy, and since to assume that all of these conditions are forms of partial decortication is to beg the question, we have little reason to believe that convulsive laughter and weeping are due primarily to the interruption of cortico-thalamic inhibitory tracts.

There is no other convincing clinical evidence of the release of emotional expression by any form of cortical lesion. The frontal lobe symptoms of excitement or euphoria (15) may be so interpreted, but they may also be explained as positive reactions or excitation, due to a lower level of comprehension of social situations. In any event there is no evidence that release of the thalamus rather than of other cortical regions from frontal inhibition is responsible for them. The phenomena are simply too complex to serve as evidence for any theory.

Thus we see that, although normal inhibition of the thalamic centers for expressive movement is indicated, there is some uncertainty as to the source of the inhibition.

The rage response is more readily elicited and is more violent in the decorticate than in the normal animal and this justifies the postulation of a normal inhibition of the rage reaction by the cortex. But it is quite possible that variations in the excitability of other emotional reactions may be conditioned in entirely different ways and it is still unsafe to generalize from the condition of the decerebrate animal to the various clinical pictures of emotional hyperexcitability.

The Motor Centers and Emotional Experience. The only direct evidence concerning the discharge to the cortex from the thalamic motor centers for emotional expresion is that derived from cases of spasmodic laughter and weeping. Dana (12), Wilson (32) and others have pointed out that many patients with these symptoms disclaim emotions appropriate to the expression,[3] and Dana, Wilson, Cannon (10) and Bard (2) have cited such dissociation of emotional experience from expression as evidence against the James-Lange theory. It is to the same extent, however, evidence that discharge to the cortex from the thalamic motor centers for emotional expression is not the basis of the subjective quality of emotion. For the motor discharge is specific in different emotional expressions, as Bard (2) has pointed out, and we have no basis for assuming that the center can discharge one emotional pattern to the effectors and another to the cortex. We must therefore recognize on the

---

[3] In one patient of this type, whom I have studied, spasmodic laughter could be induced by reference to his very distressing home situation. He not only denied amusement but claimed that he felt very sad and depressed during the spasm of laughter. This is evidence that there may be an intense emotional experience which is the opposite of that represented by the thalamic discharge.

basis of these clinical cases that the thalamic motor centers, which are concerned with the elaboration of emotional expression, are not the source of corticopetal impulses which determine the subjective character of emotion.

To preserve the thalamic theory this forces the postulation of another thalamic nucleus which contributes the emotional quality and may be dissociated from the motor nuclei. But this assumption immediately involves further difficulties. To contribute emotional excitation to the cortex, the nucleus must be excited, either by sensory impulses relayed in the thalamus or by descending impulses from the cortex. It must be dissociated from the thalamic motor nuclei by the same lesions which free the latter from cortical inhibition, since it still contributes appropriate emotions when the action of the motor nuclei is inappropriate. It must be excited by other sensory impulses or cortical processes than those which activate the motor nuclei, since the "emotional" and motor nuclei can be aroused to opposite activities by the same stimulus. We seem to be approaching here the extravagances of the diagrammatic theories of aphasia, and I shall not pursue the matter further.

Before such speculations are justified, it must be demonstrated that the thalamus does contribute something to emotional experience. The only positive evidence which has been adduced in support of the origin of centripetal affective or emotional impulses within the thalamus is that presented by Head in his studies of pathological changes in somesthetic sensation. He reported changes in the character of somesthetic sensations following thalamic lesions, which he interpreted as affective disturbances due to interference with the functions of a specific thalamic center. In the following discussion I shall attempt to show that the symptoms reported by him are not due to disturbance of affect and that they are not confined to lesions involving the thalamus and its cortical connections.

Affective Reinforcement of Sensory Impulses by the Thalamus

The facts from which Head deduced his theory of thalamic function were the following symptoms in cases of thalamic lesion:

1. Pricking, scratching, heat, pressure, or continued stroking may be felt by the patient as intolerably disagreeable or painful upon the affected side when like stimuli on the normal side have no such disagreeable character.

2. In other patients stimuli which are felt as painful on the normal side are not felt as painful on the affected side, although their pricking, scratching, or other qualitative character is recognized.

3. In hyperalgesia the absolute threshold is not lowered, but the emotional effects of the adequate stimulus are heightened.

4. Warmth and, rarely, tickling may be felt as abnormally pleasant on the affected side.

5. In a few patients showing increased affectivity of pain, auditory stimuli, especially those of an emotional character, produce tingling and other unpleasant sensations in the affected parts of the body.

To account for these facts Head assumed that there is a center in the thalamus which adds the affective character to the somesthetic sensations. Hyperalgesia and increased pleasantness of warmth were interpreted as due to release of this center from cortical inhibition, hypoalgesia to interference with the activities of the center, or with its afferent path to the cortex.

We must raise two questions concerning this interpretation: Are the "affective" changes specifically dependent on the thalamus? Are the facts relevant to the problem of emotion?

Pathological "Affective" Changes Restricted to Somesthetic Sensations. We may first dismiss briefly the claim that the thalamic lesions involve a general change in affective experience. The evidence advanced for this was the report of emotional disturbance by music, of which Head records two cases. These cases have been cited by Bard (2) as evidence that "the feeling tone of any sensation is a product of thalamic activity." But what Head actually reported was that the music caused unpleasant somesthetic sensations. "One of our patients was unable to go to his place of worship, because he 'could not stand the hymns on his affected side' and his son noticed that during the singing his father constantly rubbed the affected hand" (19, p. 560). Again, "As soon as the choir began to sing, a 'horrid feeling came on the affected side, and the leg was screwed up and began to shake.'" [4] In no case was the affect referred to the source of emotional stimulation, to the music, but always to sensations of somatic reaction to the stimulus. Only one interpretation of the reports is possible: that the emotional stimuli gave rise to expressive reactions which, owing to the hyperaesthesia on the affected side, were felt there more acutely. Nothing more than an abnormality of somesthetic sensation is indicated by the observations; certainly not a general increase in affectivity.

There is, I believe, no case on record of affective disorders involving other sense modalities in a manner similar to that described for somesthesis. Photophobia occurs in certain retinal conditions and in migraine but not after central nervous lesions, and it involves pain on photic stimulation, not an affective reaction to light. Disagreeable olfactory hallucinations are frequent and may have a sensory basis, but they result from lesions within the olfactory system and I have not seen an account

---

[4] The origin of the motor activity exhibited in this case remains entirely obscure. It might be interpreted as an excessive discharge of "emotionally expressive" movement to the leg, implying release of an emotional center from inhibition, but might also be a secondary reaction due to the greater intensity of somesthetic impulses from the affected side.

of any change in the affective character of olfactory sensations from lesions in the thalamus or internal capsule. Certainly no such affective changes were reported for Head's cases. It is noteworthy also that sensations of posture showed no alteration in affective character in his cases.

The release of an affective or emotional center in the thalamus from cortical or other inhibition should result in a change in the affective value of all stimuli capable of arousing emotion, if the region is to be regarded as a general center of affect or of emotion. Such a general change in the level of affect does not occur after thalamic lesions. The affective changes produced are restricted to the narrow group of somesthetic sensations— pain, heat, tickle, and warmth. The clinical evidence cannot be cited legitimately as bearing upon the general problem of affectivity or emotion.

The phenomena are peculiar to a single limited group of sense modalities. Since these are not the only sensory impulses relayed in the thalamus and since the sense modalities included in the group are peculiarly related in several ways, we must inquire whether the affective changes are a property of the thalamus or of some characteristic of these special modalities.

The Locus of Somesthetic "Affect." Hyperalgesia may result from lesions anywhere along the conduction path from the end organ to the thalamus.[5] Rivers and Head (28) reported an excessive painfulness of pain stimulation during regeneration of cutaneous nerve and this fact has been confirmed by more recent investigators. Hyperalgesia occurs in neuritis and other diseases of peripheral nerve. It has been ascribed to irritative lesions but persists in cases of long standing where active irritative processes are improbable.

It is also of common occurrence in lesions or diseases of the cord. In syringomyelia it has been ascribed to irritation, but it is noteworthy that in such cases there is no evidence of motor irritation. After traumatic destruction of parts of the cord hyperaesthesia and hyperalgesia may be pronounced. In Brown-Séquard paralysis, after hemisection of the cord, it is a characteristic feature (7). Kocher (23) lists ipsilateral hyperaesthesia for touch, pain, and sometimes heat and cold as characteristic symptoms of hemisection of the human cord. Hyperalgesia has been described in numerous experiments with animals. Most of these experiments were acute, but some of Martinotti's animals (25) were apparently kept beyond the irritative stage. Head (19) recognized the existence of hyperalgesia in spinal lesions, although he did not report it in the cases which he studied, and minimized its importance for his theory.

Thus hyperalgesia is not a result only of lesions within the thalamus but may arise from damage anywhere along the afferent path. From the reports one can discover no difference in the character of the "affective"

[5] A number of pertinent cases have been reported by Davison and Schick (13).

disturbance corresponding to the site of lesion. The same description of diffuse, burning, intolerable pain is given by all types of patients showing hyperalgesia, whether due to peripheral, spinal, or thalamic lesion. The ascription of a specific "affective" change to cases of thalamic lesion, different from the condition in spinal and peripheral lesions, is not justified by the published statements of the patients.

Various theories have been advanced to explain the origin of the hyperaesthesias. An early attempt to account for the condition in Brown-Séquard paralysis was that of Kocher (23). He pointed out that the hyperalgesia is more frequent and more severe in cases of complete than of partial transsection of the cord. He made the assumptions that the painfulness of pain is determined by summation and irradiation in transmission through the central gray; that in partial hemisection there is some ipsilateral as well as contralateral conduction of pain; and that in complete hemisection all the pain impulses are relayed to the opposite side of the cord and so caused to irradiate more widely. The theory involves a somewhat teleological conception, that pain impulses blocked from one path must follow another, which is contrary to what we know of the mechanism of conduction.[6] Nevertheless the emphasis which the theory places upon the factors of irradiation and summation may furnish the clue to the nature of hyperfunction, as we shall see when we examine the characteristics of the sensory impulses.

To account for hyperalgesia after nerve section Head (19) proposed a theory of reduced inhibition. In support of the theory he reported experiments on the glans penis. Stimulation of this region by water of 40 degrees induced severe pain. When the temperature was raised to 45 degrees the sensation changed to one of heat. When the corona as well as the glans was stimulated at this temperature, the sensation again changed to one of pleasurable warmth. From these facts Head deduced that fibers conducting other sense modalities are capable of inhibiting pain impulses. He did not speculate concerning the locus of these inhibitory processes but his theory seems to necessitate the view that the inhibition takes place in the thalamus, since increased affective value of pain or of pleasurable sensations is involved.

In this form the theory encounters several difficulties. If the various types of sensory impulses remained isolated until they reached the thalamus and there discharged into a common pool, there would be reason to ascribe the inhibition to the thalamus. But the same types of sensory dissociation are produced by spinal as by thalamic lesion, though not always in the same combinations. There is therefore no reason to ascribe the mutual influence of sense modalities to the thalamus rather than to

[6] The Porter phenomenon in the conduction of respiratory impulses does seem to involve just such an all-or-none change in path as was postulated by Kocher (23).

other points along the sensory paths, or to assume that inhibitory processes take place there rather than in the spinal gray.

Lewandowsky (24) states that hyperalgesia from spinal lesions may be present with or without associated defects of other sense modalities. Even admitting, as Head claims, that the measurement of sensitivity by earlier investigators leaves much to be desired, this statement indicates that the degree of hyperalgesia is independent of the severity of other sensory defects. The theory of inhibition would seem, however, to imply that the degree of sensitiveness to pain should be proportional to the amount of other sensory loss. Further, the theory fails to account for hyperaesthesia of spinal origin to tactile stimuli, as it appears in the exaggerated unpleasantness or even the painful character of tickle.

Finally, recent evidence upon the relation of cold, heat, and pain to vasoconstriction and dilatation (27) suggests an entirely different explanation for the results of Head's experiments on the glans and for hyperalgesia after nerve section. If, as Nafe suggests, cold, heat, and pain may be mediated by the same receptors and depend upon the degree of vasomotor tension, the intensity of pain stimulation by heat may be dependent upon the local vasomotor reactions, and not upon any higher central nervous process.

Thus the data presented by Head do not justify the assumption that the "affective" aspects of somatic sensation are controlled exclusively by the thalamus. Lesions anywhere along the sensory pathway may produce the same "affective" symptoms and there is no decisive evidence for localizing the phenomena at any specific point along the afferent path.

Common Characteristics of Somatic Sensations which Show "Affective" Disturbances. Among the somesthetic sensations those which are concerned with spacial localization do not show any pathological increase in intensity or affectivity. Tactile discrimination and localization of posture may be defective but never become painful or abnormally pleasurable. Only unlocalized touch, pain, pressure, temperature, and tickle become pathologically unpleasant, and warmth and tickle may show the character of increased pleasantness.

All of these have in common a tendency to summation and to collateral irradiation. They are not accurately localized and when they are of pathological intensity their diffuseness is greatly increased. The normal irradiation of pain is evident at spinal levels in the spread of reflex avoiding reactions and in referred pains. Light tactile stimuli likewise summate at spinal levels, as in the adequate stimulus to the scratch reflex.

Temperature and pressure are closely related to pain and there are recent indications that pain may depend upon summational effects as well as upon specific fibers. Heinbecker, Bishop, and O'Leary (20) have presented evidence that the painful character of pricking stimuli depends upon summation of a number of impulses. Nafe (27) has summarized the evidence that sensations of heat, cold, and pain may originate in different degrees of vasomotor constriction. Gasser (17) suggests that the pressure impulses conducted by large afferent fibers may under some conditions arouse pain.

The above evidence indicates that the painful character of these sensations may be a function of special conditions of summation, rather than of the arousal of special pain fibers or the addition of a specific affective quality, and that what Head interpreted as a specific emotive function of the thalamus is really a phenomenon of summation and irradiation arising from the unique characteristics of conduction of this limited group of sensory paths.

We know little about the conditions underlying warmth, tickle, and the sexual sensations, the so-called pleasurable sensations. They have in common the character of diffuse, poorly localized tingling, and are slow in development and subsidence. In summation and irradiation they resemble pain and differ from other sense modalities. That they are closely interrelated is indicated by studies of the erogenous zones, studies which also suggest a vasomotor element. They cannot be elicited by single stimuli, but must be built up by slow summation. Sexual sensations are sometimes abolished by low unilateral spinal lesions which do not destroy tactile sensitivity of the genitalia. Since the specific receptors are probably tactile, this disturbance of the pleasurable character of the sensation must be due to local interference with irradiation or summation.

The painful and pleasurable sensations thus form a group unified by peculiarities of summation and irradiation which are not exhibited by any other sense modalities. No other modalities show the pathological alterations in "affective" character which occur in this group. The conclusion seems justified that the pathological changes in "affect" are bound up with the special properties of conduction of this limited group of somesthetic impulses. These properties are not specific to the thalamus, but occur wherever the impulses reach a center, spinal gray, medulla, or thalamus. The especial importance of the thalamus may be ascribed to the fact that it contains the largest and most intricate nuclei within which these impulses are relayed and thus offers maximal opportunity for any abnormalities of conduction.

We do not yet know enough about the behavior of somesthetic impulses in summation and irradiation to understand their various central effects, but can infer something from the properties of the motoneuron pool (30). The suggestion has been made that when a pool has alternative outlets, the first impulses to arrive may prime one path, which will then be facilitated by impulses which might otherwise have initiated another reaction. Under pathological conditions not only primacy, but also number and rate of succession of impulses might be determining factors, and a slight change in timing or intensity could alter the path of afferent discharge and so the subjective character of the effects of the stimulus. Changes in relative dominance among impulses from various receptors would account for alterations in "affect" resulting from partial destruction of conduction paths as well as from injury to centers and so explain hyperalgesia from injury to peripheral nerve and to spinal tracts.

This is, in a way, a theory of release from inhibition (change in dominance of impulses in a center) but it does not involve, as does Head's theory, the conceptions of the specific inhibition of a center, of a localized source of inhibitory impulses, or of a restricted center for the emotional reinforcement of sensory impulses.

The available evidence justifies the conclusion that the "affective" character of somatic sensations is correlated with their peculiarities of conduction, and probably their relations to vasomotor reflexes, and that their "affective" character may be altered by lesions which disturb conduction at any of the synaptic junctions through which the impulses are relayed. There is no support for the assumption that the thalamus has a unique influence upon the "affective" character of the sensations.

Pleasure-Pain and Affect. One further question, concerning the pathological changes in somesthetic sensation produced by lesions in the afferent paths, must be discussed. Are they primarily changes in affect, or changes in the intensity and localization of specific sensations? The relation of pain and sensations of pleasure to unpleasantness and pleasantness is still a controversial matter. There seems however to be a general agreement that the sensations are correlated but not identical with affect. Tickle may be unendurable, the warm flush of fever decidedly unpleasant. Pain may be sought as a source of masochistic pleasure. Investigators who still argue for a sensory basis of affect (26, 21) do not identify it with pleasure and pain, but with bright and dull pressures. It cannot be argued, therefore, that the sensations of warmth and tickle constitute pleasantness and of pain unpleasantness. They may induce, but are not themselves, affect.

The reports of the patients with hyperalgesia are concerned primarily with changes in the character of sensation; the pain is more intense, more burning, more diffuse on the affected than on the normal side. The reports concerning the changes in sensations of warmth may be similarly interpreted. The abnormality is primarily in the nature of the cutaneous sensations. They are intensified, rendered more diffuse and persistent. Such pathological sensations are no more to be identified with affect than are normal ones. Their association with nervous lesions does not provide evidence for a specific affective center, but only shows that the affective reaction, whatever be its nature, is more intense for sensations of pathological quality or intensity.

We may question, then, whether the reported observations on clinical cases with thalamic lesions are in any way relevant to the question of the existence of an affective center in the thalamus. Not only are there no general changes in affect produced by such lesions, but even for the limited group of somesthetic sensations we cannot be sure that the pathological disturbances are affective and not merely sensory.

The Maintenance of Emotional Activity

One of the most important psychological functions which has been ascribed to emotion is the maintenance of attitudes or of motivational tension. Current theories of psychopathology are based upon "unconscious emotional drives" and, in fact, the whole development of modern dynamic psychology centers around such concepts. Perhaps there is no need to assume an extraneous "drive" to account for perseveration of behavior or of hysterical symptoms, but the persistence of activity in the absence of environmental stimuli is one of the major problems of physiological psychology and is characteristic of much behavior called emotional. Does the thalamus provide a mechanism for this dynamic function?

Theories proposed to account for persistent behavior have assumed the maintenance of activity, either by circular reflexes (22), by persistent endocrine stimulation of muscles with resultant sensory excitation, or by some sort of reverberation of tonic excitation within the central nervous system (14). Presumably, if the dynamic aspects of emotion derive from the thalamus, the nucleus there must maintain excitation, either by initiating circular reflexes, or by its own internal activity. Lacking direct evidence for such activity, we can only inquire whether the release of the thalamic emotional center from cortical inhibition increases the duration as well as the excitability of emotional response.

The Persistence of Emotional Expression. Bard (1, 2) has reported that there is practically no after-discharge in the sham rage of the decorticate animal. The reaction continues so long as the irritating stimulus is applied, but stops immediately with the termination of the stimulus. From his descriptions fear and sexual reactions seem to persist somewhat beyond the stimulus, but not apparently longer than in normal animals. Unequivocal data are not available concerning the duration of emotional disturbance in normal cats. In the rat, with which I am more familiar, the after effects of a fight may persist and render the animal unsafe to handle for several hours, and it is probable that similar persistence of emotional disturbance can be demonstrated in the normal cat. There is apparently no indication of continued emotional reactions in decorticate animals which corresponds to the persistent emotional upset which is so often seen in normals. There is thus no evidence that the thalamus serves as a reservoir of emotional tension or contributes in any way to the motivational aspects of emotional behavior.

Restlessness. Restless pacing is a characteristic of many decorticate animals. Although it might be taken as evidence for some subcortical driving mechanism, it can also be explained in terms of the general increase in excitability of lower centers after decortication and in itself does not constitute evidence for a specific dynamic center in the thalamus, any more than do the contractures of hemiplegia, or the stepping movements of a low spinal preparation. This applies also to the excitement and restlessness in cases of frontal lobe injury. Some tendency to maintain activity once initiated may be considered as characteristic of all central nervous function (8). There is certainly no evidence that it is more characteristic of the thalamus than of other regions.

Summary

Among the variety of phenomena which have been included under the topic of emotion are (a) a supposedly unique experience, (b) the hypothetical impulsions and drives which make man the neurotic animal, and (c) such bodily activities as are not directly orienting, locomotor, manipulative, digestive, or linguistic. A review of the evidence fails to reveal participation of the thalamus in any but the third of these classes. The thalamus contains centers in which some, at least, of the patterns of expressive movement are integrated. These, however, must be regarded as strictly motor centers, since the evidence for dissociation of expression from emotion, which has been advanced against the James-Lange theory, is equally applicable to show that the thalamic centers for expression cannot contribute the quality of emotion.

The supposed evidence that the thalamus adds the affective or emotional character to sensations breaks down completely when subjected to critical analysis. The affective changes resulting from thalamic lesions are restricted to a small group of somesthetic sensations and cannot be interpreted as a general change in affectivity. The changes correlate definitely with the special properties of conduction, summation, and irradiation of this group of sensory processes and not at all with a specific locus in the thalamus. The pathological changes following thalamic lesions are primarily in the character of the sensations, in intensity, duration, localization, and are therefore not relevant to the problem of affect. There is no evidence whatever that the thalamus contributes facilitative impulses which might form a basis for the motivational aspects of emotion. Thus, the only part of the thalamic theory of emotion which has factual support is the localization of motor centers for emotional expression within the hypothalamus. It seems certain that these motor centers do not contribute directly to other aspects of emotion and there is no evidence for the existence of other affective or emotional centers.

REFERENCES

1. Bard, P. On emotional expression after decortication with some remarks on theoretical views, *Psychol. Rev.*, 1934, **41**, 309–329, 424–429.

2. Bard P. The neuro-humoral basis of emotional reactions. In Murchison, C. A. (Ed.) *A Handbook of general experimental psychology.* Worcester, Mass.: Clark Univ. Press, 1934, 264–311.

3. Bechterew, W. v. Die Bedeutung der Sehhügel auf Grund von experimentellen und pathologischen Daten, *Virchow's Arch. pathol. Anat.*, 1887, **110**, 322–365.

4. Bechterew, W. v. Unaufhaltsames Lachen und Weinen bei Hirnaffektionen, *Arch. Psychiat. Nervenkr.*, 1894, **26**, 791–817.

5. Bechterew, W. v. *La psychologie objective.* Paris: Alcan, 1913.

6. Bechterew, W. v. *Die Funktionen der Nervencentra.* Jena: Fischer, 1909.

7. Brown-Séquard, E. Recherches sur la voie de transmission des impressions sensitives dans la moelle épinière, *Gas. med. Paris*, 1855, **10**, 564–568, 579–581.

8. Brown, T. G. On the nature of the fundamental activity of the nervous centers, *J. Physiol.*, 1914, **48**, 18–46.

9. Brown, T. G. Note on the physiology of the basal ganglia and midbrain of the anthropoid ape, especially in reference in the act of laughter, *J. Physiol.*, 1915, **49**, 195–215.

10. Cannon, W. B. The James-Lange theory of emotions: a critical examination and an alternative theory, *Amer. J. Psychol.*, 1927, **39**, 106–124.

11. Cannon, W. B. Again the James-Lange and the thalamic theories of emotion, *Psychol. Rev.*, 1931, **38**, 281–295.

12. Dana, C. L. The anatomic seat of the emotions, *Arch. Neurol. Psychiat., Chicago*, 1921, **6**, 634–639.

13. Davison, C., and Schick, W. *Proc. Assoc. nerv. ment. Dis.*, 1935, **15**, 457–496.

14. Ebbecke, U. *Die kortikalen psychophysischen Erregungen.* Leipzig: 1919.

15. Feuchtwanger, E. Die Funktionen des Stirnhirns, *Monogr. Geb. Neurol. Psychiat.*, 1923, **38**, iv–194.

16. Fodéra, M. Recherches expérimentales sur le système nerveux, *J. Physiol. exper. pathol.*, 1823, **3**, 191–217.

17. Gasser, H. S. Conduction in nerves in relation to fiber types, *Proc. Assoc. Res. nerv. ment. Dis.*, 1935, **15**, 35–59.

18. Harlow, H. F., and Stagner, R. Psychology of feelings and emotions, *Psychol. Rev.*, 1932, **39**, 570–589; 1933, **40**, 184–195.

19. Head. H. *Studies in neurology.* London: Frowde, Hodder & Stoughton, 1920. Vols. I, II.

20. Heinbecker, P., Bishop, G. H., and O'Leary, J. O. Pain and touch fibers in peripheral nerves, *Arch. Neurol. Psychiat., Chicago*, 1933, **29**, 771–789.

21. Hoisington, L. B. *Pleasantness and unpleasantness as modes of bodily experience.* Worcester: The Wittenberg Symposium, 1928. Pp. 236–246.

22. Kempf, E. J. *The autonomic functions and the personality.* Washington: Nerv. ment. Dis. Publ. Co., 1918.

23. Kocher, T. Die Verletzungen der Wirbelsäule zugleich als Beitrag zur Physiologie des menschlichen Rückenmarks, *Mitteil. Grenzgeb. Med. Chir.,* 1896, **1**, 415–660.

24. Lewandowsky, K. Die zentralen Sensibilitätsstörungen, *Handb. Neurol.,* Berlin, 1910, **4** (II), 773–814.

25. Martinotti, C. Hyperaesthesie nach Verletzung des Halsmarkes, *Arch. Physiol.* (Suppl.), 1890, 182–189.

26. Nafe, J. P. A quantitative theory of feeling, *J. genet. Psychol.,* 1929, **2**, 199–211.

27. Nafe, J. P. The pressure, pain, and temperature senses. In Murchison, C. A. (Ed.) *A handbook of general experimental psychology.* Worcester, Mass.: Clark Univ. Press, 1934.

28. Rivers, W. H. R., and Head, H. A human experiment in nerve division, *Brain,* 1908, **31**, 323–450.

29. Rosenblueth, A., and Ortiz, T. The crossed respiratory impulses to the phrenic, *Amer. J. Physiol.,* 1936, **117**, 495–513.

30. Sherrington, C. S. Some functional problems attaching to convergence, *Proc. roy. Soc.,* 1929, **105**, 332–361.

31. Tilney, F., and Morrison, J. F. Pseudobulbar palsy clinically and pathologically considered, *J. nerv. ment. Dis.,* 1912, **39**, 505–535.

32. Wilson, S. A. K. Pathological laughing and crying, *J. Neurol. Psychopath.,* 1924, **4**, 299–333.

33. Woodworth, R. S., and Sherrington, C. S. A pseudoaffective reflex and its spinal path, *J. Physiol.,* 1904, **31**, 234–243.

22. CONDITIONAL REACTIONS IN THE RAT [1]

Borovski (1, 2) has reported experiments in which he attempted to establish in the rat a differential reaction to two stimulus objects so arranged that the direction or sense of reaction should be determined by an additional variable in the situation. He used two discrimination boxes connected in series. The same stimuli were presented in both boxes, but with their reaction-value reversed in association with other stimuli. In one experiment a triangular and a circular hole, through which the animals crawled, served as stimuli, and the rats were required to choose the circle if the ground surrounding the figures were white, the triangle, if the ground were black. The rats failed this problem. In a second experiment the animals were trained to choose the larger of two circular openings and the smaller of two triangular, the attempt being to make the positive or negative reaction to size conditional upon the form of the objects. This problem was apparently learned.

The experiments were reported only briefly and criticism may be wide of the mark, but for the second experiment no evidence was given that the animals were reacting to the same cues, that is, to the comparative size of the openings, under the two conditions. In view of the defects of the apparatus used, as revealed by the discussions of Munn (6, 7) and of Fields (3), and of the failure of the animals where the figures were kept constant on a variable ground, it seems probable that in the second experiment the animals were responding to entirely different cues in the two situations, with no identification of the common factor of size; that there was no genuine reversal of the sense of reaction but only the formation of two independent habits based upon differences in the partial forms of the stimuli.

To demonstrate a reversal of reaction, conditional upon some additional stimulus, it will be necessary to show, first, that the stimuli in the two situations are equivalent for the animal and, second, that after the reversal of response has been established the animal is still reacting to

[1] EDITORS' NOTE: From *J. Psychol.*, 1938, **6**, 311–324. Reproduced by permission of The Journal Press. From the laboratory of physiological psychology, Harvard University.

the same properties of the differentiating stimulus under the two conditions.

The experiments reported below were designed to meet these requirements and to test the ability of the rat to change the sense of reaction to one pair of stimuli in accordance with the presence of one or another additional stimulus. This task requires only the association of the direction of reaction to specific stimuli with the modifying conditions. A further series of tests was carried through to see whether or not continued training in a variety of such specific tasks might lead the animals to a further generalization, dissociated from the specific character of the stimuli. This generalization would take the verbal form "*any* stimulus which is correct in situation *A* is incorrect in situation *B*."

Establishment of a Conditional Reaction

Three rats were trained with the "jumping" technique to choose an erect and avoid an inverted equilateral triangle on a black ground (Fig. 22.1). When a criterion of 20 successive errorless trials had been reached,

Fig. 22.1.   Fig. 22.2.

similar triangles on a ground horizontally striped with alternate black and white lines, 8 mm. in width, were presented (Fig. 22.2). With these the animals were first given 20 critical trials, that is, trials in which they were allowed to reach food, irrespective of the figure chosen, to determine whether the figures on the striated ground were equivalent to the training figures. All animals chose the erect triangle (originally positive) in at least 18 of the 20 trials.

With the figures on striped ground they were next trained to choose the inverted triangle and avoid the erect, a reversal of the original training. When they reached the criterion, the figures on the black ground were again presented and training again reversed. This alternate training with the black and striped grounds was continued until immediate reversal, with no more than one error in 20 successive trials, was obtained with each change of ground. The successive training scores are shown in Table 22.1. The figures are for trials preceding the criterion of 20 without error, and for the numbers of trials in which the animals chose the negative stimulus one or more times, each such trial being counted as one error. Next the animals were each given 20 trials in which the black and striped

Table 22.1. Record of Training and Tests to Establish Reversal of Response to Figures, in Accord with the Character of the Ground

Ground and figure	Animal 1		Animal 2		Animal 3	
	Trials	Errors	Trials	Errors	Trials	Errors
Black ground, erect triangle +	40	8	40	17	70	12
Striped ground, inverted triangle +	360	135	140	52	190	52
Black ground, erect triangle +	0	0	7	1	3	1
Striped ground, inverted triangle +	8	5	30	5	27	5
Same, new cards, wider stripes	40	17	6	1	20	4
Black ground, erect triangle +	0	0	0	0	0	0
Striped ground, inverted triangle +	7	2	0	0	1	1
Black ground, erect triangle +	2	1	0	0	0	0
Striped ground, inverted triangle +	3	1	0	0	2	1
Errors in 20 trials, grounds alternated	...	1	...	0	...	3

grounds were presented in alternate trials, to control the possibility that they had merely learned to continue a successful mode of reaction throughout a set of trials. The numbers of errors made in this test are also given in Table 22.1.

The first reversal of training involved many more trials and errors than had the original training. With the next change of ground, selection of the erect triangle on black ground was immediate by all animals, the single errors made by two animals following 6 and 2 positive responses to the erect triangle. The next reversal with striated ground required brief retraining.

At this point new cards with 1.4 cm. horizontal striations were substituted for the original striated cards, to avoid the chance of continued training to some secondary cue. All the animals were slightly disturbed by this change but relearned quickly. The broad and narrow stripes were used indiscriminately in later tests.

After 5 to 8 reversals of training the animals all reversed their reactions immediately with the changes in the ground. With the grounds changed in alternate trials they then made an average of 1.3 errors in 20 trials. In subsequent experiments to determine the effective stimuli, tests with the situations alternated in successive trials were usually carried out between series of critical trials with other test figures. A total of 260 additional trials with the grounds alternated in successive trials was obtained from the three animals. In these they made a total of 17 errors, or 94 per cent correct.

As evidence that the animals were reacting in each situation to the same difference between the triangles, and that a genuine reversal of the sense of reaction was determined by the black or striated ground, the following points have been brought out by the experiments thus far reported: (a) The first critical trials with the striped ground showed an identification of the figures under the two conditions. (b) The first training to the inverted triangle on striated ground required several times as much practice as had the original training. Numerous experiments have shown that, with nonequivalent figures, training on one problem somewhat facilitates learning of a second. There was, then, an interference between the two habits.

This evidence is not conclusive. It is possible that the animals abandoned reaction to the visual stimuli and came to rely upon some cues from the experimenter or that they developed reactions to visual cues which were unique for each situation, such as part-figures (5) formed by the intersection of the triangles and striations, and disregarded the original cues. To test these possibilities and to define the basis of the differential reactions a series of critical trials was given with the various patterns shown in Figs. 22.3 to 22.14. The method in these tests was that which I have described for determining the equivalence of stimuli; 10 training trials, in this case usually alternately with black and striated ground (occasionally with striated ground only when reaction to this situation had become unstable) followed immediately by 10 critical trials with new figures; on the next day 10 training and 10 critical trials.

The results of these tests are summarized in Table 22.2. In only a few cases are the scores ambiguous. It is safe to accept a score below 20 or above 80 per cent as indicative of a definite choice and a score between 40 and 60 per cent as chance.[2]

The frequent chance scores and a deliberate control of the experimenter's position and movements rule out reactions to secondary cues. The responses were certainly to some visual stimuli. Figure 22.7 bears the same arrangement of stripes as Fig. 22.2 and the chance scores with this figure, together with the accurate transfer to new cards with the white triangles and striations, shows that the animals were not reacting to special cues in the ground.

Figures 22.3, 22.4, 22.12 (for one animal), and 22.14 were equivalent

---

[2] In a series of critical trials, errors are most apt to be made in the first few trials of the series, and a score of 80 per cent in the first 20 trials is highly predictive of still greater accuracy, if the critical trials are continued.

Fig. 22.3

Fig. 22.4

Fig. 22.5

Fig. 22.6

Fig. 22.7

Fig. 22.8

Fig. 22.9

Fig. 22.10

Fig. 22.11

Fig. 22.12

Fig. 22.13

Fig. 22.14

Table 22.2. Scores in Critical Trials with Control Figures to Define the Basis
of Reaction to the Figure in Relation to the Ground *

Figure no.	Description	Animal no.		
		1	2	3
	Black ground, new cards	100	95	95
	Striped ground, new cards	0	0	10
	5-cm. triangles, black ground	100	95	100
3	5-cm. triangles, striped ground	10	15	20
	10-cm. triangles, gray ground (50% white)	100	100	100
4	Spotted ground	10	20	15
5	Encircled triangles	50	50	95
6	Striped triangles, black ground	100	75	100
7	Black triangles, striped ground	60	50	50
8	Vertical stripes in ground	50	50	50
9	Outlines, striped ground	...	5	50
10	One broad stripe in ground	100	70	100
11	Second stripe below	80	50	80
12	Second stripe above	...	40	0
13	Four stripes	...	50	0
14	Five stripes	10	0	0

* Scores are given as percentage of 20 critical trials in which the erect triangle was chosen.

to triangles on striated ground. In them there is no common figure formed
by the intersection of the lines in the ground with the triangles. The possibility that the reaction was not to the triangles but to independent cues
included in the black and striped grounds seems adequately ruled out.
The results of the tests justify the conclusion that the rats were reacting
to the triangles as figures and that a genuine reversal of the sense of
reaction was determined by the character of the ground. The tests are not
adequate to reveal the exact nature of the adequate stimulus, for either
the triangles or the ground. The reaction transferred to the smaller figures,
to the striped triangles, and in one case to the outline (Fig. 22.9), so
that response to the general proportions of the figures is suggested.
Response to the 50 per cent gray ground was as to black, so the stripes
were seen as distinct. For rat number 3, choosing the inverted triangle
in Figs. 22.3, 22.4, 22.12, 22.13, and 22.14, the reversal of response
seemed determined by little more than the presence of some white objects
in the ground. The response of number 2 was more specific, as several
horizontal lines were required for reversal. Since past experience has
shown the difficulty of defining the adequate stimulus more precisely

than has been done here, and since the main object of the experiment had been accomplished, no further tests of this character were carried out.

Failure in Generalization of a "Second Order"

The next experiments were undertaken in an effort to generalize the reaction from the specific figures (triangles) so that a *spontaneous* reversal of reaction might be given with any new pair of figures, learned on black ground, when they were first placed on striated ground. To this

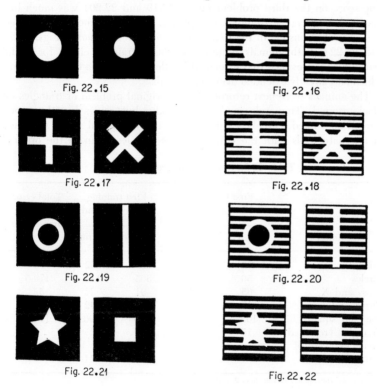

Fig. 22.15

Fig. 22.16

Fig. 22.17

Fig. 22.18

Fig. 22.19

Fig. 22.20

Fig. 22.21

Fig. 22.22

end the training, successive reversals, and final tests with black and striped ground in alternate trials, described in the experiments with triangles, were repeated with the four additional pairs of figures shown in Figs. 22.15 to 22.22. Rat number 1 failed to reach the criterion of immediate reversal with change of ground after 750 trials with the circles and was dropped from the experiment. . . .

The first of these problems, to choose the larger of two circles (Fig. 22.15), was learned quickly by . . . [the two remaining] animals. The

same figures on striped ground (Fig. 22.16) were not equivalent, however, and reversal of the reaction took an inordinate amount of training.
The failure of transfer might have been predicted from earlier experiments on discrimination of size, in which the great importance of total
white area irrespective of its form was demonstrated.[3]

The problem, *cross vs. X* (Figs. 22.17 and 22.18), was learned quickly.
Number 2 in critical trials and subsequent training with striped ground
came near to spontaneous reversal which, however, was never repeated.
The score on the third problem (Figs. 22.19 and 22.20) was much like
that with the original triangles, except that the equivalence tests showed
less accurate transfer. In the fourth problem, *star vs. square* (Figs. 22.21
and 22.22), both animals required so much training either for initial
learning or for reversal that it seemed fruitless to continue the experiment,
which had already extended over nine months.

The animals were next returned to the original problem of triangles on
black ground. They relearned this quickly, but reversal with striped
ground consumed scarcely less training than the original score. Accuracy
in alternate trials with the two situations was less than in the original

Table 22.3. Summary of Training Scores [*]

Stimuli	First training, black ground		First training, striped ground		Total errors before immediate reversal
	Trials	Errors	Trials	Errors	
Triangles	55	14.5	165	52	75
Circles	50	13.5	305	113	179.5
Cross and X	65	18.5	91	32	52
Circle and bar	17	7.5	100	42	54
Star and square	155	53	200	96+	failed
Triangles (repeated)	15	4	97	25	....
Triangles (vertical stripes)			84	24	

[*] The average scores of numbers 2 and 3 are given.

experiment and was not improved above 90 per cent with an additional
100 trials of training. The animals were retrained with triangles on black
ground, then trained for reversal of reaction to inverted triangle on vertical stripes (Fig. 22.8). Even with this condition, closely resembling the
reversal with horizontal stripes, the learning scores were high.

[3] Because of this slow reversal I have trained four animals in discrimination between
the two circles on striped ground as an initial problem. None had improved above a chance
score in 150 trials. Evidently the discrimination is inherently difficult and the poor training
scores have no especial significance in the present experiment.

Finally the rats were again given a series of critical trials with the remaining pairs of figures, circles, *cross vs. X*, etc., on black and striated grounds. With all of the figures on black ground, they showed good retention of the reaction, but failed to reverse their reactions with the figures on striations.

Table 22.3 summarizes the training data on the various problems, giving the numbers of trials and errors for initial learning of the figures on black ground and for the first reversal of training with striped ground; also the total number of errors before immediate reversal of reaction with change of ground was obtained. Although there is some downward trend of the figures until the fifth problem, there is no indication that the long training had produced any tendency of the animals to reverse the sense of reaction directly when a new pair of figures was presented for the first time on striped ground, or even that the rate of reversal under training had been significantly modified.

Discussion

In a previous study (5) I reported briefly several experiments involving the same principle as the present one and giving only negative results. In one of those experiments three stimulus cards were arranged so that the animal must choose between the two laterally placed cards which bore different patterns and of these must choose the one like the pattern on the middle card. After a few jumps to the middle card, always resulting in a fall, the animals seemed to pay no further attention to it and did not improve above chance after 200 trials of training. The same result followed when the card to be matched was placed above or below the dividing line between the two cards to be discriminated.

In another experiment the rats were trained with apparatus presenting three stimulus cards of which two bore identical patterns and the third a different one, as two circles and a cross. The animals were required to choose the unique figure (cross) and to avoid the two alike (circles). When this was learned, training was reversed; to choose one circle and avoid either of two crosses. Some animals were carried through as many as 10 reversals of training in the effort to get them to choose whichever of the two figures, cross or circle, was not duplicated. No animal ever reversed his reaction spontaneously when the situation was changed and, in fact, each successive reversal required more training than the preceding, until the animals finally fixed upon one of the stimulus cards or developed a position habit which could not be broken by further training.

The failure of these former experiments and the success of the present ones in establishing a discriminative reaction conditional upon an added variable are to be understood in terms of the specific situations involved. In the experiment requiring matching, the card to be matched had not the same significance for reaction as the stimulus cards (something to be jumped against) and thus came to be disregarded, as are visual patterns in the Yerkes box. In the experiment requiring the selection of one figure vs. two alike, the conditioning factor (duplication) was also dissociated from the immediate situation involved in discrimination. The animals could learn to choose the cross and avoid either of the two circles, but the factor of duplication was not a part of the stimulus reacted to in jumping. In the present experiments the connection of figure and ground is sufficiently close to permit of a ready association between the differentiating and reversing factors.

The different results of these experiments might lead to the conclusion that the conditional reaction really consists of two independent discrimination habits based upon the total stimulus patterns (positive to the pattern formed by the inverted triangle and stripes, etc.), thus avoiding any implication of a reversal in the sense of reaction. So interpreted, the behavior would involve no different problem from that presented by the formation of discrimination habits between any two pairs of unrelated stimuli. The problem is certainly not so simple, however. In all the tests the only differentiating features for the black and striated grounds are the figures, which are ordinarily differentiated from the ground by the rat as by the human subject. Except for the circles, the figures were identified at first in the two situations. In the final review of the problems the original responses to the figure on black ground were retained whereas the responses to the striped ground were lost and the figures in the two situations again identified. It seems quite certain that the figures retained their differentiating character and were not simply blended into two independent total patterns.

Further, there is adequate evidence (4, 5) that the discrimination of circles of unequal size involves a relational basis of response and is not reduced to an absolute basis within the limits of training of the present experiments. For the circles, the reaction with either ground is based upon the relation, $A > B$, and the response to this relation changes with the character of the ground. Since we must assume a reversal in the sense of reaction for this one case, there is no reason to consider that the other tests involve a different principle.

In an earlier experiment (5) I trained rats with a three-door apparatus to choose a cross and avoid either of two triangles, to choose a circle and avoid either of two crosses, and so through as many as 10 problems. In neither that nor the present experiment was there any indication that the animals could derive the general principle from the series of specific instances. Although the time spent in training was relatively great, the actual number of specific situations from which the general principle might be derived was small, so that failure in the tests is by no means proof that the rat cannot form such generalized responses. In order to increase the number of specific instances and still bring them within the life span of the rat, however, the rate of learning would have greatly to exceed that observed in the present experiments. Other instances of reversed training have not shown a lesser interference of opposed habits, so it seems unlikely that any modification of the present type of experiment can give positive results.

The results in the different attempts to establish conditional reactions show that what seem minor variations in the training situation may determine success or failure in the problem, and it may be that the effectiveness of the specific instance in pointing to the general principle may be greatly increased by some variation in training technique.

Summary

Rats were trained to choose one member of a pair of figures exposed on a black ground, then to choose the other member of the pair exposed on a striated ground. They eventually learned to give the appropriate reaction immediately on change of the ground. Evidence is presented which indicates that the response was in each case to the original figures, conditional upon the character of the ground, rather than to total undifferentiated patterns.

Successive training in five such problems failed to establish a generalized reaction, involving a spontaneous reversal of response with new figures, or even to show any improvement in the rate of learning to reverse the response.

REFERENCES

1. Borovski, W. M. Experimentelle Untersuchung über den Lernprozess: IV. Über Labilität der Gewohnheiten, Z. vergl. Physiol., 1930, 11, 549–564.

2. Borovski, W. M. Experimentelle Untersuchung über den Lernprozess: V. Zur Analyse der Sitzungsbegriffe; Tierpsychologie, Biol. Zbl., 1930, 50, 566–572.

3. Fields, P. E. Concerning the discrimination of geometrical figures by white rats, J. comp. Psychol., 1932, 14, 63–77.

4. Gulliksen, H. The relationship between the degree of original learning and degree of transfer, Psychometrika, 1936, 1, 37–43.

5. Lashley, K. S. The mechanism of vision: XV. Preliminary studies of the rat's capacity for detail vision, J. gen. Psychol., 1938, 18, 123–193.

6. Munn, N. L. Concerning visual form discrimination in the white rat, J. genet. Psychol., 1929, 36, 291–302.

7. Munn, N. L. Visual pattern discrimination in the white rat, J. comp. Psychol., 1930, 10, 145–166.

23. EXPERIMENTAL ANALYSIS OF INSTINCTIVE BEHAVIOR [1]

Some of the most remarkable observations in the literature of comparative psychology are reported in Kepner's study of Microstoma (21). This creature, related to the more familiar planaria and liver flukes, is equipped with nematocysts or stinging cells like those of the hydroids, which it discharges in defense and in capture of prey. In discharging, the stinging cell evaginates a threadlike barbed tube through which a poison is ejected. The striking fact about the creature is that it does not grow its own weapons, but captures them from another microscopic animal, the fresh water polyp, Hydra. The Hydras are eaten and digested until their undischarged stinging cells lie free in the stomach of Microstoma. The nettles are then picked up by ameboid processes of the cells lining the stomach and passed through the wall into the mesoderm. Here they are again picked up by wandering tissue cells and carried to the skin. The stinging cells are elliptical sacks with elastic walls, which are turned in at one end as a long coiled tube. In discharging, the wall of the sack contracts and forces out the barbed poison tube, from one end of the sack. The nettle cell can therefore only fire in one direction. When the mesodermal cell carries the nettle to the surface, it turns around so as to aim the poison tube outward. It then grows a trigger, and sets the apparatus to fire on appropriate stimulation.

When Microstoma has no stinging cells it captures and eats Hydras voraciously. When it gets a small supply of cells these are distributed uniformly over the surface of the body. As more cells are obtained they are interpolated at uniform intervals between those already present. When a certain concentration of the cells is reached, the worm loses its appetite for Hydras and, in fact, will starve to death rather than eat any more of the polyps, which are apparently not a food but only a source of weapons.

[1] EDITORS' NOTE: From *Psychol. Rev.*, 1938, **45**, 445–471. Reproduced by permission of the American Psychological Association. From Harvard University. Presidential Address delivered before the New York meeting of the Eastern Psychological Association on April 2, 1938.

Here, in the length of half a millimeter, are encompassed all of the major problems of dynamic psychology. There is a specific drive or appetite, satisfied only by a very indirect series of activities, with the satisfaction of the appetite dependent upon the concentration of nettles in the skin.

There are recognition and selection of a specific object, through the sensory-motor activities of the animal. Later there is recognition of the undischarged stinging cell by the wandering tissue cells, and some sort of perception of its form, so that it may be aimed. The uniform distribution of the nematocysts over the surface of the body is a splendid illustration of a gestalt, food for speculation concerning vectors and dynamic tensions.

Actually the phenomena of growth so closely parallel those of behavior, or rather behavior parallels growth, that it is impossible to draw a sharp line between them, and animistic theories of growth have been as numerous as mechanistic theories of behavior. Kepner, in fact, postulates a group mind among the cells of the body to account for the internal behavior of Microstoma, to me a *reductio ad absurdum* of mentalistic hypotheses, whether applied to worms or man.

Nevertheless, the naturalistic literature contains many such descriptions, made by careful and accurate observers, of instinctive behavior so complex and precise in its execution that we can only stand aghast at the inadequacy of our concepts of its mechanism. Its genuine relevance to the problems of psychology is well illustrated by the classical definition of instinct as the faculty which animals have instead of intellect which yet makes their behavior seem intelligent.

I am well aware that instincts were banished from psychology some years ago, but that purge seems to have failed of its chief objective. The anti-instinct movement was aimed primarily at the postulation of imaginary forces as explanations of behavior. It was only incidental that these had also been assumed to be constitutional. The psychology of instincts was a dynamics of imaginary forces and the anti-instinct movement was primarily a crusade against such a conceptual dynamism. Somehow the argument got twisted. Heredity was made the scapegoat and the hypostatization of psychic energies goes merrily on. Desires and aversions, field forces and dynamic tensions, needs and vectors, libidoes and means-end-readinesses have the same conceptual status as had the rejected instincts and, besides, lack the one tie to physiological reality which the problem of genetic transmission gave to the latter. The anti-instinct movement was a critique of logical method which failed of effect because it was aimed at a single group of concepts. Its history is a striking example of the lack of transfer of training or the futility of formal discipline.

Although the distinction of genetic and environmental influences has little importance in many fields of psychology, it is of real significance for problems of the physiological basis of behavior. This is true because information concerning the mechanics of development and the histological organization produced by growth is far more exact than any available data concerning the changes produced by learning. Fundamental principles of neural integration may be inferred from innate structure and the behavior dependent upon it. The plasticity and variability of learned behavior precludes any similar correlations with structural patterns.

In spite of a vast literature, there have been few systematic attempts to carry the study of instincts beyond the descriptive stage. Physiologists have been preoccupied with the mechanism of the spinal reflex and students of behavior either have been content to consider instincts as constellations of reflexes clustering around external stimuli or have neglected this side of the problem entirely and, like von Bechterew (4), considered instinct as synonymous with motivation. There are actually two problems here, whose mutual relations are by no means solved. On the one hand are the more or less precise reactions to definite objects. The primiparous female rat gathers paper or other material and constructs a crude nest, cleans her young of the foetal membranes, retrieves the young to a definite locality, distinguishing them often from quite similar objects, assumes a nursing posture, and the like. These are reactions to specific stimuli. The problems which they suggest are those of neural integration: the nature of the stimulus which elicits the response, the pattern of motor activities by which a given result is achieved and, ultimately, the neurophysiology of the behavior.

In contrast to these precise sensory-motor adjustments is the activity which can only be described as reaction to a deficit. The restless running about of the mother rat deprived of her litter, the homing of the pigeon, or the inhibition of feeding responses in the chick removed from companions presents an entirely different system of reactions from those exhibited in the presence of litter, nest, or companions. This reaction to deprivation of some stimulus presents the typical problem of motivation.

For brevity I shall speak of the specific sensory-motor reactions, such as the spider's construction of a web or the courtship display of birds, as the instinctive pattern, in contrast to the deficit reactions. The distinction is not always clear. When the hummingbird builds a nest she reacts specifically to lichens and fibrous material but the building to a definite form also suggests reaction to a deficit. The distinction is not a classification of activities but a suggestion of two different problems, reaction to an obvious stimulus and reaction in a situation where there is no external stimulus, or at least none as yet discovered, which is adequate to account for the observed behavior.

In many instinctive activities a further problem arises from the periodic appearance of both the mechanism and the deficit reaction. The migration of fishes, the seasonal nesting of birds, the receptivity of the female rat during oestrus, all such periodic variations in responsiveness raise the problem of the causes of variation in the excitability of the sensory-motor mechanism and of the reaction to deficit. I shall designate this as the problem of activation of the instinct.

For a number of years we have been trying to discover the mechanisms underlying the reproductive behavior of animals. This activity was chosen for study because it presents the most precise instinctive behavior of mammals which can be brought under laboratory observation and because it exhibits a wide variety of problems, both of integrated behavior and of motivation. The work has developed in several directions. I shall summarize the results and attempt to relate them to some of the more general problems of the mechanism of behavior.

Innate Components of Sensory Organization

The majority of studies of instinct have dealt with the motor aspects of behavior or with the products achieved. The honey-dance of the bee (14, 15), the nest of the oriole, the elaborate procedure by which the spider spaces the radial strands of the web (29) are so striking as to attract attention away from the problem of the sensory control of the behavior. The general outcome of such studies is familiar. The end attained, the web, the nest, is fairly constant and characteristic of the species. The series of acts by which it is constructed varies with every new element in the environment. Such stereotyped results attained by diverse means have formed the excuse for interpretations of instinct in terms of purpose or entelechy.

Granting the facts, there is still an alternative to such finalistic speculations, which are meaningless to those of us who ask *how* the result is attained. The apparent working toward a goal, which cannot be foreseen, is very difficult to express in terms of a motor mechanism, since the motor activities are variable and therefore cannot be interpreted as a predetermined sequence, run off automatically like an automatized habit. This variability in motor activity compels a search for some controlling factor and this might lie in the characteristics of the animal's perceptual organization. It is possible that the nest, or other product of activity, presents a sensory pattern which is "closed" for the animal, in the sense in which this term has been applied to visually perceived forms. The nest might then be built by somewhat random activity, modified until it presents a satisfactory sensory pattern.

With this possibility in mind, a number of our experiments have been directed toward a descriptive analysis of the animal's sensory organization, when there has been no opportunity for modification by learning. The visual system is best adapted for such studies. Anatomically the system is very complexly organized, with the different parts of the retina projected with great accuracy upon the optic lobes or visual cortex (23). We have evidence that this precise anatomic pattern develops normally in the absence of any photic stimulation. Structurally it is probably the most elaborate portion of the nervous system so that, if anatomic differentiation has any functional significance, we should expect to find some innate functional organization in the visual system.

Studying the first visual reactions of rats reared to adulthood in total darkness, Hebb (18, 19) has found that the animals respond immediately to objects, as contrasted with background. Something of figure-ground organization is immediately given. They learn readily a differential reaction to figures which cannot be explored in any way except visually. This means that the figures must be distinguished visually before association with motor reactions can occur. The animals show transposition for size and brightness when they have experienced only two absolute units in the series. This demands the immediate perception of relational properties.

Russell and I (25) have found that rats reared in darkness show an accurate discrimination of visual distance and, without training, regulate the force of jumping to the distance to be crossed. This involves a direct control of motor activity through some innate sensory organization.

These experimental results are in accord with the most careful studies of the congenitally blind children who have had vision restored suddenly (35). So far as one can interpret the literature, these children distinguish figure from ground, distinguish objects as of different shapes, although they are unable to describe them, and have also some perception of distance.

In a series of experiments on discrimination of visual patterns I have found that the general characteristics of the figure-ground relation, as worked out by Rubin (34) and Wertheimer (49) for man, apply also to the rat. The evidence also points to the conclusion that the formation of the discrimination habit depends upon a perception of relations which is prior to the learning process. When a pair of stimuli is presented, one with positive, the other with negative reinforcement, the positive or negative reactions are associated only with that property of each stimulus which differentiates it from the other. A couple of experiments will illustrate the nature of the evidence. A group of animals was trained for 150 trials to choose an 8-cm. circle opposed to a black card; another group to choose a 5-cm. circle under the same conditions. All were then trained to choose the 8-cm. circle when opposed to the 5-cm. The previous training had no effect whatever upon the learning scores with the pair of figures. The property of size was not associated with the reaction so long as the object was alone. The same result is obtained when animals are trained with a single figure and tested for recognition of its form.

If an animal is trained to choose the larger of two circles he will spontaneously choose the larger of any pair of figures. The reaction is not differentiated for form. If he is trained with two different forms, he is undisturbed by wide variations in the size of the figures. So, in every discrimination habit the response is not to a specific pattern but to some property which distinguishes the two figures and which must be differentiated before the motor responses can be associated with it. Furthermore, when the nature of these differentiating properties is tested, they turn out to be relational: relative size, relative direction, proportions, and the like. Such evidence, I believe, disposes of the theory that reactions to relational properties are due to irradiation of conditioned reactions to absolute properties.

These lines of evidence from the animal work support the conclusion already reached by the members of the Gestalt school, that the fundamental organization in perception is innate. And this organization has very definite characteristics, a preference, as it were, for certain specific arrangements of the physical elements of the stimulus.

Motor Action Based on Perceptual Organization

In only one of these observations is there a predetermined motor response; that is the regulation of the force of jumping to the distance seen. It is not necessary, however, that specific motor responses be directly elicited by the sensory organization, in order that the latter should be effective in directing the form of activity. Once motor reactions are associated with some aspects of the stimulus, or with an equivalent stimulus, the innate organization may exercise a selective action upon the various associated reactions. Thus the fluctuations of the staircase illusion may determine alternative associated motor responses, which have been built up by experience with three-dimensional situations and which themselves are certainly not responsible for the fluctuations of the illusion. Innate perceptual organization might similarly exercise a selective influence among motor activities not innately associated with the objects eliciting the reactions.

There is good evidence that animals without previous experience may give specific reactions to biologically significant objects and that the recognition or discrimination of these objects may be quite precise. I became interested in this problem first through observations on the brooding of the sooty terns. If these birds were given eggs of a related species to hatch they would invariably reject the foster children within a short time after hatching, throwing the chicks out of the nest and sometimes killing them. Strange chicks of their own species were accepted during the first few days of brooding. The chicks of the two species did not differ greatly in appearance, yet the discrimination was certain. I was unable to discover the sensory basis of the reaction, beyond getting indications that it depended upon a complex of stimuli, not wholly visual. The history of these birds was of course unknown but the number of individuals observed, considered in relation to the death rate of the colony, made it certain that some at least were dealing with their first brood.

Later Stone took up a similar problem, that of sex recognition, under conditions where the history of the animals and the patterns of sensory stimulation could be controlled. His studies of the effective stimulus to sexual activity are the most thorough available. More recently Borovski (7) has reported observations on the recognition of their eggs by gulls and Beach has completed a number of experiments dealing with the sensory control of the rat's reactions to her young. Although the adequate stimulus has in no case been completely defined, certain important general principles have come out of these studies.

When we first began work in the field it seemed probable that the exciting stimulus would turn out to be simple—an odor, a localized tactile stimulus such as that which induces the clasping reflex in the frog, or the like, and that this would initiate a chain of precise reflexes. Sensory controls have made this hypothesis seem untenable. Vision, olfaction, audition, tactile sensitivity of the snout and vibrissae, of the paws or skin of the ventral surface can be eliminated singly without preventing the appearance of normal patterns of reaction when the stimulus object is first presented. The arousal of sexual excitement by the female in heat or the cleaning and first retrieving of the young is not dependent upon excitation through any one sense modality. The results of the experiments parallel those dealing with the performance of the maze habit, which is little if at all disturbed by the elimination of any single sense modality. Even the elimination of several sensory paths together may not interfere with the reaction. Thus in a familiar experiment Stone (38) observed copulatory activity in a male, reared in isolation, and with vision, olfaction, and tactile sensitivity of the vibrissae and ventral skin eliminated. Similar results have been obtained by Beach in reactions of females to their young.

These results indicate either that we have missed some simple cue, through inadequacy of technique, or that the same pattern of instinctive behavior may be initiated through different sense modalities and patterns of stimuli. Swann's studies of olfactory discrimination (44) showed that a remnant of the olfactory bulb too small to be identified by gross dissection may mediate olfactory discrimination. This fact might be urged against Stone's conclusions, but Beach has confirmed Stone's observations with animals in which complete destruction of the olfactory bulbs was verified by histological examination. Like sources of error are improbable in experiments dealing with other sense modalities. Beach finds that desensitizing the lips and snout by section of the sensory root of the fifth nerve interferes with the retrieving of young by the female, but it interferes also with the finding and picking up of food, so that this operative control is inconclusive.

The experiments based on sense privation thus point to the conclusion that the exciting stimulus in instinctive recognition of mate or young is not mediated exclusively by any one sense modality.

A second experimental method for analysis of the adequate stimulus has consisted of the successive elimination of properties of the stimulus object in an effort to determine the minimal characters which will elicit the normal pattern of response. Two points have come out clearly in this work. The first is that a wide range of variation in any property of the stimulus is possible, without destroying its effectiveness.

Borovski (7) found that gulls would retrieve eggs to their nests from some distance. He substituted other things for the eggs. The birds retrieved objects of various sizes, weights, textures, and specific heats, ranging from small pebbles to potatoes and billiard balls. But any marked departure from a rounded or oval form led to rejection of the substitute. Cubes, angular stones, and the like were not retrieved. Texture also seemed important, since mudballs were rejected. I have observed that the terns are greatly disturbed by a lump of mud or wax stuck on an egg and distorting its form, although painting or dyeing the eggs in variegated colors is without effect. The adequate stimulus of the egg may thus be defined as a rounded object of certain limited size and texture, and this, in the setting of the nest, elicits specific retrieving, cleaning, and brooding behavior.

Stone (37) could define the stimulus to sexual excitement in the male rat only as an object within certain limits of size, exhibiting a definite jerking movement. The analysis of the female's recognition of her young is still less complete, but size and surface texture seem to provide the chief cues by which the young are identified.

Thus far no investigator has found any single property of the stimulus object which cannot be varied within limits without disrupting the reaction. The stimulus is not a single characteristic color or odor, but seems to be a pattern, having the same characteristics of organization which we have found in studies of visual discrimination of objects. The complete analysis of sensory control of reactions to the mate or young seems scarcely less difficult than the problem of sensory control of homing has proved to be. The experiments thus far carried out have scarcely done more than emphasize the need for exhaustive studies in the field.

It is really imperative that we make a serious effort to define the adequate stimulus, not only in studies of instinct but equally in studies of reflexes and of learning. Psychological theories based upon the relations of stimulus and response remain sheer nonsense so long as the stimulus is defined only as whatever the experimenter puts in front of the animal. We have gone far enough in this work to be sure that the animal rarely reacts to what the experimenter regards as the stimulus. In any complex situation the true basis of reaction can be discovered only by systematic variation of all the parts and properties of the supposed stimulus.

The second point of significance revealed by studies of the stimulus to instinctive behavior is that the effective properties of the stimulus vary with the total situation. The primiparous mother rat will retrieve a number of objects having some resemblance to infants, selecting them from among food objects and nest materials. Temperature, odor, shape, color, surface texture, brightness and size may be somewhat altered without interfering with retrieving. But in the nest the subsequent behavior toward the objects varies with their character. The mother may start to lick a stuffed skin which she has retrieved and discover the stitches in it. She promptly pulls at these, soon removes the sawdust and discards the skin. The nest situation plus the retrieved object calls out new responses and if the sensory pattern of the substitute stimulus does not conform to the requirements of this total situation, the normal course of behavior is disrupted. I have observed that the sooty tern is stimulated to assume the brooding posture by the contact of a chick under the breast but the reaction is only momentary unless the bird is on its own familiar nest.

The accumulated observations suggest that the instinctive behavior is dependent upon a complex of stimuli. Some of the reactions are elicited only by the total integrated pattern. Others may be aroused by single elements of the stimulus and interfering reactions are likely to be excited when the stimulus has abnormal traits which themselves elicit other instinctive or habitual responses.

Such an interplay of specific sensory demands may well form the basis of apparently purposive activities. The nest of the rat is a very primitive affair in comparison with the structures built by many animals. Kinder (22) found that animals which had had no previous experience with any nests materials collected material as promptly and built nests indistinguishable from those constructed by experienced animals. Sturman-Hulbe (43) found little evidence of a basis for selection of materials beyond ease of manipulation and, possibly, specific heat. The range of materials tested was slight, however.

The actual construction of the nest, that is, the determination of its form, seems to meet the requirements of low heat conductivity underneath, contact with the body at the sides, and, less consistently, exclusion of light. The arrangement of optimal conditions in these three respects dictates the form of the nest. The combination of sensory factors is fairly clear and is consistent with the hypothesis of perceptual control that I have suggested. That they are in any sense relational or involve any perception of form is doubtful, in the case of the rat, however.

The available evidence is not sufficient to establish the thesis that the perceptual organization of the animal determines the goal of behavior but the studies of the rat do suggest control by a complex sensory pattern. What the situation is in the case of more elaborate construction, such as the nests of the weaver birds, can only be determined by actual analysis of the process of construction.

The Distinction of Reflex and Instinct

The changes in the character of the responses and in the nature of the adequate stimulus under different environmental conditions, for example, the cleaning of the young in the nest and not during retrieving and the like, are, in a sense, a confirmation of the chain-reflex theory of instinct. It is true that the instinctive behavior creates situations which in turn serve as stimuli to further activities. To dismiss the activity as reflex is, however, to ignore its characteristic features.

Many writers have attempted to differentiate between reflex and instinct, but the final criterion has been only a vague difference in complexity. Our conception of the nature of reflex is derived largely from avoiding reactions elicited by protopathic stimuli and from the muscle-shortening reflexes. These are elicited by a localized group of sensory endings. Locus, intensity, and modality of the stimulus are its determining properties. In the contrast to this, sexual and maternal behavior seem chiefly determined by the pattern or organization of the stimulus, with locus of incidence upon the sensory surface or sense modality secondary. In this respect the instincts present the organismal problem as the reflexes do not. This difference in the nature of the adequate stimulus justifies, I believe, the retention of the term instinct to stress the importance of the problem of sensory organization.

The Activation of the Sensory-motor System

Many sensory-motor reactions are performed apparently as soon as the growth of essential nervous structures is completed. The pioneer studies of Herrick and Coghill (20) marked the way for the many later investigations correlating the appearance of early reflexes with the growth of nervous connections. In many of the early reflexes the mechanism is capable of functioning as soon as growth is completed. But there are, also, many activities which appear only at some interval after the completion of neuron growth. The work of Tilney and Casamajor (45) suggests that the late appearance of some of the so-called delayed reflexes or instincts may be due to late myelinization of tracts, but the maturation of instinct as studied by Breed (8) and Bird (6) is probably due to a diversity of causes in which neural growth is less important than general development of muscular strength and control.

Reproductive behavior presents a unique situation among instinctive activities in that it is delayed long after the development of the nervous system and is conditioned by the attainment of sexual maturity. Recent studies of hormonal activation of sexual behavior raise important problems, both of neural integration and of motivation. The work of Steinach (36), Stone (37), and a number of more recent investigators shows the dependence of the behavior of the male upon the testicular hormone. Many studies show the importance of endocrine products in the regulation of the oestrus cycle and the relation of the behavior of the female to this cycle. The experiments of Wiesner and Sheard (53), Riddle (31, 32), and others indicate something of the dependence of maternal behavior upon pituitary secretions.

The interrelations of the hormones are complex and the literature upon this subject is vast. I shall not take time to review the evidence on the physiological action of the various hormones. More important for us who are interested in behavior than the details of the biochemistry and interaction of the endocrine products is the question of how they act to induce the appearance of specific patterns of behavior. The introduction of male hormone into the blood stream somehow sensitizes the animal to the stimuli presented by the female in heat. What is the mechanism of such sensitization?

The difficulty of the problem is enormously increased by the variability of behavior under normal conditions. There seems to be no item of behavior except parturition and the removal of the fetal membranes from the young which is wholly restricted to the mother rat. Norman has found that nests are sometimes built and young retrieved in a manner indistinguishable from that of the best mothers by virgin females and even by males. Stone and others have observed female mating reactions on the part of normal males and Beach the masculine behavior of normal virgin females. The mere observation of such behavior in experiments involving injection of a hormone therefore does not justify the conclusion that the hormone is responsible for the behavior. There are distinguishing characteristics of what we have considered as normal behavior. The parturient female collects her young into the nest immediately or within a few hours after their birth. Virgin females and males show such behavior only after much longer exposure to young, often with an intervening period during which the young are devoured. It is not impossible to establish definite criteria by which hormonal effects may be recognized but the necessary criteria are quantitative rather than qualitative. The validity of the criteria employed by earlier workers is somewhat called in question. We can only consider the problem of activation on the basis of observations which should be checked again with more attention to the range of normal variation.

With this reservation it seems worth while to consider the mechanism of activation, if only to define the problem more clearly.

1. Does the hormone stimulate the growth or formation of new nervous connections, as the chemical organizers in Spemann's experiments stimulate differentiation of structure? A number of observations may be urged as arguments against this possibility. Castration abolishes the male reaction. Injection of the male hormone may restore it promptly and it may be repeatedly revived by repeated injection of the hormone. It is unlikely that each of these repeated activations involves a renewed growth with intervening degeneration of the mechanism. In the experiments of Wiesner and Sheard retrieving of the young grew less persistent as the young approached weaning age and began to venture from the nest. The retrieving reaction could be restored to its initial vigor, either by injection of pituitary hormones or by giving the mother newborn young to nurse. The responses to the younger infants were apparently immediate. We cannot ascribe the initiation of neuron growth to this stimulus and so have no reason to assume that the hormone produces such an effect. This and other evidence point to the conclusion that the neural mechanism is already laid down before the action of the hormone, and that the latter is only an activator, increasing the excitability of a mechanism already present.

2. Does the hormone act merely by increasing the general excitability of the organism? Reduced sexual activity during starvation or physical illness (40) and the fact that male hormone increases the excitability of the sympathetic system as measured by vasomotor reflexes (50) lend plausibility to this assumption. I have found, however, that castration does not alter general activity for a month or so, nor is there other valid evidence for a reduction in general excitability which is common to castrated males, females in the dioestrum, and nonparturient females, which should be the case if the hormones acted as general excitants. Finally, the strongest argument against this hypothesis is the apparent specificity of the different hormones for different patterns of behavior as illustrated by Moore's reversal of sex behavior (27) by interchanging the gonads of the two sexes.

3. The hormones induce specific changes in various organs, such as the vascular changes in the uterine mucosa, the rapid enlargement of the testis, or lactation in the mammary glands. It is possible that these altered states initiate sensory impulses which facilitate the mechanisms of the

secondary sexual reactions. This is the mechanism implied in Moll's evacuation theory (26) of the sex drive and in the ascription of various phases of maternal behavior to lactation. The suppression of the oestrus cycle and of receptivity in the female rat during lactation, and the correlation of sexual behavior with phases of the oestrus cycle suggest an elaborate interplay of such mechanisms.

The evidence against this somatic sensory reinforcement is rather compelling, however. Stone tested the evacuation theory by removing as much as possible of the reproductive system from males and observing their behavior after treatment with male hormone. He found sexual excitability, responsiveness to the female in heat, in castrated animals from which all of the accessory reproductive glands had been removed, leaving no anatomic basis for the tension of accumulated secretions assumed as the source of sensory reinforcement in the evacuation theory. Several investigators (52) have reported the hormonal induction of oestrus without the induction of mating behavior. Ball (2) has observed the normal signs of sexual excitement in females from which the uterus and vagina had been removed. Wiesner and Sheard have reported and Norman has confirmed the fact that normal retrieving of young occurs in parturient females from which the mammary glands were removed in infancy. The mechanical stimuli of lactation therefore cannot be an important factor in the induction of this phase of maternal behavior.

In each of these experiments the organs to which the function of sensory reinforcement would naturally be ascribed have been removed without abolishing excitability to the appropriate stimuli. Still more conclusive evidence on this matter comes from instances of reversal of sexual behavior. In gynandromorphic insects with head of one sex, thorax and abdomen of the other, sexual behavior is reported to follow the sex of the head, not that of the reproductive system (51). Reversal of sexual behavior in hens with tumors of the ovary has long been known (28). In the experiments of Moore the gonads were interchanged between male and female rats and corresponding reversal of behavior noted, the feminized males retrieving young and the masculinized females showing male behavior.

Such observations and experiments seem to preclude the evacuation theory of sexual activation and to minimize the importance of any sensory reinforcement from somatic organs in the production of specific reproductive responses. Of course they do not rule out all possible peripheral mechanisms which might provide effective facilitation for specific reflexes. Certain possibilities have not yet been explored, such as that of an altered temperature control during pregnancy which might precipitate nest building, as Kinder (22) has suggested, or localized changes in vasomotor reflexes which might alter local cutaneous sensitivity. Nevertheless, the organs showing greatest structural changes under hormone influences and those to which sensory facilitation has been ascribed have been removed without destroying the secondary sexual reactions and the observations on reversal of sexual behavior make it pretty certain that somatic sensory impulses cannot be the determiners of specific reaction patterns.

4. There remains only the last alternative, that the hormones act upon the central nervous system to increase the excitability of the sensory-motor mechanism specifically involved in the instinctive activity. Direct evidence for this is lacking and we have no conception of the way in which various organic compounds might exercise a selective effect upon specific nervous elements or schemata. There are, however, many instances of the restricted influence of drugs, both upon localized structures, as in the case of strychnine, and upon psychological functions, as in the action of mescal. There is also some slight evidence for the local sensitization of nervous tissue to organic toxins, with a selective action of later doses upon the sensitized tissue. The hypothesis of a specific action of the hormones upon nervous organization is therefore not without parallel in the literature of pharmacology. The problem here is clear enough. Techniques of direct investigation, as by serological tests of the affinity of specific structures for different hormones, are still lacking.

Neural Structure and Instinct

Gross Localization. The probable locus of action of the hormone within the central nervous system leads to the question of the neurological basis of instinct. The notion of a sharp distinction of levels must be abandoned. Zeliony (55) and Culler and Mettler (10) have demonstrated the possibility of conditioning in the decorticate animal, so that the cerebral hemispheres are no longer to be regarded as the exclusive seat of the learning process. Instinctive activities are also not exclusively a function of subcortical structures. In submammalian forms many complicated instincts can be carried out in the absence of the forebrain, as illustrated by Rogers' studies of the reproductive activities of decerebrate pigeons (33). In these birds such complex learning as is required by differential reaction to visual forms is also independent of the forebrain (16) so that these animals do not provide evidence for a separate localization of instinct and learning. In mammals instinctive activities may suffer severely from total or partial decortication. I have found that the rat's reactions to visual distance are disturbed by injuries to the visual cortex but are unaffected by extensive destruction of the optic centers of the thalamus and midbrain. Mating behavior has not been observed in male rats lacking more than half of the neocortex. It is difficult to keep such animals at a normal level of general vigor and their impotence might be ascribed to lowered vitality. They usually fail, however, to show any specific reactions to cage mates and in this respect are quite different from animals which are undernourished or ill. Stone (41) has found normal mating behavior in male rabbits with large cortical lesions and Brooks (9) in completely decorticate male and female rabbits, so long as the olfactory system remains intact. The difference between the rat and rabbit thus seems to correspond to the degree of specificity of the adequate stimulus in the two genera. Brooks has reported normal mating in rabbits deprived of olfactory bulbs and with the neocortex intact. This confirms our conclusion concerning alternative effective stimuli.

The studies of Beach (3) show the dependence of many aspects of maternal behavior upon the cortex. Using such criteria as the time of initiation of nest building before parturition, the removal of the foetal membranes, grade of nest, retrieving, and the removal of the nest and young from unfavorable conditions, he has compared the performance of normal mothers with that of others having various cerebral lesions. Practically every item of the behavior showed deterioration in proportion to the extent of cerebral injury.

None of the primary reactions dropped out as a result of the cerebral lesions. Collecting nest material, nest building, cleaning the young, retrieving were observed in all animals, but in case of those with extensive lesions the activities were not fitted together into an effective organization. Nests were poorly constructed and inadequate as protection to the young. One or two of the litter might be cleaned, the rest left to die in the foetal membranes. In retrieving tests the young were carried about but not collected into a single group, and so on.

The results of this study are of especial importance in emphasizing, by contrast, the degree of integration of activities in the normal pattern. Dunlap (13) has averred that there are no instincts, although there is instinctive behavior, meaning by this that such categories as maternal behavior are created by the observer out of an aggregate of activities which, in themselves, have no physiological coherence. The analysis of cerebral function in maternal behavior favors an opposite interpretation. The partially decerebrate mother shows all of the component activities which are revealed by the maternal behavior of the normal animal, but these elements are so poorly coordinated that she cannot rear her litter. The normal pattern of maternal behavior involves a total integration of the component activities which makes it a functional unit and in mammals this unity is given by the activity of the cerebral cortex.

Histologic Structure. In the visual system there is a high degree of precision in the topographic arrangement of the fibers. A statistical study of the distribution of normal cells in the lateral geniculate nucleus shows after lesions in the visual cortex that the axons which reach the cortex reproduce exactly the relative spacial positions of the cells in the nucleus;

that is to say, the concentration of cells is uniform, right up to the edge of a degenerated area in the nucleus. But this accuracy of growth is apparently rare and it constitutes in the visual system not a precise set of sensory-motor connections, but a cortical field in which the spacial relations of retinal excitation are reproduced and whose parts are still equipotential for the integrative processes.

Experimental studies of nerve growth and regeneration seem to establish the fact that in general there is little specificity in the connections of individual fibers. The transplantation experiments of Detwiler (11) and of Weiss (47, 48) show that the distribution of the fibers to the muscles may be quite random and yet coordinated movements are effected as soon as growth is completed, without any opportunity for the intervention of practice to establish the patterns of integration. This, rather than the precision of the afferent visual pathway, must represent the usual state of affairs in the growth of nerves and tracts. No exact sensory-motor connections are established, yet the instinctive reactions may have a high degree of precision.

In general the neurological problems which have arisen in the study of instincts are identical with those of cerebral function in learning. The same questions of equivalence of stimuli, of substitute responses, and of similar effects of various cerebral lesions appear, whether the activities are innate or learned. We are no nearer to an answer to such questions in one case than in the other but I believe that there is more hope of solution of these problems through the study of instincts than of learning.

The Physiology of the Drive

I have reviewed the evidence that the endocrines must act directly upon the central nervous system to activate the instinctive pattern. The same evidence may be applied to the problem of reactions to deficit. The experimental studies have in fact dealt with gross activities such as retrieving or mating which involve both reaction to deficit and specific sensory-motor patterns, both preparatory and consummatory activity. This means that the various motivational factors observed in maternal behavior cannot be ascribed to somatic sensory reinforcement, any more than can the hormonal activation of the reactions.

Most of the current theories concerning the nature of primitive drives have been derived by analogy with the hunger mechanism and assume some continued visceral activity, comparable to the contractions of the empty stomach, as the source of masses of excitation whose irradiation in the nervous system increases the general responsiveness of the animal. This analogy has certainly been overworked, especially as it is by no means assured that hunger motivation is itself synonymous with the hunger pangs. The work of Richter (30) and Wada (46) shows a correlation between rhythmic bodily activities and hunger contractions, but the activities of the animal under hunger motivation are not rhythmic. The rat in the maze does not stop running between hunger pangs. Even for hunger motivation we must assume, I believe, some source of continued excitation which is no more than activated by the hunger contractions.

When the theories of motivation by somatic sensory facilitation were developed, there was little evidence that activity could be sustained within the central nervous system. The maintenance of tension or activity through some form of circular reflex was more in accord with the conception that all excitation must pass over immediately into motor response, as first formulated by Dewey (12). The recent demonstration of recurrent nervous circuits, perhaps capable of indefinite reverberation, by the anatomic and physiologic studies of Lorente de Nó, relieves us from the necessity of finding a peripheral mechanism to account for the maintenance of activity or for the dynamic tensions which are implied by the phenomena of motivation. The studies of the sexual and maternal motivation strongly suggest a central nervous mechanism which is merely rendered excitable by hormone action. What this means is that the seeking activities or reactions to a deficit, such as are measured by the obstruction method, are not a reaction to a continuous peripheral stimulus, such as is assumed in the evacuation theory, but are the expression of some central nervous activity or state.

The relation between the reactions to deficit and the excitability of the specific patterns of behavior is obscure. It is generally stated that the drive is first aroused, as by endocrine action, and that this, in turn, causes the appearance of the instinctive sensory-motor reactions. An increase in the excitability of sexual reactions is accepted as evidence for intensification of the drive. But the phenomenon actually observed is only a more ready excitation of specific responses. There is no need to postulate an extraneous drive to account for the fluctuations in the threshold of such reactions. The mechanism is present and under the influence of the hormone or of excitation by an adequate stimulus its excitability is increased.

Only in cases of reaction to a deficit is there any justification for introducing the notion of a drive as a source of facilitation. An increase in general activity or in exploratory behavior indicates an increased responsiveness to stimuli not obviously related to the specific sensory-motor patterns of the instinctive behavior. There is also inhibition of reactions to other stimuli, as when the chick removed from companions refuses to eat. This is a selective facilitation of activity and the facilitation originates with the organism. Does it call for the postulation of some source of energy apart from that of the specific sensory-motor patterns? The evidence indicates that the facilitation is probably independent of somatic stimulation and is of central nervous origin. Stimulation of an instinctive pattern will increase the intensity of the apparent drive. Thus sexual excitement in the male rat is aroused only by the very specific pattern of the female in heat, but once the animal is so excited, he will respond to less definite patterns of stimulation. The waning retrieving activity of the female is intensified by supplying her with a younger litter. Motivation of the hungry animal in the maze is really effective only after the maze has been associated with the getting of food. In these cases the apparent motivation seems to derive from a specific sensory-motor mechanism.

I suspect that all cases of motivation will turn out to be of this character; not a general drive or libido, or disturbance of the organic equilibrium, but a partial excitation of a very specific sensory-motor mechanism irradiating to affect other systems of reaction. In his *Dynamic Psychology* Woodworth (54) suggested that habits might acquire dynamic functions, that a mechanism might become a drive, as he expressed the matter. I should carry this notion a step further and suggest that physiologically all drives are no more than expressions of the activity of specific mechanisms.

Summary

I have reviewed the material on reproductive behavior chiefly to illustrate what seem to me the fundamental problems of instinct. Practically the whole of physiological theory concerning the integration of behavior, whether of spinal reflex or of speech, is based upon inference from the relations of stimulus and response. Instinctive behavior raises questions of the nature of the adequate stimulus which seem to differentiate such activities sharply from spinal reflexes. An essential first step toward an understanding of the mechanism of instinct is the analysis of the properties of the stimulus situation which are really effective in arousing the behavior. This has proved to be a very difficult task, ramifying into all of the problems of perception. Understanding of the motor activities seems to hinge upon these perceptual problems. Little of the behavior can be described in terms of stereotyped movements; rather the whole repertoire of learned and reflex movements may be elicited until some definite sensory pattern is produced. The phenomena are identical with those from which I have inferred the equivalence of reactions and Bethe (5) the principle of "sliding coupling."

I feel that the problem of motivation is also closely identified with the problem of the specific patterns of instinctive response. Hormone action, or reinforcement by sensory impulses from the viscera, seems to do nothing more than activate some central nervous mechanism which maintains excitability or activity. There is no good reason to assume that this mechanism is distinct from the sensory-motor organization which is later active in the consummatory reaction. The current trend in social psychology and psychopathology is to elevate the drive to the position formerly occupied by instinct, as some general motivating force apart from specific sensory-motor systems. Actually the term is nothing more than a general designation of reactions to deficit and its hypostatization as a real force can only blind us to the fact that each such reaction constitutes a special problem involving, perhaps, a unique mechanism.

REFERENCES

1. Avery, G. T. Notes on reproduction in guinea pigs, *J. comp. Psychol.*, 1925, **5**, 373–396.

2. Ball, J. Sex behavior of the rat after removal of the uterus and vagina, *J. comp. Psychol.*, 1934, **18**, 419–422.

3. Beach, F. A. The neural basis of innate behavior: I. Effects of cortical lesions upon the maternal behavior pattern in the rat, *J. comp. Psychol.*, 1937, **24**, 393–434.

4. Bechterew, W. v. *La psychologie objective*. Paris: Alcan, 1913.

5. Bethe, A., and Fischer, E. Die Anpassungsfähigkeit (Plastizität) des Nervensystems, *Handb. norm. path. Physiol.*, 1931, **15** (II), 1045–1130.

6. Bird, C. The effect of maturation upon the pecking instinct of chicks, *Ped. Sem.*, 1926, **33**, 212–233.

7. Borovski, V. M. The relation of the gull to its nest, eggs, and young (Russian), *Reflexksi, Instinkti, Naviki*, 1936, **2**, 139–174.

8. Breed, F. S. Maturation and use in the development of instinct, *J. Anim. Behav.*, 1913, **3**, 274–285.

9. Brooks, C. M. The role of the cerebral cortex and of various sense organs in the excitation and execution of mating activity in the rabbit, *Amer. J. Physiol.*, 1937, **120**, 544–553.

10. Culler, E., and Mettler, F. A. Conditioned behavior in a decorticate dog, *J. comp. Psychol.*, 1934, **3**, 291–303.

11. Detwiler, S. R. *Neuroembryology*. New York: Macmillan, 1936.

12. Dewey, J. The reflex arc concept in psychology, *Psychol. Rev.*, 1896, **3**, 357–370.

13. Dunlap, K. Are there any instincts? *J. abn. Psychol.*, 1919, **14**, 307–311.

14. Frisch, K. v. Über die "Sprache" der Bienen, *Zool. Jb., Abt. zool. Physiol.*, 1923, **40**, 1–186.

15. Frisch, K. v., and Rösch, G. A. Neue Versuche über die Bedeutung von Duftorgan und Pollenduft für die Verständigung im Bienenvolk, *Z. vergl. Physiol.*, 1926, **4**, 1–21.

16. Gemelli, A., and Pastori, G. Sulla rieducabilita di animali scerebrati, *Bol. Soc. Ital. Biol. Sper.*, 1930, **5**, 1–6.

17. Giersberg, H. Gehirntransplantationen bei Amphibien, *Zool. Anz.*, 1935, **8** (Suppl. Bd.), 160–168.

18. Hebb, D. O. The innate organization of visual activity: I. Perception of figures by rats reared in total darkness, *J. genet. Psychol.*, 1937, **51**, 101–126.

19. Hebb, D. O. The innate organization of visual activity: II. Transfer of

response in the discrimination of brightness and size by rats reared in total darkness, *J. comp. Psychol.*, 1937, 24, 277–299.

20. Herrick, C. J., and Coghill, G. E. The development of reflex mechanisms in Amblystoma, *J. comp. Neurol.*, 1915, 25, 68–86.

21. Kepner, W. A. *Animals looking into the future.* New York: Macmillan, 1925.

22. Kinder, E. F. A study of the nest-building activity of the albino rat, *J. exp. Zool.*, 1927, 47, 117–161.

23. Lashley, K. S. The mechanism of vision: VIII. The projection of the retina upon the cerebral cortex of the rat, *J. comp. Neurol.*, 1934, 60, 57–79.

24. Lashley, K. S. The mechanism of vision: XV. Preliminary studies of the rat's capacity for detail vision, *J. gen. Psychol.*, 1938, 18, 123–193.

25. Lashley, K. S., and Russell, J. T. The mechanism of vision: XI. A preliminary test of innate organization, *J. genet. Psychol.*, 1934, 45, 136–144.

26. Moll, A. *Handbuch der Sexualwissenschaften.* Leipzig: F. C. Vogel, 1926.

27. Moore, C. R. On the physiological properties of the gonads as controllers of somatic and psychical characteristics: I. The rat, *J. exp. Zool.*, 1919, 28, 137–160.

28. Morgan, T. H. *Heredity and sex.* New York: Columbia Univ. Press, 1914.

29. Peters, H. Studien am Netz der Kreuzspinne (Aranea diadema, L.): II. Über die Herstellung des Rahmes, der Radialfäden, und der Hilfsspirale, *Z. Morph. Ökol. Tiere*, 1937, 1, 126–150.

30. Richter, C. P. Animal behavior and internal drives, *Quart. Rev. Biol.*, 1927, 2, 307–343.

31. Riddle, O., Lahr, E. L., and Bates, R. W. Maternal behavior induced in virgin rats by prolactin, *Proc. Soc. exp. Biol. Med.*, 1935, 32, 730–734.

32. Riddle, O., Lahr, E. L., and Bates, R. W. Aspects and implications of hormonal control of the maternal instinct, *Proc. Amer. phil. Soc.*, 1935, 75, 521–525.

33. Rogers, F. T. An experimental study of the corpus striatum of the pigeon as related to various instinctive types of behavior, *J. comp. Neurol.*, 1922, 35, 21–59.

34. Rubin, E. J. *Visuell wahrgenommene Figuren.* Kopenhagen: Gyldendalske, 1921.

35. Senden, M. v. *Raum- und Gestaltauffassung bei operierten Blindgeborenen vor und nach der Operation.* Leipzig: 1932.

36. Steinach, E. Geschlechtstrieb und echt sekundäre Geschlechtsmerkmale als Folge der innersekretorischen Funktion der Keimdrüsen, *Zbl. Physiol.*, 1910, 24, 551–566.

37. Stone, C. P. The congenital sexual behavior of the young male albino rat, *J. comp. Psychol.*, 1922, 2, 95–153.

38. Stone, C. P. Further study of sensory functions in the activation of sexual behavior in the young male albino rat, *J. comp. Psychol.*, 1923, 3, 469–473.

39. Stone, C. P. A note on "feminine" behavior in adult male rats, *Amer. J. Physiol.*, 1924, 68, 39–41.

40. Stone, C. P. Delay in the awakening of copulatory ability in the male

albino rat incurred by defective diets: I. Quantitative deficiency, *J. comp. Psychol.*, 1924, **4**, 195–224; II. Qualitative deficiency, *J. comp. Psychol.*, 1925, **5**, 177–203.

41. Stone, C. P. The effects of cerebral destruction on the sexual behavior of rabbits: I. The olfactory bulbs, *Amer. J. Physiol.*, 1925, **71**, 430–435; II. The frontal and parietal regions, *Amer. J. Physiol.*, 1925, **72**, 372–385; III. The frontal, parietal, and occipital regions, *J. comp. Psychol.*, 1926, **6**, 435–448.

42. Stone, C. P., and Barker, R. G. Spontaneous activity, direct and indirect measures of sexual drive in adult male rats, *Proc. Soc. exp. Biol. Med.*, 1934, **32**, 195–199.

43. Sturman-Hulbe, M., and Stone, C. P. Maternal behavior in the albino rat, *J. comp. Psychol.*, 1929, **9**, 203–238.

44. Swann, H. G. The functions of the brain in olfaction: II. The effects of destruction of olfactory and other structures upon the discrimination of odors, *J. comp. Neurol.*, 1934, **59**, 175–201.

45. Tilney, F., and Casamajor, L. Myelinogeny as applied to the study of behavior, *Arch. Neurol. Psychiat.*, Chicago, 1924, **12**, 1–66.

46. Wada, T. An experimental study of hunger in its relation to activity, *Arch. Psychol.*, 1922 (57).

47. Weiss, P. Das Resonanzprinzip der Nerventätigkeit, dargestellt in Funktionsprüfungen an transplantierten überzähligen Muskeln, *Arch. ges. Physiol.*, 1931, **226**, 600–658.

48. Weiss, P. Further experimental investigations on the phenomenon of homologous response in transplanted amphibian limbs, *J. comp. Neurol.*, 1937, **66**, 181–209, 481–535, 537–548; 1937, **67**, 269–315.

49. Wertheimer, M. Untersuchungen zur Lehre von der Gestalt. I. *Psychol. Forsch.*, 1921, **1**, 47–58; II, *Psychol. Forsch.*, 1923, **4**, 301–350.

50. Wheelon, H., and Shipley, J. L. The effects of testicular transplants upon vasomotor irritability, *Amer. J. Physiol.*, 1915, **39**, 395–400.

51. Whiting, P. W., and Wenstrup, E. J. Fertile gynandromorphs in Habrobracon, *J. Hered.*, 1932, **23**, 31–38.

52. Wiesner, B. P., and Mirskaia, L. On the endocrine basis of mating in the mouse, *J. exp. Physiol.*, 1930, **20**, 273–279.

53. Wiesner, B. P., and Sheard, N. M. *Maternal behavor in the rat.* Edinburgh: Oliver, 1933.

54. Woodworth, R. S. *Dynamic psychology.* New York: Columbia Univ. Press, 1918.

55. Zeliony, G. P. Observations sur des chiens auxquels on a enlevé les hémisphères cérébraux, *C. R. Soc. Biol.*, Paris, 1913, **74**, 707–709.

24. THE MECHANISM OF VISION.

XVI. The Functioning of Small
Remnants of the Visual Cortex [1]

Although the rat's detail vision is abolished by complete destruction of the striate areas of the cerebral cortex, the capacity for discrimination of simple geometrical figures is little affected by extensive lesions within these areas, so long as some part of the cortical projection of the binocular field remains intact. Previous experiments have shown both postoperative retention of habits based upon discrimination of simple figures and postoperative formation of such habits after destruction of more than 90 per cent of the visual cortex (12). A more accurate determination of the smallest area which can mediate detail vision and of the character of that vision is of interest in relation to several problems.

The functioning of residual bits of cortical tissue immediately adjacent to large lesions bears directly upon questions of disordered behavior arising from metabolic or circulatory disturbance, and upon the problem of diaschisis. Experiments reported earlier have shown few symptoms which could be ascribed to metabolic disturbances in the neighborhood of lesions and Tsang's studies (21) show an actual increase in density of capillaries along the borders of a cut in the cortex. The experiments reported below indicate that cerebral tissue at the very edge of a sharply defined lesion may function normally.

For the visual system there are many lines of evidence pointing to a close functional interrelation of all parts of the cortical field, as illustrated by the phenomena of contrast, of dependence of acuity upon illumination of the surroundings, of illusions, and the like. Diaschitic effects should therefore be especially prominent after lesions within the visual area, if diaschisis plays any important part in the production of symptoms, and a great reduction of tissue should disrupt functional organization. The discrimination of visual objects typically involves a high grade of perceptual organization in which the total pattern or interrelation of the parts

[1] EDITORS' NOTE: From *J. comp. Neurol.*, 1939, **70**, 45–67. Reproduced by permission of The Wistar Institute. From Harvard University.

of the stimulus is dominant for behavior. The various "gestalt" or "field" theories developed to account for such organization stress the importance of spacial distribution of excitation. It is important to know the spacial limits within which the "field" properties can operate and the character of the disturbances resulting from limitation of the field. Loss of function in small residual areas would favor the theory of diaschisis and disturbances of the normal figure-ground relations, or the like, would lend support to theories of organization in terms of some dynamic tensions.

Extreme limitation of the size of the visual field might reduce it to dimensions which could no longer include the whole of the object to be recognized. In such a case of tubular vision the form of the object to be recognized must be reconstructed by integration of the parts seen successively. Loeb (14) ascribed the "psychic blindness" described by Munk (16) to limitation of the visual field by scotomas rather than to an agnosia. Any study purporting to deal with visual agnosia in animals must take into account the limitations of function imposed by a restricted visual field.

In the experiments reported here the attempt has been made to determine the smallest remnant of the visual cortex which can still mediate the discrimination of visual figures. Rather crude preliminary tests have also been given to define the character of spacial vision in cases which failed in discrimination of figures and to establish the dependence of reaction upon the total figure in cases which did discriminate.

Failure in tests is difficult to interpret since it may be due to central scotoma, to cortical blindness resulting from diffuse inflammatory changes in the residual tissue, to visual agnosia, or to a nervous excitability which sometimes appears in the operated animals, leading them to balk after a few falls in the jumping apparatus and so fail even in tests which they have previously passed. Only positive evidence of discrimination is therefore conclusive and the interpretation of failures must be tentative until confirmed by consistent results with a large number of cases.

Anatomic Data

After lesions in the visual areas of the cortex the cells of the lateral geniculate nucleus, whose axon terminations have been destroyed, undergo complete degeneration. It is therefore a simple matter to determine the number of geniculo-striate fibers which remain intact by counting the undegenerated neurons in the nucleus. The spacial relations of the retinal cells are accurately maintained in projection to the lateral geniculate nucleus and the cortex, so that it is possible to estimate the extent of the intact visual field and the position of the areas of scotoma from counts and maps of the neurons in the lateral geniculate nuclei.

The anatomic projection of the retina upon the lateral geniculate nucleus and the cortex, as determined in previous studies (6, 7), is shown diagrammatically in Fig. 24.1. This anatomic projection is confirmed by the behavior of animals with large lesions in the striate areas. Thus rat number 7, in the present series, always bent his head sharply downward when reacting to visual objects, as if he were able to see only in the upper part of the median visual field. His right lateral geniculate nucleus was completely degenerated and in the left there were nerve cells only in the

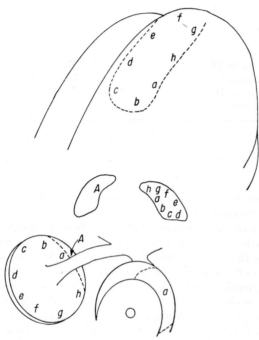

Fig. 24.1. The anatomic projection of the retina upon the lateral geniculate nucleus and area striata of the cerebral cortex in the rat. A coronal section of the nucleus and the dorsolateral surface of the occipital half of the cerebrum are shown. The letters indicate corresponding points. After Lashley and Frank (12).

regions marked *h* in Fig. 24.1, corresponding to the projection of the lower temporal retina, or the upper nasal part of the visual field.

The numbers of cells at each level from the retina are given in Table 24.1. The methods of counting at different levels have been reported in an earlier study (11). The figure for the lateral geniculate nucleus, 34,000 cells, was obtained by actual count of all cells in serial sections through

Table 24.1. The Numbers of Nerve Cells at Successive Levels in the
Visual System of the Rat

Level	Total number of nerve cells [*]	
Rod nuclei	9,180,000	
Cone nuclei [†]	120,000	Retina
Bipolar cells	3,530,000	
Ganglion cells	192,000	
Lateral geniculate	34,000	Thalamic relay
Lamina VII	68,800	
Lamina VI	135,400	
Lamina V	147,700	Cortex
Lamina IV	127,000	
Lamina III–II	176,000	

[*] The figures given are for one eye, lateral geniculate nucleus, and cerebral hemisphere.
[†] In an earlier paper (5) I questioned whether the oval nuclei described by Menner (15) could be interpreted as cone nuclei, since many of them, like rod nuclei, seemed to be attached to the myoid by a slender fiber. The more recent work of Walls (23) seems to establish these nuclei as a criterion of cones in the rat's retina.

the nucleus of one specimen and confirmed by estimates from the volume and cell concentration in the nuclei of other animals. In the retina the ganglion cells are most numerous in the middle of the temporal quadrant and decrease in concentration toward the periphery of the retina (5). In the center of the binocular field there are about four times as many per unit area as in the zone near the ora serrata. The total number of cells in the lateral geniculate nucleus is not sufficient to account for the observed visual acuity of the rat except with the assumption that the binocular field has an even greater proportionate representation in the nucleus than is indicated by the distribution of ganglion cells of the retina. The cells of the lateral geniculate nucleus are uniformly distributed. It is safe to assume, therefore, that a given area from the binocular field is represented by at least four times as many cells of the nucleus as is a peripheral area of equal size. These facts give some basis for computing the size of the residual visual field from counts of undegenerated cells in the lateral geniculate nuclei.

Methods

Testing. Fourteen adult male rats from a fully pigmented strain were trained to twenty consecutive errorless trials in three visual problems. Training was the "jumping" apparatus (4) requiring the animals to jump against the stimulus patterns presented at two openings in irregular alternation, with food for a correct choice, a fall for an incorrect one. The animals learned to choose a 6-cm. white square and avoid a black card (Fig. 24.2), to choose 2-cm. horizontal striations and avoid vertical (Fig. 24.3), and to choose an erect and avoid an inverted equilateral triangle, 10 cm. to the side (Fig. 24.6).

On completion of training they were subjected to operation. Under ether anesthesia the entire striate area of the right hemisphere was de-

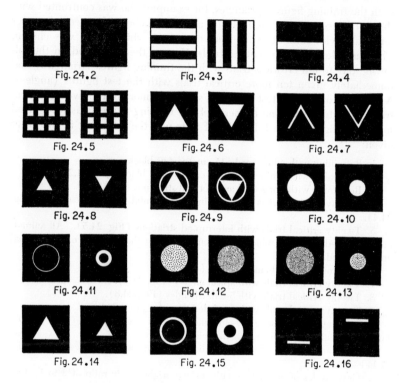

Figs. 24.2 to 24.16. Pairs of stimulus cards used in the tests. Figures 2, 3, 6, and 10 were used for training, the others in tests for equivalence of stimuli. Uniform gray is indicated by stippling. × 1/12.

stroyed by cautery. On the left hemisphere the mesial and caudal portions of the striate area were removed, leaving intact some small portion of the lateral margin, the projection of the binocular field.

Fourteen days after operation the animals were tested for retention with the white square versus black and retrained on succeeding days with the striations and triangles. In addition to the original training figures, a series of equivalence tests were given to determine the capacity of the animals to recognize properties of those figures in a different setting. Thus, after retraining with triangles, the animals were confronted with lines forming only the apical angles of the triangles, to see if these would be identified with the solid triangles, as they are by the majority of normal animals. The tests for equivalence of figures were carried out in each case as follows: when the animal had made twenty consecutive errorless trials with the training figures (triangles, for example), he was confronted with the test figures (apical angles) and allowed to choose between these for ten trials, with food at every trial, no matter which figure was chosen. These are designated as critical trials. He was then retrained on the following day to ten errorless trials with the training figures (triangles) and immediately given ten more critical trials with the test figures (angles). A choice of one of the test figures in sixteen or more of the twenty critical trials indicates that some property of the training figures was recognized in the test figures. The full series of tests was the following in the order given:

1. Retraining with white card (15 cm.) versus black.
2. Retraining with white square (6 cm.) versus black (Fig. 24.2).
3. Retraining with horizontal and vertical striations (Fig. 24.3).
4. Twenty critical trials with a single horizontal and vertical line (Fig. 24.4).
5. Twenty critical trials with interrupted striations (Fig. 24.5). (All animals but one failed this test, which has been passed by the majority of the normal animals tested.)
6. Retraining with 10-cm. triangles (Fig. 24.6).
7. Twenty critical trials with apical angles (Fig. 24.7).
8. Twenty critical trials with 5-cm. triangles (Fig. 24.8).
9. Twenty critical trials with encircled triangles (Fig. 24.9).
10. Training to choose a 10-cm. and avoid a 6-cm. circle (Fig. 24.10). Twenty critical trials with each of the following:
11. Circular outlines of unequal diameter but equal surface area (Fig. 24.11).
12. Gray circles of equal size with surface brightness in ratio of 3 to 1 (Fig. 24.12).
13. Circles of unequal size and equal total luminosity (Fig. 24.13).
14. Equilateral triangles of unequal size (Fig. 24.14).
15. Circular outlines of equal size and unequal surface area (Fig. 24.15).
16. Horizontal bars at unequal heights (Fig. 24.16).

The majority of these tests were chosen as possible indicators of the extent of scotoma. The direction of the interrupted lines of Fig. 24.5 is not apparent unless almost the entire card is seen. The interrupted lines are identified with striations by the majority of normal animals (3, 10). The discrimination of a difference in size is possible only if both figures are seen as a whole. With circles of different size (Fig. 24.10), however,

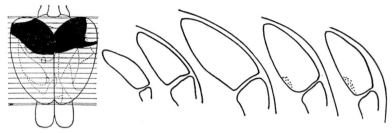

Fig. 24.17. Diagrams of the anatomic findings in animal number 1. At the left is a dorsal view of the cerebral hemispheres with the extent of the lesions indicated in solid black. To the right of this, five coronal sections at equal intervals through the left lateral geniculate nucleus, pars dorsalis, are shown with partial outlines of the pars ventralis and optic tract. Successive levels from the most anterior are arranged from left to right. The position of undegenerated neurons is indicated by stippling. In this case no part of the striate area could be identified. The same arrangement is followed in subsequent figures, in which the remaining area striata is indicated by vertical hatching.

discrimination may be based upon linear dimensions, surface area, distance of the figures from the frame, curvature of the edges of the figures, or total reflected light. The animal with all of the visual cortex destroyed apparently reacts to them on the basis of total reflected light. Tests 11 to 16 were introduced to define the basis of reaction to Fig. 24.10.

Other tests were intended to establish reaction to form. The discrimination of striated fields may involve form-perception, perhaps only direction (19), or a primitive optokinetic reaction such as results from moving striated fields (20). The single lines (Fig. 24.4) and interrupted lines (Fig. 24.5) give some control of these alternatives. Discrimination of triangles may be based upon total figures, upon direction of lines in the perimeter, distance of the base line from the frame, and the like. Tests 7, 8, and 9 give some control of these properties.

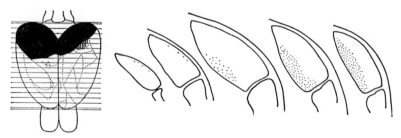

Fig. 24.18. Diagrams of the anatomic findings in animal number 3, arranged as in Fig. 24.17.

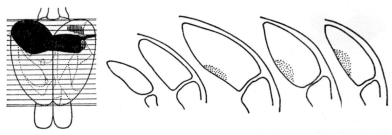

Fig. 24.19. Diagrams of the anatomic findings in animal number 4, arranged as in Fig. 24.17.

I have previously reported extensive tests of the visual capacity of the normal rat (10). Owing to the great variation in the behavior of normal animals it has not been possible to establish consistent norms of behavior in many of the tests employed, but at least 75 per cent of the normal animals tested have transferred without additional training from the training figures (3, 6, and 10) to the figures following them in the series.

Anatomic Methods. On completion of the tests the animals were killed with ether. Complete serial sections through the lateral geniculate nuclei and cortical lesions were prepared with thionin stain for study of retrograde degeneration. The lesions were reconstructed by the usual graphic method and the remaining portions of the area striata were identified by the cytoarchitecture and mapped with the lesions.

The entire right area striata was destroyed in all cases and careful examination of the right lateral geniculate nuclei, pars dorsalis, failed to reveal any recognizable neurons, except a few spindle-shaped cells along the margin of the pars ventralis.

By the aid of a mechanical stage and cross-hatched eyepiece counts of

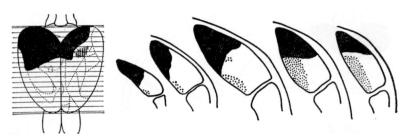

Fig. 24.20. Diagrams of the anatomic findings in animal number 5, arranged as in Fig. 24.17.

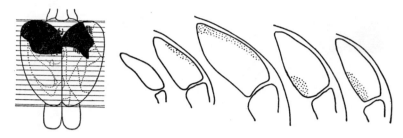

Fig. 24.21. Diagrams of the anatomic findings in animal number 6, arranged as in Fig. 24.17.

neurons in the left lateral geniculate nuclei, pars dorsalis, were made under a magnification of 250 diameters. For the cases in which the degenerated areas of the nucleus obviously exceeded half its total volume all cells in all sections were counted (numbers 1 and 3 to 12 inclusive). In other cases (10 and 14) cells in alternate sections were counted. Rough estimates indicated that more than 15,000 cells remained intact in the remaining cases. No attempt was made to correct the numbers obtained for loss by erosion on the microtome knife, which is probably slight with collodion material.

To record the position of the undegenerated cells in the nucleus, camera drawings of five sections at equal intervals through a normal nucleus were made and used as a diagram. On this the approximate position of the cells is indicated by stippling (Figs. 24.17 to 24.25). The figures thus show the extent of the lesions (solid black), the region of the cortex in which the characteristic granular layer (lamina IV) of the area striata was identifiable (hatched), and the position of the remaining nerve cells in the left lateral geniculate nucleus, pars dorsalis (stippling).

The borders of the degenerated regions in the nucleus are quite sharp.

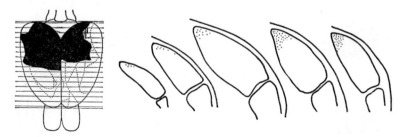

Fig. 24.22. Diagrams of the anatomic findings in animal number 7, arranged as in Fig. 24.17.

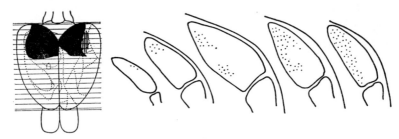

Fig. 24.23. Diagrams of the anatomic findings in animal number 8, arranged as in Fig. 24.17.

I have made a number of counts of cells in measured areas in the middle of the intact zones and at the margins bordering degenerated regions. If the cortical lesion shows a sharp edge without diffuse degenerative changes, the cell concentration in the nucleus is uniform up to the edge of the degenerated region of the nucleus. This indicates a very exact spacial projection of the nucleus upon the cortex. In some cases (numbers 1, 3, and 7) there were scattered cells within the degenerated areas and both these and the cells along the margins of the intact areas showed marked chromatolysis and swollen nuclei.[2]

Experimental Results

The preoperative training scores of the animals fell within the usual range, with an average of thirty-two trials and eight errors for learning

[2] Marked changes in the staining properties of neurons and other pathological changes in nerve tissue do not always indicate functional disturbance. Good detail vision may persist when inflammatory changes have so completely obliterated the cytoarchitectural arrangement of the striate areas that the typical cell layers can nowhere be identified. After partial lesions in the striate area, ganglion cells disappear completely from a limited area of the lateral geniculate nucleus and those which remain in other regions are always less sharply stained than cells in other nuclei and appear somewhat shrunken, yet detail vision may be normal.

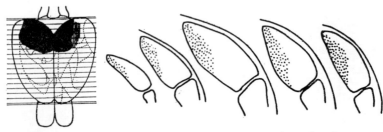

Fig. 24.24. Diagrams of the anatomic findings in animal number 9, arranged as in Fig. 24.17.

striations (Fig. 24.3) and sixty-four trials, eleven errors, for triangles (Fig. 24.6). The postoperative scores are summarized in Table 24.2. Five of the animals refused to jump after some retraining tests (marked *R* in Table 24.2). In all these cases training for 20 days or more failed to reestablish regular jumping.

The scores of numbers 9 to 14 are nearly normal. In these cases the area striata of the right hemisphere was completely destroyed, but one-third or more of the left, including the projection of the temporal retina, was intact. Their records will therefore not be considered in detail. They failed a rather larger proportion of the tests for equivalence of stimuli than do normal animals and showed a greater deterioration of the habits formed before operation than can be ascribed to the lapse of time.

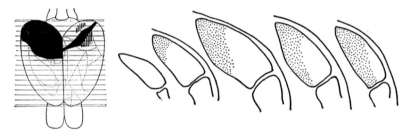

Fig. 24.25. Diagrams of the anatomic findings in animal number 10, arranged as in Fig. 24.17.

The animals with greater amounts of destruction are described below in individual protocols.

Number 1 (Fig. 24.17) jumped readily to the 15-cm. white card versus black, but made a chance score with the 6-cm. card versus black and after a number of falls refused to jump; remained refractory for 3 weeks, then developed a lung infection and was killed. There was no evidence of detail vision and his behavior was much like that of an animal with the entire visual cortex destroyed. The right lateral geniculate nucleus, pars dorsalis, was completely degenerated. The left nucleus contained not more than 300 neurons, and these were scattered, much shrunken and abnormal in appearance. No striate cortex could be recognized. There was probably no functional visual cortex.

Number 2 jumped to the white card versus black only after 20 days of training. When he began to jump he chose the large white card versus black but failed to reach the criterion in 100 trials. When the smaller white square was presented he refused to jump and in the 30 days following could be induced to jump only to the 15-cm. white card.

The right area striata was completely destroyed. On the right side the dorsal half of the lateral geniculate nucleus, the optic tract, the pretectile nucleus, and

Table 24.2. Records of Postoperative Training and Critical Trials in Tests for Detail Vision [a]

Animal no.	1	2	3	4	5	6	7	8	9	10	11	12	13	14	15	16	Cell count
										Test number							
1	10–1																300
2	100–7 FC	R															15,000+
3	0–0	R	6–4 R														2,218
4	10–1	10–1	20–6[b]														713
5	142–32	100–25 FC	40–5[b]														2,656
6	0–0	100–24 FC	70–39 F	160–52 FC[c]	10 F	130–29	R	2	10 F[f]	120–17	16[d]	2	0	0	0	10 F	1,100
7	0–0	30–4 70–8	50–28 (10–1)[e]	60–13[e]												11 F	682
8	0–0	60–11	60–15	0	9 F	100–13	10 F	3	8 F	10–2	12 F	11 F	10 F	0	10 F	4	4,631
9	10–1	20–3	30–7	3	10 F	80–19	8 F	4	10 F	50–10	10 F	6 F	4	0	10 F	9 F	9,608
10	0–0	0–0	50–6	0	9 F	10–1	10 F	10 F	10 F	40–3	9 F	10 F	5	1	7 F	10 F	14,782
11	10–1	10–1	40–10	2	12 F	130–21	10 F	8 F	8 F	70–17	10 F	8 F	4	0	8 F	10 F	15,000+
12	0–0	0–0	10–1	0	10 F	90–7	9 F	0	1	130–18	6 F	9 F	4	1	19	10 F	15,000+
13	0–0	10–2	20–4	1	1	40–5	4	0	8 F	50–13	10 F	1	10 F	0	10 F	0	15,000+
14	0–0	0–0	40–3		10 F	30–3	4		10 F	120–27		8 F	8 F		14 F	8[d]	15,000+

[a] Training scores are given as hyphenated numbers representing trials–errors preceding twenty errorless trials. A single figure is given for critical trials, representing the number of times in twenty trials that the card shown on the right of each pair in the text figures was chosen. Preference for either figure in 80% of the trials indicates an identification of the test with the training figures. The numbers of the tests in the first row correspond to the list of tests in the text and the numbering of the figures from 2 to 16.

[b] Ill, training discontinued.
[c] Trained on figure 4 after failure with striated fields.
[d] Definite choice of smaller figure.
[e] Only one error on striations after training with single lines.
[f] Experiment interrupted.

F, failed to give evidence of discrimination or transfer.
FC, failed to attain the criterion of accuracy.
R, refused to jump after a few trials.

the lateral margin of the superior colliculus had been destroyed by the cautery. The greater part of the left lateral geniculate nucleus was normal.

The behavior of this animal is consistent with that of others with similar lesions previously reported (12, 13). The combined destruction of parts of the striate areas and the colliculi seriously interferes with jumping even when detail vision is retained.

Number 3 (Fig. 24.18) jumped to the white card versus black only after 20 days of training. He jumped fairly readily to a single figure, but balked whenever two figures were presented. In two weeks of daily testing only 6 jumps to the striated cards were obtained.

The right area striata was destroyed. The right geniculate nucleus, optic tract and superior colliculus were severely damaged. The left lateral geniculate nucleus contained 2,218 neurons, none of normal appearance.

Number 4 (Fig. 24.19) and number 5 (Fig. 24.20) both jumped readily, discriminated the 6-cm. white square from black, but failed to meet the criterion of accuracy in 100 trials. Both gave indications of discrimination between the striations of Fig. 24.3, but developed some lymphatic infection before training on this test was completed. They certainly had some detail vision.

In number 4 the right area striata was completely destroyed. The left nucleus contained 713 neurons, grouped in the projection field of the dorsal temporal retina.

In number 5 the dorsal third of the left nucleus with the overlying optic tract had been destroyed. There were 2,656 neurons of normal appearance in the lower inner half of the nucleus.

Number 6 (Fig. 24.21). This animal chose the white square versus black with 4 errors in 40 trials. With striated fields he showed no improvement above chance score in 100 trials, making 58 errors. He was then trained with a single horizontal stripe, 2 cm. in width and 15 cm. long, versus a similar vertical one. With these he reached an accuracy of 90 per cent after 160 trials with 52 errors. Further training for 50 trials with the striated fields still gave chance scores. Various control tests indicated that he was reacting upon the basis of the position of the bottom of the vertical stripe and not to the form or direction of the stripes.

Training was continued with circles of unequal size and the criterion reached after 120 trials and 17 errors. The scores on the various control tests showed that he tended to choose the larger continuous white surface (tests 11 and 15) and did not depend upon position of the figures or total reflected light; that is, there was some appreciation of surface area, independent of surface brightness.

The right area striata was completely destroyed. The lesion had cut across the left area striata, leaving remnants of the anteromesial and posterolateral margins. Correspondingly, two groups of cells appeared in the lateral geniculate nucleus. The total number of these was 1,100, of which not more than 400 were in the projection area of the temporal retina. Detail vision, except for crude position and area, seemed impossible.

Number 7 (Fig. 24.22) jumped readily and showed an immediate preference for the white square, although 70 trials with 8 errors were required to reach the criterion of 20 successive errorless. He showed no improvement above chance in 50 trials with striated fields. He was then trained with a single horizontal versus vertical stripe and reached an accuracy of 90 per cent after 100 trials with 22 errors. He was next tested with the striated fields and chose with an accuracy of 95 per cent. He failed with the interrupted striations in 20 critical trials.

Trained next on triangles (Fig. 24.6) he reached the criterion in 130 trials with 29 errors, transferred with 90 per cent accuracy to the 5-cm. triangles, but balked with the angles and made chance scores with the base lines (test 16) and with the encircled triangles. Since these tests had extended over more than 100 days, it was not possible to continue the training for discrimination of size. The results with the striations and triangles seemed sufficient to demonstrate the presence of detail vision involving something more than the discrimination of position and direction.

The right striate area was destroyed, with the nucleus completely degenerated. On the left hemisphere there was a small remnant of striate cortex along the posterolateral margin of the area. The remaining cells in the lateral geniculate nucleus were grouped in the dorsal tip, the projection field for the lower temporal retina. They did not exceed 700 in number and in many of them the nuclei seemed swollen and weakly stained. Their concentration also was probably less than that found in normal nuclei.

This is the most critical case of the series. There can be little doubt that the animal could distinguish the form of simple figures, although the central visual path contained only one-fiftieth of the normal number of fibers.

Number 8 (Fig. 24.23) gave immediate evidence of discrimination of white square versus black and of striations, but was slow in reaching accuracy. He gave evidence of detail vision and discriminated circles of unequal size when total reflected light was equated. The striate cortex of the right hemisphere was completely destroyed. The left lateral geniculate nucleus contained 4,631 neurons, including a large part of the temporal projection area.

The remaining cases do not call for special consideration. In all of them at least half of the left geniculo-striate system of one side was intact, including parts of the temporal projection field, and all gave evidence of detail vision. Diagrams of the lesions and distribution of cells in the lateral geniculate nuclei for numbers 9 and 10 are given in Figs. 24.24 and 24.25. The remaining cases had still larger normal areas in the nucleus.

Discussion

Cases 1, 2, and 3 are ruled from consideration by the anatomic findings and cases 4 and 5 by illness which interrupted the experiment. The remaining animals, numbers 6 to 14, were all, in some or many of the tests, significantly inferior to normal animals. Initial learning for discrimination of size was in general slower than with normal animals; 76 trials with 13 errors as contrasted with a normal average of 37 trials and 5.5 errors. Except for discrimination of the large white square from black, there was greater postoperative loss of previous habits than can be ascribed to the lapse of time alone. For striations postoperative relearning required 41 trials with 12.5 errors, exceeding the preoperative learning scores (32 trials, 8 errors). Relearning of triangles required 76 trials with 12 errors. Initial learning had required 64 trials with 11 errors. In the various tests for equivalence of stimuli no animal was up to normal performance. Although normal animals vary considerably with respect to transfer to similar figures, 75 per cent of any group will pass any of the tests included in the present series, with the exception of test 5. Almost all of the operated animals failed in the majority of the tests. For cases with more than 4,000 axons in the optic radiation, there is no clear relation between the extent or position of the lesion and success or failure in the equivalence tests.

Scotomas, Amnesia, and Agnosia. With the tests used and the variability of the scores it is not possible to distinguish clearly between the effects of restriction of the visual field and the possibility of some deterioration of higher integrative processes. A limited visual field requires some readjustment of visual fixation, as illustrated by the unusual posture of number 7 when inspecting the stimulus cards, and with large figures perhaps a relearning to react to limited parts of the total figure. Extensive scotomas might thus give rise both to an apparent postoperative loss of memory, and also to a slowing of initial learning. Even in transfer tests limitation of the visual field may significantly alter the appearance of the test figures. This is illustrated by the unique reversal of reaction from the larger of two circles to the smaller circular outline (Fig. 24.11) which appears in the record of number 6. With his limited visual field (v.i.) the smaller circle certainly presented a larger white surface than did a segment of the larger circular outline. The observed failures in the tests may reasonably be ascribed to scotoma but the existence of other defects is not ruled out.

Least Cell Number Permitting Detail Vision. The record of number 7 shows some discrimination of figures superior to any results which have been obtained from animals with both striate areas completely destroyed. Striations and triangles were discriminated and the equivalence of striations to single lines and of small to large triangles was demonstrated. The transfer from larger to smaller triangles rules out reaction to position of these figures and indicates some sort of form perception. Detail vision of a limited sort thus seems possible with a maximum of 682 cells in the geniculo-striate system, one-fiftieth of the number of visual fibers normally reaching one area striata. Number 4 with 713 cells in the lateral geniculate nucleus also gave evidence of discrimination of striations. This latter discrimination has been obtained with a few animals lacking the visual cortex, but only after long training, whereas number 4 gave some indication of immediate postoperative retention of the reaction. His illness prevented adequate tests, but the incomplete record supports the findings with number 7.

Number 6, with 1,100 cells, discriminated the single lines of Fig. 24.4 on the basis of position and distinguished size, corrected for total reflected light (Fig. 24.13). All but 400 of the cells in his lateral geniculate nucleus were in the field of the nasal retina and therefore could not have participated in the reaction to the stimulus cards, with the forward fixation required by the jumping apparatus. His performance was better than that of animals completely lacking the striate areas, but he gave no evidence of discriminating the form of the figures.

Comparison of the records of numbers 6 and 7 seems thus to fix the smallest number of cells in the geniculo-striate system which can mediate detail vision as between 400 and 700. No animal with a larger number of cells failed to give evidence of detail vision, with the exception of the two cases with extensive subcortical lesions.

Size of the Minimal Effective Area. If 700 cells near the fixation point represent something near the minimal requirement for detail vision under the conditions of these experiments, what is the visual angle covered by them? The total number of cells in the normal lateral geniculate nucleus, pars dorsalis, is 34,000 or 50 times the minimal effective number. Owing to the great curvature of the cornea and lens of the rat's eye, the total visual field of one eye subtends about 208 degrees (5). The visual angle for the minimal effective area cannot be directly proportional to the number of cells, however, for the normal acuity of the rat requires a greater concentration of cells per unit area in the central than in the peripheral projection zone.

The rat can distinguish striations subtending a visual angle of about 30 minutes (5, 10). Since the total visual field of one eye embraces about 208 degrees, more than 100,000 separate central paths would be required to give the maximum acuity over all parts of the retina, or three times the actual number. There are about four times as many ganglion cells per unit area near the fixation point in the retina as in the extreme periphery. If the distance of separation of the ganglion cells determines the field of overlap of fibers from the myoids and hence the acuity, acuity would be twice as great at the fixation point as at the periphery of the visual field. Assuming that acuity does fall off at a uniform rate to one-half from center to periphery, a rough calculation gives a requirement for normal acuity of at least 36,000 separate central paths, a close approximation to the actual number of cells in the geniculo-striate system.

To carry this assumption a step further, four times as many central paths near the fixation point as at the peripheral retina would be required to supply a unit area and give double the acuity of the peripheral retina.

The 700 cells found effective for detail vision would cover, near the fixation point, not one-fiftieth, but one two-hundredth of the visual field. This would be included by a visual angle of about 14 degrees.

Approaching the problem in another way the small number of ganglion cells in the normal lateral geniculate nucleus makes it highly probable that each cell at that level conducts impulses from a single acuity unit of the retina and so, in the binocular field, covers an angle of 30 minutes. Seven hundred cells would thus cover an area bounded by about twenty-six acuity units, or a visual angle of 13 degrees.

These two methods of estimation, based upon somewhat different assumptions, give the same result: 700 cells in the nucleus cover a maximal visual angle of about 13 or 14 degrees. With the jumping apparatus as used, a 10-cm. figure, such as the larger triangles or circles, covers a visual angle of 28 degrees or four times the area included in the minimal effective visual field. The transfer from large to 5-cm. triangles (test 8) by rat number 7 indicates that in learning the larger triangles he had been able to reconstruct the total form from successive fixations of different parts of the figure, since he failed to transfer to the more limited parts presented in the angles and base lines and therefore was probably not reacting to position or direction of a limited part of the figures.

The striate cortex of one hemisphere has a surface area of about 20 sq. mm. If the axons of the cells of the lateral geniculate nucleus are distributed to it uniformly, 700 cells in the radiation would correspond to one-fiftieth of the area or 0.4 sq. mm. The identifiable remnant of the fourth layer in number 7 was about 1.5 sq. mm. in area. The radiation to the medial part of this remnant was probably interrupted by the lateral extension of the lesion in front of the area (Fig. 24.22).

The Normal Functioning of Small Areas. Pieron (18), Buytendijk (2), Pavlov (17), and others have ascribed the similar effects of cortical lesions in different areas upon such activities as maze learning to circulatory disturbances or other remote effects of the surgical destruction of tissue. The present experiments show that a remnant of a functional cortical area immediately adjacent to a lesion and not more than 1.5 sq. mm. in area is able to carry out such integrative functions as are involved in the discrimination of visual patterns and the mediation of habits based upon the discrimination. In a previous experiment (12, p. 370) we found that lesions along the margins of the striate areas, penetrating the fiber layer, did not produce a postoperative loss of visual habits and in a series of cases all possible transcortical connections of the striate areas were severed without abolishing the visual reactions. Bard (1) has shown that in the cat the placing reactions may survive the removal of all of the cortex back of the sigmoid gyrus and that the destruction of the latter alone abolishes the reactions. The results with the visual cortex bear out this evidence that certain functions may be maintained by cerebral tissue in close proximity to a lesion and that the interruption of a considerable part of the transcortical connections of such areas does not seriously interfere with their activities.

Both the placing reactions and visual discrimination involve the accurate differentiation of the spacial position of the stimulus upon the sensory surface. As I have pointed out (9), it is these functions of spacial orientation which reveal the highest degree of subordinate localization within the functional cortical area. It appears also that the normal activity of the parts of such areas in some functions is largely independent of their interconnections with other parts of the cortex or even of other parts of the same specialized area. This autonomous activity of the striate cortex in detail vision is in such sharp contrast with the disturbances in maze and latch-box learning after similar lesions as to suggest that the two types of function are mediated by fundamentally different integrative mechanisms (9).

Summary

The entire right and a large part of the left striate area of the visual cortex was destroyed in each of a series of rats and the animals were then tested for detail vision. Discrimination of visual figures was observed in animals with not more than 700 neurons in the geniculo-striate system, about one-fiftieth of the number normally present in each lateral geniculate nucleus. The experiment shows that the simpler integrative processes involved in visual discrimination and learning may be carried out in a normal or nearly normal manner by a minute remnant of a cerebral area immediately adjacent to an extensive lesion. It therefore argues against any trophic changes in the residual tissue as important causes of defects observed in other functions after similar lesions.

REFERENCES

1. Bard, P. Studies on the cerebral cortex: I. Localized control of placing and hopping reactions in the cat and their normal management by small cortical remnants, *Arch. Neurol. Psychiat., Chicago*, 1933, **30**, 40–74.

2. Buytendijk, F. J. J. An experimental investigation into the influence of cortical lesions on the behavior of rats, *Arch. néerl. Physiol.*, 1932, **17**, 370–435.

3. Krechevsky, I. A note on the perception of linear Gestalten in the rat, *J. genet. Psychol.*, 1938, **52**, 241–246.

4. Lashley, K. S. The mechanism of vision: I. A method for rapid analysis of pattern-vision in the rat, *J. genet. Psychol.*, 1930, **37**, 453–460.

5. Lashley, K. S. The mechanism of vision: V. The structure and image-forming power of the rat's eye, *J. comp. Psychol.*, 1932, **13**, 173–200.

6. Lashley, K. S. The mechanism of vision: VII. The projection of the retina upon the primary optic centers in the rat, *J. comp. Neurol.*, 1934, **59**, 341–373.

7. Lashley, K. S. The mechanism of vision: VIII. The projection of the retina upon the cerebral cortex of the rat, *J. comp. Neurol.*, 1934, **60**, 57–79.

8. Lashley, K. S. The mechanism of vision: XII. Nervous structures concerned in the acquisition and retention of habits based on reactions to light, *Comp. Psychol. Monog.*, 1935, **11**, 43–79.

9. Lashley, K. S. Functional determinants of cerebral localization, *Arch. Neurol. Psychiat., Chicago,* 1937, **38**, 371–387.

10. Lashley, K. S. The mechanism of vision: XV. Preliminary studies of the rat's capacity for detail vision, *J. gen. Psychol.*, 1938, **18**, 123–193.

11. Lashley, K. S. The mechanism of vision: IX. The numerical relations of cells in the visual system of the rat, *Ukr. Psikhonevrol. Akad.*, 1938.

12. Lashley, K. S., and Frank, Margaret. The mechanism of vision: X. Postoperative disturbances of habits based on detail vision in the rat after lesions in the cerebral visual areas, *J. comp. Psychol.*, 1934, **17**, 355–380.

13. Layman, J. D. Functions of the superior colliculi in vision, *J. genet. Psychol.*, 1936, **49**, 33–47.

14. Loeb, J. Die Sehstörungen nach Verletzungen der Grosshirnrinde, *Arch. ges. Physiol.*, 1884, **34**, 67–172.

15. Menner, E. Zapfen in der Retina der Maus, Z. *Zellforsch. mikr. Anat.*, 1930, 9, 53–62.

16. Munk. H. *Über die Funktionen der Grosshirnrinde.* Berlin: 1881.

17. Pavlov, I. P. A reply of a physiologist to psychologists, *Psychol. Rev.*, 1932, **39**, 91–127.

18. Pieron, H. *Le cerveau et la pensée.* Paris: 1923.

19. Poppelreuter, W. Zur Psychologie und Pathologie der optischen Wahrnehmung, Z. *ges. Neurol. Psychiat.*, 1923, **83**, 26–152.

20. Smith, K. U. The postoperative effects of removal of the striate cortex upon certain unlearned visually controlled reactions in the cat, *J. genet. Psychol.*, 1937, **50**, 137–156.

21. Tsang, Yü-Chüan. Vascular changes following experimental lesions in the cerebral cortex, *Arch. Neurol. Psychiat., Chicago,* 1936, **35**, 1280.

22. Tsang, Yü-Chüan. Visual sensitivity in rats deprived of visual cortex in infancy, *J. comp. Psychol.*, 1937, **24**, 255–262.

23. Walls, G. L. The visual cells of the white rat, *J. comp. Psychol.*, 1934, **18**, 363–366.

25. PATTERNS OF CEREBRAL INTEGRATION INDICATED BY THE SCOTOMAS OF MIGRAINE [1]

The scotomas characteristic of ophthalmic migraine have been described by a number of investigators.[2] The visual disturbance precedes or accompanies other symptoms of migraine and is usually of short duration. It is generally restricted to one half of the visual field, the right or the left, and ranges in size from a scarcely noticeable blind spot to total hemianopia. A great variety of forms have been mentioned in the literature, but those which have been described in detail are of much the same type. The scotoma starts as a disturbance of vision limited to the neighborhood of the macula and spreads rapidly toward the temporal field. With increase in size the disturbed area moves or "drifts" across the visual field, so that its central margin withdraws from the macular region as its peripheral margin invades the temporal. Spread from the temporal toward the macular region has also been described and is apparently more frequent when complete hemianopia develops. The area may be totally blind (negative scotoma), amblyopic or outlined by scintillations. A scotoma of the last type takes the form of "fortification figures," so called from the suggestion of a map of the bastions of a fortified town. They appear as series of parallel, white or colored scintillating lines, forming angles or polygons along the margins of the scotomatous area. The scotomas are symmetric for the two eyes and so are almost certainly the result of a cortical disturbance.

Two characteristics of the scotomas have not previously been reported and are of some interest as suggesting the nature of the inherent organization of cortical activity. These are (a) the maintenance of the

[1] EDITORS' NOTE: From *Arch. Neurol. Psychiat., Chicago*, 1941, **46**, 331–339. Reproduced by permission of the American Medical Association. From Harvard University.
[2] For an account of the symptomatology of ophthalmic migraine, with references, see Richter (11). The most detailed description of scotomas is that of Jolly (3).

characteristic shape of the scotoma during its drift across the visual field and (b) the "completion of figure" described by Gelb and Poppelreuter as occurring in scotomas of traumatic origin.

Over a period of years I have had opportunity to observe and map a large number of such scotomas, uncomplicated by any other symptoms of migraine. The scotoma usually occurs first as a small blind or scintillating spot, subtending less than 1 degree, in or immediately adjacent to the foveal field. This spot rapidly increases in size and drifts away from the fovea toward the temporal field of one side. Usually both quadrants of one side only are involved, the right and left being affected with about equal frequency. Occasionally the scotoma is confined to one quadrant. Rarely, there is complete hemianopia, and in one instance, in more than one hundred, there was complete blindness in both lower quadrants, with sparing of the macula.

Rate of Drift

The outline of the scotoma is readily charted by fixating a mark on a sheet of paper, moving a pencil toward the blind area along different radii and marking the places at which the point of the pencil disappears—the usual method for crude demonstration of the blind spot. When this is done, each scotomatous area is found to have a distinct shape, and when the charting is repeated at brief intervals, this specific shape is roughly preserved as the area drifts across the visual field. Figures 25.1, 25.2, 25.3, and 25.4 show the successive positions and shapes of four such areas charted at intervals of from two to five minutes. Occasionally the shape is not well preserved, as in the area shown in Fig. 25.1. Generally, however, within the region between the macula and the optic disk [3] the form is maintained, as shown in Figs. 25.2 and 25.4, and occasionally, as in Fig. 25.3, successive charting reveals almost perfect correspondence of forms. As the scotoma drifts to the temporal field accurate mapping becomes impossible, since the pencil point can no longer be clearly seen.

Not only does the form of the scotomatous area remain constant as it drifts across the visual field, but when there are fortification figures, these also maintain their characteristic pattern in each part of the area. The size of the fortification figures does not increase with increase in the size of the scotoma, but additional figures are added as the area grows. It is not possible to sketch the figures accurately. The rate of scintillation is near 10 per second [4] and the form changes rapidly, but small figures

---

[3] The blind spots do not, of course, interfere with binocular charting of the scotoma. In the figures the outline of the blind spot of the homolateral eye is inserted to indicate the position and size of the scotoma in relation to the visual field.

[4] This rate is above the maximum for counting but well below the flicker fusion point. The rate may be related to the alpha rhythm.

can be distinguished from large and simple angles from polygonal figures. Differences of the sort indicated in Fig. 25.3 are unmistakably present and persist while the area drifts for considerable distances across the field. I have the impression, without adequate data to confirm it, that the size and shape of the fortification figures are constant for each radius of the field. That is, the pattern is finer and less complicated in the upper quadrants than in the lower, as indicated in Figs. 25.4 and 25.5. If true, this suggests that the pattern is a function of the anatomic substratum, rather

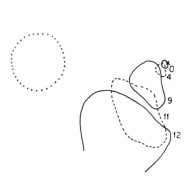

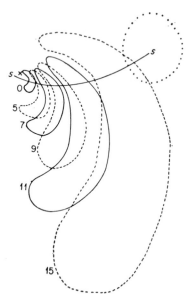

Fig. 25.1. Maps of a negative scotoma confined to the lower left quadrant. The successive sketches were made at intervals of no, four, nine, eleven, and twelve minutes after the area was first noted. Alternate sketches are outlined with broken lines to avoid confusion. The fixation point is marked by *x*. The dotted circle is an outline of the blind spot of the homolateral eye, to indicate the size of the visual field. In this instance the form was not well maintained.

Fig. 25.2. Maps of a scintillating scotoma sketched at the intervals, expressed in minutes, shown at the left. Scintillations were confined to the region above the line *ss*. Arrangement as in Fig. 25.1.

than of the nature of the propagated disturbance. More certainly, when the fortification figures are limited to one part of the area, they continue in that part only throughout the entire drift, as shown in Fig. 25.2.

Whatever the precipitating cause of the disturbance, these facts indicate that an inhibitory process, in the case of blind areas, or an excitatory process, in the case of scintillations, is initiated in one part of the visual cortex and spreads over an additional area. As the process spreads, activity at the point where it was initiated is extinguished, and the process of extinction also spreads over the same area at about the same rate as does the active process.

The increase in size of the scotoma as it passes toward the peripheral areas does not necessarily mean that the disturbance starts from a point and spreads to larger areas. Apparent size in the visual field is not related to the size of the excited region of the striate cortex, since the cortical field of the macula is probably as large as that of all the remaining retina (10). Apparent size must be determined at a later stage of integration, and in the case of smaller scotomas the actual extent of cortical area involved in the disturbance is probably constant as the disturbance drifts.

The drift of the scotomatous area is what might be expected from the spread of excitation across a succession of reverberatory circuits, as de-

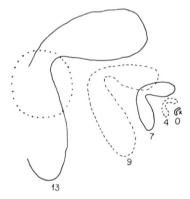 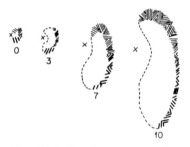

Fig. 25.3. Successive maps of a negative scotoma, arranged as Fig. 25.1.

Fig. 25.4. Successive maps of a scintillating scotoma, to show characteristic distribution of the fortification figures. The x in each case indicates the fixation point.

scribed by Lorente de Nó (8), with the activity of the circuits extinguished at the inner margin of the blind area at the same rate as it is propagated to new circuits at the advancing margin. The rate of propagation may eventually have some significance. For a number of observations the rate is fairly uniform. Ten to twelve minutes is required for spread of the outer margin from the region of the macula to the blind spot of the homolateral eye. The rate beyond this point is rapid and difficult to estimate, but the total time required for the disturbance to spread from the macula area to the temporal field is approximately twenty minutes. A negative area of the size shown in Fig. 25.2 is determined by an inhibitory phase lasting for about five minutes. The development and the recovery of complete hemianopia each requires about fifteen to twenty minutes, indicating a propagation of the disturbance at about the same rate, with a longer period of inhibition, sometimes lasting half an hour.

The anteroposterior length of the striate area is about 67 mm. (1). The disturbance starts very near the mid-line of the visual field, which is probably projected near the occipital pole; propagation to the temporal margin requires about twenty minutes. These figures give a rate of 3 mm. per minute or less for the propagation of the disturbance.

In each attack the disturbance seems to spread with different characteristics along different radii of the visual field. Thus, in the scotoma sketched in Fig. 25.2 scintillations were confined to the upper quadrant and the duration of the inhibited phase was apparently greater in the lower part of the field than in the upper, as measured by the width of the band. The constriction in the band, shown in Fig. 25.3, indicates a negative phase of short duration, passing out along a definite radius above the margin of the lower quadrant. Poppelreuter (9) has pointed out that in scotomas of traumatic origin there are indications of dynamic organization of the visual field such that effects of fatigue, etc., tend to spread along the radii of the field, and the evidence from the scotomas of migraine leads to a similar conclusion. No anatomic basis for such phenomena is known at present, but some anteroposterior polarization of the striate cortex is indicated.

Fig. 25.5. Sketch to show apparent differences in the fortification figures. The coarser and more complicated figures appear generally in the lower part of the field.

The scintillations must represent a phase of intense excitation. The lines are of dazzling brightness, subjectively of the order of direct sunlight reflected from a white surface. They occur along the advancing margin of the area,[5] followed by the blind region, as if a wave of strong excitation were followed by a phase of total inhibition (Fig. 25.4). However, part or all of the area may show no signs of excitation, yet advance at the same rate (Fig. 25.2, lower part). From this it seems that the inhibitory phase may spread without a preliminary phase of excitation, and at the same rate. Occasionally the negative phase fails to develop, and objects may be seen in the field immediately behind, or even between, the fortification figures, as shown in the sketches of Jolly (3). The propagation of the excitatory phase with or without a subsequent

---

[5] In the early stages, when the area is near the macula, it may be entirely filled with scintillations, but later these form a band of varying width along the advancing margins. Circular bands radiating from a point have been reported.

protracted inhibitory phase and the propagation of the inhibitory phase without evidence of previous excitation raise an important problem of the interrelations of these processes.

Limitation of Spread

The definite limitation of symptoms to those of primary visual disturbance argues for a sharp functional separation of the striate areas from adjacent regions of the cortex. The disturbance, spreading to a scintillating or negative scotoma, is evidently intense, or at least dominant over other cortical activities; yet it appears to be blotted out completely at the margin of the striate cortex. Except for a very slight torticollis associated with complete hemianopia, I have been unable to detect any additional symptoms during or after the scotoma. It seems to move off the side of the visual field and leave no aftereffects whatever. The absence of any symptoms associated with the peristriate areas indicates that the disturbance does not spread beyond the margin of the primary visual cortex. The interconnections between architectonic areas must therefore be of a very different nature from those of a single area.

In experiments with animals I have been unable to demonstrate any symptoms of visual disturbance after knife cuts which partially sever the striate cortex from surrounding areas, even when difficult problems of visual generalization are used in the tests (6). The complete blocking of the excitatory wave of the scotoma suggests that in man also there may be a greater autonomy of function in the different architectonic areas than is generally assumed to be the case.

Repetitive Patterns

The activity within the scintillating area is perhaps of some theoretic interest. The scintillations have the form of distinct parallel lines, which cannot be counted but give the impression of groups of five or more. These seem to sweep across the figure toward the advancing margin and are constantly renewed at the inner margin, like the illusion of movement of a revolving screw. The pattern of lines and angles is much the same in the experience of all persons who have reported them. Its significance is in the reduplication of activity throughout a considerable area. Repetitive patterns of activity have been reported in other cases of pathologic cortical activity. They are frequently mentioned as characteristic of the visual hallucinations following mescal poisoning (4), and perhaps are represented on the motor side of the convulsive movements of an epileptic attack.

Such repetitive patterns should be predicted from the free spread of excitation through a uniform neural field having the structural arrangement of reverberatory circuits described by Lorente de Nó (7). Although nothing is known of the actual nervous activity during the migraine, the picture suggests that the propagated disturbance is so intense as to be independent of the afferent supply of the cortex and that the patterning represents the type of organization into which the cortical activity falls as a result of inherent properties of the architectonic structure. I have elsewhere outlined briefly a theory of cortical integration based on interference of spreading waves of excitation (12), and the patterning shown in the migraine scotomas is consistent with that theory.

Completion of Figure

The "principle of completion" in visual organization was first pointed out by Fuchs (2) and confirmed by Poppelreuter (9). It states that certain simple geometric patterns (square, circle, triangle, stripes) when exposed so that a part falls within the blind field of a patient with hemianopia of traumatic origin are always perceived as complete figures, although it is certain that the part falling within the scotomatous area is not actually seen. When the migraine scotoma is without scintillations the same phenomenon may be observed. Two examples stand out in my experience in which there was opportunity for careful observation.

A negative scotoma may completely escape observation, even when it is just off the macula, unless it obscures some object to which attention is directed. Talking with a friend, I glanced just to the right of his face whereon his head disappeared. His shoulders and necktie were still visible, but the vertical stripes in the wallpaper behind him seemed to extend right down to the necktie. Quick mapping revealed an area of total blindness covering about 30 degrees, just off the macula. It was quite impossible to see this as a blank area when projected on the striped wall or other uniformly patterned surface, although any intervening object failed to be seen.

On another occasion, with complete hemianopia, including the macula, it was possible to divide a complex object on any line of fixation. A human face was sharply divided by fixating the tip of the nose, so that half, including one nostril only, was visible. At the same time it was impossible so to fixate a circular object that only half was seen. Fixating a chalk mark on the middle of a billiard ball failed to make any part of the ball invisible, although the ball was considerably larger than the readily divided nose.

These observations are of interest as showing that filling in the blind spot and the completion of figures in scotomatous areas are not the result of habits of disregarding blind areas or of identifying part figures. The phenomena appear immediately with new blind areas. They must, then, represent some intrinsic organizing function of the cortex. The figures completed are reduplicated patterns of very simple symmetric figures.

The relation of this fact to the tendency to reduplication in fortification figures and other patterns of "spontaneous" activity of the visual areas is suggestive of a common mechanism.

Such phenomena can be made intelligible by the assumption that the integrative mechanism of the striate cortex tends to reproduce a pattern of excitation, aroused in one region, in any other region also if the latter is not dominated by different afferent patterns. Such a reduplication of patterns should result from the spreading of waves of excitation from points of initial stimulation, by analogy with the transmission of wave patterns on the surface of a liquid. Recent work on the histology of the cortex reveals an anatomic basis for radiation of such waves, in that the interconnections are so numerous as to constitute virtually a homogeneous conducting mechanism.

Summary

Maps of the scotomas of ophthalmic migraine sketched at brief intervals during an attack suggest that a wave of intense excitation is propagated at a rate of about 3 mm. per minute across the visual cortex. This wave is followed by complete inhibition of activity, with recovery progressing at the same rate. Sometimes the inhibition spreads without the preceding excitatory wave. Limitation of the disturbance to the primary visual cortex raises questions as to the nature of the interconnections between architectonic fields. The observations are interpreted in relation to the possible integrative effects of radiating waves of excitation in the cortex.

REFERENCES

1. Filimonoff, I. N. Ueber die Variabilität der Grosshirnrindenstruktur, *J. Psychol. Neurol., Lpz.*, 1932, 44, 1–96.

2. Fuchs, W. Untersuchungen über das Sehen der Hemianopiker und Hemiamblyopiker: II. Die totalisierende Gestaltauffassung. In Gelb, A., and Goldstein, K. *Psychologische Analysen hirnpathologischer Fälle.* Leipzig: Barth, 1920.

3. Jolly, F. Ueber Flimmerskotom und Migräne, *Berl. Klin. Wchnschr.*, 1902, 39, 973–976.

4. Klüver, H. *Mescal.* London: Kegan Paul, 1928.

5. Lashley, K. S. Mass action in cerebral function, *Science*, 1931, 73, 245–254.

6. Lashley, K. S. The mechanism of vision: XVII. Autonomy of the visual cortex, *J. genet. Psychol.*, 1942, 60, 197–221.

7. Lorente de Nó, R. Studies on the structure of the cerebral cortex: II. Continuation of the study of the ammonic system, *J. Psychol. Neurol., Lpz.*, 1934, 46, 113–177.

8. Lorente de Nó, R. Analysis of the activity of the chains of internuncial neurons, *J. Neurophysiol.*, 1938, 1, 207–244.

9. Poppelreuter, W. *Die psychischen Schädigungen durch Kopfschuss.* Leipzig: Voss, 1917.

10. Poliak, S. The main afferent fiber system of the cerebral cortex in primates, *Univ. Calif. Publ. Anat.*, 1932, **2**, 1.

11. Richter, H. Die Migräne, *Handb. Neurol.*, 1935, **17**, 166–245.

26. AN EXAMINATION OF THE "CONTINUITY THEORY" AS APPLIED TO DISCRIMINATIVE LEARNING [1]

Some years ago Spence (16) proposed a theory of the nature of discriminative learning which he opposed to an earlier suggestion of mine to the effect that such learning involves a series of "attempted solutions" and should therefore be classed as an instance of learning by trial and error, rather than as one of direct conditioning. Krechevsky (8, 9) has been active in developing a systematic theory which has much in common with my original suggestion, and a rather extensive controversial literature dealing with the subject has accumulated. The position opposed to the theory of Spence, which has borne various names, has recently been rechristened the "Lashley theory" (19). Since Spence's treatment of the foundling seems less than just, I am willing to accept the responsibilities of paternity, though from a certain purposive cast in the infant's features I suspect that I am cuckold.

Without reviewing the discussion in detail I shall state the chief questions at issue, examine the evidence which has been published, and present additional evidence which seems crucial. The theory of Spence was deduced from the fundamental assumptions of conditioned-reflex theory. The validity of some of those assumptions is questionable, but they are not readily tested and it is not necessary to do so in order to evaluate the derived theory of discriminative learning.

The basic proposition of this conditioned-reflex theory of discrimination has been stated succinctly by McCulloch (13, p. 76). "According to association theory, all stimuli acting at the time of response become associated with that response." [2] This is the proposition which is denied

---

[1] EDITORS' NOTE: From *J. gen. Psychol.*, 1942, **26**, 241–265. Reproduced by permission from The Journal Press. From the laboratory of physiological psychology, Harvard University.

[2] In the discussions of Spence and McCulloch reference is made to "stimuli" and to "aspects of a stimulus." Hull (3) has previously described the "elements" or "components of the stimulus complex" as independently associated and exciting response by an additive action. This difference in terminology may be a source of confusion. I take it that no distinction is implied. Thus a white circle on a black ground has properties of form, surface area, linear dimensions, surface luminosity, total luminosity, contrast, etc. These are called stimuli or aspects, elements or components of the stimulus, according to the usage of the various writers.

in the present discussion. Since conditioned-reflex theory further assumes that each stimulation combined with a reaction increases the effectiveness of that stimulus for eliciting the reaction, it follows that there will be a continuous strengthening of the association, as a function of the number of times that such combined stimulation has occurred. This derived proposition has been termed the "continuity theory." Special assumptions concerning the quantitative relations are irrelevant to the present discussion.

From these propositions Spence goes on to account for discrimination in terms of the familiar Pavlovian theory of differential conditioning. The theory regards discrimination as composed of two independent reactions determined by the relative excitatory strengths of the stimuli discriminated, as built up by reinforcement or reduced by experimental extinction. This aspect of the theory will be considered here only in so far as it implies that all of the differentiating properties of the stimuli are associated and contribute by summation to the excitatory value of the stimulus as a whole (3).

The assumptions of the opposed theory are:

1. The mechanism of nervous integration is such that when any complex of stimuli arouses nervous activity, that activity is immediately organized and certain elements or components become dominant for reaction while others become ineffective. This constitutes a "set" to react to certain elements. Such an organization is in part described by gestalt principles of perception, in part by principles of attention.

2. In any trial of a training series, only those components of the stimulating situation which are dominant in the organization are associated. Other stimuli which excite the receptors are not associated because the animal is not set to react to them.

From these assumptions it follows that learning will not be continuously cumulative throughout training but will vary with the perceptual organization and "set" of the animal. It follows also that the discriminative reaction will usually be based upon only a limited part of the total number of differentiating properties of the stimuli. The cues to which the animals react will depend upon the particular perceptual organization which was dominant during learning. This dominance is regarded as the result of (a) an active process of comparing by which the traces of the two stimuli are brought into a common perceptual field and (b) inherent organizing tendencies which concentrate activity upon the "conspicuous" differences between the stimuli. The particular aspects of the stimulus which are associated cannot be predicted on the basis of the theory of differential conditioning.

In my original statement I suggested (10) that position reactions, responses to irrelevant cues, and the like, represent attempts at solution of the problem and that practice during such false attempts is ineffective for learning. The phrase "attempt at solution" is anthropomorphic but conforms with the usage in older descriptions of learning by trial and error, which did not imply voluntarism. To clarify the phrase in conformity with the above assumptions requires elaboration. The animal comes to the situation with certain perceptual and sensory-motor organizations. The situation elicits these in an order which is unexplained (perhaps "chance," or relative excitability of different systems) but is clearly not a simple function of the external situation. To say that the animal "tries" one organized response implies no more than that the reaction to one rather than another of two physically equivalent stimuli is determined by some unknown internal factor. To ascribe other meaning to the statement is to admit that man has some volitional function which animals lack. Some phases of the discussion may have arisen from the ambiguity of this expression, but the major issue concerns the effectiveness of practice during the dominance of aspects of the problem situation other than those to be learned.

Since the postulated shifts of perceptual organization are difficult to demonstrate in an animal, the occurrence of systematic position reactions or systematic errors is accepted as indicative of a set to react to spacial or kinesthetic cues which may prevent the association of simultaneously acting differential stimuli. For this reason discussion has centered on the question whether association with the stimulus-to-be-learned occurs during the dominance of reaction to position. Absence of systematic errors does not preclude the existence of some other set or perceptual organization which might interfere with learning but, if this exists, it must then be revealed through some other form of behavior, difficult to identify at present.

Indecisive Experiments

Two types of experiment designed to test the regularly cumulative effect of practice have been reported. Using the string-pulling technique, McCulloch and Pratt (14) trained different groups of rats with one of two weights positive for certain numbers of trials, then reversed training and determined the amount of interference resulting. They found retarding effects from all amounts of initial negative training, roughly proportional to the number of errors made. Krechevsky (8) repeated the experiment using a difficult problem of visual discrimination and obtained opposite results. These two experiments have been exhaustively discussed (7, 8, 9, 13, 15, 16, 19).

As his major criticism of Krechevsky's experiment Spence has stressed the possibility that the conditions were not adequate for stimulation. He repeats that "the mere presence of the cue stimulus somewhere in the experimental situation does not guarantee its impingement on the ani-

mal's sensorium at or near the critical moment of response." "Impingement on the sensorium" is ambiguous. Hull (4, p. 11) identifies it with
making a "junction with the system of visual end organs," which perhaps
means excitation of receptor cells. The rat's visual field includes something more than 300 degrees. The binocular field covers between 50 and
100 degrees, depending on convergence (11). When the animal orients
to jump in the discrimination apparatus the image of the differential stimulus necessarily falls on the binocular field of the retinae, so that the
question of adequate stimulation seemed controlled in Krechevsky's experiment. However, Spence now seems to require that the animal "look
at" a particular "aspect" of the situation (19, p. 432) and suggests that
when the rat fixates the lower part of the stimulus cards the stimuli on
the upper part of the cards (12 degrees distant) do not impinge on its
sensorium. "They did not 'see' the rows of black squares because they
were fixating other aspects of the stimulus complex." These statements
imply that the "sensorium" is identified with "focus of attention," and
both Spence and McCulloch indicate that they consider such statements
to be, in fact, a discussion of attention. If so, the original proposition
becomes "all stimuli in the focus of attention at the time of response
become associated with that response," and their whole discussion becomes pointless. If not, the criticism of Krechevsky's experiment is invalid.
The outcome of this discussion of the McCulloch and Pratt experiment is
that the proponents of each theory have suggested possible but unproved
defects in the experiment unfavorable to their assumptions and the results
remain contradictory and inconclusive. . . .[3]

Test of the Major Hypotheses

The question whether all stimuli acting at the time of response become
associated with the response or whether the set of the animal determines
a selective association can be tested by very simple experiments.[4] If the
animal is given a preliminary organization or set to respond to one component of a stimulus and then is trained in a situation where this component is combined with another, conditioned-reflex theory requires that
both components be associated. The alternate theory predicts that no
new association will be formed, provided that the new component does
not arouse a perceptual organization dominant over the first.

These alternatives were tested by the following experiments: Four rats

[3] EDITORS' NOTE: Most of pages 245 to 257 of original article are not reproduced here.
[4] Spence published his original formulation as a theory of discriminative learning (16)
without limitation as to the kind of stimuli discriminated. Later (17) he applied the theory
to the discriminative learning of visual forms. We are now informed (19) that ". . . the
manner in which complex patterns are reacted to is not dealt with at all. Indeed the whole
problem of patterning is omitted from discussion because our present interest is centered
on the learning process *in situations where the perceptual response is as simple as possible.*"
Since the simplicity of a perceptual response cannot be defined in terms of the objective
situation, the theory may no longer be capable of factual evaluation.

were trained to choose the larger of two circles, 10 and 6 cm. in diameter, averaging 95 trials, 14 errors for learning. This, presumably, established a set to react on the basis of size. When they had reached the criterion of 20 successive errorless trials, an equilateral triangle, 10 cm. to the side, was substituted for the larger circle. All chose the triangle without error in 10 critical trials. They were then given 200 training trials with the large triangle positive, the small circle negative, making an average of 1.5 errors in the 200 trials.[5] Two hundred trials is more than twice the usual practice required for learning triangle vs. circle as an initial problem. By conditioned-reflex theory this training should have established a discriminative reaction to the triangle and circle as figures, since the new stimuli (or stimulus components) receive facilitation throughout 200 trials and should therefore be associated with the reaction.

The next step in the experiment was to present the animals with a triangle and circle of equal surface area (50 sq. cm.) in critical trials, that is, in preference tests. In 20 trials with new figures, each of the animals jumped to one door of the apparatus, right or left, in 19 or 20 trials, showing no preference whatever for either triangle or circle. Retraining with the large triangle and small circle for 20 trials (without error) was next followed by preference trials with a small triangle and large circle, reversing the size relations. All animals chose the large circle in 20 of 20 critical trials. In spite of the opportunity for association of reaction with the differentiating shapes of the figures and the absence of any common attributes of form in the positive and negative situations which might extinguish such an association, form was not associated.

Several experiments of this general pattern have been carried out with essentially the same result. If the animals are given a set to react to one aspect of a stimulus situation, large amounts of training do not establish association with other aspects, so long as the original set remains effective for reaching the food. In the one instance where a suggestion of association with the new aspect of the stimulus appeared, the patterns added to the original size difference were conspicuously different and of such a character as to obscure somewhat the difference in size; a six-pointed star with long points vs. a triangle of larger surface area but smaller linear dimensions.

Such experiments flatly contradict the fundamental proposition of the conditioned-reflex theory of discriminative learning. In terms of excitatory

[5] This procedure rules out questions of the sensory adaptation of the animal, such as were raised in criticism of the experiment of Krechevsky. In order to react to the "size" of an object the animal must fixate the object. Size is not a function of a part of the object but of the whole object. (The possibility that reaction is to a limited part, as to the curvature of a side, has been eliminated by many experiments in which marked changes in form do not disturb a reaction associated with size.) There is no peripheral mechanism which will fixate or focus the size of an object and not its form. If the size of the object stimulates the sense organ, so must its form.

value for the reaction the first training, in the experiment reported, facilitates reaction to the larger circle by the effects of 81 positive reactions and reduces the excitatory value of the smaller by whatever amount 14 punished errors may give. Two hundred trials add to the excitatory value of "large" by a proportionate amount, and 1.5 errors detract from "small." At the same time the *forms* receive the same or a greater amount of facilitation. Even though the curve of effectiveness of training is one of diminishing returns, the reduced effects after the initial training should apply only to the initial stimuli, so that the relative effects of the later 200 trials would be greater for form than for size. When the animals are presented with forms of equal size, since in association the various components of the stimulus have single additive function in arousing response (4), the positive stimulus still has left, after the subtraction of 81 units of excitatory value, the 200 units from the second training series. Similarly, the negative stimulus loses 14 units of inhibition but has remaining the additional 1.5. The difference of 201.5 greatly exceeds the amount necessary to arouse a differential reaction. This, however, does not occur.

There are a number of recorded experiments which show that, even without an experimentally induced set, the animal usually associates only a few of the stimuli with respect to which the positive and negative situations differ. Chang (1) trained rats in a differential reaction between figures which differed with respect to both size and form. Those animals which were trained to choose the larger of the two figures reacted exclusively on the basis of size, those trained with the small figure positive reacted exclusively to the form. The reason for selection of the specific properties is irrelevant to the present argument. In each case the association involved only one of the discriminable properties of the stimuli.

I have reported a variety of experiments in which, after animals had been trained in differential reaction to complex patterns of stimuli, tests to determine the basis of reaction showed that (*a*) parts of stimulus patterns which might have served as differentiating cues acquired no excitatory value for the reaction; (*b*) differentiating dimensions, size, brightness, pattern and the like may remain unassociated; (*c*) individual differences between animals with respect to what is associated are so great that only rarely can the selection be ascribed to the conditions of training; (*d*) elements of the situation which are associated are generally those which combine readily according to gestalt laws of perception; (*e*) items which are not readily organized into figures (dots scattered at random, for example) cannot be associated with a differential reaction, within the usual limits of training (12).

All such evidence is inconsistent with the proposition that all stimuli which affect the sense organs during a reaction are associated with that reaction. The experiments which have been reported as supporting the continuity theory have been shown to be inconclusive and evidence from more direct tests of the matter is decisively opposed to the theory. Only those stimuli or aspects of a stimulus to which the animal is set to react during training will elicit the discriminative reaction after training.

The bearing of systematic position errors upon the problem remains undetermined. There is no positive evidence that learning of the differential stimuli occurs while the animal is set to react to position and inference from the influence of set toward other aspects of the stimulus situation leads to the conclusion that such learning probably does not occur. The matter is of slight importance, however, since the major premise of the continuity theory has been shown by other methods to be false.

Other Forms of Conditioned-reflex Theory

A variant of conditioned-reflex theory of discriminative learning is that of Gulliksen and Wolfle (2). These authors do not assume, as does Spence, that all simultaneously acting stimuli are associated with the response, but that directional reactions are associated with the positive and negative stimuli as a unit. That is, the combined stimuli on the two doors of the jumping apparatus constitute a single configuration and the interchange of the figures on the two doors produces a different total configuration. With one of these the animal associates a jump to the right and with the other, a jump to the left (primary assumption).

In support of this assumption the authors describe an experiment. The jumping apparatus was arranged to present a large and a small circle which throughout training were kept in a constant position. Rats were trained to jump to one of these, e.g., always to the large circle on the right. When this was learned the animals were tested by interchange of the two figures to determine whether they would react to the changed visual situation or would continue to jump to the same side of the apparatus. The majority continued the original direction of jumping. From this fact the authors conclude that the rats had learned a directional response. They then go on to develop a theory which assumes that the directional response was to the *visual stimuli*. "Seventeen of the 24 animals responded to the test configurations on a directional basis and only seven on a brightness basis." Of course the experiment shows nothing of the sort. With similar training blind rats would all have responded on a directional basis, but could scarcely have been accused of reaction to the test configurations. The experiment proves nothing except, perhaps, that the majority of rats do not develop discriminative reactions under such conditions.

Although the authors' elaborate development of their hypothesis is consistent with some facts of learning, the primary assumption is in direct contradiction to many established facts.

1. In an experiment reported earlier (12) I trained rats to choose one of three circles differing in size. Different animals were trained positive to the largest, to the intermediate, and to the smallest circle, exposed in a jumping stand with three doors. According to the hypothesis the permutations in position of the three figures give six configurations to be associated with three directional responses. The hypothesis predicts that the rate of learning will be the same, no matter which reaction is required to be associated with each configuration, since each association is an independent directional response to a distinct configuration (provided, of course, that there are no preexisting directional associations with any of the configurations, and in such experiments these are known to be slight and easily counteracted by training). The actual outcome of the experiment was that learning is quick when the smallest or largest circle is positive and impossible when the intermediate is positive. The prediction of the hypothesis is contrary to fact.

2. Animals were trained to a triangle and circle, triangle positive. The theory predicts that when two circles or two triangles are presented the animal's reaction will in either case be the same, since in both cases the configurations no longer present cues to directional response. Actually the animals jump readily to either triangle and refuse to jump to the circles. The prediction is contrary to fact.

It is unnecessary to cite further examples to prove that the fundamental postulate of the Gulliksen-Wolfle theory is false.

"Purposive" Character of "Attempts at Solution"

In comparing theories of discriminative learning I have refrained from discussing the "purposive" character of the behavior, which has aroused some earlier controversy, beyond pointing out that the phrase "attempt at solution" does not imply indeterminate behavior unless one assumes indeterminism in human choice reactions. Such expressions are objectionable because of the halo of metaphysical association which surrounds them and have, perhaps, led to some misunderstanding of the implications of the two opposed theories (19, p. 287).

The meaning which the phrase "attempt at solution" sought to convey, derived from the general conception of trial-and-error learning, is that reactions like alternation, left-going, or "seeing" the size of a visual figure, are organized reactions, in the sense that digging, gnawing, etc., in a problem-box situation are organized, independently of the immediate conditions of training. This implies further a functionally substitutive character of the various organizations.

When it comes to this aspect of the problem we are all in the same cul de sac. The objective fact is that when an animal has obtained food in a certain place he may later maintain a bodily orientation in the direction of that place, exhibiting patterns of movement not previously associated with the immediate situation but necessary to maintain the orientation. I have said that such behavior exhibits equivalence of reactions. Others have termed it "goal-directed behavior" and the like. Spence presupposes it in his statement, "It may be assumed that the organism has acquired, in its past experience, reaction tendencies of orienting toward and approaching each of the stimuli . . ." (16, p. 434). Krechevsky seeks to relate the sensory-motor components of the discriminative reactions to the same problem, saying in Tolmanesque language, that not only is orientation maintained by substitution of motor patterns but by substitution of perceptual organizations (7). None of us has done more with the problem than to state it in terms which are derived from and related to our individual fields of interest. All the statements represent efforts to escape from the implications of a metaphysical finalism, but no solution of the problem.

Quantitative Hypotheses in Theories of Discriminative Learning

In the quantitative formulation of his theory Spence has sought to account for the successive appearance of the organized reactions in terms of relative increase or decrease of the excitatory values of the stimuli through the effects of repetitive association. This may be possible, by making certain additional assumptions concerning the relative excitability of various perceptual organizations, but there are indications that the ease with which various configurations are organized in perception does not obey simple quantitative laws and is relatively independent of external conditions of stimulation, so that whether a rat sees and reacts to the size or shape of an entire figure, or to only a corner of it, or to the distance from the frame, and the order in which such reactions appear cannot be defined as a function of the number of facilitations or inhibitions which each of these receives during training. Certain perceptual configurations may "spring out" of a situation as a result of determining factors too obscure and complex for present analysis and may completely change the rate of learning. Thus a figure lacking identifiability (20, p. 88) may be impossible of memorization (recognition) until some portion of it is suddenly perceived as the crude outline of a familiar object. This one experience then suffices for future recognition.

Perhaps the basic difference in point of view which has given rise to this discussion is with respect to the origin of perceptual organization. Pavlov and his followers have assumed that all elements of a stimulus which excite the receptor are, primitively, equally effective for behavior, and have sought to account for perceptual organization in terms of stimulus contiguity and repetition. Opposed to this is the view that perceptual organization is a function of inherent characteristics (nervous structure) of the organism and always antedates association. Such a conception should, in turn, be distinguished from that expressed in field theories, which seem to hold that the process of organization (closure) is identical with fixation in memory.

I am not unsympathetic with the type of quantitative theory which members of the Pavlovian group have been trying to develop. Learning theory must ultimately be cast in some such form, if it is to deal adequately with the established quantitative relations between practice and improvement. But a survey of the phenomena of learning suggests that other variations in addition to repetitive facilitation must be taken into account as important factors in determining the rate of association in discriminative learning. One of those variables is the ease with which figural organization can be imposed upon physically independent items in the stimulus. For the present this variable cannot be quantified and until it can be, quantitative theories of learning are apt to prove abortive.

Summary

The fundamental proposition of theories of discriminative learning, as derived from general conditioned-reflex theory, is that all stimuli which are exciting the receptors during a reaction are associated with that reaction. From this the "continuity theory" of discriminative learning has been derived. Experiments published in support of the continuity theory have been examined and showned to be indecisive. Other evidence has been presented which is incompatible with the assumptions of that theory.

REFERENCES

1. Chang, M. Transposition of size- and pattern-discrimination in the white rat, *Sci. Rep. Nat. Tsing Hua Univ.*, 1936, **2** (B), 89–110.
2. Gulliksen, H., and Wolfle, D. L. A theory of learning and transfer, *Psychometrika*, 1938, **3**, 128–149, 225–251.
3. Hull, C. L. A functional interpretation of the conditioned reflex, *Psychol. Rev.*, 1929, **36**, 498–511.
4. Hull, C. L. The problem of stimulus equivalence in behavior theory, *Psychol. Rev.*, 1939, **46**, 9–30.
5. Krechevsky, I. "Hypotheses" versus "chance" in the pre-solution period in sensory discrimination-learning, *Univ. Calif. Publ. Psychol.*, 1932, **6**, 27–44.
6. Krechevsky, I. The genesis of "hypotheses" in rats, *Univ. Calif. Publ. Psychol.*, 1932, **6**, 45–64.
7. Krechevsky, I. A note concerning "the nature of discrimination learning in animals," *Psychol. Rev.*, 1937, **44**, 97–133.
8. Krechevsky, I. A study of the continuity of the problem-solving process, *Psychol. Rev.*, 1938, **45**, 107–133.
9. Krechevsky, I. An experimental investigation of the principle of proximity in the visual perception of the rat, *J. exp. Psychol.*, 1938, **22**, 497–523.

10. Lashley, K. S. *Brain mechanisms and intelligence.* Chicago: Univ. of Chicago Press, 1929.

11. Lashley, K. S. The mechanism of vision: V. The structure and image-forming power of the rat's eye, *J. comp. Psychol.*, 1932, **13**, 173–200.

12. Lashley, K. S. The mechanism of vision: XV. Preliminary studies of the rat's capacity for detail vision, *J. gen. Psychol.*, 1939, **18**, 123–193.

13. McCulloch, T. L. Comment on the formation of discrimination habits, *Psychol. Rev.*, 1939, **46**, 75–84.

14. McCulloch, T. L., and Pratt, J. G. A study of the pre-solution period in weight discrimination by white rats, *J. comp. Psychol.*, 1934, **18**, 271–290.

15. Pratt, J. G. An experimental analysis of the process of solving a weight discrimination problem in white rats, *J. comp. Psychol.*, 1938, **25**, 291–314.

16. Spence, K. W. The nature of discrimination learning in animals, *Psychol. Rev.*, 1936, **43**, 427–449.

17. Spence, K. W. Analysis of the formation of visual discrimination habits in the chimpanzee, *J. comp. Psychol.*, 1937, **23**, 77–100.

18. Spence, K. W. Gradual versus sudden solution of discrimination problems by chimpanzees, *J. comp. Psychol.*, 1939, **25**, 213–224.

19. Spence, K. W. Continuous versus non-continuous interpretations of discrimination learning, *Psychol. Rev.*, 1940, **47**, 271–288.

20. Thorndike, E. L. *Human learning.* New York: Century, 1931.

27. STUDIES OF CEREBRAL FUNCTION IN LEARNING. *XII. Loss of the Maze Habit after Occipital Lesions in Blind Rats* [1]

In a number of experiments dealing with the effects of cerebral damage in the rat a reliable correlation between the extent of surface destruction and the loss of efficiency in various tasks has been demonstrated. The correct interpretation of this relationship is still obscure. Several alternative explanations have been proposed and attempts made to test their validity, but lack of precise data concerning the extent of diverse functional areas of the rat's brain has rendered some of the tests inconclusive. Recent anatomic analysis of the sensory projection fields (11), supported by accumulated data on the sensory functions of the cortex, now makes possible a more thorough control of important variables. The principal factors which might produce increasing deterioration with increasing size of lesion, together with such controls as have been previously reported, are listed below.

1. **Indirect Effects of the Lesion.** Damage to the central nervous system might cause a lowered efficiency of nervous tissue not involved in the lesion through the toxic action of products of cell degeneration, changes in circulation with resultant trophic disturbances (17), mechanical distortion and pressure, or diaschisis (16). The action of such agencies has sometimes been assumed to be proportionate to the extent of the lesion. These suggestions have been effectively ruled out by experiments showing (*a*) that the quantitative relation persists for long intervals after the cerebral insult (9, 14); (*b*) that mechanical distortion by dilatation of the ventricles with resultant circulatory changes does not produce deterioration (13); and (*c*) that small remnants of a cortical area may carry on their specialized functions in an apparently normal manner (1, 9).

2. **Invasion of Critical Areas.** The performance of any given function may be dependent upon the normal activity of some limited cortical area. If so, the larger the lesion, the greater the chance of invading this critical area and destroying the function. I have shown that the correlation between extent of lesion in the occipital cortex and postoperative loss of habits based on brightness dis-

[1] EDITORS' NOTE: From *J. comp. Neurol.*, 1943, **79**, 431–462. Reproduced by permission of The Wistar Institute. From Harvard University and Yerkes Laboratories of Primate Biology.

crimination is due to the relative frequency of invasion of the binocular projection field by small and large lesions (10). However, in other tasks such as maze running the relation between extent of lesion and deterioration of performance is equally close and the possibility of a single critical area is precluded by the fact that deterioration is produced by lesions in different parts of the cortex which involve no common area.

3. **Summated Sensory Defects.** Learning the maze and similar tasks involves the integration of visual, olfactory, tactile, and other sensory cues. The larger the lesion, the greater the chance of depriving the animal of more than one of these sense modalities and so reducing the number of cues available for orientation or of destroying the sensory basis of preexisting habits. Hunter (6) and Finley (4) have pointed out that, although loss of one sense modality may have little effect on maze performance, combined loss of two or more modalities may produce serious deterioration (2) and have assumed that loss of the maze habit after cerebral lesions is primarily due to sensory defects. Tests of the influence of sense privation of central origin have taken three forms:

a. The effects of peripheral sense privation have been compared with the effects of destruction of the corresponding cerebral sensory fields. It has been found that cerebral lesions produce a more serious deterioration than does peripheral sense privation, even when several sense modalities are impaired (10, pp. 24–28).

b. Since different senses do not contribute equally to maze learning, lesions of the same magnitude should not produce equal degrees of deterioration. A first study (9) indicated equal deterioration from equal lesions in different areas but a later study (14) gave equivocal results.

c. The theory of strict localization ascribes diverse and unique functions to each cortical area. On such a theory a primary sensory area such as the area striata has no other function than the integration of excitation from its particular sense organ. Consequently, if a sense modality is eliminated by removal of the sense organ, the corresponding sensory area of the cortex should play no further part in the activities of the animal and its destruction should not affect habits acquired after sense privation.

To test this assumption, animals blinded by enucleation of the eyes were trained in a maze, then subjected to operation which destroyed the visual cortex, and tested for retention of the habit. Lesions in the occipital region were found to be as effective in eliminating the maze habit in such animals as in animals trained with vision (9, 20).

These various control experiments were carried out before the specialized areas of the rat's cortex had been accurately mapped. In most cases lesions involving one sensory area extended into one or more additional cortical fields. Finley (4) has recently emphasized the possible importance of slight invasion of one cortical field when combined with total destruction of another. The value of this suggestion is questionable, since small lesions generally produce little disturbance in the functions of a specialized field, but the available evidence on the influence of such composite lesions is inconclusive and a more comprehensive study of the matter is required before the cumulative effect of loss of diverse sensory functions can be evaluated.

4. Progressive Invasion of "Association Areas" with Increasing Size of Lesion. No direct tests of this possibility are available. I have reported in various past experiments the records of cases with destruction of possible association areas by small lesions without significant loss of the maze habit, so that it is clear that the habit is not dependent upon any single associative area.

5. Interference with Interaction of Diverse Functional Areas. Cerebral lesions may interrupt specific transcortical connections between areas not directly damaged. Thus deterioration following a lesion might express both the loss of a specific cortical area and interference with the functional interaction of other areas, the latter in proportion to the extent of damage. The importance of long transcortical connections seems to have been somewhat exaggerated, since recent anatomic studies fail to reveal the elaborate system of transcortical fibers described by earlier anatomists (3). I have found that partial isolation of the visual cortex does not seriously affect its function in the control of reactions to complex visual situations (12).

6. Reduced Dynamic Action of the Cortex. Goltz (5) first called attention to the relation between extent of lesion and degree of intellectual defect. He sought to explain the relation as a result of a reduction in the capacity for attention. Because of the apparent equality of effects of cerebral lesions in various areas upon maze learning and retention I have suggested that various parts of the cortex have some common function and that destruction of any region may reduce the efficiency of the rest. This is a sort of residual hypothesis which cannot at present be tested directly and receives support only if the more concrete theories of localization and interaction of specific functions prove inadequate to account for the effects of cerebral lesions.

In indirect support of this hypothesis the evidence for loss of the maze habit after destruction of the visual cortex by animals which were peripherally blinded before training was cited as showing that the visual cortex has some function in maze learning in addition to visual reception (9). Since the lesions in those blind animals extended beyond the limits now established for the area striata, the experiments failed to establish loss of the habit from damage to the visual area alone.

Object of the Present Experiments

Ideally, a conclusive test for nonvisual functions of the visual cortex should consist of training peripherally blinded animals, then measuring the effect of lesions strictly limited to the area striata. Such an experiment is practically impossible since the minimal size of lesion which produces measurable deterioration of maze performance approximates the area of the visual cortex and since the topographic relations of the area striata are such that extensive damage to it necessarily involves some damage to adjacent structures. The complementary experiment involving comparison in blind animals of destruction of the striate cortex plus adjacent areas with destruction of those areas alone is also impracticable because destruction of retrosplenial areas and of the dorsal convexity of the hippocampus cannot be carried out without extensive damage to the overlying visual areas.

It is possible, however, to compare the effects of total destruction of the striate areas plus adjacent structures with the effects of interruption of sensory paths to the occipital lobes, to determine whether loss of the maze habit after occipital lesions is due to other sensory defects in addition to blindness. It is also possible in a series of cases with occipital lesions to determine whether the invasion of any particular area, in addition to the visual, contributes to deterioration of the habit, and to test the effects of damage to at least some of the more accessible nonvisual structures, such as the hippocampal lobes, upon the maze performance of blind animals.

The experiments reported below were planned to give data on the following points: (a) The effects of peripheral blindness upon maze performance. (b) The effects of cutting the posterior thalamic radiation with minimal damage to the cortex. This operation destroys most if not all of the sensory connections of the occipital lobe and also, in a majority of cases, resulted in extensive damage to the hippocampal lobes. (c) The effects of total destruction of the striate cortex, with some adjacent areas, on the performance of animals which had learned to traverse the maze without visual cues. (d) Comparative effects of destruction of the striate area in combination with various adjacent structures.

Topographic Relations of the Rat's Visual Cortex

The cortical projection of the rat's visual system seems to be limited to the area striata, as identified by the granular structure of lamina IV. The following description is based upon a comparison of the rat's cortex with the figures and criteria given by Rose (18) for the mouse and my previous study of the projection of the sensory thalamus (11). The mesial and occipital borders of the area striata are bounded by the area peristriata and by the area retrosplenialis agranularis, which forms the lip of the longitudinal fissure and the caudal margin of the hemisphere (Fig. 27.1). The lateral margin of the striate area is in contact with the area ectorhinalis and with the projection field of the lateral nucleus, pars posterior. The latter seems to be a continuation of the area parietalis. Rose describes an area occipitalis adjacent to the anterolateral margin of the striate area but I doubt the functional validity of this division. The mesial portion of his area occipitalis certainly receives fibers from the lateral nucleus and the lateral portion from the medial geniculate nucleus.

The anterior margin of the striate area is bounded by the area parietalis, which is the projection field of the nucleus lateralis, pars principalis. The presubicular and subicular areas underlie the caudal portion of the striate area and the cephalic margin of the area covers the dorsal convexity of the cornu Ammonis.

The total thickness of the visual cortex does not exceed 2 mm., so that it is impossible to remove it without some damage to underlying structures.

Plan of Experiments

Three groups of animals were used to test the effects of peripheral and cortical blinding and of occipital lesions.

Group I. Blinded by enucleation of the eyes. Trained to errorless performance in the maze.

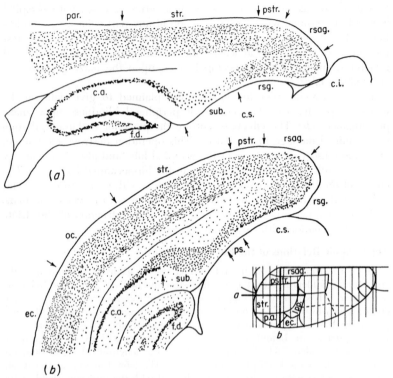

Fig. 27.1. Sketches of sagittal (a) and coronal (b) sections of the rat's cortex to show topographic relations. c.a., cornu Ammonis; c.i., inferior colliculus; c.s., superior colliculus; ec., area ectorhinalis; f.d., fascia dentata; l.p.p., field of lateral nudeus, pars posterior; oc., area occipitalis; p.a., post-auditory area; par., area parietalis; ps., area presubicularis; pstr., area peristriata; rsag., area retrosplenialis agranularis; rsg., area retrosplenialis granularis; str., area striata; sub., subiculum. × 14.

Group II. Normal animals trained in the maze; eyes enucleated; retrained to errorless performance (postblind retention tests).

Groups I and II combined. When both groups had reached errorless performance without visual cues the striate areas were destroyed. After 10 to 15 days for recovery they were retrained for fifty trials (postoccipital retention test). The average scores for the two groups in this test were not reliably different, so the data have been treated together.

Group III. Normal animals trained to errorless performance in the maze. Incisions were made with a fine knife through the posterior thalamic radiation on each side. After 10 days for recovery they were retrained to the criterion. These animals were selected from a large number used in another experiment to test the effects of cutting various thalamo-cortical paths. All cases from the larger series involving extensive damage to the optic radiation were included, except four, which were excluded because of extensive damage to or complete isolation of the visual cortex, invasion of the colliculi, or complete destruction of the radiation of the ventral nucleus.

Methods

Animals. Male black rats from a strain derived from a cross of Wistar albinos with trapped wild were used. They averaged 120 days of age at the beginning of the experiment.

Operations. All operations were performed under deep ether anesthesia. The thalamic radiations were cut with a small iris knife. The visual cortex was destroyed by thermocautery.

Histological Methods. The brains were sectioned and stained with thionin. Cortical lesions were reconstructed by the usual graphic method. The diagrams used to represent them were prepared to show the projection fields of the various thalamic nuclei (11). The cross lines represent intervals of 1 mm. in the adult brain.

All of the thalamic nuclei of each brain were examined for retrograde degeneration and that found was recorded on a 5-point scale ranging from 0 to 4, the highest figure indicating degeneration as severe as that following hemidecortication.

The areas surrounding the occipital lesion were examined and damage to the retrosplenial, subicular, and ectorhinal areas, and to the hippocampal lobes, which would not be revealed by study of the thalamus, was recorded. Damage to the hippocampi is shown on a diagram representing these structures unrolled on a horizontal plane.

Training. With food as incentive, the rats were trained in an eight cul de sac, rectangular, enclosed maze (9, maze III) with five trials per day to a criterion of five consecutive errorless trials. The floor of the maze was arranged with electric contacts wired to a counter, so that errors were summed automatically for each trial. After training all animals were given a rest period of 10 days, then retrained to the criterion before operation.

Effect of Peripheral Blinding upon Initial Learning

For groups [I (blind) and II (normal)] the average scores in initial learning [2] were the following:

[2] EDITORS' NOTE: Four tables giving original training and postoperative retraining scores for individual animals as well as the analysis of the lesions of individual animals have not been reproduced. Group I consisted of 23 animals, group II of 19 animals, and group III of 11 animals.

	Trials		Errors	
Group II (normal)	17.4 ± 1.2	σ = 7.4	50.4 ± 3.9	σ = 25.6
Group I (blind)	23.7 ± 1.2	σ = 8.7	116.0 ± 9.1	σ = 64.0
Difference	6.3 ± 1.7		65.6 ± 10.0	
Percentage difference	37		131	

The blind animal is evidently slower in learning than is the normal. He wanders somewhat at random, retraces frequently, and gives less evidence of early generalization of direction in the maze. The error score is much increased above the normal. The number of trials required for learning is, however, not much greater than that required by normal animals and the difference is barely reliable. The proportionately greater increase in error scores than in trial scores produced by blinding indicates that although the blind animal has difficulty in gaining orientation, he has relatively little difficulty in remembering the correct path once orientation has been acquired or adequate cues identified.

Effect of Peripheral Blinding upon Retention

The importance of visual cues for maze learning is also indicated by the inaccuracy of maze performance following the blinding of animals which learned the maze with vision intact. . . . The average scores for the group are the following:

	Trials		Errors	
Initial learning	17.4 ± 1.2	σ = 7.4	50.4 ± 3.9	σ = 25.6
Preliminary retention	2.5 ± 0.5	σ = 3.2	1.4 ± 0.2	σ = 1.6
Postblind retention	11.6 ± 1.6	σ = 10.7	46.3 ± 7.1	σ = 46.3

As in initial learning by blind animals, the error score is more seriously affected than that for trials. Postblind relearning required 65 per cent of the trials and 86 per cent of the errors for initial learning. The variability of performance is greatly increased; the standard coefficient of variability for both trials and errors in postblind retention tests is double that for initial learning. Some of the animals were little disturbed by blinding (e.g., numbers 24, 31, 33); others required as much practice for relearning as did members of group I for initial learning.

There is a significant correlation between the initial and postblind training scores of group II for both trials and errors; $p = 0.48 \pm 0.12$. The slower learners among normal animals were those most dependent on vision. This fact confirms Krechevsky's observation (7) that "maze-dull" rats are visually dominant.

These tests after enucleation of the eyes give a measure of the effect of peripheral blinding for comparison with that of cortical damage. The range of postblind loss is from perfect retention to a maximum of 42 trials with 178 errors for relearning. The great variability in the extent to which different animals are dependent on vision in maze learning confirms a similar observation by Finley (4).

No increase in variability appears in the initial learning after blinding. The standard coefficients of variability for initial learning are for normal animals, 0.42 for trials and 0.51 for errors; for blind animals, 0.37 for trials and 0.55 for errors. Forced use by some rats of a nonpreferred sense does not retard their learning enough to spread the distribution. Finley has suggested that individual differences in the employment of different sense modalities will account for variation in the effects of identical lesions, which I have reported previously. The explanation is plausible as applied to postoperative retention but is not applicable to initial learning after brain lesions, where the variability of effect of similar lesions is equally great, unless further assumptions are made concerning the reduction of the general plasticity of the animal by cerebral damage (8).

Effect of Interrupting the Posterior Thalamic Radiation

The animals of group III were trained with vision intact to the criterion, and given preoperative retention tests. The posterior radiation was then cut with a minimum of damage to the overlying cortex. After a 10-day rest period the rats were again trained to the criterion. . . . Their average scores, in comparison with those of group II after peripheral blinding, are given below.

	Initial learning		Preoperative retention		Postoperative retention	
	Trials	Errors	Trials	Errors	Trials	Errors
Group III (central)	14.8±1.4	48.0±6.0	3.6±0.5	4.4±0.7	6.8±1.2	43.1±11.8
Group II (peripheral)	17.4±1.2	50.4±3.9	2.5±0.5	1.4±0.2	11.6±1.6	46.3± 7.1
Difference	3.6±1.8	2.4±7.2	1.1±0.7	3.0±0.9	4.8±2.0	3.2±13.8

The scores of these two groups are closely comparable throughout. The rats with interruption of the posterior radiation made a slightly better trial score in postoperative tests than did the peripherally blinded rats, but the difference is not reliable and the error scores are almost identical. Variability of the two groups was about equal, ranging in postoperative tests from nearly perfect retention to requirement of more practice than for initial learning.

In one animal of group III, number 53, there was extensive damage to the thalamus with interruption of the optic tracts, destruction of the lateral geniculate nuclei and of the pretectal region and of part of the ventral nucleus. If the score of this animal is omitted, the postoperative averages for the remainder are reduced to 5.5 ± 1.0 trials and 27.2 ± 6.5 errors.

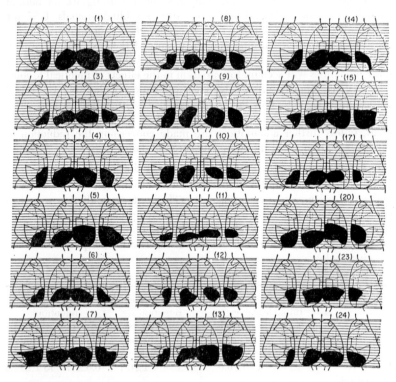

Fig. 27.2. Diagrams of cerebral lesions in animals number 1 to 24 of groups I and II.

The brains of the rats in group III were analyzed for thalamic degeneration and injuries to cortical and subcortical structures. The cortical lesions are shown in Fig. 27.3, numbers 43 to 52. . . . In four of the animals the optic radiation had been completely interrupted. In two of these the auditory radiations were also completely destroyed (numbers 44 and 51). In the majority the radiations of the pars posterior of the lateral nuclei were completely interrupted. In other cases there was rather extensive invasion of the fields of the ventral nuclei. Number 51 shows the most extensive damage including total degeneration of the lateral and medial geniculate nuclei, of the pars posterior of the lateral, and of the lateral and central divisions of the ventral nucleus, with subtotal degeneration of the lateral nucleus. The loss of the habit in this animal was little greater than the average loss produced by peripheral blinding.

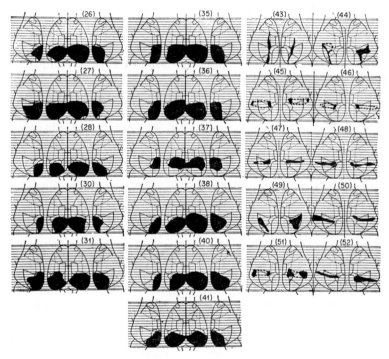

Fig. 27.3. Diagrams of cerebral lesions in animals number 26 to 41 of groups I and II, and of numbers 43 and 52 of group III. Cuts which interrupted projection fibers without damaging the cortex are represented by broken lines.

Eight of the eleven animals suffered damage to the hippocampal lobes. The locus and extent of damage are indicated in Fig. 27.4, numbers 44 to 52. The black areas on the diagrams represent total destruction of the fimbria, Ammonshorn and gyrus dentatus underlying them. Shallower lesions are indicated by stippling. The lesions in the hippocampal structures of this group equal in extent most of those produced in combination with destruction of the striate areas, described below, yet without causing greater loss of the habit than results from peripheral sense privation.

The data . . . suggest . . . that the size of the postoperative scores increases somewhat in proportion to the amount of damage to nonvisual structures. The maximal effect of such composite lesions is, however, not greater than the maximal produced by peripheral blinding and is far less than the average loss produced by destruction of the occipital cortex in groups I and II, reported below. The experiment shows that interruption of the optic and auditory radiations, even when combined with severe damage to the hippocampal lobes and invasion of the field of the ventral nucleus, does not produce a significantly greater loss than follows peripheral blinding.

Effects of Destruction of the Occipital Cortex in Animals Which Know the Maze without Visual Cues

Seventeen rats from group I and twelve from group II had reached the criterion of five consecutive errorless trials after peripheral blinding. They were rested for 10 days, retrained to the criterion, and subjected to destruction of the occipital cortex. As stated above, the postoperative scores of the two groups were not significantly different, so they have been combined for statistical treatment. . . . The cortical lesions and damage to the hippocampal lobes are shown in Figs. 27.2 and 27.3, numbers 1 to 41. The brains were analyzed for retrograde degeneration in the thalamic nuclei. . . .

Only one of the twenty-nine animals (number 4) reached the criterion of five consecutive errorless trials within fifty trials of retraining. The others were all making numerous errors at the end of fifty trials, when the experiment had to be discontinued. Their average scores for the fifty postoperative trials are given below in comparison with the corresponding scores of the animals with interruption of the posterior thalamic radiation, no one of which required as many as 50 trials for relearning.

	Groups	Trials	Errors
Occipital lesions	(I and II)	50+	415.9 ± 25.9
Posterior radiation	(III)	6.8 ± 1.2	43.1 ± 11.8

Extrapolation of the learning curves indicates that the group would not have reached the criterion with an average of less than 700 errors. Compared with the effects of peripheral blinding or of interruption of the posterior thalamic radiation, destruction of the occipital cortex produces a far greater deterioration. Even though training was not continued to the criterion, almost ten times as many errors were made after occipital lesion as after peripheral blinding.

In all cases there was total degeneration of the lateral geniculate nuclei, showing that the entire visual cortex had been destroyed or cut off from the thalamus. In addition there was some invasion of adjacent structures in all cases. Interpretation of the results therefore requires an evaluation of the effects on maze performance of the lesions outside of the striate cortex.

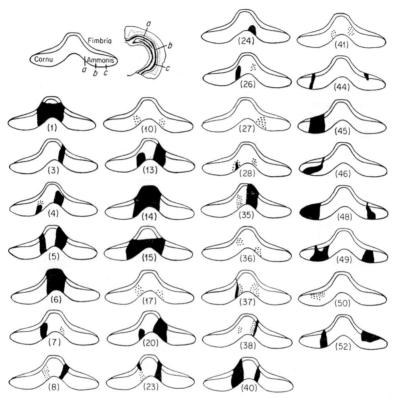

Fig. 27.4. Diagrams of lesions to the hippocampal lobes and fimbria. The lobes are represented as unrolled with proportions as indicated at the left above. Superficial injuries not reaching the fascia dentata are stippled; deeper lesions solid black. Numbers 1 to 41, animals of groups I and II; numbers 44 to 52, animals of group III.

Comparison of Effects of Destruction of the Visual Cortex in Combination with Various Other Structures

Tectum. In three animals there was invasion of the colliculi. They were number 6 with 875 errors, number 14 with 962 errors, and number 35 with 453 errors. The first two of these had nearly total bilateral destruction of the inferior colliculi; the third only a slight invasion on the left. The average errors for these three animals is 763.3, as compared with 375.4 for the remaining twenty-six. Except for injury to the colliculi, their lesions did not differ significantly from those of other animals in the group. Although the number of cases is too small to give reliability to the difference, the conclusion seems justified that the midbrain lesions in numbers 6 and 14 were responsible for the marked retardation. The cases with midbrain lesions have therefore been excluded from analyses of effects of damage to other structures.

Hippocampal Lobes. Lesions to the hippocampus are shown in Fig. 27.4. For comparative treatment the lesions were grouped into five classes: 0, no injury; 1, shallow injuries, not penetrating to the fascia dentata; 2, deeper injuries, without section of the fimbria; 3, deep injuries with unilateral section of the fimbria; 4, deep injuries with bilateral section of the fimbria. . . .

Grade of lesion	Number of cases	Average errors
0	5	391.4
1	8	335.1
2	2	266.5
3	6	438.6
4	5	393.6

These figures give no indication of any trend corresponding to the degree of injury to the hippocampal structures. The averages for animals without injury and for those with maximal injury are almost identical.

In some animals of group III, with interruption of the posterior radiation there was damage to the hippocampus as great as in many cases after occipital destruction. These lesions are shown in Fig. 27.4, numbers 44 to 52. A similar classification of cases gives the following averages for group III, omitting number 53, because of the severe damage to the thalamus:

Grade of lesion	Number of cases	Average errors
0	3	32.3
3	3	12.0
4	3	38.3

Two of the animals with maximal hippocampal lesion and one in each of the other groups of three had a total degeneration of both lateral geniculate nuclei. The combination of total cortical blindness with damage to the hippocampus produced no such loss of the maze habit as followed destruction of the occipital cortex. In group III the lateral convexities of the hippocampus were chiefly involved; with occipital lesions, the dorsal convexities. There is, however, no reason to assume that one part of the hippocampus is more important for maze learning than another.

Auditory Cortex. In twelve of the twenty-nine animals of groups I and II there were indications of degeneration in one or both medial geniculate nuclei. The average of errors for these twelve cases was 369. The average for the fourteen cases in which no degeneration of the medial geniculates could be detected was 381 errors. Invasion of the auditory cortex produced no increase in errors.

Field of the Anterior Nuclei. In eight of the animals there was no trace of degeneration in the anterodorsal or anteroventral nuclei. The others showed for the most part slight degeneration in the dorsolateral margins of the nuclei. The average for cases without degeneration was 338 errors; for cases with degeneration of the anterior nuclei, 392 errors. The difference is not reliable and certainly does not indicate any pronounced differential effect of invasion of the retrosplenial area.

Field of the Lateral Nucleus, Pars Posterior. In practically all of the animals the posterior part of the lateral nucleus, adjacent to the lateral geniculate nucleus, showed total or subtotal degeneration. Effects of damage to its cortical field therefore cannot be determined by comparison of cases in groups I and II. However, the radiation to this field was totally interrupted bilaterally in six cases of group III without significant increase in error scores above that of animals without such interruption. Further, the pars posterior of the lateral nucleus probably receives fibers from the optic tract. It certainly has no other primary sensory supply, so its cortical field must be classed as either a visual receptive or a visual associative area.

Field of the Lateral Nucleus, Pars Principalis. In twelve cases the pars principalis was normal. The average error score for these was 353, whereas for the fourteen cases with some degeneration of the nucleus the average was 395 errors. The difference is not reliable and does not indicate any significant effect of the slight invasion of the area parietalis.

Subicular Area and Caudal Pole. At its caudal pole the striate cortex adjoins a field included by Rose (18) in the area retrosplenialis agranularis which, however, does not appear to receive fibers from the anterior nuclei. The striate area also overlies the subicular area, which was damaged in a few cases. The average for thirteen cases with damage to one or both of these regions was 379 errors; for cases without such damage the average was 372 errors. The difference is not significant and there is no indication that either the subicular areas or the caudal part of the retrosplenial are especially significant for the maze habit.

Postauditory Cortex. Lesions in the caudal portion of the area ectorhinalis are not followed by discoverable thalamic degeneration. I have suggested (11) that this region may be homologous to the lower temporal field of primates, which has few projection fibers (21). The area, caudad to the auditory cortex, was invaded in all animals, with a range from total destruction to almost no involvement. The cases were divided into four groups according to the amount of destruction of the region, from 1, with slight injury, to 4, with almost total destruction. The average error scores for the four grades were the following: (1) 470 errors; (2) 344 errors; (3) 392 errors; (4) 317 errors. There is no relation between the degree of involvement of the region and the amount of loss of the maze habit. In animals 43, 44, and 49 of group III, with an average of ten errors in relearning, there was invasion of the postauditory cortex as severe as in many cases with destruction of the visual cortex (e.g., numbers 12 and 30) and profound deterioration. No especial significance for maze performance can therefore be ascribed to the postauditory region.

Comparative figures for cases with and without damage to various cerebral structures are summarized in Table 27.1. In no case is there a reliable difference between the scores of animals with lesions in a particular structure and those without, instances where the scores were slightly increased by damage to one structure being balanced by an equal number where they were apparently decreased. If the severe deterioration of the cases with destruction of the occipital cortex is to be ascribed to the damage to such nonvisual structures, then no one seems to contribute more than any other to efficiency of performance.

The possibility remains to be tested that lesions in each of these struc-

Table 27.1. Summary of the Effects of Damage to Various Cerebral Structures Combined with Total Destruction of the Striate Areas and Field of the Pars Posterior of the Lateral Nucleus

	Average errors	
	With involvement	Without involvement
Hippocampal lobes	362	391
Auditory cortex	369	353
Lateral nucleus, pars principalis	395	353
Retrosplenial areas (anterior nuclei)	382	338
Subicular areas	379	372
	Maximal	Minimal
Postauditory cortex	317	470

tures contributes to the deterioration and that, although the effects of damage to any one are not measurable, the summated effects of damage to several produce large error scores. This may be tested by comparison of animals with different total amounts of damage.

Extent of Lesion. The range of cortical destruction for the twenty-six cases is from 9.5 to 29.4 per cent of the surface area of the pallium. Rank order correlation between extent of lesion and errors in retraining is only 0.10 ± 0.14. Two factors make for a small correlation in this group. The range of variation is not great, more than half of the cases falling within a range of 10 per cent. Postoperative training was not carried to completion and, since previous studies have shown a correlation between extent of lesion and trials for relearning, as well as for errors, some part of the higher correlations found previously is due to errors accumulated in the later stages of retraining, to which this group was not subjected. . . .

The correlation between the magnitude of . . . [lesions] and errors in postoperative tests is only $p = 0.07 \pm 0.14$. There is thus no indication that the loss of the habit increases progressively with increase in the total amount of damage to nonvisual structures. . . .

Cases with Minimal Involvement of Nonvisual Structures. Although the series includes no case with lesions wholly restricted to the striate cortex, there are several in which the damage to nonvisual structures is very slight. These are numbers 3, 8, 9, 10, 12, 26, and 28. Their average number of errors is 355, as compared with 375 for the entire group. The difference is not reliable. Number 12 had the least damage to nonvisual structures of any animal; total degeneration of the lateral geniculate nuclei with very slight unilateral invasion of the retrosplenial area and of the postauditory area. The hippocampal lobes and fields of the anterior and medial geniculate nuclei were not involved. The error score of this animal was 440; slightly higher than the average for the entire group.

This analysis has failed to reveal a pronounced deteriorating effect of invasion of any one of the diverse nonvisual structures accidentally included in the occipital lesions. It has also given no indication of a cumulative effect of slight damage to various fields. A further check of the effects of such damage is provided by the cases of group III, in which cortical blindness was combined with lesions in the hippocampal lobes, auditory and postauditory cortex, or the radiations of the lateral and ventral nuclei. Although the lesions in group III did not involve exactly the same combinations of structures as were damaged in the animals of groups I and II, the total damage to nonvisual structures was in some cases quite as severe and failed to produce any such marked deterioration as followed destruction of the occipital cortex.

In view of this evidence, the conclusion is justified that the severe effects of the cerebral lesions of groups I and II were not due to invasion of nonvisual structures, but to the extensive destruction of the cerebral visual areas themselves. Destruction of the visual cortex in animals which have learned the maze without visual cues results in a total disorganization of the habit and a retardation in relearning greatly exceeding that produced by peripheral blinding and as severe as that found in previous experiments to result from similar lesions in animals trained with vision.

Lindley (15) and Casper (2) by peripheral elimination of vision and olfaction, singly and in combination, have shown that maze learning is progressively retarded by increasing sensory loss. On the basis of such evidence Hunter (6) and Finley (4) have maintained that the correlation between extent of cerebral lesion and deterioration of the maze habit is due to the fact that large lesions produce more severe sensory defects than do small. Finley has extended the generalization from the experiments on sensory control of maze learning to include nonsensory cerebral functions. She has reported an experiment (4) which is interpreted as showing that destruction of the visual cortex produces no more disturbance of maze performance than does peripheral blinding, that lesions which invade more than one functional area of the cortex result in a more serious disturbance than injury to one area alone, and, hence, that the correlation between extent of cortical damage and severity of deterioration is due solely to the cumulative effects of loss of diverse functions. A study of her data reveals that she was misled by inaccurate anatomic analysis of her data and that her conclusions are not borne out by the facts presented.

Analysis of Dr. Finley's Experiments. Finley trained rats on an elevated maze for fifty-three trials, tested their accuracy for twelve additional runs alternately in light and darkness, subjected them to lesions in the occipital region, and again tested performance for seventeen trials in alternate light and darkness. Her animals were then divided into two groups on the basis of the character of the lesions. In group 1, consisting of twenty-eight cases, the lesions were stated to be "limited to the visual cortex." In group 2, with eleven animals, the lesions were deeper and in most cases slightly damaged the dorsal convexities of the hippocampal lobes, "extending also, in certain instances, beyond one or both striate areas." Conclusions were based upon a comparison of the performance of these two groups with each other and with the scores of blind animals reported by other investigators. Two main conclusions bearing upon the functions of the striate cortex and of vision in maze performance were drawn.

1. "Under the conditions described, interference with the central reception of visual cues results in no greater loss of accuracy for rats running an elevated maze then does the enucleation of their eyes or the elimination of visual stimuli, and the effect of central interference differs in no detectable way from that of peripheral."

2. "Lesions involving approximately the same surface area of the rat's cortex,

but affecting more than one functional area or brain center, may produce very much greater losses of accuracy in maze running than lesions limited to a single functional area" (4, p. 235).

The author uses "interference with central reception" as synonymous with damage to the striate areas. Her results are too complex for detailed analysis here, but the following considerations show the inconclusive character of the experiment:

Group 1. Postoperative loss in this group was slight and not clearly ascribable to the cerebral damage. The animals were not trained to errorless performance in darkness before operation and the test procedure, involving alternate trials in light and darkness, evidently results in a spread of the disturbing effects of darkness to subsequent trials in light (Finley's Fig. 3, preoperative tests). Such spread of effect, which is the general result of the introduction of any novel element during maze learning, combined with the general shock effect of the operation, is sufficient to account for the slight falling off in the performance of the group, without postulation of any defect of vision.

The anatomic data do not indicate any significant visual defects in group 1. The lesions are confined to the mesial edge of the striate areas and in no case invade the projection areas for the binocular field. Such lesions have not been found to interfere with visual performance in other tests. Neither the behavioral nor anatomic data justify the conclusion that there was any significant postoperative interference with vision in the majority of the animals.

The second conclusion listed above is largely based upon the statement that the lesions in animals of group 1 were "limited to the visual cortex." This statement is obviously incorrect. Finley's diagrams indicate for every case an invasion of the peristriate and retrosplenial areas; in fact, the microphotographs reproduced in her Fig. 4b and c, p. 213, as representative of the lesions in group 1, show lesions largely restricted to the retrosplenial and peristriate areas with very slight invasion of the mesial border of the striate area. The lesions are superficial and small in area, including little more than 6 per cent of the surface area of the cortex. In previous work lesions of this magnitude have never been found to produce a measurable effect upon maze performance.

Group 1 is thus actually a series of cases with small lesions involving two or more architectonic areas, probably without significant visual defect, and without demonstrated behavioral symptoms.

Group 2. The animals of this group made somewhat poorer records than those of group 1 and their lesions were reported as involving nonvisual structures, in contrast to the restriction to visual structures in group 1. The diagrams of the lesions of group 2 actually do not show invasion of any nonvisual, neocortical structures which were not also involved to an equal or greater extent in the animals of group 1. The only consistent difference in nonvisual structures damaged in the two groups is the invasion of the hippocampal lobes in some cases of group 2. Such invasion appears to be very superficial, involving at most a few hundred cells (Finley's Fig. 4a, p. 213). My data reported above on the effects of section of the optic radiation combined with much more severe damage to the hippocampus rule out the ascription of any serious influence upon maze performance to such small lesions.

Many of the animals of group 2 show invasion of the projection area of the binocular field and therefore probably had effective visual defects. That some vision was still retained is indicated by their significantly better scores in light than in darkness (Finley's Fig. 5, p. 215), but part of the relatively slight average postoperative loss may have been due to visual defect.

Since the lesions of group 2 invaded the hippocampal lobes they were evidently deeper and so involved effective destruction of larger cortical areas than did those of group 1. Even without allowance for this difference in depth of lesion, and the lesions in group 1 were apparently in most cases very superficial, the lesions of group 2 are roughly 50 per cent greater in surface area than those of group 1.

The assumption that the greater deterioration of group 2 was due to invasion of functional areas not involved in group 1 is thus not justified by the facts. All that the experiments actually show is that small lesions, whether restricted to the visual cortex or involving other cerebral areas as well, produce little or no disturbance of maze performance; that deeper and more extensive lesions produce relatively more disturbance, which may be the result of any of three uncontrolled variables: visual defect, invasion of the hippocampus, or total extent of damage. The facts presented are in no way inconsistent with the theory of mass action or with my earlier conclusion concerning the effects of destruction of the visual cortex upon the maze performance of blind animals, and they provide no support to the conclusions which Finley drew from the experiment.

Interpretation of the Relative Effects of Destruction of the Striate Areas and of Damage to Adjacent Structures. Although Finley's attempt to get conclusive evidence on the question of a nonvisual function of the visual cortex failed, her criticism of my earlier experiment is justified, since that experiment was carried out before the visual areas had been mapped accurately and since more recent work has shown that the lesions resulting in loss of the maze habit in blind animals invaded nonvisual structures as well as the striate areas. The present experiments do not avoid the same difficulty. Extensive destruction of the striate areas necessarily results in some injury to adjacent structures, but the controls reported seem adequate to show that such accidental injuries are not responsible for the severe deterioration following the extensive occipital lesions. The important points of evidence are the following:

1. Destruction of the occipital cortex in animals which were running the maze accurately without visual cues resulted in a deterioration of performance at least ten times as great as that following the peripheral blinding of animals which had learned the maze with vision. The effects of the occipital damage are therefore much more severe than those resulting from peripheral blinding.

2. Interruption of the optic radiations combined with damage to nonvisual structures produces only slight loss. Destruction of the visual cortex combined with similar damage to nonvisual structures results in nearly ten

times as great a deterioration. This severe loss therefore cannot be ascribed to the accidental invasion of the hippocampus, or of the fields of the medial geniculate, ventral, or lateral nuclei.

3. Comparison of cases with and without damage to each of the nonvisual structures which were involved in the destruction of the striate cortex reveals that injury to no one of these structures (with the possible exception of the colliculi, damaged in three cases) contributes more to the deterioration than injury to any other. If the severe loss following occipital lesions is due to invasion of adjacent structures, then this effect is a cumulative one, not ascribable to any particular structure.

4. Quantitative analysis of the effects of injuries to nonvisual structures in various combinations fails to reveal any relation between the severity of the defect and the number of such structures or the total extent of damage to nonvisual areas involved in the lesions. There is no evidence of a cumulative effect of damage to diverse occipital structures, within the narrow range of these experiments.

In view of these results it seems impossible to ascribe the severe deterioration following the occipital lesions to the accidental involvement of nonvisual structures. In some way the extensive destruction of the striate cortex must be responsible for the severity of the symptoms.

Effects of Extent of Lesion. Within the present experiments the range of extent of lesion is small and bears no relation to the severity of deterioration. Finley's experiments (4), involving lesser damage to essentially the same structures, provide some control of the effects of extent of damage. I have estimated roughly the surface area of the lesions in her cases by comparison of the lesions with the extent of the striate cortex shown in her diagrams. Since the mazes used were dissimilar and the animals were not trained to the same criterion, the effects of the lesions are best expressed for comparison as a percentage of the initial training scores in each experiment. I have arbitrarily chosen the first seventeen trials of initial training and of postoperative tests, corresponding to the seventeen trials of postoperative training used by Finley. The following table shows the effects of various amounts of damage:

	Percentage lesion	Average errors in first 17 postoperative trials	Errors expressed as percentage of 17 initial trials
Group 1 (Finley)	6.2	8.5	35
Group 2 (Finley)	9.6	22.0	90
Groups I and II (Lashley)	19.0	186.5	265

Interpretation of this table is complicated by the fact that Finley's animals were to some extent dependent on vision, whereas my animals had been trained to errorless performance after enucleation of the eyes; my cases also involved damage to cerebral areas laterad to the striate areas, which were not invaded in any of Finley's animals. However, such interference with vision as occurred from striate lesions in Finley's cases would have resulted in increased effectiveness of the lesions and reduction of the difference between her groups and mine, that is, in apparent effectiveness of extent of lesion. My cases with interruption of the posterior radiation show that the severe loss of groups I and II is not due to the damage to structures laterad to the striate areas. It therefore seems clear that the greater losses shown by the blind animals with larger lesions are due primarily to the extent of destruction of the visual cortex.

Bearing of the Experiments upon the Theory of "Mass Action." These results confirm my earlier conclusion that the area striata, the primary visual area, has some important function in maze learning in addition to the reception and integration of visual impulses. The nature of this function is still in question. If it is a specialized, unique function of the area, it is most probably concerned with space perception. Probably the most important process in maze learning is the development of a generalized orientation (19); the fitting of the maze pattern into the animal's system of space coordinates. The central visual mechanism, providing as it does the most accurate spatial data of any sense modality, might well be dominant in such a function but several lines of evidence oppose this interpretation. Tsang's studies (20) rule out any coordinate system built up by visual experience as affected in these studies and it is unlikely that the system is innately organized in the visual cortex. The correlation between postblind scores and initial learning presented on page 438 indicates that those animals which are most dependent on vision tend to learn most slowly. Similar visual dominance in maze-dull rats has been reported by Krechevsky (7). If the maze coordinates were primarily visual, one should expect the visual animals to be superior. Finally, disturbance of spatial orientation, other than visual, is not characteristic of visual agnosia in man.

If the visual cortex is not especially concerned in generalized orientation, the only other suggestion which has been made concerning its possible function in blind rats is some general facilitation of other parts, such as I have postulated under the term "mass action." Such an hypothesis is not inconsistent with the known facilitative action of other nervous structures.

The present experiments do not give direct evidence upon the factors determining the correlations between extent of lesion and loss of efficiency. There can be little question that elimination of several sense modalities by larger lesions contributes significantly to their effectiveness in reducing efficiency. In a study of the effects of interrupting sensory radiations, to be reported later, I have found a close relationship between the loss in maze performance and the amount of degeneration in the nuclei of the sensory thalamus. On the other hand, as in the present comparison of section of the posterior radiation and destruction of the occipital cortex, the deterioration from cortical damage is generally more severe than that following corresponding peripheral sensory loss or motor defects (10). Demonstration that the maze performance of blind animals depends upon the primary visual cortex suggests a nonsensory function whose loss may contribute to a general deterioration and to the cumulative effects of large lesions.

Summary

Comparison of the effects on maze performance of enucleation of the eyes, section of the posterior radiations, and destruction of the occipital lobes leads to the following conclusions.

1. Section of the posterior radiations combined with damage to the hippocampal lobes, to radiations of the ventral nucleus and of the lateral, pars posterior, and to the auditory and postauditory cortex produces no more serious deterioration than does peripheral blinding.

2. Total destruction of the visual cortex, combined with invasion of adjacent structures, similar to that involved in section of the radiation, produces severe deterioration, at least ten times as great as that following peripheral blinding.

3. Analysis of the effects of destruction of the area striata in combination with damage to various other structures indicates that the latter did not contribute significantly to the loss of the maze habit.

4. The visual cortex has some important function in maze learning which is exercised in the absence of any visual stimuli.

REFERENCES

1. Bard, P. Studies of the cerebral cortex: I. Localized control of placing and hopping reactions in the cat and their normal management by small cortical remnants, *Arch. Neurol. Psychiat.*, Chicago, 1933, **30**, 40–74.

2. Casper, B. The normal sensory control of the perfected double-alternation spatial maze habit in the albino rat, *J. genet. Psychol.*, 1933, **43**, 239–292.

3. Clark, W. E. Le Gros. Observations on the association fiber system of the visual cortex and the central representation of the retina, *J. Anat.*, 1941, **75**, 225–235.

4. Finley, C. B. Equivalent losses in accuracy of response after central and after peripheral sense deprivation, *J. comp. Neurol.*, 1941, **74**, 203–237.

5. Goltz, F. Ueber die Verrichtungen des Grosshirns, *Arch. ges. Physiol.*, 1881, **26**, 1–49.

6. Hunter, W. S. A consideration of Lashley's theory of equipotentiality of cerebral action, *J. gen. Psychol.*, 1930, **3**, 455–468.

7. Krechevsky, I. Hereditary nature of "hypotheses," *J. comp. Psychol.*, 1933, **16**, 99–116.

8. Krechevsky, I. Brain mechanisms and variability, *J. comp. Psychol.*, 1937, **23**, 121–138.

9. Lashley, K. S. *Brain mechanisms and intelligence.* Chicago: Univ. of Chicago Press, 1929.

10. Lashley, K. S. Studies of cerebral function in learning: XI. The behavior of the rat in latch-box situations. XII. Nervous structures concerned in the acquisition and retention of habits based on reactions to light, *Comp. Psychol. Monogr.*, 1935, **11** (52), 1–79.

11. Lashley, K. S. Thalamo-cortical connections of the rat's brain, *J. comp. Neurol.*, 1941, **75**, 67–121.

12. Lashley, K. S. The mechanism of vision: XVII. Autonomy of the visual cortex, *J. genet. Psychol.*, 1942, **60**, 197–221.

13. Lashley, K. S., McDonald, W. T., and Peters, H. N. Studies of cerebral function in learning: X. The effects of dilatation of the ventricles upon maze learning, *Amer. J. Physiol.*, 1933, **104**, 51–61.

14. Lashley, K. S., and Wiley, L. E. Studies of cerebral function in learning: IX. Mass action in relation to the number of elements in the problem to be learned, *J. comp. Neurol.*, 1933, **57**, 3–55.

15. Lindley, S. B. Maze learning ability of anosmic and blind rats, *J. genet. Psychol.*, 1930, **37**, 245–265.

16. Monakow, C. von. *Die Lokalisation im Grosshirn.* Wiesbaden: J. F. Bergmann, 1914.

17. Piéron, H. *Le cerveau et la pensée.* Paris: Alcan, 1923.

18. Rose, M. Cytoarchitektonischer Atlas der Grosshirnrinde der Maus, *J. Psychol. Neurol., Lpz.*, 1929, **40**, 1–51.

19. Tryon, R. C. Studies in individual differences in maze learning: VI. Disproof of sensory components: Experimental effects of stimulus variation, *J. comp. Psychol.*, 1939, **28**, 361–415.

20. Tsang, Yü-Chüan. The functions of the visual areas of the cortex of the rat in the learning and retention of the maze, *Comp. Psychol. Monogr.*, 1934, **10** (50), 1–56.

21. Walker, A. E. *The primate thalamus.* Chicago: Univ. Chicago Press, 1938.

28. PERSISTENT PROBLEMS IN THE
EVOLUTION OF MIND [1]

The comparative psychologist must try to ask questions of his animals and to understand their answers. When Pfungst demonstrated that the horses of Elberfeld, who were showing marvelous linguistic and mathematical ability, were merely reacting to movements of the trainer's head, Mr. Krall (see 16), their owner, met the criticism in the most direct manner. He asked the horses whether they could see such small movements and in answer they spelled out an emphatic "*no*." Unfortunately, we cannot all be so sure that our questions are understood or obtain such clear answers. In 1913 Szymanski tried to find out whether the dog can recognize pictures of objects. The dogs not only failed to recognize the pictures but even failed to distinguish the objects. After long testing with the best methods that he could devise, Szymanski concluded that the dog's vision is so poor that he can only distinguish light from darkness. A number of us in this country were equally unsuccessful in demonstrating detail vision in dogs and rodents. For a period of ten years we were forced to believe these animals practically blind, in spite of common experience to the contrary. Then by chance we hit upon the method of having the animal jump against the objects to be distinguished. This "look before you leap" method put the questions in a way that was intelligible even to rats. They learned in 1 trial discriminative reactions that had formerly taken more than 100; they learned in 10 trials tasks that they had previously failed after 7,000 trials of training. Except for differences in acuity, their perception of visual form turned out to be almost as good as my own. Dogs did equally well. Evidently when an animal fails in a task, it is not safe to conclude that he lacks capacity for that task, unless we can be sure that the question was properly asked.

Sometimes the answers are unexpected and often ambiguous. When I started work with chimpanzees, I presented what seemed a very simple problem: to associate a white box with food. I placed a white and a black

[1] EDITORS' NOTE: From *Quart. Rev. Biol.*, 1949, **24**, 28–42. Reproduced by permission of the Williams and Wilkins Co. From Harvard University and the Yerkes Laboratories of Primate Biology.

box on a table before the cage, each box attached to a rope extending to
the bars of the cage. The white box alone always contained food and if
the black box were pulled in, I snatched away the other rope. When this
had happened half a dozen times, my subject, Mimi, a husky female,
grasped a rope in each hand, pulled one in until she could wrap it around
her foot for a firm grip. She thus freed both hands to pull in one rope,
while retaining complete control of the other. If the first box were empty,
she usually won the tug of war for the second. Her solution of the problem
was better than my own, so I judge it highly intelligent. But when I finally
regained control of the situation, Mimi took more than 200 trials to form
the simple association between the white box and food, a task which the
rat, under optimal conditions, can learn in a single trial.

I describe these misadventures in animal training to emphasize the
tentative character of the conclusions to be drawn from the accumulated
mass of studies of animal behavior. It has been said that American rats
learn only by trial and error, whereas European rats learn by insight.
Certainly, investigators in America have been only too prone to put a rat
in a dark box where it can do nothing but press a lever and, because it
does nothing else, to conclude that all its behavior is of the same character. Unless the experimenter has wide experience with the animals that
he studies and adapts his questions to their modes of behavior, the results
give little information about their true capacities. There are remarkably
few comparative studies which are really significant for the evolution of
behavior. A great part are meaningless for the problem, either because the
questions were improperly put or because the tests were made with a
single species and comparable data are available for no other. In consequence, the evolution of mind can as yet be sketched in only the most
general terms, with no certainty that the actual level of development of
any species has been determined, and with comparative data on but few
functions.

The Origin of Mind

The study of mental evolution has been handicapped by a metaphysical
dualism. Early students were concerned with the question of where mind
or consciousness first appears among animals. They accepted the Cartesian
distinction between mind and body and felt it necessary to trace the
evolution of conscious states along with the evolution of the brain and
of behavior. Various criteria of mind were proposed, the most familiar
being "associative memory," emphasized by Jacques Loeb, but none was
satisfactory and many students turned away from the problem as insoluble.

Behaviorism met the issue by denying that the conception of mind has
any definite meaning. The first statements of this position were not rigorously formulated, and behaviorism has been assailed for denying self-

evident facts of experience, whereas the denial was that the facts constitute evidence for a meaningful distinction between experience and behavior. The position of behaviorism can be stated more rigorously today, largely as the result of the application of operational concepts as tools of logical criticism (6, 17, 37).

Subjective experience reveals only a complex of activity, varying from moment to moment, without constant structure or content. The characteristic is the organization. The organizing process is not experienced; that is, thoughts think themselves, just as the words of a sentence fall spontaneously into grammatical order. The elements which are organized, sensations, feelings, etc., cannot be described or defined. They are abstractions from the mental structure which have in themselves no attributes distinguishing them from physical abstractions. I shall not attempt here to validate this statement beyond pointing out that William McDougall (30), the most aggressive recent advocate of mind-body dualism, was forced to postulate atoms of mind-stuff, adsorbed on physical atoms, as the elements of mental structure. The question of what may happen to such mental atoms in these days of atomic fission was not foreseen when he wrote in 1913.

Psychological analysis reveals nothing but varying organization or structure. Studies of the physiology of the nervous system and analysis of behavior reveal the same principles of organization as are discovered by subjective analysis (21). The question, "What is the mental state of an animal?" means then: What is the level of organization of its activities? The question can have no other meaning because no other conception of mind can be derived from experience.

I should not have burdened you with this matter, save that eminent biologists, e.g., Lillie (27), Herrick (11), Sherrington (35), still maintain that mind, where it appears, performs a unique function in integrating behavior. They have not, however, indicated the nature of this function or defined the behavior which is its unique product. They postulate two modes of biological action but do not suggest the nature of the distinction between them. Even so keen a philosophical biologist as Woodger (43), though he insists that the concept of mind has no place in biological science, accepts the distinction between public and private knowledge, without realizing that private knowledge is, on analysis, only private ignorance. The questions of where mind or consciousness enters in the phylogenetic scale and of the nature of conscious experience as distinct from physiological processes are pseudo-problems, arising from misconceptions of the nature of the data revealed by introspection. A comparative study of the behavior of animals is a comparative study of mind, by any meaningful definition of the term.

The Nature of Behavioral Evolution

The interest of early students of comparative psychology was in finding the origin of human mental traits. Darwin and Romanes could point out behavior of animals which suggested similarity of emotional characters, memory, and intelligence to that of man, and could show that the similarity increased with increasing bodily similarity to man. They could not specify what was changing in evolution or the nature of the steps between different levels of behavior. We are in a scarcely better position today. It is not possible to classify unit factors in behavior and to trace the development of distinct entities, as one may trace the evolution of the heart, the gill arches, or the limbs. For such a classification it is necessary to know the mechanisms by which the behavior is produced and to trace the evolution of these mechanisms. This is still impossible for any except the simplest and most primitive forms of behavior. The problems can, however, be defined more clearly than was possible a generation ago.

A sharp distinction has often been made between instinct and intelligence, with the implication that these represent divergent lines of evolutionary development. Instinctive behavior is described as genetically determined, stereotyped, and relatively unmodifiable; intelligent behavior as the product of experience, plastic and adaptable. Analysis of behavior included under the two categories does not, I believe, justify the distinction. The differences are in degree only, not in kind.

Intelligence is generally defined as the capacity to profit by experience, or the capacity to learn, and its evolution is described in terms of performance in situations requiring learning. This view is based on a confusion in definitions. Learning involves both the ability to form associations and also the ability to solve problems, to discover the significant relations in the situation. The typical learning curve is compounded of trial-and-error discoveries, of insight, and of memory. Under favorable conditions every animal, at least above the level of the worms, can form a simple association in a single trial. In this sense the capacity to learn was perfected early and has changed little in the course of evolution. It is not the fact of learning but what is learned that differentiates animals in the evolutionary scale. The learning of higher animals involves a perception of relations which is beyond the capacity of the lower.

As an illustration of this, compare the learning behavior of a spider monkey and a chimpanzee in a matching problem. The monkey was set the task of choosing either a red or green square according as a red or green square was shown as a model. The monkey made no improvement above chance in nearly 1,000 trials (Fig. 28.1, *a*). The model was then placed in contact with the color to be chosen (*b*). Correct choice followed within a dozen trials. With the model returned to the original position

(c), there was a chance score for 600 trials. The colored models were then increased in size to form a background; the task to choose red on red, green on green (d). This was learned very quickly. With the original small model, chance scores again. With the colored grounds just making visual contact with the squares, every trial was correct (e). Breaking

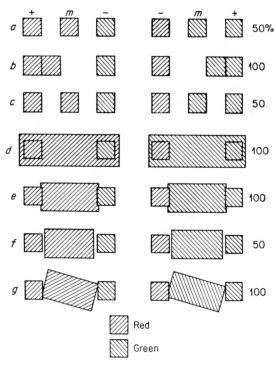

Fig. 28.1. Record of scores made by a specimen of *Ateles geoffroyi* in training to choose one of two colored squares to match the color of a model *m*. The percentages given at the right represent the final level of accuracy attained in each of the seven situations.

the visual contact by 2 mm. (f) gave chance scores again. Rotating the model to visual contact gave errorless choice (g); rotating back, chance scores. I continued training by such methods for 18,000 trials with this one monkey, but he never learned to choose the matching object. He saw the model as a pointer when it was placed in contact with the object, but a piece of white paper served equally well to indicate the choice. He saw the colored background as a signal but disregarded the color similarity, for he learned just as quickly to choose the red object on a white background and the green on a black. The relation of similarity was not grasped. The macaque can learn this task of matching, though he requires much special training. The chimpanzee grasps it quite readily.

An attempt to analyze the learning process here results in the discovery of apparently different processes. Associations with one or another aspect of the situation are formed readily, but what is associated depends upon some sort of insight into the relations of the variable elements of the situation. For the spider monkey, visual continuity seems essential. Visual objects which are not in contact are not related. For the chimpanzee this aspect of the situation is less important.

Analysis of learning or of adaptive reactions almost always gives results of this kind. Schneirla's comparison of maze learning in ants and mammals (33) indicates qualitative differences in the maze relations to which these animals react. The modes of response of different animals are found to be based upon different types of relational organizing which are refractory to further analysis. So far as evidence is available, the capacities for these relational concepts are genetically determined. The limits of capacity of each order of animals are set by the kinds of relations among objects that it can perceive. The development of the individual is a slow maturation of such capacities. Intelligence tests, which are selected as representative of the average capacities at different ages, are tests for the presence of relational concepts and represent a series of qualitatively different stages of development much like those illustrated from the matching behavior of the monkeys.

In contrast to the usual statements, instinctive behavior is actually plastic and adaptive. Its range may be restricted by the perceptual and conceptual limitations of the organism, but within that range, the instinctive acts are directly adapted to the requirements of the situation. The web of the orb-weaver may seem, superficially, to present a stereotyped pattern but when one examines the arrangement of foundation lines, the attachment of the radii to them to produce equal spacing, or the neat repairing of the torn web, one must recognize that the construction involves an appreciation of spatial relations which is fundamentally of the same nature as the concepts of relations that are basic to intelligent behavior in man.

The mechanisms of instinctive and intelligent behavior thus seem fundamentally the same. Both are the expression of modes of the perception of relationships, and these modes are genetically determined. Higher levels of intelligence are based on a greater variety of types of organization, but this does not mean that they are any less dependent upon genetic factors.

A more important distinction for the evolution of nervous mechanisms is that between behavior mediated by anatomically restricted pathways and "relationally determined" behavior. These two types are illustrated among protozoa by the reactions of the Ciliata and Rhizopoda. In *Euplotes,* for example, the stroke of the cirri is controlled by impulses transmitted over fibers of the neuromotor apparatus (40), which are limited and invariable conducting paths. In *Ameba,* on the contrary, although reaction may take place at a distance from the point of stimulation, the character of the response seems to be determined by the existing conformation of the pseudopodia, as indicated in Kepner's studies (14) of the feeding behavior of *Ameba.* In the one case the behavior is mediated by a precise anatomic structure, and the evolutionary problem involves the accurate control of form in ontogeny; in the other, a transient physiological state is responsible for the behavior, and the ontogenetic problem is of a different character. Among higher animals this distinction appears between reactions determined by stimulation of specific receptor cells and behavior in which the *mode* of organization is genetically determined but in which the receptor and effector mechanisms are variable.

Correlation of Behavior with the Evolution of the Nervous System

The evolution of mind is the evolution of nervous mechanisms, but only the simpler of these can as yet be analyzed directly. Comparative studies of the brain and of behavior are, therefore, still largely separate in method and problems. I shall try to relate some of the data derived from the two approaches and to point out lines of investigation which seem to bear upon fundamental questions.

The phylogenetic history of gross changes in the nervous system can be traced in some detail. In a few cases where the relations are simple and direct it has been possible to show correlations between specific structures and behavior, as in the segmental reflexes which produce the crawling movements of the earthworm, or the relation between the dominant use of the nose as a tactile organ by the pony and the great extent of its representation in the sensory area of the cortex (1). For more complicated reactions, however, such as the instinctive behavior of insects and birds or the behavior which is called intelligent, no such detailed correlations have been possible.

There are obvious changes in the gross structure of the nervous system with ascent in the evolutionary scale and these have been seized upon as the probable basis of increase in behavioral capacity. Evidence in support of such interpretations is by no means conclusive. The history of the nervous system presents a few points of radical change in structure. These points should show maximal changes in the types of activity of the animals, if gross structure is important in the reaction system. The most conspicuous of these are: the substitution of the nerve net in metazoa

for the neuromotor apparatus of protista; the appearance of the synaptic
type of conduction in echinoderms; the development of the dorsal nerve
cord and its dominance over the ventral ganglionic chain; and the appearance of the neopallium in mammals. None of these changes seems to
have introduced anything new in behavior, when it first appeared. The
behavior of hydra is no better coordinated than that of some of the
suctoria. The synapse perhaps conferred on the nerve net the capacity
for independent reflexes, but paramecium and the hypotricha have independent reflexes as well as coordinated movements of groups of cilia.
The primitive vertebrates are inferior to the higher invertebrates in every
behavioral capacity that has been tested. The primitive mammal with an
extensive neopallium is not superior in behavior to birds like the crow
or parrot. Such studies as exist do not reveal qualitative differences in
behavior corresponding to radical changes in the plan of gross structure
of the nervous system. It might be said that, although such changes
confer no advantage at the start, they open the way for later advancement.
Such a statement, however, adds in no way to an understanding of the
reason for the potential limitations of any form of the nervous system.
H. G. Wells has represented insect-like inhabitants of the moon as pos-
sessed of superhuman intelligence, and the neurologist can point to no
characteristic of the brain structure of insects which would preclude such
a development.

Since I am most familiar with the behavior and neurology of mammals,
among which the differences are chiefly in those forms of behavior which
are designated as intelligent, I shall confine the discussion largely to the
evolution of the brain in relation to intelligence and shall try to picture
the kind of change that has been responsible for this phase of the evolution of behavior.

Attempts to correlate the level of intelligence with nervous structures
have been limited almost entirely to studies of mammals. Brain weight,
ratio of brain to body weight, degree of fissurization, vascularity, and
relative development of different lobes of the cerebrum are the chief
characters that have been studied. It has been held that the associative
areas of the mammalian brain have increased, relatively more than
sensory and motor areas, with ascent in the evolutionary scale, but the
areas have never been actually measured. The conclusion is based upon
measurements of vaguely defined lobes which do not represent functional
divisions or strictly homologous parts in different species. Definition of
cortical areas in terms of their cytoarchitecture might provide a better
index of changes in proportions, but comparative measurements of such
areas have not been made. Moreover, George Clark and I (25) have
found individual variations in cell structure greater than those upon
which many of the areal divisions have been based. Cerebral architecture

is then unreliable as an index of function. From rough measurements of actual functional areas, determined by anatomic analysis of their connections, for the rat and monkey, I question that there has been any very significant change in the relative proportions of the different functional areas of mammalian cortex in the development from rodent to primate.

The only neurological character for which a correlation with behavioral capacity in different animals is supported by significant evidence is the total mass of tissue, or rather, the index of cephalization, measured by the ratio of brain to body weight, which seems to represent the amount of brain tissue in excess of that required for transmitting impulses to and from the integrative centers (5). We must seek the clue to behavioral evolution in the number and interconnections of the nerve cells or in their biochemical characteristics, not in their gross structural arrangement.

Variation and Functional Regulation in the Nervous System

An examination of the general principles upon which the nervous system is organized throws somewhat more light upon its possible mode and direction of evolution. The system is in some ways the most highly differentiated and exactly genetically determined structure in the body. It is also in other respects the most plastic and adaptable. Each of these seemingly incongruous characters presents special problems of phylogenetic development.

The precision of organization is illustrated by the visual system of mammals. In this system there is virtually a point to point or cell to cell connection between the retina and the occipital lobes of the cerebral cortex, predetermined in growth. Nerve fibers originate in the ganglion cell layer of the retina, are relayed in the thalamus, and the connections continued to the cerebral cortex in a nearly exact reproduction of the retina. I have found in the rat that the topological arrangements of cell bodies in the thalamic nucleus and of their axon terminations in the cortex vary at most by two to three cell diameters in a nucleus containing more than 34,000 cells and not more than 1 cell in 100 is displaced to this extent. This precise arrangement is not simply a result of parallel growth of fibers, for the retinal fibers are distributed at random in the optic nerve and seem to undergo a complete intercrossing between the thalamic nucleus and the cortex (20). Other sensory systems seem to be as precisely arranged, though they have been studied less thoroughly.

The functioning of such systems is rigidly determined in mammals. Damage to them results in irrecoverable loss, and there is no evidence that their mode of action can be modified in any way by learning. They are also phylogenetically very old. The arrangement of the visual paths in marsupials and man is essentially the same. Such evolutionary changes as have occurred involve only increase or decrease in number and addition or loss of certain types of cells and increase in the proportion of uncrossed fibers, but without change in the basic spatial pattern.

Systems with such accurately determined connections have been regarded as the prototype of all integrative organization. The simple reflex arc has been represented as a restricted chain of connected cells transmitting impulses from sense organs to muscles without mutual interference. More complicated behavior has been interpreted as a product of the additive activity of such paths. This view of the nervous mechanism has underlain a criticism of evolution by random variation, which has been a principal argument of Lamarckians and advocates of some form of guided evolution. They have maintained that chance variation cannot account for the evolution of behavior, because organized behavior calls for correlated variation in the genetic determiners for hundreds or thousands of connections between individual cells, and the chance of such correlated variation is infinitely small.

Evidence is accumulating, however, that the principle of organization within integrative centers, such as the cerebral cortex, is entirely different from this simple chain conduction. The precise sensory paths transmit to the central mechanisms a pattern of excitation corresponding to the spatial and temporal distribution of stimulation on the sensory surfaces. From this point neither anatomic nor physiologic evidence lends any support to the conception of restricted anatomic pathways connecting sensory and motor centers.

The evidence of this statement comes chiefly from what we have called stimulus equivalence. An illustration of this is a fact so familiar as to be generally overlooked: *Objects remain the same with innumerable changes in visual fixation.* The general principle is that reactions are to relations within the mass of stimuli—to proportions, and the like—and are independent of the excitation of particular nerve fibers. Direct experimental work on the nervous system supports this statement. Excitations from the retina are transmitted to a definite part of the cerebral cortex, the area striata, and visual integrations apparently take place within this area only. Any other part of the cerebral cortex, in the rat at least, can be destroyed without interfering with complex visual reactions. I have found that all but 2 per cent of the visual area of the rat's brain can be destroyed without affecting these types of organization, and it need not be the same 2 per cent in all cases. The integration is somehow inherent in every part of the visual area (19).

How far this concept can be carried is uncertain. It seems to hold true for learned reactions as well as for innate modes of organization. When a rat has been trained in a differential visual response, any part of the cerebral cortex may be removed without destroying memory of the stimuli, so long as enough of the visual cortex remains to permit any visual reactions at all. All attempts to analyze the nervous basis of mammalian instincts, of habits, and of modes of behavior designated as intelligent have given similar results. I started experimental studies of the brain in the expectation that definite conditioned-reflex arcs could be traced from sensory to motor regions. No experimental result has ever been consistent with this expectation. One example must suffice. A number of rats were trained in a maze and long knife cuts made through the cortex and underlying fibers, dividing the brain in a great variety of ways (Fig. 28.2). No evidence could be obtained that these cuts affected the habit in any way, no matter what cortical areas were divided or separated by them. The capacity to form new habits was also unaffected. The best learning score in my records of several hundred animals was made by a rat with both hemispheres split from end to end. There is similar though less detailed evidence from monkeys in which the frontal or occipital

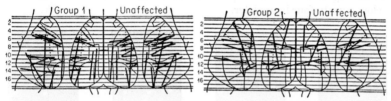

Fig. 28.2. Composite diagrams of incisions, penetrating the fiber layers of the cerebral cortex of the rat, which failed to produce a significant effect upon maze performance. Each pair of symmetrically placed lines in the two hemispheres represents the incisions in one animal. Group 1, postoperative initial learning; group 2, postoperative retention. (After Lashley, 24.)

lobes or motor areas have been partially isolated. In man a wound which pierces the occipital lobe may produce a blind spot without distorting the spatial relations of the remaining functional parts of the field. The visual integrations are apparently not dependent upon the direct interconnections of different parts of the visual cortex.

I have been struck by the fact that even very extensive destruction of brain tissue does not produce a disorganization. Behavior becomes simplified but remains adaptive. In one experiment rats were trained on a latch box which required pushing down a lever, turning, and stepping on a platform to open the door to the food box. The normal animal accidentally works these latches by climbing or stepping on them. After a few trials, his behavior changes radically; he may seize the lever with his teeth and pull it down, turn, and make a quick thrust against the platform with his fore feet. The necessary movement of the objects is somehow analyzed from the totality of chance activities, and the rat's movements are directed to manipulate the latches. Rats with large brain lesions learn this problem with about the same average practice as normal ones, but their performance is different. A rat lacking about 40 per cent of the cortical surface first opened the box by scrambling up the front of the food box over the latch and falling off backward onto the platform. He continued this procedure throughout training, became skilful in falling and could eventually open the box more quickly than a normal animal, but he never reacted to the latches as separate objects. His reactions were organized at a simpler level, as associated movements without insight into the significance of the latches. Nevertheless, he was not confused; what was noted was associated quickly and efficiently. Uncomplicated destruction of brain tissue in man likewise does not produce confusion. Compressing tumors, diffuse disease, drugs, or traumatic shock may produce confusional states, but these agents change the chemistry of the whole system. A patient may talk coherently during and immediately after a frontal lobotomy and develop a state of confusion only as oedema develops twenty-four hours later.

Fig. 28.3. Structured and unstructured arrangements of dots. Recognition of the groupings on the right is difficult for the rat, as for man.

A second point of major importance is that the nervous system is not a neutral medium on which learning imposes any form of organization whatever. On the contrary, it has definite predilections for certain forms of organization and imposes these upon the sensory impulses which reach it. Vision has been most adequately studied in this respect, and definite laws of visual organization have been established, which hold for all vertebrates. The animals react to objects, that is, to organized patterns of stimuli. The basic patterns of this organization are apparently inherent in the structure of the visual system. Certain patterns of excitation become units for behavior. Thus, dots arranged in simple geometrical designs are readily recognized as a definite figure. The same dots in another arrangement lose all coherence (Fig. 28.3). It might seem that the geometrical figures are recognized by us because they are familiar and have names. However, rats, for whom such geometrical forms cannot have acquired any meaning, learn to recognize them very quickly and are unable to distinguish the groups of randomly scattered dots after many weeks of training.

A number of laws of geometrical perception have been worked out.

Coherence of the figure is determined by continuity of line or direction, continuity and contrast of surface, simplicity of outline, and the like; quantitative relations like larger, brighter, or more distant are immediately perceived. These modes of organization are innate; we have raised rats in total darkness and discover the same laws of visual organization in their first reactions when brought into the light (9, 10, 26). Reports of men who have first seen after removal of congenital cataract confirm these results (34).

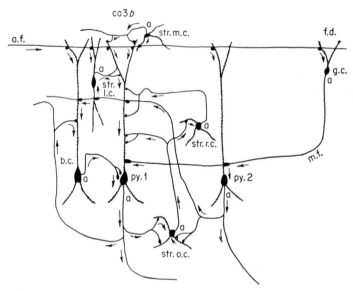

Fig. 28.4. Connections between a single afferent fiber (a.f.) and an efferent pyramid (py. 1) of the Ammonshorn, illustrating the complexity of recurrent connections in the cortical lattice. (After Lorente de Nó, 28.)

In its functional organization the nervous system seems to consist of schemata or basic patterns within which new stimuli are spontaneously fitted. Even in the case of learned activities the learning may and perhaps most frequently does involve the organization of a new generalized schema rather than the formation of a limited association. This is most clearly illustrated in the case of language. The grammatical form of each language is learned, but once it is acquired new words or new ideas are spontaneously given the structural peculiarities of the language.

The physiology of such organizations is far from being understood, but anatomic studies suggest that a network or lattice of nerve cells forms the basis of the central integrative processes. The evidence of this comes chiefly from the work of Lorente de Nó (28), which is epoch-making for the understanding of the action of the central nervous system. The cerebral cortex consists of a network of nerve cells connected together in circuits of different lengths. Figure 28.4 shows some of the interconnections between the cells of the cortex. An excited cell transmits impulses to adjacent cells, and the excitation may be returned from various distances, through one or a thousand links. Since the activation or inhibition of a cell is dependent upon the number and frequency of the impulses transmitted to it, it is obvious that a system so organized will have its own inherent patterns of response. Figure 28.5 represents a situation where each cell is connected with two adjacent ones. If two impulses arriving in quick succession produce inhibition, the pattern of activity shown in the figure would be produced by a series of impulses. Actually the diagram is much oversimplified and would not produce such a result

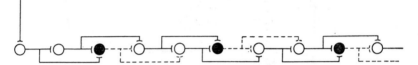

Fig. 28.5. Diagram to illustrate the principle of pattern formation in a lattice of neurons.

except on some improbable assumptions concerning the development of inhibition. However, it serves to illustrate the general principle of organization and the fact that a nervous network must necessarily develop its own intrinsic patterns of activity. The form of these patterns will vary with the number and reactive properties of the cells which are interconnected. I shall designate these patterns of interacting cells as neural schemata.

Different functional systems have characteristically different arrangements of cells, which appear to be fairly uniform within the system. Figure 28.6 shows groups of cells from the same layer in the postcentral, temporal, and occipital areas of the monkey. In two there are a great variety of cell sizes and irregular arrangement; in the other, uniformity in size and regular arrangement in vertical chains. There are probably corresponding differences in intercellular connections, although nothing positive is known about this.

It is not yet possible to analyze the activities of such systems in any detail. Biophysicists, under the leadership of N. Rashevsky, have made some progress toward formulation of the elementary properties of the nervous lattice (13) and I have discussed possible application of the theory to the problems of stimulus equivalence and adaptive behavior (23). Köhler and Wallach (15) have approached the same problems from a consideration of the electric properties of active nerve cells and have developed a theory of field effects which provides a more explicit interpretation of some of the phenomena of perception.

The common characteristic of all these theories of nervous integration is the recognition that a network of nerve cells has inherent properties of organization which are dependent upon the spatial and physico-chemical properties of the system as a whole. The significance of such views of nervous mechanisms for the problem of evolution is their implication concerning what is genetically determined in behavior and concerning the potentialities of the system for correlated variation and self-regulation.

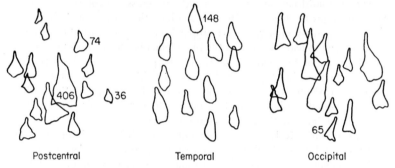

Postcentral   Temporal   Occipital

Fig. 28.6. The arrangement of cell bodies in lamina III in the postcentral, temporal, and occipital regions of Macaca. (After Lashley and Clark, 25.)

Those systems which show a predetermination of intercellular connections, such as the paths from the eye to the striate cortex, have an essentially spatial organization. The relative positions of the cell bodies determine the relative positions of axon terminations. The neuron specificities do not imply individual genetic determination but can arise as a product of biochemical gradients such as play a general role in the differentiation of structure. Correlations in the evolution of such systems with modifications of sense organs or limb structure follow from the general principles of morphogenesis.

Within the integrative network the variables which determine the character of organization are the number of cells forming various circuits, the amount of proliferation of axon terminations and end buds, refractory periods, and the like. These are anatomic and physiologic characters which may be common to large areas or even to the entire system. The genetic control of such characters presents a quite different problem from the determination of individual interneural connections. The mechanisms of their ontogeny may be no more specific than are those which control the development of dermal or other structures. Variation or mutation may change such characters, with resultant changes in the integrative patterns developed within the nervous network, but so long as the tissue retains the fundamental characters of the network, its activities will be organized according to the same general principles. Just as extensive lesions may result in a simplification of reactions without producing a disorganization, so mutations may modify the fundamental capacities or modes of integration without producing a functional disorganization, so long as a lattice of nerve cells is maintained.

Apparent Discontinuity in the Evolution of Behavior

The anatomist can sometimes trace the progress of evolution by quantitative changes in structure. He may see how the form of a limb or tooth has developed by changes in its proportions or by the addition, subtraction, or reduplication of identifiable elements. Such insight into the modifications of behavior is rarely if ever possible. The three types of reaction to the object presented in the matching experiment described above, as a pointer, as a signal, and as a model, seem qualitatively different. We cannot see how growth of one of these modes of responding can transform it into another. The same outcome appears in all attempts to measure quantitatively the development of any behavioral function. The measures of human intelligence consist of groups of tasks assigned to each chronological age, according as some arbitrary percentage of children of that age can pass the tests. A quantitative scale in terms of average age is thus produced and is assumed to measure something which is called intelligence. If the individual test items of different ages are compared, however, they give no evidence of continuity of growth. There is no common function in noting the absence of ears from a sketch of the human head and finding the incongruity in a logical contradiction (two different age level tests). The processes by which the different tasks are carried out seem to form a discontinuous series. This is true of both phylogenetic and ontogenetic development. Different levels of capacity are largely characterized by different types of integrative activity. Even the development of language, to which a major part of human superiority has often been ascribed, seems to be primarily the expression of forms of relational organization which are absent in lower mammals, rather than a means to such organization, as has sometimes been held.

For example, one of the most important of language activities is the use of the series of ordinal numbers. Almost all mathematical procedures depend upon it. The ordinal numbers involve the matching of two arrays of objects and the recognition of their common property of serial order.

This can be done to some extent at least without language, as when a child sets up two parallel rows of matching blocks. It is not the invention of the symbols which makes possible the function, but the extension of the capacity for matching objects, shown by the chimpanzee, to the more abstract concept of arrangement. The chimpanzee, or even the rat, can learn the order of a single series, but no animal has given any evidence of the generalization of the order of one set of objects to another. Without such generalization the conception of number and the development of number-names is impossible.

In contrast to the apparently discrete qualitative changes in the kinds of integration involved in performance of different tasks at different levels in the evolutionary scale, the growth of the nervous system presents a continuous quantitative change. As I pointed out earlier, the only established structural correlate with evolution in complexity of behavior is based upon brain weight. In a number of experiments I have found that the severity of deterioration is proportional to the quantity of cerebral tissue destroyed. Cell division in the brain is completed in the early years, and the intellectual growth of the individual must be due to maturation of cells, expressed as a proliferation of axons or as changes in the physiological characters of the nerve cells. In all these cases a quantitative change in nervous tissue seems to correlate with a series of qualitative changes in behavioral capacity.

It is possible that a more penetrating psychological analysis may discover the common processes underlying what seem to be qualitative diversities in the organization of behavior, and so reveal a quantitative continuity of behavioral development. Students of genetic psychology have frequently assumed that mental development is a continuous quantitative growth. Spearman (36), for example, has equated intelligence with the level of an hypothetical mental energy. Thorndike (41) has suggested that it depends upon the number of potential associative bonds which have not yet been preempted by learning. Such speculations, however, do not help us to understand the reasons for such differences in modes of response as are illustrated by the reactions of spider monkeys and of chimpanzees in the matching situation. Some phenomena suggest that the kind of relation perceived may be a function of the complexity and number of the nervous schemata which can be activated and integrated at one time. An example from bird behavior may make the meaning of this statement clearer. The nesting sooty tern holds territorial rights to an area surrounding her nest, and attacks any trespassers. She will rush to the defense of any chick which is attacked, even in a neighbor's territory. Having rescued a chick from the attacks of a neighbor, she herself will immediately attack it, if it runs away. If during her attack the chick runs under her breast, she responds with the hovering reaction, but after a few seconds she begins to peer about and, finding herself away from her nest, stands up, takes a few steps, turns and attacks the chick which she has just hovered. The immediate reaction is to a limited range of stimuli, and adjustment to the conflicting demands of the whole situation is slow. The superior insight into the situation, which makes the bird's behavior seem inadequate and ridiculous to the human observer, lies in the fact that more of the elements of the situation are effective at the same time for us and our reaction to the combination is more rapid.

The perception of relations which seem qualitatively different, such as those of pointing and of likeness in the matching problem, might possibly be reduced to such quantitative terms, depending upon the number of elements in the situation which can be integrated simultaneously. An increasing number of cells and axon connections might make possible the development of a more complex structure, without change in the fundamental mode of organization, just as a larger piece of a regenerating hydroid can develop more nodes of differentiation and so a more complex pattern of tentacles than a smaller one (7). Thus far, attempts to analyze processes of generalization into such quantitative terms have been unsuccessful.

A second alternative is that continued research on the finer structure of the nervous system may discover changes in the type of interneural connections which correspond to qualitative changes in behavior. There is little indication of this in current investigations, but techniques for detailed analysis of the finer structural relations in the nervous system are not at present available. Until this problem of continuous or discontinuous steps in the development of the nervous system and of behavior has been solved, a significant correlation of the two will not be possible.

Genetic Determination of Specific Types of Behavior

With such a view of nervous organization, what may be the basis of such specific instinctive behavior as the orb-weaving of spiders, or the selective recognition of objects like the egg of the bird or of the young of the species by various birds and mammals? There are indications that the human cerebrum has a predilection for certain types of geometrical organization. In hemianopia most objects are cut off sharply at the edge of the blind field, but simpler geometrical figures like a square or circle cannot be so divided. When only half of such a figure falls within the seeing field, its form is spontaneously completed; it is seen as an entire square or circle (8, 32). In one type of migraine, blind spots filled with scintillating lines develop. The form taken by these lines, the so-called fortification figures, is uniform for all subjects and probably represents a preferential pattern of the cortical tissue in spontaneous discharge (22).

We have raised the question whether differences in the behavior of animals could be correlated with differences in such tendencies to nervous patterning. Earlier experiments by Hertz (12) indicated that, whereas for mammals such simple figures as the square or triangle are most readily identified, patterns of radiating lines, like flower forms, are most readily identified by bees. This was interpreted as indicating a difference in the types of perceptual organization in insects and vertebrates. It turned out that the effective stimulus for the bee is the flicker produced by the lines as it flies above them (42) and its ready response to flower patterns is not evidence for a different patterning of neural impulses, but the example serves to illustrate the general type of neural mechanism for which we must search in the analysis of instincts. The nesting tern seems to notice no difference when her eggs are dyed red or black but is immediately and greatly disturbed if their smooth contour is altered by sticking on a bit of clay or putty. For her, smoothness of outline is the essential character of the egg. This is the sort of property that can be most easily interpreted in terms of the inherent tendencies to functional organization in the nervous network.

I do not mean to imply by this that the geometry of the web of the spider is exactly represented in the spider's brain, that the orb tends to be completed as the circle or square is completed in hemianopia. The process of web-spinning is much too complicated for this, but various elementary actions that contribute to the structure of the orb are understandable in such terms. The angle of radii may be determined by the angle at which the legs are held (31); the completeness or incompleteness of the orb may depend upon the readiness with which certain postures are assumed in relation to gravity. Detailed analysis of the steps in web construction will be necessary before explanation of the finished product can be attempted. The simple nest of the rat is piled and pushed about until it satisfies certain sensory requirements of reduced heat loss. The orb of the spider is perhaps a composite of several such sensory requirements, combined with some specialized geometrical perceptions such as are illustrated by the rat's more ready recognition of a triangle or circle than of irregular ink blots which differ even more in shape.

A study of complex instincts requires a detailed analysis of the exact stimulus or combination of stimuli which call forth the behavior, combined with descriptions of the behavior elicited. This has been attempted under controlled conditions only for some instinctive behavor of birds (29) and for the mating and maternal behavior of the rat, and in no case has the analysis been carried to the limits which are necessary to define the actual properties of the objects which elicit the instinctive responses. It is possible to arrange the webs of different spiders into a series which illustrates their evolution from the tangle of threads of *Theridion* to the perfect orb of *Gasteracantha*, but the webs are the products of behavior and do not tell what has changed in the spiders themselves or how their behavior has altered. The behavior of different species in web-spinning has not been analyzed.

At present there is no factual basis upon which a theory of the heritable mechanisms of specific patterns of behavior can be based. Instinctive acts have generally been described in terms of their products. They must be subjected to analysis in terms of the exact exciting stimuli and of the movements elicited. The behavior of related species must be compared from this point of view. Only then can the evolutionary steps in behavior be profitably compared.

Comparative Stability of Behavior Traits

Among morphological characters there appear to be very great differences in phylogenetic stability; some basic structural patterns have remained relatively unchanged throughout mammalian and even vertebrate evolution, while others have run the scale of imaginable changes. These differences may be due either to selection pressure or to inherent tendencies to variation. In either case there is some basis for prediction of further changes. In behavioral patterns there are similar differences in stability. I pointed out that the topological arrangement of afferent systems is remarkably constant among vertebrates. The correlated functions of sensory perception are similarly uniform. Studies of visual perception in birds, rodents, and monkeys have not revealed significant differences from man.

Emotional behavior seems likewise to have undergone relatively little change, at least in mammalian evolution. The chemistry of the endocrines is remarkably constant and the reactions of the nervous system to them are equally so. The same types of nervous derangement follow glandular disorders in dogs and in man (38). The subordinate chicken (2) and the subordinate chimpanzee (4) become aggressive and dominant under large doses of testosterone.

All investigators who have worked closely with the champanzee agree that these apes resemble man far more closely in their emotional and interpersonal reactions than in the behavior designated as intelligent. Descriptions of the social reactions of groups of dogs, associated as in sledge teams, correspond quite closely to the social reactions of the chimpanzees. For example, the dominant male dog and dominant male chimpanzee both grant feeding privilege to the receptive female. It is difficult to objectify and quantify such behavior. Judgments of emotion and temperament in animals are still largely intuitive and prescientific, as indeed they are also in human psychology, but fundamental patterns of emotional reaction and temperamental types seem to have undergone little change in mammalian evolution. The major changes are rather the result of the development of intelligent foresight and the inhibition of action in anticipation of more remote prospects.

Thus two aspects of nervous functioning seem to have remained remarkably stable in mammalian evolution. The highly differentiated structural arrangements, such as the cortical projection of fibers of the visual system, are fundamentally the same in all mammals. Their structure is understandable in terms of tissue polarization in the early spatial differentiation of the embryo. The endocrine-neural relations, influencing the general level of neural activity and the activation of specialized systems, such as those of mating and maternal behavior, seem even more primitive, with mechanisms little changed throughout the vertebrate series.

Conclusion

Evolutionary changes between marsupials and man have been almost exclusively an increase in the capacity to discover significant relations among the elements of a situation and to adjust behavior in terms of a maximum number of such relations. It is obvious that we have as yet only the vaguest notion of the neural mechanisms which produce such an organization of behavior. At the level of simple perception a start has been made toward understanding the principles of integration in terms of the properties of a network or lattice of interacting nerve cells. For more complex behavior or more abstract functions we can only guess that the same general principles apply in the interaction of neural schemata established in different lattices.

The student of physical evolution must deal with gene variation and the resultant changes in structure. The student of behavior has to consider an additional step: from gene to brain structure, from brain structure to behavior. The interpretation of nervous organization that I have described somewhat simplifies the first of these steps. Precise neural connections, where they occur, are clearly the result of the spatial characteristics of the developing organism and can be dealt with in the same terms as other structures differentiating in a polarized field. The changes in the integrative network are most probably quantitative; indeed, the difference in behavioral capacity between man and the chimpanzee may be no more than the addition of one cell generation in the segmentation of the neuroblasts which form the cerebral network.

The step from neural structure to an understanding of the details of behavior is more obscure, but I believe that the general principles of organization are within our grasp. Progress toward an understanding of the evolution of behavior depends upon our ability to analyze the properties of the nerve net and to discover the phylogenetic differences in its structure.

REFERENCES

1. Adrian, E. D. *The physical background of perception.* Oxford: Clarendon Press, 1947.
2. Allee, W. C. Social dominance and subordination among vertebrates, *Biol. Symp.*, 1942, **8**, 139–162.
3. Allport, G. *Personality.* New York: Henry Holt, 1939.
4. Birch, H., and Clark, G. Hormonal modification of social behavior: II. The effects of sex-hormone administration on the social dominance status of the female-castrate chimpanzee, *Psychosom. Med.*, 1946, **8**, 320–331.
5. Bonin, G. von. Brain-weight and body-weight of mammals, *J. gen. Psychol.*, 1937, **16**, 379–389.
6. Boring, E. G. Mind and mechanism, *Amer. J. Psychol.*, 1946, **59**, 173–192.
7. Child, C. M. Axial development in aggregates of dissociated cells from Corymorpha palma, *Physiol. Zool.*, 1928, **1**, 419–461.
8. Fuchs, W. Untersuchungen über das Sehen der Hemianopiker und Hemiamblyopiker. In Gelb, A., and Goldstein, K. (Eds.) *Psychologische Analysen hirnpathologischer Fälle.* Leipzig: Barth, 1920. Pp. 419–561.
9. Hebb, D. O. The innate organization of visual activity: I. Perception of figures by rats reared in total darkness, *J. genet. Psychol.*, 1937, **51**, 101–126.
10. Hebb, D. O. The innate organization of visual activity: II. Transfer of response in the discrimination of brightness and size by rats reared in total darkness, *J. comp. Psychol.*, 1937, **24**, 277–299.
11. Herrick, C. J. The natural history of experience, *Phil. Sci.*, 1945, **12**, 57–71.
12. Hertz, M. Über figurale Intensitäten und Qualitäten in der optischen Warhnehmung der Biene, *Biol. Zbl.*, 1933, **53**, 10–40.
13. Householder, A. S., and Landahl, H. D. *Mathematical biophysics of the central nervous system.* Bloomington: Principia Press, 1944.
14. Kepner, W. A. *Animals looking into the future.* New York: Macmillan, 1925.
15. Köhler, W., and Wallach, H. Figural aftereffects: an investigation of visual processes, *Proc. Amer. phil. Soc.*, 1944, **88**, 269–357.
16. Krall, K. *Denkende Tiere: Beiträge zur Tierseelenkunde auf Grund eigener Versuche.* Leipzig: F. Engelmann, 1912.
17. Lashley, K. S. The behavioristic interpretation of consciousness, *Psychol. Rev.*, 1923, **30**, 237–272, 329–353.
18. Lashley, K. S. The mechanism of vision: VIII. The projection of the retina upon the cerebral cortex of the rat, *J. comp. Neurol.*, 1934, **60**, 57–79.
19. Lashley, K. S. The mechanism of vision: XVI. The functioning of small remnants of the visual cortex, *J. comp. Neurol.*, 1939, **70**, 45–62.
20. Lashley, K. S. Thalamo-cortical connections of the rat's brain, *J. comp. Neurol.*, 1941, **75**, 67–121.
21. Lashley, K. S. Coalescence of neurology and psychology, *Proc. Amer. phil. Soc.*, 1941, **84**, 461–470.
22. Lashley, K. S. Patterns of cerebral integration indicated by the scotomas of migraine, *Arch. Neurol. Psychiat., Chicago*, 1941, **46**, 331–339.

23. Lashley, K. S. The problem of cerebral organization in vision, *Biol. Symp.*, 1942, **7**, 301–322.

24. Lashley, K. S. Studies of cerebral function in learning: XIII. Apparent absence of transcortical association in maze learning, *J. comp. Neurol.*, 1944, **80**, 257–281.

25. Lashley, K. S., and Clark, G. The cytoarchitecture of the cerebral cortex of Ateles: a critical examination of architectonic studies, *J. comp. Neurol.*, 1946, **85**, 223–306.

26. Lashley, K. S., and Russell, J. T. The mechanism of vision: XI. A preliminary test of innate organization, *J. genet. Psychol.*, 1934, **45**, 136–144.

27. Lillie, R. S. Some aspects of theoretical biology, *Phil. Sci.*, 1948, **15**, 118–134.

28. Lorente de Nó, R. Studies on the structure of the cerebral cortex, *J. Psychol. Neurol., Lpz.*, 1933, **45**, 381–438; **46**, 113–177.

29. Lorenz, K. Der Kumpan in der Umwelt des Vogels. *J. Orn., Lpz.*, 1935, **83**, 137–213.

30. McDougall, W. *Body and mind.* London: Methuen, 1911.

31. Peters, H. Studien am Netz der Kreuzspinne (*Aranea diadema*, L), *Z. Morph. Ökol. Tiere*, 1937, **1**, 126–150.

32. Poppelreuter, W. *Die psychischen Schädigungen durch Kopfschuss.* Leipzig: Voss, 1917.

33. Schneirla, T. C. Studies on the nature of ant learning, *J. comp. Neurol.*, 1941–43, **32**, 41–82; **35**, 149–176.

34. Senden, M. von. *Raum- und Gestaltauffassung bei operierten Blindgeborenen vor und nach der Operation.* Leipzig: Barth, 1932.

35. Sherrington, S. *Man on his nature.* Cambridge: Cambridge Univ. Press, 1947.

36. Spearman, C. *The nature of intelligence and the principles of cognition.* London: Macmillan, 1923.

37. Stevens, S. S. The operational definition of psychological concepts, *Psychol. Rev.*, 1935, **42**, 517–527.

38. Stockard, C. R. *The genetic and endocrine basis for differences in form and behavior.* Philadelphia: Wistar Inst. Anat. Biol., 1941.

39. Szymanski, J. S. Versuche über die Fähigkeit der Hunde zur Bildung von optischen Assoziationen, *Arch. ges. Physiol.*, 1918, **171**, 317–323.

40. Taylor, C. V. Demonstration of the function of the neuromotor apparatus in *Euplotes* by the method of microdissection, *Univ. Calif. Publ. Zool.*, 1920, **19**, 403–471.

41. Thorndike, E. L., Bregman, E. O., Cobb, M. N., and Woodyard, E. *The measurement of intelligence.* New York: Columbia Univ. Press, 1926.

42. Wolf, E., and Zerrahn-Wolf, G. Flicker and the reactions of bees to flowers, *J. gen. Physiol.*, 1937, **20**, 511–518.

43. Woodger, J. H. *Biological principles.* New York: Harcourt, Brace, 1929.

29. IN SEARCH OF THE ENGRAM [1]

When the mind wills to recall something, this volition causes the little [pineal] gland, by inclining successively to different sides, to impel the animal spirits toward different parts of the brain, until they come upon that part where the traces are left of the thing which it wishes to remember; for these traces are nothing else than the circumstance that the pores of the brain through which the spirits have already taken their course on presentation of the object, have thereby acquired a greater facility than the rest to be opened again the same way by the spirits which come to them; so that these spirits coming upon the pores enter therein more readily than into the others.

So wrote Descartes just three hundred years ago in perhaps the earliest attempt to explain memory in terms of the action of the brain. In the intervening centuries much has been learned concerning the nature of the impulses transmitted by nerves. Innumerable studies have defined conditions under which learning is facilitated or retarded, but, in spite of such progress, we seem little nearer to an understanding of the nature of the memory trace than was Descartes. His theory has in fact a remarkably modern sound. Substitute nerve impulse for animal spirits, synapse for pore and the result is the doctrine of learning as change in resistance of synapses. There is even a theory of scanning which is at least more definite as to the scanning agent and the source of the scanning beam than is its modern counterpart.

As interest developed in the functions of the brain the doctrine of the separate localization of mental functions gradually took form, even while the ventricles of the brain were still regarded as the active part. From Prochaska and Gall through the nineteenth century, students of clinical neurology sought the localization of specific memories. Flechsig defined the association areas as distinct from the sensory and motor. Aphasia, agnosia, and apraxia were interpreted as the result of the loss of memory images, either of objects or of kinesthetic sensations of movements to be made. The theory that memory traces are stored in association areas

[1] EDITORS' NOTE: From *Society of Experimental Biology Symposium No. 4: Physiological Mechanics in Animal Behaviour* (Cambridge University Press). Reprinted by permission of The Company and Biologists Limited. From Harvard University and the Yerkes Laboratories of Primate Biology.

adjacent to the corresponding primary sensory areas seemed reasonable and was supported by some clinical evidence. The extreme position was that of Henschen, who speculated concerning the location of single ideas or memories in single cells. In spite of the fact that more critical analytic studies of clinical symptoms, such as those of Henry Head and of Kurt Goldstein, have shown that aphasia and agnosia are primarily defects in the organization of ideas rather than the result of amnesia, the conception of the localized storing of memories is still widely prevalent (52).

While clinical students were developing theories of localization, physiologists were analysing the reflex arc and extending the concept of the reflex to include all activity. Bechterew, Pavlov and the behaviourist school in America attempted to reduce all psychological activity to simple associations or chains of conditioned reflexes. The path of these conditioned reflex circuits was described as from sense organ to cerebral sensory area, thence through associative areas to the motor cortex and by way of the pyramidal paths to the final motor cells of the medulla and cord. The discussions of this path were entirely theoretical, and no evidence on the actual course of the conditioned reflex arc was presented.

In experiments extending over the past 30 years I have been trying to trace conditioned reflex paths through the brain or to find the locus of specific memory traces. The results for different types of learning have been inconsistent and often mutually contradictory, in spite of confirmation by repeated tests. I shall summarize today a number of experimental findings. Perhaps they obscure rather than illuminate the nature of the engram, but they may serve at least to illustrate the complexity of the problem and to reveal the superficial nature of many of the physiological theories of memory that have been proposed.

I shall have occasion to refer to training of animals in a variety of tasks, so shall give a very brief description of the methods used. The animals studied have been rats and monkeys with, recently, a few chimpanzees. Two lines of approach to the problem have been followed. One is purely behavioural and consists in the analysis of the sensory excitations which are actually associated with reactions in learning and which are effective in eliciting the learned reactions. The associated reactions are similarly analysed. These studies define the patterns of nervous activity at receptor and effector levels and specify certain characteristics which the memory trace must have. The second approach is by surgical destruction of parts of the brain. Animals are trained in various tasks ranging from direct sensory-motor associations to the solution of difficult problems. Before or after training, associative tracts are cut or portions of the brain removed and effects of these operations on initial learning or postoperative retention are measured. At the termination of the experiments the brains are sectioned and the extent of damage reconstructed from serial sections. The brains are also analysed for secondary degeneration, so far as available histological methods permit.

Elimination of the Motor Cortex

I first became sceptical of the supposed path of the conditioned reflex when I found that rats, trained in a differential reaction to light, showed no reduction in accuracy of performance when almost the entire motor cortex, along with the frontal poles of the brain, was removed. This observation led to a series of experiments designed to test the part played by the motor cortex or Betz cell area in the retention of various habits. The matter can be tested either by removing the motor cortex or by sever-

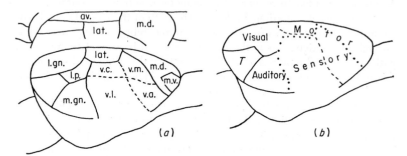

Fig. 29.1. Functional divisions of the rat's brain. (*a*) The projection fields of the principal thalamic nuclei: av., anteroventral; lat., lateral; l.gn., lateral geniculate; l.p., lateral, pars posterior; m.d., median dorsal; m.gn., median geniculate; m.v., median ventral; v., the various divisions of the central nucleus. The projection fields of the median nuclei (m.d., m.v.) correspond to the prefrontal areas of primates. (*b*) Location of visual, auditory, and overlapping sensory-motor areas. (After Lashley, 44.) The region marked *T* is probably homologous with the temporal association area of primates.

ing its connexions with the sensory areas of the brain. Both methods have been used with the rat and the monkey.

The sensory and motor areas of the brains of these animals have been mapped by anatomic methods and by electric stimulation. Figure 29.1 shows the principal areas of the rat's brain, the separate auditory and visual areas and the overlapping sensory and motor areas. Figure 29.2 is a composite from several sources of the chief sensory and motor areas of the brain of the macaque monkey.

Incisions were made through the cortex and underlying fibres of the rat's brain such as to sever the visual areas more or less completely from the motor regions of the brain. The rats were then trained in what I have called the conditional reaction. They are taught to jump to a white triangle and to avoid a white X when both figures are on a black background, but to choose the × and avoid the triangle if the background is striped; the direction of choice is conditional upon the character of the background. This is the most difficult visual generalization that we have been able to teach the rat. Animals with incisions like those shown in Fig. 29.3, which practically separate the motor regions from the visual, were able to learn this reaction as quickly as did normal controls (42).

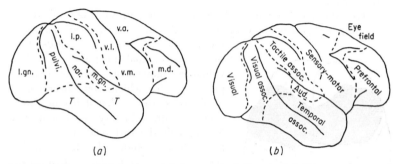

Fig. 29.2. Functional divisions of the monkey's brain. (a) The projection of the principal thalamic nuclei. Abbreviations as in Fig. 29.1. The homologies between the divisions of the central and lateral nuclei are uncertain. (b) Location of functional areas.

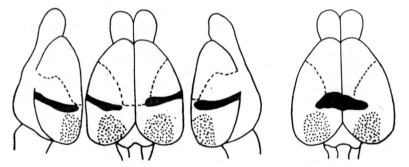

Fig. 29.3. Lesions partially separating the visual area (stippled) from the motor areas (outlined by dashes) of the rat's brain without disturbing visual learning.

Monkeys were trained to open various latch boxes. The motor areas were then removed, as shown in Fig. 29.4. Note that these lesions involved both the Betz cell area and the premotor area, including parts of the eye fields around the arcuate sulcus. This operation produces a temporary paralysis, but after 8 to 12 weeks this paralysis recovers to such an extent that the animals are capable of the movements required to open the boxes. During this recovery period they did not have access to the training boxes.

When sufficiently recovered, they were tested and opened the boxes promptly without random exploratory movements. The tasks require both visual recognition of the latches and semiskilled movements, such as turning a crank. Removal of the motor areas did not produce a loss of memory for the movements (33). Jacobsen has since confirmed these observations with a chimpanzee from which the motor cortex was removed (24).

These experiments seem to rule out the motor cortex or Betz cell area as containing any part of the conditioned-reflex arc. The traditional view of the function of this area regards it as the region of final integration of skilled voluntary movements. My own interpretation, to which few neurologists would subscribe, is that it has no direct concern with voluntary movement, but is a part of the vast reflex postural system which includes the basal nuclei, cerebellar and vestibular systems. Certainly there is no evidence that it forms a part of the conditioned reflex circuit.

For the rat the experiments rule out the whole frontal region of the brain from participation in visual habits. In the monkey there remains another possibility. The so-called visual associative area (area 18) has direct connexion with the cortex of the arcuate sulcus (area 8), and this in turn with the premotor cortex (area 6). This last area is also motor and perhaps equivalent in function with the Betz cell area (5). The cortex of the arcuate sulcus and of a considerable surrounding area was removed from five monkeys that had been trained in a variety of visual discriminative reactions. After the operations they showed perfect retention of all their visual habits (45). Jacobsen (24) has reported loss of certain latchbox habits in monkeys after removal of area 6, but there are indications that this may be a kinesthetic-sensory area (17, 57), and the loss cannot be ascribed to disturbance of its function as a final common motor path. I have removed it in combination with area 4 without disrupting motor habits (33).

I have occasionally seen the type of defect reported by Jacobsen after prefrontal lobe lesions, as also reported by Kennard (27), but it has not

Fig. 29.4. Extent of cortical lesion which did not abolish latch-box habits. The lesion is bounded caudally by the central fissure and extends forward to include the arcuate sulcus.

occurred consistently and its occurrence remains unexplained. I did not find it after removal of area 6 in conjunction with the Betz cell area.

Transcortical Conduction

There is evidence, not only that the motor cortex does not participate in the transmission of the conditioned-reflex pattern, but also that the transmission of impulses over well-defined, isolated paths from one part of the cortex to another is inessential for performance of complicated habits. The maze habit of the rat almost certainly involves the utilization of several sensory modalities, visual, tactile and kinesthetic. In a rather complicated set of experiments I attempted to test the importance of connexions across the cortex for maze performance. Rats were trained on the maze, then knife cuts were made through the cortex and underlying fibres, separating different functional areas or cutting through functional areas. The incisions were long, averaging half of the entire length of the cerebral hemispheres. After recovery the animals were tested in retention of the maze habit. In other experiments the incisions were made before training and their effect upon the rate of initial learning was tested. In neither initial learning nor in retention could any certain effect of separating the various parts of the cortex be demonstrated. If the incisions interrupted sensory tracts to the cortex, there was loss of the habit, but uncomplicated separation of cortical areas produced no effect on performance. Figure 28.2 gives composite diagrams of incisions which were without effect on maze performance (44).

Both the anatomic evidence of Le Gros Clark (7) and the physiological evidence from strychninization of the cortex (4) show that the primary visual area has direct axon connexions only with the immediately adjacent cortex. In experiments which I shall report in more detail in considering the function of associative areas, I removed the greater part of this band of cortex surrounding the visual areas from five monkeys that had been trained in a variety of visual habits (Fig. 29.5). This operation almost certainly destroyed all the relay connexions across the cortex from the macular fields. It produced no loss of visual habits based on discrimination of the colour, brightness, or form of objects (45).

Miss Wade trained monkeys in habits which are abolished by destruction of the frontal lobes and which require visual, tactile and kinesthetic adjustments. I cut the transcortical fibres of the frontal lobes in these animals, leaving only the projection fibres for the area. There was no disturbance of performance after the operations (unpublished experiments).

Such results are certainly puzzling. They leave us with almost no understanding of the function of the associative fibres which extend across from one part of the cortex to another. The results are difficult to accept, yet they are supported by various other lines of evidence. Smith (54) and Akelaitis (1) have reported careful studies of human patients in whom the corpus callosum (the great commissure of fibres connecting the two hemispheres) had been severed in an effort to stop the spread of Jacksonian epilepsy. These investigators were not able to demonstrate any effects of the operation except a slight slowing of reaction time, which was equally great, whether the reaction was on the same or opposite side of the body to that stimulated. Sperry (55) has divided the arm motor and sensory areas of the monkey's brain into a number of small square divisions (Fig. 29.6) by careful subpial section. Although the operations were intended to sever only the intrinsic fibres of the cortex, they actually destroyed most of the longer loop fibres as well. Such animals do not show

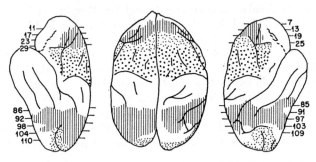

Fig. 29.5. Lesions, marked by hatching, which destroyed the greater part of the so-called visual associative areas in a monkey without affecting visual functions.

any postoperative incoordination of the movements of the different segments of the arm and use the arm efficiently in the performance of habitual movements.

It is difficult to interpret such findings, but I think that they point to the conclusion that the associative connexions or memory traces of the conditioned reflex do not extend across the cortex as well-defined arcs or paths. Such arcs are either diffused through all parts of the cortex, pass by relay through lower centres, or do not exist.

There is the possibility that the chief associative connexions between functional areas of the cortex are by connexions through the thalamus. I doubt this for two reasons. The techniques that have been used to demonstrate cortical efferents to the thalamus, the Marchi stain and strychninization of the cortex, are unreliable indices of the direction of fibres. The supposed cortico-thalamic fibres follow the paths of the afferent fibres and may not be efferent. Secondly, in the rat at least there is little evidence of an elaborate system of intrathalamic association fibres. After a cortical injury thalamic nuclei degenerate completely without leaving a residue of internuncial cells. The question of the importance of intrathalamic association is not settled, and none of the available anatomic or physiological techniques is capable of giving conclusive evidence.

A few experiments by Ingebritsen (23) on the spinal cord suggest that the essential pattern of a learned reaction can be transmitted by a diffuse nervous network. Ingebritsen made double hemisections of the spinal cord of rats, severing one half at the second, the other at the fifth cervical level. These lesions cut all long fibres connecting the brain with the spinal motor centres of the limbs. Nevertheless, such rats retained maze habits and were able to learn to operate latch boxes requiring that they rise on

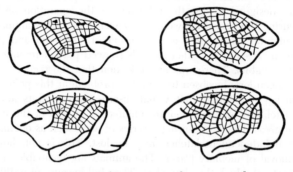

Fig. 29.6. Pattern of incisions in the motor and sensory areas of two monkeys which did not produce incoordination movements. (After Sperry, 55.)

the hindfeet and depress a lever with the forepaws. . . . There are no long fibres, either sensory or motor, crossing over between the two levels of these sections. Habit patterns cannot be acquired by the isolated spinal cord (26). Somehow, the control of the motor pattern essential for the performance of the complex acts traverses the network of short internuncial cells of the spinal cord.

The Problem of the "Association Areas"

In anatomic theories of the memory trace the association areas of the cortex have played a major part. Frontal, parietal, occipital and temporal associative areas have been distinguished as regions of the cortex, relatively lacking in massive connexions with the lower centres of the brain. On the basis of some clinical evidence, but chiefly because of their anatomic relations, these areas have been considered as associative and as the storehouses of memory images of sensations derived from the adjacent sensory areas. Thus areas 18 and 19 of Brodmann's questionable divisions have been called the visual associative areas, areas 5 and 7 tactile associative, and areas 20, 21, and 22 of the temporal lobe the auditory association areas. The prefrontal area was considered by Hitzig to be a higher integrative region because he believed that it showed the greatest evolutionary growth in the primate brain. Special memory functions were also ascribed to it, however.

S. I. Franz reported that the removal of the frontal association areas of cats destroyed recently formed habits but left old, well-established habits unaffected (15). The actual observation was that the cats lost their habits of opening latch boxes but would still come when called. His operations destroyed much of the motor areas as well as the prefrontal cortex. I later trained monkeys on latch boxes and removed the prefrontal cortex, in an experiment designed to test the influence of the operation on learning ability. During the period allowed for recovery one of the animals found the experimental boxes piled in the corner of the room and promptly opened them. Tests of the other animals showed perfect retention of the manipulative habits. There was no indication that the recently acquired habits had been lost. Jacobsen took up the problem at this point and carried it further. He found that visual discriminative habits and simple habits of latch-box manipulation are unaffected by loss of the prefrontal association areas. Habits requiring a series of acts, such as opening a box with several independent latches, may be lost. This is not, however, a simple removal of memory traces. The animals are incapable of relearning the functions which they have lost. They fail because of a difficulty in going on from one task to the next, not from loss of memory of the individual items of the task (25).

Loss of the delayed reaction after removal of the prefrontal lobes of the monkey has been interpreted as a loss of immediate memory. However, this task and others, which are affected by prefrontal injury, all involve a series of conflicting actions. Difficulty in maintaining a constant set or attitude is the real basis of the loss. Such an interpretation fits better with clinical findings than does the hypothesis of memory defect.

We have recently been testing the relation of other associative areas to memory functions in the monkey. Five spider monkeys were trained on a variety of visual tasks. A band of cortex surrounding the primary visual areas and including the visual associative areas of Campbell and Brodmann was then removed (Fig. 29.6), and the animals were tested for retention of habits based on discrimination of colours, of geometric forms, and of a number of familiar objects, such as visual recognition of their home cages, of the caretaker, and the like. No loss of any visual memories could be demonstrated (45).

Similar experiments with habits of tactile discrimination are now being completed. The monkeys are required to reach through a hole in a partition and to distinguish variously shaped covers of food dishes by touch alone. They learn readily such tasks as to choose a cylinder and reject a prism, if both are smooth, but to choose the prism, if both are coated with sandpaper. When they had reached a standard criterion of accuracy, the parietal associative areas (Brodmann's areas 5 and 7) were removed. No animal has shown significant loss of the habits based on tactile discrimination after removal of these areas alone (Dr. Josephine Blum).

Removal of the lateral surfaces of the temporal lobes alone has also not affected visual or tactile habits.

A number of experiments with the rat have shown that habits of visual discrimination survive the destruction of any part of the cerebral cortex except the primary visual projection area. Similarly for auditory habits and the auditory cortex. There is no indication of specialized memory areas outside the primary sensory fields. Although there are not clearly distinguished associative areas in the rat's cortex, I have become somewhat sceptical of the existence of any great difference in the extent of associative areas, as between the rat and monkey. The best anatomic index that we have of the functional differentiation of a cortical area is its connexions with the thalamus. The prefrontal cortex of man is the projection field of the dorsomedial and ventromedial nuclei. The corresponding nuclei in the rat's thalamus project to a large frontal region, perhaps proportionately as large as the prefrontal lobes of man (40). This region also includes the electrically excitable points for the head and part of that for the forelegs. It has therefore been classed as motor, but it is equally justifiable to class it as corresponding to the human prefrontal cortex.

It has been claimed that the differentiation of a number of cerebral areas contributes to man's superior intelligence by avoiding confusion of functions, but, if the anatomic relations in man and the rat were reversed, it would be concluded with equal assurance that, because intellectual activity requires close integration of different functions, the advantage lies with the brain in which functional areas are not sharply set off. Such *post hoc* arguments based on anatomic grounds alone have little value for functional interpretations. Many current conceptions of cerebral physiology are based upon just such dubious inferences from anatomic data.

The outcome of the experiments involving removal of the associative areas of the monkey was unexpected, in spite of the fact that it confirms the earlier results with the rat. The conclusion, which seems to be forced by the accumulated data, runs counter to the accepted tradition concerning the organization of the cerebral cortex. Memory traces, at least of simple sensory-motor associations, are not laid down and stored within the associative areas; at least not within the restricted associative area supposedly concerned with each sense modality. Memory disturbances of simple sensory habits follow only upon very extensive experimental destruction, including almost the entire associative cortex. Even combined destruction of the prefrontal, parietal, occipital and temporal areas, exclusive of the primary sensory cortex, does not prevent the animal from forming such habits, although preexisting habits are lost and their reformation is greatly retarded.

These results, showing that the so-called associative areas are not essential to preservation of memory traces, have been obtained with rats and monkeys. Is there a greater cortical differentiation in anthropoid apes and man? We have experimental data only on the prefrontal associative cortex of the chimpanzee and of man. Bilateral removal of the entire prefrontal granular cortex in five chimpanzees in our laboratory has not resulted in any memory defect. One two-year-old animal, lacking prefrontal and parietal areas, removed in early infancy, falls well within the normal range in all aspects of development. Adult chimpanzees, trained in such complicated habits as choosing an object, like a model shown, retain the habits after removal of the entire prefrontal cortex. We have not been able to demonstrate loss of any memory or, in fact, of any function after such operations.

Clinical data, with amnesias following apparently small lesions, seem to contradict such experimental findings. However, lesions in the human brain are mostly the result either of tumor growth or of severe traumatism, both of which probably produce widespread changes in addition to the local injury. The surgical removal of parts of the frontal lobes in the recent topectomy studies has not produced such severe defects as usually result from traumatic destruction of the lobes (51).

The Role of Subcortical Structures

Perhaps we have been looking in the wrong place for the conditioned-reflex arcs or memory traces. Are they formed somewhere else than in the cortex? Experiments on the thalamus and other subcortical structures are technically difficult, and there is little direct evidence on this question. Since the classical experiments of Goltz a number of investigators have studied the capacity of the totally decorticate animal to learn. The outcome of these experiments is that such animals can form simple sensory-motor associations, although with extreme slowness in comparison with the rate of the normal animal (18, 53). We must ask, however, whether such learning occurs when the cortex is intact.

When the sensory or associative areas of the cerebral cortex are destroyed, the corresponding nuclei of the neo-thalamus degenerate, so this portion of the subcortex is eliminated from consideration by the same experiments which rule out the cortical association areas. The only experiments bearing upon the participation of other subcortical centres suggest that subcortical learning does not occur when the cortex is functioning.

Fischel (14) has maintained, solely from comparative psychological studies, that the basal ganglia are the seat of the space-coordinate elements of motor habits. I have destroyed the greater part of these structures in rats, trained in the discrimination box, without producing loss of orientation. The animals may perform forced circus movements but, in spite of this, they maintain their orientation in the problem box (31). The basal ganglia in man are subject to various degenerative diseases. The symptoms of such diseases are, in general, tremors and other disturbances of coordination at a primitive level, but without evidence of apraxia or other disorder of the learned patterns of motor coordination. The evidence seems conclusive that in mammals the basal nuclei are not an essential link in the patterning of learned activities.

It has been widely held that although memory traces are at first formed in the cerebral cortex, they are finally reduced or transferred by long practice to subcortical levels. The evidence for this has been the apparently greater fragility of recently formed habits than of old habits; the supposedly greater resistance of the latter to brain injuries. The amnesias following electroshock therapy indicate that it is the age of the trace and not the amount of practice that has built it up which determines its survival, and a difference of a few minutes in the age of memories may suffice to determine their loss or survival. This is scarcely evidence for reduction to lower levels of the nervous system. The chief argument for the dropping out of memory traces from the cortex has seemingly run somewhat as follows: Consciousness is a function of the cerebral cortex; long-practised habits become automatic and are performed without conscious control; therefore they are no longer mediated by the cerebral cortex. Both premises of this syllogism are probably false, and the conclusion would not follow if they were true.

When rats are trained in a habit based upon the discrimination of intensities of light, to choose a brightly lighted alley and avoid a dimly lighted one, the removal of the striate cortex completely abolishes the habit. The animals are able to relearn the reaction and require as much practice as they did for initial learning. One group of animals was trained in this habit and given 1,200 trials of overtraining, daily practice for a period of 3 months. Their behaviour strongly suggested automatization of the habit. The striate areas were then removed. The habit was lost, just as in the case of animals which are operated as soon as they give evidence of the presence of the habit. The long overtraining did not eliminate the participation of the cortex (30).

This visual habit can be formed in the absence of the visual cortex, and the rates of learning with and without the visual area are exactly the same. The average for 100 normal animals is 125 trials; for nearly 100 without the visual areas it is 123 trials. After such animals, lacking the visual cortex, have learned the brightness reaction, any other part of the cerebral cortex may be destroyed without disturbing the habit. Apparently no other part of the cortex takes over the learning function (32). If, in addition to removal of the striate areas, the pretectile region of the thalamus and the optic tectum are destroyed, the animals cannot learn the discrimination reaction (37). These facts indicate that, in the absence of the visual cortex, the learning of the brightness reaction is carried out by the optic tectum. However, so long as the visual cortex is intact, removal of the tectum has no effect whatever upon the performance of visual habits. The tectum apparently does not participate in visual learning so long as the cortex is intact (37).

Dunlap (8) has advanced the hypothesis that complex serial habits, such as those of maze running, playing a musical passage, or speaking a sentence, are at first chains of sensory-motor reactions in which excitations from muscular contractions in one movement of the series serve as stimuli to elicit the next. He holds that, with continued practice, there is a short-circuiting of these conditioned reflex pathways through the cerebellum and that the peripheral elements drop out. McCarthy and I (47) attempted to test this hypothesis by training rats in the maze, removing the cerebellum, and testing for retention. The operations greatly disturbed the motor coordination of these animals. Some of them practically rolled through the maze, but they rolled without entering the blind alleys. There was no loss of memory of the sequence of turns in the maze.

These few experiments are, of course, by no means conclusive. They constitute, however, the only direct evidence available, and they definitely point to the conclusion that, if the cerebral cortex is intact, the associative connexions of simple conditioned reflexes are not formed in the subcortical structures of the brain.

The studies which I have reported thus far point to the conclusion that habits based upon visual discrimination are mediated by the striate areas, by the primary visual cortex, and do not involve the activity of any other part of the cerebral cortex. The conduction of impulses is from the retina to the lateral geniculate nuclei, thence to the striate areas, and from them down to some subcortical nervous mechanism. The path beyond the striate cortex is unknown. It may be direct to the spinal cord. There is some evidence that the pyramidal paths contain many fibres from all parts of the cerebral cortex, not from the Betz cell area only.

It seems probable that the same restriction of simple discriminative habits to the primary sensory areas holds also for other sensory modalities. The evidence is less complete, but what there is is consistent with the data on the visual system.

The evidence thus indicates that in sensory-motor habits of the conditioned reflex type no part of the cerebral cortex is essential except the primary sensory area. There is no transcortical conduction from the sensory areas to the motor cortex, and the major subcortical nuclear masses, thalamus, striatum, colliculi and cerebellum, do not play a part in the recognition of sensory stimuli or in the habit patterning of motor reactions.

The Engram within Sensory Areas (Equipotential Regions)

The experiments reported indicate that performance of habits of the conditioned reflex type is dependent upon the sensory areas and upon no other part of the cerebral cortex. What of localization within the sensory areas? Direct data upon this question are limited, but point to the conclusion that so long as some part of the sensory field remains intact and there is not a total loss of primary sensitivity, the habit mechanism can still function. Thus, in a series of experiments attempting to locate accurately the visual cortex of the rat, parts of the occipital lobes were destroyed in a variety of combinations. In these experiments it appeared that, so long as some part of the anterolateral surface of the striate cortex (the projection field of the temporal retina corresponding to the macula of primates) remained intact, there was no loss of habit. Any small part of the region was capable of maintaining the habits based on discrimination of intensities of light (37).

In a later experiment an attempt was made to determine the smallest amount of visual cortex which is capable of mediating habits based upon detail vision. The extent of visual cortex remaining after operation was determined by counting undegenerated cells in the lateral geniculate nucleus. Discrimination of visual figures could be learned when only one-sixtieth of the visual cortex remained (39). No comparable data are available on postoperative retention, but from incidental observations in other experiments I am confident that retention would be possible with the same amount of tissue.

In an early study by Franz (16) the lateral surfaces of the occipital lobes of the monkey were destroyed after the animals had been trained in pattern and colour discrimination. These operations involved the greater part of what is now known to be the projection field of the macula. There was no loss of the habits. I have destroyed the cortex of the retrocalcarine fissure (the perimacular field) without destroying visual memories. The results with monkeys thus support the more ample data for the rat; the visual memory traces survive any cortical lesion, provided some portion of the field of acute vision remains intact.

This lack of definite habit localization might really have been predicted from psychological data alone. Analysis of the effective stimuli in discriminative learning reveals that the association is independent of particular sensory nerve fibres. It is a response to a pattern of excitation which may vary widely in position on the sensory surface and consequently in cortical projection. The reactions involved in motor habits show the same sort of functional equivalence; a motor habit is not a predetermined set of muscular contractions but is a series of movements in relation to bodily posture and to the complex pattern of the environment. The writing of one's name, for example, is not a stereotyped series of contractions of particular muscles but is a series of movements in relation to the body planes which can be performed with any motor organ and with any degree of amplitude.

I have not time here to report in detail the experiments which justify the conclusion that neither the afferent path nor the efferent is fixed by habit. The mass of evidence accumulated by gestalt psychologists shows conclusively that it is the pattern and not the localization of energy on the sense organ that determines its functional effect. Similar motor equivalence is demonstrated by a variety of less systematic evidence. The psychological studies, like the more limited direct experiments on the brain, point to the conclusion that the memory trace is located in all parts of the functional area; that various parts are equipotential for its maintenance and activation.

Facilitative Functions in Learning and Retention (Mass Action)

The experiments thus far reported have been concerned almost entirely with discriminative habits requiring only an association between a single sensory stimulus and a motor response. A very different picture develops in experiments with other types of learning. If rats are trained in the maze and then have portions of the cortex removed, they show more or less loss of the habit. If a small amount of cortex is destroyed, 5 to 10 per cent, the loss may be scarcely detectable. If large amounts, say 50 per cent or more, are destroyed, the habit is completely lost, and relearning may require many times as much practice as did initial learning. The amount of loss, measured in terms of the practice required for relearning, is, on the average, closely proportional to the amount of cortex destroyed. Figure 29.7 shows the relation for one group of rats on a relatively difficult maze with eight culs de sac. There is some evidence that the more difficult the task, the greater the relative effect of the larger lesions (34, 48). Similar results have been obtained with latch-box learning and retention (36). So far as it is possible to analyse the data from more than 200 diverse operations, the amount of loss from a given extent of cortical destruction is about the same, no matter what part of the cerebral hemispheres is destroyed, provided that the destruction is roughly similar in both hemispheres.

The explanation of this quantitative relationship is difficult. In learning the maze the rat certainly employs a variety of sensory cues, visual, tactile, kinesthetic, olfactory, possibly auditory. Brain injuries destroy various sensory fields and the larger the lesion the greater the reduction in avail-

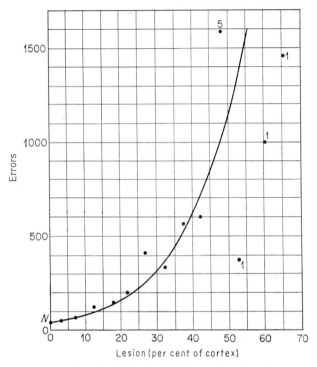

Fig. 29.7. The relation of errors in maze learning to extent of cerebral damage in the rat. The extent of brain injury is expressed as the percentage of the surface area of the iso-cortex destroyed. Data from 60 normal and 127 brain-op-erated animals are averaged by class intervals of 5 per cent destruction. The curve is the best fitting one of logarithmic form. For lesions above 45 per cent the number of cases (indicated by numerals on the graph) is too small for relia-bility. (After Lashley and Wiley, 48.)

able sense data. The production of different amounts of sensory deficit would thus appear to be the most reasonable explanation of the quantita-tive relation between habit loss and extent of lesion (13, 22). Sensory deficit certainly plays a role in it. In the experiment on effects of incisions through the cortex, which was described earlier, the severity of loss of the maze habit correlated highly with the interruption of sensory pathways, as determined from degeneration of the thalamus.

However, sensory loss will not account for all of the habit deterioration. There is evidence which shows that another more mysterious effect is involved. In the first place, destruction of a single sensory area of the cortex produces a far greater deficit in maze or latch-box performance than does loss of the corresponding sense modality. A comparison was made of the effects on retention of the latch-box habits of combined loss of vision, vibrissae touch, and the anesthesia to touch and movement produced by sectioning the dorsal half of the spinal cord at the third cervical level. This latter operation severs the columns of Gall and Burdach, which convey tactile and kinesthetic impulses, and also severs the pyramidal tracts which have a dorsal position in the rat. The combined peripheral sense privation and section of the pyramids produced less loss of the latch-box habits than did destruction of a single sensory area of the cortex (36). Secondly, when blind animals are trained in the maze, the removal of the primary visual cortex produces a severe loss of the habit with serious difficulty in relearning, although the animals could have used no visual cues during the initial learning (43).

A possible explanation of this curious effect was that the rat forms concepts of spatial relations in visual terms, as man seems to do, and that the space concepts are integrated in the visual cortex. The visual cortex might then function in the formation of spatial habits, even when the animal loses its sight. To test this Tsang (56) reared rats blind from birth, trained them as adults in the maze, then destroyed the visual cortex. The resultant loss of the maze habit by these animals was as severe as in animals which had been reared with vision. The hypothesis concerning the formation of visual space concepts was not confirmed.

Our recent studies of the associative areas of the monkey are giving similar results to those gained with rats. Visual and tactile habits are not disturbed by the destruction singly, either of the occipital, parietal, or lateral temporal regions, so long as the primary sensory fields remain. However, combined destruction of these regions, as shown in Fig. 29.8, does produce a loss of the habits with retarded relearning. Higher level functions, such as the conditional reaction, delayed reaction, or solution of the multiple stick problem, show deterioration after extensive damage in any part of the cortex. The capacity for delayed reaction in monkeys, for example (to remember in which of two boxes food was placed), may be seriously reduced or abolished by removal either of the prefrontal lobes or of the occipital associative cortex or of the temporal lobes. That is, small lesions, embracing no more than a single associative area, do not produce loss of any habit; large lesions produce a deterioration which affects a variety of habits, irrespective of the sensory-motor elements involved.

Results such as these have led me to formulate a theory of mass action or mass facilitation. It is, essentially, that performance of any function depends upon two variables in nervous activity. The reaction mechanism, whether of instinctive or of learned activity, is a definite pattern of integrated neurons with a variable threshold of excitability. The availability of such patterns, the ease with which they can be activated, is dependent upon less specific facilitative effects. This facilitation can come from a variety of sources. Some instinctive behaviour seems to require hormonal activation, probably a direct chemical effect upon specific nervous elements. Emotional facilitation may produce a temporary activation. Continued activity of related mechanisms may facilitate the whole group of associated reactions; a sort of warming-up effect.

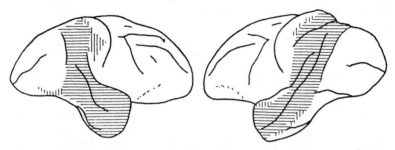

Fig. 29.8. Minimal lesion which produces disturbances in tactile or visual memory in the monkey.

There are indications (28), although little systematic evidence, that the severity of postoperative amnesia varies with the intensity of motivation. Rats trained in a discrimination without punishment with electric shock for errors may show loss of the habit after lesions which do not produce loss in animals which were trained with punishment. The greater effects of cortical lesions in monkeys than in rats may be in part a result of the greater difficulty in getting consistent motivation in the higher animals. In man an amnesia often seems to be a difficulty rather than impossibility of recall; recall may be possible but only with extreme effort and fatigue. I believe that the evidence strongly favours the view that amnesia from brain injury rarely, if ever, is due to the destruction of specific memory traces. Rather, the amnesias represent a lowered level of vigilance, a greater difficulty in activating the organized patterns of traces, or a disturbance of some broader system of organized functions.

In interpreting apparent loss of memory after cerebral damage, extreme caution is necessary. The poor performance in tasks may be due to the destruction of specific associative connexions, but is instead generally, I believe always, the result rather of interference with a higher level functional patterning. Some experiments of Dr. Klüver's (personal communication) illustrate this point. Monkeys were trained in a variety of discriminative reactions calling for use of different sense modalities by a method that required them to pull in the stimulus objects by attached strings. Extensive lesions in different cortical areas all caused loss of these habits. The monkeys simply pulled the strings at random. They were retrained in the discrimination of weights. When this was learned, the habits based on other sense modalities (reactions to intensities of light, for example) returned spontaneously. What had been disturbed by all the operations was the set or attitude to compare stimuli, not the specific memory of which one was correct.

This example perhaps illustrates at a primitive level the characteristic of amnesias as seen clinically. Apparent loss of memory is secondary to a disorder in the structuring of concepts. Some physiological mode of organizing or integrating activity is affected rather than specific associative bonds.

The Complexity of the Memory Trace

The experiments that I have reviewed deal with only a small part of the whole problem of the memory trace; with those aspects which can most readily be studied in experiments with animals. Immediate memory presents a different type of problem. It is highly probable that immediate memory is maintained by some sort of after-discharge of the originally excited neurons. Such persistent activity can scarcely be the basis of more permanent memory, although Ebbecke (10) and Edgell (11) have formulated theories of memory in terms of persistent states of excitation. It is by no means certain that all memory is mediated by a single type of mechanism; that motor skills and eidetic images, for example, have any physiological properties in common. The attempt to account for all memory by any single theory involves assumptions which are not supported by any evidence now available.

Much of learning theory has been based upon supposedly isolated and simple instances of association, on the assumption that these represent a primitive prototype of all memory. However, an analysis of even the conditioned reflex indicates that it is not the simple, direct association of stimulus and response that it has been thought to be. I served as experimenter and subject for several years in experiments employing both the salivary method of Pavlov and the motor reactions of Bechterew. The experience convinced me that, far from being a simple sensory-motor reaction, the conditioned reflex is very complicated (29). The S-R diagram is misleadingly schematic. The effective stimulus is not only the object which the experimenter designates as S, but a whole background of other objects constituting the situation in which the experiment is conducted. Every stimulus has a space setting. When, for example, the rat is trained to react to a triangle, he fails to respond if the figure is rotated through more than 10 to 15 degrees (12). This means that the memory trace of the figure is tied in with the space coordinates of the animal's postural system. This system of space coordinates is a part of the postural reflex system which pervades every aspect of behaviour. There is scarcely a memory which does not have spatial orientation, either with reference to the planes of the body or to external space in addition.

Most skilled acts, from running a maze to playing a musical phrase or speaking a sentence, involve a timed series of actions which cannot be accounted for as a simple chain of conditioned reflexes (46). The serial timing of actions is among the most important and least studied of behavioural problems. Almost all memories except those of automatized motor habits are dated, as Bergson (3) has emphasized; that is, they have a temporal position in the series of memories which constitutes the individual's past. The memory trace is associated with this series as well as with the particular objects which make up its central core.

The conditioned reflex also includes an element of affective reinforcement. Corresponding to the nature of the conditioning stimulus, there is fear of electric shock, objectively demonstrable by cardiac and respiratory changes, anticipation of acid in the mouth with slight nausea, or expectation of food (29). Unless this affective element is aroused, the conditioned reflex does not occur. So-called extinction of the conditioned reflex is not a weakening of the specific association, but a waning of this affective reinforcement. Other types of association also have dynamic aspects. The amnesic aphasias seem to be due less to a weakening of specific associations than to a reduction in some general form of facilitation. Henry Head has expressed this as a reduction of "vigilance," without attempting to define further the nature of the function which is disturbed.

A variety of evidence (50) shows that, in a memorized series of nonsense syllables, associations are formed, not only between adjacent words but also between words remote from each other in the series. This, I believe, is an illustration at a primitive level of the fact that every memory becomes part of a more or less extensive organization. When I read a scientific paper, the new facts presented become associated with the field of knowledge of which it is a part. Later availability of the specific items of the paper depends upon a partial activation of the whole body of associations. If one has not thought of a topic for some time, it is difficult to recall details. With review or discussion of the subject, however, names, dates, references which seemed to be forgotten rapidly become available to memory. Head (20) has given instances of such recall by multiple reinforcement in his studies of aphasia. Although there are no systematic experiments upon this "warming-up" effect, it is a matter of common experience and is evidence, I believe, that recall involves the subthreshold activation of a whole system of associations which exert some sort of mutual facilitation.

All this is by way of indicating the probable complexity of the memory trace of even the simplest associations. The engram of a new association, far from consisting of a single bond or neuron connexion, is probably a reorganization of a vast system of associations involving the interrelations of hundreds of thousands or millions of neurons.

Some Quantitative Considerations

It has been customary to assume that, since the nervous system contains so many millions of neurons, there must be a large reservoir of cells or of synaptic connexions which can be modified and reserved for specific memory functions. Dunlap (9) has expressed the view that every individual has far more brain cells than he is ever called upon to use, and has urged this as an argument against any congenital restriction of ability. A similar view has been implied in the identification of intelligence as the individual's number of unpreempted and available memory bonds. However, only the vaguest sort of anatomic data have been available to support such theories. Analysis of actual cell numbers involved in a reaction system gives little indication of a reserve of unused connexions and raises a very difficult question as to the way in which the same system can mediate different functions.

I have counted or estimated the number of cells at different levels in the visual system of the rat. The numbers, which I believe are correct within approximately 10 per cent, are given in Table 29.1. You will note that there is a marked concentration of paths from the retinal myoids to the lateral geniculate nucleus, such that an average of nearly 300 myoids feed into each thalamo-cortical path. At the cortical level there is some dispersion, but it is not great. In the receptive layer (lamina iv) there are fewer than four neurons for each afferent fibre, and in the whole visual cortex there are only nineteen neurons for each afferent fibre.

The rat's maximal visual acuity is about 30 min. of arc, as determined by behavioural tests and from the resolving power of the lens system. Because of the extreme curvature of the cornea and lens the visual field of one eye subtends about 210 degrees. If acuity were uniform throughout the retina, it would require more than 80,000 fibres to represent each acuity unit of the retina by one central fibre. The concentration of ganglion cells falls off from 130 per hundredth square millimetre at the fixation point to 65 at the ora serrata (35). Assuming that acuity decreases proportionately, some 40,000 separate paths are required to represent each acuity unit at the cortex by a single afferent fibre. This corresponds fairly

Table 29.1. The Number of Neurons at Each Level in the Visual System
of the Rat (Unilateral)

Level	Total no. of neurons	Ratio to fibres in radiation
Retinal cells:		
Rods	9,180,000	273·0
Cones	120,000	
Bipolar	3,530,000	104·0
Ganglion	260,000	13·1
Lateral geniculate	34,000	1·0
Cortical cells:		
Lamina vii	68,800	2·0
Lamina vi	135,400	4·0
Lamina v	147,700	4·3
Lamina iv (granular)	127,000	3·7
Laminae ii–iii	176,000	5·2
Total cortical	654,900	19·2

well to the 34,000 geniculo-striate paths actually counted. Since acute
vision is continuous under light stimulation, it follows that all of the
geniculo-striate cells must be firing constantly when the eye is stimulated
by the usual lighted environment. Further, since there are not more than
nineteen neurons in the visual area for each afferent fibre, it is almost certain that every cell in the striate cortex is firing during light stimulation.
Certainly there is no large reserve of cells which can be set aside for
excitation only in specific habits.

Corresponding counts of cells in the visual system of the monkey have
recently been made by Chow and Blum (personal communication). The
number of neurons in the lateral geniculate nucleus and visual cortex is
enormously greater than in the rat, about 1 and 140 millions respectively,
but the ratio of cortical cells to central pathways is only 140 to 1, so again
there is no great reserve of cells for mnemonic purposes.

The rat is capable of retaining scores, probably hundreds, of visual
habits involving discrimination of complex figures (38), and retention
may sometimes be demonstrated a year after training. As I reported
earlier, there is good evidence that visual habits are dependent upon the
striate cortex and upon no other part of the cerebral cortex. The efferent
path from the striate cortex is not known. It is not via cortico-tectile fibres.
If by cortico-thalamic fibres, there are far fewer neurons within the thalamic

nuclei than in corresponding cortical areas, and there is certainly no reserve of cells there for the storing of memories. There seems to be no justification for assuming that the specific shunting of nervous impulses constituting various memories occurs at some level beyond the visual cortex or that memory traces are stored elsewhere than in the cortex.

If the data on the restriction of visual memory to the striate cortex are correct, and they are supported by a variety of experiments, the conclusion seems inevitable that the same cells which bear the memory traces are also excited and play a part in every other visual reaction of the animal. In all probability, the same sort of quantitative relations holds for the other sense modalities.

Even if the associative areas are functional in memory, they do not provide the supposed excess of cells. The visual cortex is directly connected only to a band of cortex directly adjacent, the visuopsychic area of Campbell. The boundaries of this are indeterminate, but it certainly contains no more cells than does the striate area, probably fewer. There is no geometrical multiplication of cells and pathways. Many millions of cells of the striate cortex must be firing constantly into the adjacent area, so that its cells also must be constantly bombarded with nervous impulses and constantly firing. The conclusion is justified, I believe, by such considerations and is supported by electrical studies, that all of the cells of the brain are constantly active and are participating, by a sort of algebraic summation, in every activity. There are no special cells reserved for special memories.

Lorente (49) has shown that each neuron may bear a hundred or more end-feet or separate synapses. However, considering the enormous complexity of the nervous activity involved in performance of even the simplest habit, it is doubtful that even the multiplication of cell number by a hundredfold will provide separate connexions that function only for single specific memories.

The alternative to the theory of preservation of memories by some local synaptic change is the postulate that the neurons are somehow sensitized to react to patterns or combinations of excitation. It is only by such permutations that the limited number of neurons can produce the variety of functions that they carry out. Local changes in the cell membrane, such that combined excitation by several synapses excite the cell, would provide a possible mechanism for such response to patterns, but speculation about this mechanism without direct evidence is likely to be as futile as speculation concerning changes in resistance in the synapse has been.

Summary

This series of experiments has yielded a good bit of information about what and where the memory trace is not. It has discovered nothing directly of the real nature of the engram. I sometimes feel, in reviewing the evidence on the localization of the memory trace, that the necessary conclusion is that learning just is not possible. It is difficult to conceive of a mechanism which can satisfy the conditions set for it. Nevertheless, in spite of such evidence against it, learning does sometimes occur. Although the negative data do not provide a clear picture of the nature of the engram, they do establish limits within which concepts of its nature must be confined, and thus indirectly define somewhat more clearly the nature of the nervous mechanisms which must be responsible for learning and retention. Some general conclusions are, I believe, justified by the evidence.

1. It seems certain that the theory of well-defined conditioned reflex paths from sense organ via association areas to the motor cortex is false. The motor areas are not necessary for the retention of sensory-motor habits or even of skilled manipulative patterns.

2. It is not possible to demonstrate the isolated localization of a memory trace anywhere within the nervous system. Limited regions may be essential for learning or retention of a particular activity, but within such regions the parts are functionally equivalent. The engram is represented throughout the region.

3. The so-called associative areas are not storehouses for specific memories. They seem to be concerned with modes of organization and with general facilitation or maintenance of the level of vigilance. The defects which occur after their destruction are not amnesias but difficulties in the performance of tasks which involve abstraction and generalization, or conflict of purposes. It is not possible as yet to describe these defects in the present psychological terminology. Goldstein (19) has expressed them in part as a shift from the abstract to the concrete attitude, but this characterization is too vague and general to give a picture of the functional disturbance. For our present purpose the important point is that the defects are not fundamentally those of memory.

4. The trace of any activity is not an isolated connexion between sensory and motor elements. It is tied in with the whole complex of spatial and temporal axes of nervous activity which forms a constant substratum of behaviour. Each association is oriented with respect to space and time. Only by long practice under varying conditions does it become generalized or dissociated from these specific coordinates. The space and time coordinates in orientation can, I believe, only be maintained by some sort of polarization of activity and by rhythmic discharges which pervade the entire brain, influencing the organization of activity everywhere. The position and direction of motion in the visual field, for example, continuously modify the spinal postural adjustments, but, a fact which is more frequently overlooked, the postural adjustments also determine the

orientation of the visual field, so that upright objects continue to appear upright, in spite of changes in the inclination of the head. This substratum of postural and tonic activity is constantly present and is integrated with the memory trace (46).

I have mentioned briefly evidence that new associations are tied in spontaneously with a great mass of related associations. This conception is fundamental to the problems of attention and interest. There are no neurological data bearing directly upon these problems, but a good guess is that the phenomena which we designate as attention and interest are the result of partial, subthreshold activation of systems of related associations which have a mutual facilitative action. It seems impossible to account for many of the characters of organic amnesias except in such general terms as reduced vigilance or reduced facilitation.

5. The equivalence of different regions of the cortex for retention of memories points to multiple representation. Somehow, equivalent traces are established throughout the functional area. Analysis of the sensory and motor aspects of habits shows that they are reducible only to relations among components which have no constant position with respect to structural elements. This means, I believe, that within a functional area the cells throughout the area acquire the capacity to react in certain definite patterns, which may have any distribution within the area. I have elsewhere proposed a possible mechanism to account for this multiple representation. Briefly, the characteristics of the nervous network are such that, when it is subject to any pattern of excitation, it may develop a pattern of activity, reduplicated throughout an entire functional area by spread of excitations, much as the surface of a liquid develops an interference pattern of spreading waves when it is disturbed at several points (41). This means that, within a functional area, the neurons must be sensitized to react in certain combinations, perhaps in complex patterns of reverberatory circuits, reduplicated throughout the area.

6. Consideration of the numerical relations of sensory and other cells in the brain makes it certain, I believe, that all of the cells of the brain must be in almost constant activity, either firing or actively inhibited. There is no great excess of cells which can be reserved as the seat of special memories. The complexity of the functions involved in reproductive memory implies that every instance of recall requires the activity of literally millions of neurons. The same neurons which retain the memory traces of one experience must also participate in countless other activities.

Recall involves the synergic action or some sort of resonance among a very large number of neurons. The learning process must consist of the attunement of the elements of a complex system in such a way that a particular combination or pattern of cells responds more readily than before the experience. The particular mechanism by which this is brought about remains unknown. From the numerical relations involved, I believe that even the reservation of individual synapses for special associative reactions is impossible. The alternative is, perhaps, that the dendrites and cell body may be locally modified in such a manner that the cell responds differentially, at least in the timing of its firing, according to the pattern of combination of axon feet through which excitation is received.

REFERENCES

1. Akelaitis, A. J. A study of gnosis, praxis and language following section of the corpus callosum and anterior commissure, *J. Neurosurgery*, 1944, 1, 94–102.

2. Bailey, P., Bonin, G. v., Davis, F. W., Garol, H. W., and McCulloch, W. S. *J. Neuropath. exp. Neurol.*, 1944, 3, 413–415.

3. Bergson, H. *Matière et mémoire*. Paris: 1896.

4. Bonin, G. v., Garol, H. W., and McCulloch, W. S. The functional organization of the occipital lobe, *Biol. Symp.*, 1942, 7, 165–192.

5. Bucy, P. C. The relation of the premotor cortex to motor activity, *J. nerv. ment. Dis.*, 1934, 79, 621–630.

6. Bucy, P. C., and Fulton, T. F. Ipsilateral representation in the motor and premotor cortex of monkeys, *Brain*, 1933, 56, 318–342.

7. Clark, W. E. L. Observations on the associative fibre system of the visual cortex and the central representation of the retina, *J. Anat., Lond.*, 1941, 75, 225–236.

8. Dunlap, K. The short-circuiting of conscious responses, *J. Phil. Psychol. sci. Meth.*, 1927, 24, 253–267.

9. Dunlap, K. Psychological hypotheses concerning the functions of the brain, *Sci. Mon., N.Y.*, 1930, 31, 97–112.

10. Ebbecke, U. *Die kortikalen psychophysischen Erregungen*. Leipzig: Barth, 1919.

11. Edgell, B. *Theories of memory*. Oxford: Clarendon Press, 1924.

12. Fields, P. E. Studies in concept formation: I. The development of the concept of triangularity by the white rat, *Comp. Psychol. Monogr.*, 1932, 9 (2).

13. Finley, C. B. Equivalent losses in accuracy of response after central and after peripheral sense deprivation, *J. comp. Neurol.*, 1941, 74, 203–237.

14. Fischel, W. *Die höheren Leistungen der Wirbeltiergehirne*, Leipzig: Barth, 1948.

15. Franz, S. I. On the functions of the cerebrum: the frontal lobes, *Arch. Psychol.*, 1907, (2).

16. Franz, S. I. On the functions of the cerebrum: the occipital lobes, *Psychol. Monogr.*, 1911, 13 (4).

17. Gay, J. R., and Gellhorn, E. Cortical projection of proprioception, *Amer. J. Physiol.*, 1948, 155, 437.

18. Girden, E., Mettler, F. A., Finch, G., and Culler, E. Conditioned responses in a decorticate dog to acoustic, thermal, and tactile stimulation, *J. comp. Psychol.*, 1936, 21, 367–385.

19. Goldstein, K. *Human nature in the light of psychopathology*. Cambridge, Mass.: Harvard Univ. Press, 1940.

20. Head, H. *Aphasia and kindred disorders of speech.* New York: Macmillan, 1926. Vol. II.

21. Herrick, C. J. *Brains of rats and men.* Chicago: Univ. Chicago Press, 1926.

22. Hunter, W. S. A consideration of Lashley's theory of the equipotentiality of cerebral action, *J. gen. Psychol.*, 1930, **3**, 455–468.

23. Ingebritsen, O. C. Coordinating mechanisms of the spinal cord, *Genet. Psychol. Monogr.*, 1933, **13**, 485–553.

24. Jacobsen, C. F. Influence of motor and premotor area lesions upon the retention of skilled movements in monkeys and chimpanzees, *Proc. Ass. Res. nerv. ment. Dis.*, 1932, **13**, 225–247.

25. Jacobsen, C. F. Studies of cerebral function in primates, *Comp. Psychol. Monogr.*, 1936, **13** (3).

26. Kellogg, W. N., Deese, J., Pronko, N. H., and Feinberg, M. An attempt to condition the chronic spinal dog, *J. exp. Psychol.*, 1947, **37**, 99–117.

27. Kennard, M. A. Alterations in response to visual stimuli following lesions of frontal lobe in monkeys, *Arch. Neurol. Psychiat., Chicago*, 1939, **41**, 1153–1165.

28. Krechevsky, I. Brain mechanisms and brightness discrimination, *J. comp. Psychol.*, 1936, **21**, 405–445.

29. Lashley, K. S. The human salivary reflex and its use in psychology, *Psychol. Rev.*, 1916, **23**, 446–464.

30. Lashley, K. S. Studies of cerebral function in learning: II. The effects of long continued practice upon cerebral localization, *J. comp. Psychol.*, 1921, **1**, 453–468.

31. Lashley, K. S. Studies of cerebral function in learning: III. The motor areas, *Brain*, 1921, **44**, 256–286.

32. Lashley, K. S. Studies of cerebral function in learning: IV. Vicarious function after destruction of the visual areas, *Amer. J. Physiol.*, 1922, **59**, 44–71.

33. Lashley, K. S. Studies of cerebral function in learning: V. The retention of motor habits after destruction of the so-called motor areas in primates, *Arch. Neurol. Psychiat., Chicago*, 1924, **12**, 249–276.

34. Lashley, K. S. *Brain mechanisms and intelligence.* Chicago: Univ. Chicago Press, 1929.

35. Lashley, K. S. The mechanism of vision: V. The structure and image-forming power of the rat's eye, *J. comp. Psychol.*, 1932, **13**, 173–200.

36. Lashley, K. S. Studies of cerebral function in learning: XI. The behavior of the rat in latch-box situations, *Comp. Psychol. Monogr.*, 1935, **11**, 1–42.

37. Lashley, K. S. The mechanism of vision: XIII. Nervous structures concerned in the acquisition and retention of habits based on reactions to light, *Comp. Psychol. Monogr.*, 1935, **11**, 43–79.

38. Lashley, K. S. The mechanism of vision: XV. Preliminary studies of the rat's capacity for detail vision, *J. genet. Psychol.*, 1938, **18**, 123–193.

39. Lashley, K. S. The mechanism of vision: XVI. The functioning of small remnants of the visual cortex, *J. comp. Neurol.*, 1939, **70**, 45–67.

40. Lashley, K. S. Thalamo-cortical connections of the rat's brain, *J. comp. Neurol.*, 1941, **75**, 67–121.

41. Lashley, K. S. The problem of cerebral organization in vision, *Biol. Symp.*, 1942, **7**, 301–322.

42. Lashley, K. S. The mechanism of vision: XVII. Autonomy of the visual cortex, *J. genet. Psychol.*, 1942, **60**, 197–221.

43. Lashley, K. S. Studies of cerebral function in learning: XII. Loss of the maze habit after occipital lesions in blind rats, *J. comp. Neurol.*, 1943, **79**, 431–462.

44. Lashley, K. S. Studies of cerebral function in learning: XIII. Apparent absence of transcortical association in maze learning, *J. comp. Neurol.*, 1944, **80**, 257–281.

45. Lashley, K. S. The mechanism of vision: XVIII. Effects of destroying the visual "associative areas" of the monkey, *Genet. Psychol. Monogr.*, 1948, **37**, 107–166.

46. Lashley, K. S. The problem of serial order in behavior, In Jeffress, L. A. (Ed.) *Cerebral mechanisms in behavior*. New York: Wiley, 1951. Pp. 112–136.

47. Lashley, K. S., and McCarthy, D. A. The survival of the maze habit after cerebellar injuries, *J. comp. Psychol.*, 1926, **6**, 423–433.

48. Lashley, K. S., and Wiley, L. E. Studies of cerebral function in learning: IX. Mass action in relation to the number of elements in the problem to be learned, *J. comp. Neurol.*, 1933, **57**, 3–55.

49. Lorente de Nó, R. Studies on the structure of the cerebral cortex: II. Continuation of the study of the Ammonic system, *J. Psychol. Neurol., Lpz.*, 1934, **46**, 113–177.

50. McGeoch, J. A. *The psychology of human learning*. New York: Longmans, Green, 1942.

51. Mettler, F. A. Physiologic effects of bilateral simultaneous removal of Brodmann's cytoarchitectural areas in the human, *Fed. Proc. Amer. Soc. exp. Biol.*, 1949, **8**, 109.

52. Nielsen, J. M. *Agnosia, apraxia, aphasia: their value in cerebral localization*. Los Angeles: Waverly Press, 1936.

53. Poltyrew, S. S., and Zeliony, G. P. Grosshirnrinde und Assoziationsfunktion, *Z. Biol.*, 1930, **90**, 157–160.

54. Smith, K. U. Bilateral integrative action of the cerebral cortex in man in verbal association and sensori-motor coordination, *J. exp. Psychol.*, 1947, **37**, 367–376.

55. Sperry, R. W. Cerebral regulation of motor coordination in monkeys following multiple transection of sensorimotor cortex, *J. Neurophysiol.*, 1947, **10**, 275–294.

56. Tsang, Yü-Chüan. The function of the visual areas of the cortex of the rat in the learning and retention of the maze, *Comp. Psychol. Monogr.*, 1934, **10**, 1–56.

57. Walker, A. E. *The primate thalamus*. Chicago: Univ. Chicago Press, 1938.

58. Ward, A. A., Jr., Peden, J. K., and Sugar, O. Cortico-cortical connections in the monkey with special reference to Area 6, *J. Neurophysiol.*, 1946, **9**, 453–461.

30. THE PROBLEM OF SERIAL ORDER IN BEHAVIOR [1]

The previous speakers have approached our common problem by considering the properties of the elementary units of which we believe the cerebral structure to be built up. They have considered the kinds of neural integration of behavior which can be anticipated from those properties. The remaining members of the symposium have in their research been concerned chiefly with the analysis of complex behavior, seeking to derive general principles of neural integration from the infinitely complex products of that integration. Our common meeting ground is the faith to which we all subscribe, I believe, that the phenomena of behavior and of mind are ultimately describable in the concepts of the mathematical and physical sciences. In my discussion here, I have deliberately turned to the opposite extreme from the neuron and have chosen as a topic one aspect of the most complex type of behavior that I know: the logical and orderly arrangement of thought and action. Our discussion so far has dealt chiefly with the conditions of input and of immediate switching in the nervous mechanism, without explicit consideration of what is already going on within the system.

My principal thesis today will be that the input is never into a quiescent or static system, but always into a system which is already actively excited and organized. In the intact organism, behavior is the result of interaction of this background of excitation with input from any designated stimulus. Only when we can state the general characteristics of this background of excitation, can we understand the effects of a given input.

The unpronounceable Cree Indian word "kekawewechetushekamikowanowow" is analyzed by Chamberlain (7) into the verbal root, *tusheka*, "to remain," and the various particles which modify it as follows: *ke (la) wow*, the first and last syllables, indicating second person plural; *ka*, a prefix of the future tense; *we*, a sort of imperative mode expressing a wish; *weche*, indicating conjunction of subject and object; *mik*, a suffix

[1] EDITORS' NOTE: Reprinted with permission from Jeffress, L. A. (Ed.) *Cerebral mechanisms in behavior*. New York: John Wiley & Sons, Inc., 1951. Pp. 112–136. From Harvard University and the Yerkes Laboratories of Primate Biology.

bringing the verb into agreement with a third person subject and second person object; and *owan*, a suffix indicating that the subject is inanimate and the object animate. A literal translation: "You will I wish together remain he-you it-man you" or, freely, "may it remain with you." This difference in structure between Cree and English illustrates an outstanding characteristic of verbal behavior: the occurrence of predetermined, orderly sequences of action which are unique for each language. In English the adjective precedes, in French it follows, the noun which it modifies. In English the movement or action of the subject is expressed as early as possible after the subject; in German the expression of action may be postponed until all qualifying thoughts have been expressed. In a sentence discussing this subject, Pick (20) introduces fifty-five words between the subject and the principal verb. Each Chinese word, and to a lesser extent, each English word, stands as an unchanging unit. In the highly inflective languages, such as Sioux, the form of almost every word in the sentence may be altered, according to some attribute of the subject, as when two objects rather than one or several are discussed.

The study of comparative grammar is not the most direct approach to the physiology of the cerebral cortex, yet Fournié (10) has written, "Speech is the only window through which the physiologist can view the cerebral life." Certainly language presents in a most striking form the integrative functions that are characteristic of the cerebral cortex and that reach their highest development in human thought processes. Temporal integration is not found exclusively in language; the coordination of leg movements in insects, the song of birds, the control of trotting and pacing in a gaited horse, the rat running the maze, the architect designing a house, and the carpenter sawing a board present a problem of sequences of action which cannot be explained in terms of successions of external stimuli.

Associative Chain Theories

In spite of the ubiquity of the problem, there have been almost no attempts to develop physiological theories to meet it. In fact, except among a relatively small group of students of aphasia, who have had to face questions of agrammatism, the problem has been largely ignored. It is not even mentioned in recent textbooks on neurophysiology or physiological psychology, nor is there any significant body of experimental studies bearing upon the problem. The spinal animal scarcely exhibits serial activity, so the physiologist may be excused for overlooking the phenomenon. On the other hand, psychologists have been concerned chiefly with the question of whether or not the organizing processes displayed in serial action are conscious, and very little with the organization itself. I have chosen to discuss the problem of temporal integration here, not with the expectation of offering a satisfactory physiological theory to account for it, but because it seems to me to be both the most important and also the most neglected problem of cerebral physiology. Temporally integrated actions do occur even among insects, but they do not reach any degree of complexity until the appearance of cerebral cortex. They are especially characteristic of human behavior and contribute as much as does any single factor to the superiority of man's intelligence. A clearer formulation of the physiological problems which they raise should be of value, even though a solution of the problems is not yet in sight.

I shall consider first some of the questions raised by the structure of language, then turn to other forms of serial action for indications of the nature of the nervous mechanisms involved.

To the best of my knowledge, the only strictly physiological theory that has been explicitly formulated to account for temporal integration is that which postulates chains of reflexes, in which the performance of each element of the series provides excitation of the next. This conception underlay the "motor theories" of thinking which were advocated by several psychologists early in this century. Watson (26) sought to identify thought with inaudible movements of the vocal organs, linked together in associative chains. The peripheral chain theory of language was developed in greatest detail by Washburn (25). She distinguished what she called "successive movement systems" and, although she drew her examples from memorized series of nonsense syllables, her implication was that such series are typical of all language behavior. She defined a movement system as "a combination of movements so linked together that the stimulus furnished by the actual performance of certain movements is required to bring about other movements." She described speech as a succession of vocal acts in which the kinesthetic impulses from each movement serve as a unique stimulus for the next in the series (25, pp. 11 ff.). Attempts to confirm these peripheral theories by mechanical (23) or electrical (19) recording of muscular tensions have given no valid evidence in support of them. It should be noted that, at the time when the theories were proposed, it was generally believed that conduction in the nervous system is always downstream from sense organ to muscle, and that muscular contraction must always follow promptly on stimulation. The existence of reverberatory circuits which could maintain central activity was scarcely suspected.

The introspective psychology which objected to such peripheral theories did not explicitly formulate an alternative neurological theory, but there is implicit in it a view that verbal thought is a simple chain of central processes in which each element serves to arouse the next by direct association. Titchener, for example, maintained that the meaning of a word (or of an auditory image in his system) consists of the chain of associations which it arouses; that it has no meaning until such a sequence has occurred. From this it must be inferred that he was thinking in terms of a simple associative chain, since no other relating process is suggested.

Objections to the Associative Chain Theory

A consideration of the structure of the sentence and of other motor sequences will show, I believe, that such interpretations of temporal organization are untenable and that there are, behind the overtly expressed sequences, a multiplicity of integrative processes which can only be inferred from the final results of their activity. There is an extensive controversial literature dealing with this inferred integrative activity. Pick (20) devotes almost his entire book, *Die agrammatischen Sprachstörungen*, to reviewing discussions of the subject. Most of this literature deals with the question of whether or not the integrative processes are conscious. Much of this is irrelevant to the present topic, but the advocates of so-called imageless thought did present a great deal of material indicative of the complexity of the problem of thought structure. From this, and other evidence which I shall present, I believe that the production of speech involves the interaction of at least three, possibly four, major neurological systems which are interrelated but somewhat independently variable.

Let us start the analysis of the process with the enunciation of the word. Pronunciation of the word "right" consists first of retraction and elevation of the tongue, expiration of air and activation of the vocal cords; second, depression of the tongue and jaw; third, elevation of the tongue to touch the dental ridge, stopping of vocalization, and forceful expiration of air with depression of the tongue and jaw. These movements have no intrinsic order of association. Pronunciation of the word "tire" involves the same motor elements in reverse order. Such movements occur in all permutations. The order must therefore be imposed upon the motor elements by some organization other than direct associative connections between them. So, for the individual movements in writing or typing the word, finger strokes occur in all sorts of combinations. No single letter invariably follows g, and whether gh, ga, or gu is written depends upon a set for a larger unit of action, the word.

Words stand in relation to the sentence as letters do to the word; the words themselves have no intrinsic temporal "valence." The word "right," for example, is noun, adjective, adverb, and verb, and has four spellings and at least ten meanings. In such a sentence as "The millwright on my right thinks it right that some conventional rite should symbolize the right of every man to write as he pleases," word arrangement is obviously not due to any direct associations of the word "right" itself with other words, but to meanings which are determined by some broader relations.

It has been found in studies of memorization of nonsense syllables that each syllable in the series has associations, not only with adjacent words in the series, but also with more remote words. The words in the sentence have, of course, associations with more remote words as well as with adjacent ones. However, the combination of such direct associations will not account for grammatical structure. The different positions of the word "right" in the illustrative sentence are determined by the meanings which the positions in relation to other words denote, but those meanings are given by other associations than those with the words in the spoken sentence. The word can take its position only when the particular one of its ten meanings becomes dominant. This dominance is not inherent in the words themselves.

From such consideration, it is certain that any theory of grammatical form which ascribes it to direct associative linkage of the words of the sentence overlooks the essential structure of speech. The individual items of the temporal series do not in themselves have a temporal "valence" in their associative connections with other elements. The order is imposed by some other agent.

This is true not only of language, but of all skilled movements or successions of movement. In the gaits of a horse, trotting, pacing, and single footing involve essentially the same pattern of muscular contraction in the individual legs. The gait is imposed by some mechanism in addition to the direct relations of reciprocal innervation among the sensory-motor centers of the legs. The order in which the fingers of the musician fall on the keys or fingerboard is determined by the signature of the composition; this gives a *set* which is not inherent in the association of the individual movements.

The Determining Tendency

What then determines the order? The answer which seems most in accord with common sense is that the intention to act or the idea to be expressed determines the sequence. There are, however, serious difficulties for this solution. There is not much agreement among psychologists concerning the nature of the idea. The structuralist school, under the leadership of Titchener, held that the idea consists of mental images, often the auditory images of words, and the meanings are nothing but sequences of such images. Describing the role of images in his lecturing, Titchener wrote (24), "When there is any difficulty in exposition, a point to be argued pro and con or a conclusion to be brought out from the convergence of several lines of proof, I hear my own voice speaking just ahead of me." What solution of the lecture problem for the lazy man! He need not think but only listen to his own inner voice, to the chain of associated auditory images. A behaviorist colleague once remarked to me that he had reached a stage where he could arise before an audience, turn his mouth loose, and go to sleep. He believed in the peripheral chain theory of language. (This clearly demonstrates the superiority of behavioristic over introspective psychology. The behaviorist does not even have to listen to his own inner voice.)

Seriously, such positions offer no solution for the problem of temporal integration. Titchener finds his grammar ready made and does not even raise the question of the origin of the succession of images. The chain-reflex theory, while definite, is untenable.

The third view of the nature of the idea was developed by a group known as the Würzburg School (4); exponents of imageless thought. It held that some organization precedes any expression that can be discovered by introspective or objective means. Thought is neither muscular contraction nor image, but can only be inferred as a "determining tendency." At most, it is discovered as a vague feeling of pregnancy, of being about to have an idea, a Bewusstseinslage. It is not identical with the words which are spoken, for quite frequently no word can be recalled which satisfactorily expresses the thought, and we search a dictionary of synonyms until a word or phrase is found which does seem appropriate.

In his discussion of the relation of thought to speech, Pick (20) accepts this point of view, but he asserts further that the set or the idea does not have a temporal order; that all of its elements are cotemporal. Evidence in support of this conclusion comes, for example, from translation of one language into another which has a different sentence structure. I read a German sentence, pronouncing the German words with no thought of their English equivalents. I then give a free translation in English, without remembering a single word of the German text. Somewhere between the reading and free translation, the German sentence is condensed, the word order reversed, and expanded again into the different temporal order of English. According to Epstein (9), the polyglot shifts readily from one language to another, expressing the same thought in either, without literal translation. The readiness with which the form of expression of an idea can be changed, the facility with which different word orders may be utilized to express the same thought, thus is further evidence that the temporal integration is not inherent in the preliminary organization of the idea.

The Schema of Order

The remaining alternative is that the mechanism which determines the serial activation of the motor units is relatively independent, both of the motor units and of the thought structure. Supporting evidence for this may be found in the mistakes of order, the slips and interferences which occur in writing and speaking. For some time I have kept records of errors in typing. A frequent error is the misplacing or the doubling of a letter. *These* is typed t-h-s-e-s, *look* as l-o-k-k, *ill* as i-i-l. Sometimes the set to repeat may be displaced by several words. The order is dissociated from the idea. Earlier, in preparing this paper, I wrote the phrase, "maintain central activities." I typed *min,* omitting the *a,* canceled this out and started again; *ama.* The impulse to insert the *a* now dominated the order. I struck out the *a* and completed the phrase, only to find that I had now also dropped the *a* from *activities.* This example suggests something of the complexity of the forces which are at play in the determination of serial order and the way in which conflicting impulses may distort the order, although the primary determining tendency, the idea, remains the same.

The polyglot, who has become proficient in a secondary language, who thinks in it and even dreams in it, may still tend to use the grammatical structure of his native tongue. If, as in French, that tongue applies gender to inanimate things, the English pronouns referring to them may take the gender of the French equivalents, though the French nouns are not thought. The German postponement of the verb or the Magyar use of the past infinitive may be incorporated in the new language. In such cases, the structuring seems to be dissociated both from the content and from the simple associative connections of the words themselves.

The ease with which a new structure may be imposed on words is illustrated by the quickness with which children learn hog Latin. The form which I learned involved transposing the initial sound of each word to the end of the word and adding a long *a.* Thus—at-thay an-may oes-gay own-day e-thay eet-stray. Some children become very facile at such inversions of words, and restructure new words without hesitation. From such considerations it seems to follow that syntax is not inherent in the words employed or in the idea to be expressed. It is a generalized pattern imposed upon the specific acts as they occur.

"Priming" of Expressive Units

There are indications that, prior to the internal or overt enunciation of the sentence, an aggregate of word units is partially activated or readied. Evidence for this comes also from "contaminations" of speech and writing. The most frequent typing errors are those of anticipation; the inclusion in the word being typed of some part of a word or word structure which should properly occur later in the sentence. It may be only a letter. Thus I wrote, *wrapid* writing, carrying the *w* from the second word to the first. Not infrequently words are introduced which should occur much later in the sentence, often five or six words in advance.

In oral speech, Spoonerisms illustrate the same kind of contamination. The Spoonerism is most frequently an inversion of subject and object;

"Let us always remember that waste makes haste." But it may be only a transposition of parts of the words: "Our queer old dean" for "our dear old queen." The frequency with which such contaminations occur is increased by haste, by distraction, by emotional tension, or by uncertainty and conflict as to the best form of expression. In some types of aphasia the tendency to disordered arrangement of words is greatly increased, and, in extreme cases, the attempt to speak results in a word hash with complete loss of grammatical organization. Professor Spooner, after whom such slips are named, was probably suffering from a mild form of aphasia. In these contaminations, it is as if the aggregate of words were in a state of partial excitation, held in check by the requirements of grammatical structure, but ready to activate the final common path, if the effectiveness of this check is in any way interfered with.

In his *Psychopathology of Everyday Life*, Freud has given numerous examples of similar contaminations of action outside the sphere of language. We do not need to accept his theories of censorship and suppression to account for such slips. They are of the same order as misplacements in typing and represent contaminations of coexisting, determining tendencies to action.

Such contaminations might be ascribed to differences in the relative strength of associative bonds between the elements of the act, and thus not evidence for preexcitation of the elements or for simultaneous preexcitation. However, the understanding of speech involves essentially the same problems as the production of speech and definitely demands the postulation of an aftereffect or after-discharge of the sensory components for a significant time following stimulation. Thus, in the spoken sentence, "Rapid righting with his uninjured hand saved from loss the contents of the capsized canoe," the associations which give meaning to righting are not activated for at least 3 to 5 seconds after hearing the word.[2] I shall refer later to other evidence for such long after-discharge of sensory excitations. The fact of continued activation or after-discharge of receptive elements and their integration during this activation justifies the assumption of a similar process during motor organization. The processes of comprehension and production of speech have too much in common to depend on wholly different mechanisms.

Internal and Overt Speech

One other point with respect to the organization of speech: The earlier literature on aphasia emphasized the distinction of internal and overt speech. The aphemia of Broca and the pure motor aphasia of Wernicke

---

2 Dr. Lashley ingeniously laid the groundwork for this three paragraphs earlier, when he mentions "wrapid writing." The audience all heard, "Rapid writing with his uninjured hand," etc. "Capsized canoe" required a complete and amusing about-face. (Symposium Editor)

and later writers were held to be a loss of the ability to enunciate without loss of ability to think in words and without paralysis of the organs of speech. The brain insult was assumed to affect only the transition from the thought to the enunciation of the word. We may doubt the existence of instances of such "pure" defects and question the reliability of the early clinical examinations in view of the more careful analyses that have been made since 1917, but the distinction of internal and overt speech is still valid and the transition still unexplained. Watson interpreted internal speech as inaudible movements of the vocal organs, and Jacobsen (15) and Max (19) have given evidence of changes in muscular tonus during verbal thinking or thought of movement. This is far from proving that the motor discharge is essential for the internal formation of words, however.

I once devised an instrument to record small movements of the tongue. Within the limits of its sensitivity, it showed that in silent thinking the tongue usually drops to the back of the mouth and shows no detectable movement. Verbal problems, such as the correct squaring of three-place numbers, could be carried out with no trace of overt movement. If, however, I urged the subject to hurry or if I slapped his face, his tongue came forward and showed movements corresponding to the syllabification of internal speech or of the computation he was performing. This I interpret as indicating that internal speech may be carried out wholly by processes within the nervous system, with some unessential discharge upon the final common path for vocal movements. Facilitation of the motor path, either by increased emotional tension or by "voluntary" reinforcement, increases its excitability until the same central circuits whose activity constitutes internal speech are able to excite the overt movements. This aspect of the language function is irrelevant to the problem of syntax or serial order, but is important as illustrating a further point in the dynamics of the cerebrum. Many activities seem to require for their performance both a specific patterning and also a general facilitation, a rise in dynamic level. There are, I think, indications that hemiplegia and motor aphasia are primarily expressions of a low level of facilitation rather than a loss of specific integrative connections which are involved in the use of language or in the patterning of our movements. A monkey, for example, after ablation of the precentral gyrus may seem unable to use the arm at all, but if emotional excitement is raised above a certain level, the arm is freely used. As soon as the excitement dies down, the arm is again hemiplegic. I have seen something of the same sort in a human hemiplegic. The problem of the availability of memories, which was raised earlier in the discussion here, may find a partial solution in such fluctuations in dynamic level. In many of the organic amnesias the pattern of integration seems to be retained but can be reactivated only by an abnormally intense sensory or central reinforcement.

Generality of the Problem of Syntax

I have devoted so much time to discussion of the problem of syntax, not only because language is one of the most important products of human cerebral action, but also because the problems raised by the organization of language seem to me to be characteristic of almost all other cerebral activity. There is a series of hierarchies of organization; the order of vocal movements in pronouncing the word, the order of words in the sentence, the order of sentences in the paragraph, the rational order of paragraphs in a discourse. Not only speech, but all skilled acts seem to involve the same problems of serial ordering, even down to the temporal coordination of muscular contractions in such a movement as reaching and grasping. Analysis of the nervous mechanisms underlying order in the more primitive acts may contribute ultimately to the solution even of the physiology of logic.

It is possible to designate, that is, to point to specific examples of, the phenomena of the syntax of movement that require explanation, although those phenomena cannot be clearly defined. A real definition would be a long step toward solution of the problem. There are at least three sets of events to be accounted for. First, the activation of the expressive elements (the individual words or adaptive acts) which do not contain the temporal relations. Second, the determining tendency, the set, or idea. This masquerades under many names in contemporary psychology, but is, in every case, an inference from the restriction of behavior within definite limits. Third, the syntax of the act, which can be described as an habitual order or mode of relating the expressive elements; a generalized pattern or schema of integration which may be imposed upon a wide range and a wide variety of specific acts. This is the essential problem of serial order: the existence of generalized schemata of action which determine the sequence of specific acts, acts which in themselves or in their associations seem to have no temporal valence.

I shall turn now to other phenomena of movement which may be more readily phrased in physiological terms and which may suggest some of the mechanisms underlying serial order.

Duration and Intensity of Nervous Discharge

A consideration of the control of extent and rate of movement supports the view that sensory factors play a minor part in regulating the intensity and duration of nervous discharge; that a series of movements is not a chain of sensory-motor reactions. The theory of control of movement which was dominant at the turn of the century assumed that, after a movement is initiated, it is continued until stopped by sensations of movement and position, which indicate that the limb has reached the desired position. This theory was opposed by a good bit of indirect evidence, such as that accuracy of movement is increased rather than diminished with speed. I had opportunity to study a patient who had a complete anesthesia for movements of the knee joint, as a result of a gunshot wound of the cord (16). In spite of the anesthesia, he was able to control the extent and speed of movements of flexion and extension of the knee quite as accurately as can a normal person.

The performance of very quick movements also indicates their independence of current control. "Whip-snapping" movements of the hand can be regulated accurately in extent, yet the entire movement, from initiation to completion, requires less than the reaction time for tactile or kinesthetic stimulation of the arm, which is about one-eighth of a second, even when no discrimination is involved. Such facts force the conclusion that an effector mechanism can be preset or primed to discharge at a given intensity or for a given duration, in independence of any sensory controls.

Central Control of Motor Patterns

This independence of sensory controls is true not only of intensity and duration of contraction of a synergic muscle group but is true also of the initiation and timing of contraction of the different muscles in a complex movement. The hand may describe a circular movement involving coordinated contractions of the muscles of the shoulder, elbow, and wrist in about 1/10 second, and the stopping of movement at a given position, of course, is only a small fraction of that time. The finger strokes of a musician may reach 16 per second in passages which call for a definite and changing order of successive finger movements. The succession of movements is too quick even for visual reaction time. In rapid sight reading it is impossible to read the individual notes of an arpeggio. The notes must be seen in groups, and it is actually easier to read chords seen simultaneously and to translate them into temporal sequence than to read successive notes in the arpeggio as usually written.

Sensory control of movement seems to be ruled out in such acts. They require the postulation of some central nervous mechanism which fires with predetermined intensity and duration or activates different muscles in predetermined order. This mechanism might be represented by a chain of effector neurons, linked together by internuncials to produce successive delays in firing. In some systems the order of action may be determined by such a leader or pace-setter. Buddenbrock (6) has shown for the stick insect, and Bethe (3) for a number of animals from the centipede to the dog, that removal of one or more legs results in a spontaneous change in the order of stepping. Thus, for the insects, the normal order is alternate stepping of the first pair of legs with right first, left second, right third legs advancing together. With removal of the left first leg, the right first and left second alternate and the order becomes right first, left third, right third stepping together, with left second and right second advancing together, instead of alternately. These investigators were interested in spontaneity of reorganization, rather than in the mechanism of coordination, and did not propose any theory for the latter. They did show, however, that it is necessary to remove the leg completely to get the change in pattern of movement; sensory impulses from a limb stump would prevent it. Such coordination might be explained, perhaps, by a combination of loss of excitability in the centers of the absent limb, by the excitation of the remaining anterior center as a leader or pace-setter, and the spread of alternate waves of inhibition and excitation from the more anterior to the more posterior limb centers. The spontaneous change in coordination shows, however, that the coordination is not due to the action of predetermined anatomic paths but is the result of the current physiological state of the various limb centers.

Such an hypothesis implies also the assumption of a polarization of conduction along the neuraxis, with the order of excitation determined by the spatial arrangement of the centers of the legs. I see no other possibility of accounting for the facts. The examples of circular movement and of finger coordination, involving temporal integration of movements, seem to call for a similar hypothesis. They might be ascribed to an habitual linkage of the movements through a simple chain of internuncials but for two facts. First, such series are usually reversible at any point or can be started from any point. This would require the assumption of a second set of internuncials habituated to conduct in the opposite direction, and this in turn leads to the further assumption of a polarization of conduction. Second, such patterns of coordinated movement may often be transferred directly to other motor systems than the ones practiced. In such transfer, as to the left hand for writing, an analysis of the movements shows that there is not a reduplication of the muscular patterns on the two sides, but a reproduction of movements in relation to the space coordinates of the body. Try upside-down mirror writing with the left hand and with eyes closed for evidence of this. The associative linkage is not of specific movements but of directions of movement. An analysis of systems of space coordinates suggests mechanisms which may contribute to production of such series of movements in a spatial pattern.

Space Coordinate Systems

The work of Sherrington, Magnus, and others on postural tonus and reflexes has defined one level of spatial integration rather fully, yet it is doubtful if these studies have revealed the effective neural mechanism. The work has shown that the tonic discharge to every muscle in the postural system is influenced by afferent impulses from every other muscle, toward increased or decreased activity, according to its synergic or antergic action. To these influences are added vestibular and cerebellar effects. Diagrammatically these mutual influences of the muscular system may be represented by separate reflex circuits from each receptor to every muscle, as Sherrington (21, p. 148) has done. But no neuroanatomist would, I am sure, maintain that such separate circuits or paths exist. What the experiments on posture actually show is a correlation of sensory stimulation and of tonic changes in a network of neurons whose interconnections are still undefined. The reactions isolated experimentally have the characteristics of simple directly conducted reflexes, but their combination results in patterns of movement and posture which have definite relations to the axes of the body and to gravity.

This postural system is based on excitations from proprioceptors. The distance receptors impose an additional set of space coordinates upon the postural system, which in turn continually modifies the coordinates of the distance receptors. The dropped cat rights itself, if either the eyes or the vestibular senses are intact, but not in the absence of both. The direction of movement on the retina imposes a directional orientation of the postural system. Conversely, the gravitational system imposes an orientation of the visual field. Upright objects such as trees or the corners of a room appear upright, at no matter what angle the head is inclined. Derangement of the vestibular system can disturb the distance orientation or the orientation of the receptors, as in the apparent swaying of the vertical as a result of the after-images of motion following hours of rocking in a small boat.

There are other, still more generalized systems of space coordinates. We usually keep track of the compass points or of some more definite index of direction by a temporal summation of the turns made in walking, though not always with success. Finally, there is a still more plastic system in which the concepts of spatial relations can be voluntarily reversed, as when one plays blindfold chess alternately from either side of the board.

Explanation of these activities, these complex interactions, in terms of simple isolated interconnections of all the sensory and motor elements involved seems quite improbable on anatomic grounds and is ruled out by results of our experiments on sectioning of the spinal cord. Ingebritsen (14) studied rats with double hemisection of the cord; one half of the cord cut at the second, the other at the fifth cervical segment. In the best case only a small strand of the spino-cerebellar tract of one side remained intact. These rats were able to balance in walking, oriented to visual stimuli, scratched with the right or left hind foot according to the side of the face stimulated, were able to run mazes correctly, and even learned to rise on the hind feet and push down a lever with the forepaws in opening a box.

The alternative to the isolated-path theory of the space coordinates is that the various impulses which modify postural tonus are poured into a continuous network of neurons, where their summated action results in a sort of polarization of the entire system. I shall consider later the integrative properties of such a net. For the moment I wish to emphasize only the existence of these systems of space coordinates. Their influences pervade the motor system so that every gross movement of limbs or body is made with reference to the space system. The perceptions from the distance receptors, vision, hearing, and touch are also constantly modified and referred to the same space coordinates. The stimulus is *there*, in a definite place; it has definite relation to the position of the body, and it shifts with respect to the sense organ but not with respect to the general orientation, with changes in body posture.

Memories of objects usually give them position in the space system, and even more abstract concepts may have definite spatial reference. Thus, for many people, the cardinal numbers have definite positions on a spiral or other complicated figure. What, if anything, such space characters can contribute to temporal integration is an open question. They provide a possible basis for some serial actions through interaction of postural and timing mechanisms.

Rhythmic Action

The simplest of the timing mechanisms are those controlling rhythmic activity. T. Graham Brown (5) first showed by his studies of deafferented preparations that the rhythmic movements of respiration and progression are independent of peripheral stimulation and are maintained by a central nervous mechanism of reciprocal innervation. He suggested that this mechanism of reciprocal innervation, rather than the simple reflex, is the unit of organization of the whole nervous system. He thus foreshadowed, in a way, the conception of reverberatory circuits which is coming to play so large a part in neurological theory today. Holst (13) has recently shown that the rhythmic movement of the dorsal fin of fishes is a compound of two superimposed rhythms, that of its own innervation and that of the pectoral fins. These two rhythms are centrally maintained.

Musical rhythms seem to be an elaboration of the same sort of thing. The time or beat is started and maintained at some definite rate, say 160 per minute. This rate is then imposed upon various activities. The fingers of the musician fall in multiples of the basic rate. If the leader of a quartet speeds up the time or retards, all the movements of the players change in rate accordingly. Not only the time of initiation but also the rate of movement is affected. The violinist, in a passage requiring the whole bow, will draw the bow from frog to tip at a uniform rate for the required number of beats, whether the tempo is fast or slow. With practiced violinists, the rate of movement is extremely accurate and comes out on the beat at the exact tip of the bow.

Superimposed on this primary rhythm is a secondary one of emphasis, giving the character of 3/4, 4/4, 6/4, or other time. The mechanism of these rhythms can be simply conceived as the spread of excitation from some centers organized for reciprocal innervation; as a combination of the principles of Brown and of Holst. There are, however, still more complicated rhythms in all music. That of the melodic line is most uniform. In much music, the melodic progression changes in 2, 4, or some multiple of 4 measures. In improvisation, the performer keeps no count of measures, yet comes out almost invariably in a resolution to the tonic of the key after some multiple of 8 measures. Here a generalized pattern is impressed on the sequence, but it is a simpler pattern than that of grammatical structure. It only requires the recurrence of a pattern at certain rhythmic intervals; a pick-up of a specific pattern after so many timed intervals.

There are, in addition, still less regular rhythms of phrasing and emphasis. Parallels to these can be found in speech. The skilled extemporaneous speaker rounds his phrases and speaks with a definite though not regular rhythm.

The rhythms tend to spread to almost every other concurrent activity. One falls into step with a band, tends to breathe, and even to speak in time with the rhythm. The all pervasiveness of the rhythmic discharge is shown by the great difficulty of learning to maintain two rhythms at once, as in three against four with the two hands. The points to be emphasized here are the widespread effects of a rhythmic discharge indicating the involvement of almost the entire effector system, the concurrent action of different rhythmic systems, and the imposition of the rate upon both the initiation and speed of movement. Consideration of rhythmic activity and of spatial orientation forces the conclusion, I believe, that there exist in the nervous organization elaborate systems of interrelated neurons capable of imposing certain types of integration upon a large number of widely spaced effector elements; in the one case transmitting temporally spaced waves of facilitative excitation to all effector elements; in the other imparting a directional polarization to both receptor and effector elements. These systems are in constant action. They form a sort of substratum upon which other activity is built. They contribute to every perception and to every integrated movement.

Interaction of Temporal and Spatial Systems

Integration ascribed to the spatial distribution of excitations in the nervous system has been much more intensively studied than the temporal aspects of nervous activity. Theories of integration are based almost exclusively upon space properties, time entering only in theories of facilitation,

inhibition, and after-discharge. In cerebral functions, however, it is difficult to distinguish between spatial and temporal functions. The eye is the
only organ that gives simultaneous information concerning space in any
detail. The shape of an object impressed on the skin can scarcely be
detected from simultaneous pressure, but the same shape can readily be
distinguished by touch when traced on the skin with a moving point or
when explored by tactile scanning. The temporal sequence is readily
translated into a spatial concept. Even for vision it might be questioned
whether simultaneous stimulation gives rise directly to space concepts.
The visual object is generally surveyed by eye movements, and its form
is a reconstruction from such a series of excitations. Even with tachisto-
scopic exposures, the after-discharge permits a temporal survey, and, with
visual fixation, shifts of attention provide an effective scanning.

Since memory traces are, we believe, in large part static and persist
simultaneously, it must be assumed that they are spatially differentiated.
Nevertheless, reproductive memory appears almost invariably as temporal
sequence, either as a succession of words or of acts. Even descriptions of
visual imagery (the supposed simultaneous reproductive memory in
sensory terms) are generally descriptions of sequences, of temporal reconstructions from very fragmentary and questionable visual elements. Spatial
and temporal order thus appear to be almost completely interchangeable
in cerebral action. The translation from the spatial distribution of memory
traces to temporal sequence seems to be a fundamental aspect of the
problem of serial order.

I spoke earlier of the probability of a partial activation or priming of
aggregates of words before the sentence is actually formulated from them.
There is a great deal of evidence for such preliminary facilitation of patterns of action in studies of reaction time and of word association. Reaction
time, in general, is reduced by preliminary warning or by instructions
which allow the subject to prepare for the specific act required. In controlled association experiments, the subject is instructed to respond to the
stimulus word by a word having a certain type of relation to it, such as
the opposite or a part of which the stimulus is the whole; black-white,
apple-seed. The result is an attitude or set which causes that particular
category to dominate the associative reaction. Whether such preliminary
reinforcement is to be ascribed to accumulation of excitatory state, as
defined by Sherrington (21), or to some other physiological process, the
facts of behavior assure that it is a genuine phenomenon and plays a
decisive role in determining the character of the response.

Once the existence of such states of partial activation is recognized,
their possible role in temporal integration must be considered. There are
indications that one neural system may be held in this state of partial
excitation while it is scanned by another. Here is an example. A series

of four to six numbers is heard: 3–7–2–9–4. This is within the attention or memory span and is almost certainly not remembered in the sense in which one's telephone number is remembered, for memory of it is immediately wiped out by a succeeding series of numbers. While it is retained in this unstable way, subject to retroactive inhibition, the order of the numbers can be reassorted: 3–7–2–9–4, 3–2–7–9–4, 4–9–2–7–3, and the like. It is as if, in this case, a rhythmic alternation can suppress alternate items, or a direction of arousal can be applied to the partially excited system. Another example which illustrates even more clearly the spatial characteristics of many memory traces is the method of comultiplication, used in rapid mental calculation. In attempts to play a melody backward, we have a further illustration. I find that I can do it only by visualizing the music spatially and reading it backward. I cannot auditorily transform even "Yankee Doodle" into its inverse without some such process, but it is possible to get a spatial representation of the melody and then to scan the spatial representation. The scanning of a spatial arrangement seems definitely to determine, in such cases, the order of procedure. Two assumptions are implied by this. First, the assumption is that the memory traces are associated, not only with other memory traces, but also with the system of space coordinates. By this I do not mean that the engram has a definite location in the brain; our experiments show conclusively that such is not the case. Rather, when the memory trace is formed it is integrated with directional characters of the space system, which give it position in reference to other associated traces. Second, the assumption is that these space characters of the memory trace can be scanned by some other level of the coordinating system and so transformed into succession.

This is as far as I have been able to go toward a theory of serial order in action. Obviously, it is inadequate. The assumptions concerning spatial representation and temporal representation may even beg the question, since no one can say whether spatial or temporal order is primary. Furthermore, such determining tendencies as the relation of attribute to object, which gives the order of adjective and noun, do not seem to be analyzable into any sort of spatial structure or, for that matter, into any consistent relationship. I have tried a number of assumptions concerning the selective mechanism of grammatical form (spatial relations, the relative intensity or prominence of different words in the idea, and so on) but I have never been able to make an hypothesis which was consistent with any large number of sentence structures. Nevertheless, the indications which I have cited, that elements of the sentence are readied or partially activated before the order is imposed upon them in expression, suggest that some scanning mechanism must be at play in regulating their temporal sequence. The real problem, however, is the nature of the selective mechanism by which the particular acts are picked out in this scanning process, and to this problem I have no answer.

Such speculations concerning temporal and spatial systems do little more than illustrate a point of view concerning nervous organization which is, I believe, more consistent both with what is known of the histology and elementary physiology of the brain and also with behavior phenomena than are the more widely current theories of simple associative chains of reactions.

Nearly forty years ago Becher (2, p. 243) wrote: "There is no physiological hypothesis which can explain the origin and relations of temporal forms in mental life; indeed, there is no hypothesis which even foreshadows the possibility of such an explanation." The situation is little better today, but I do feel that changing conceptions of the fundamental organization of the nervous system offer more hope for a solution of such problems than did the physiological knowledge available when Becher wrote. However, we are still very far from being able to form an explicit explanation of temporal structure.

The Fundamental Mechanism of Integration

Neurological theory has been dominated by the belief that the neurons of the central nervous system are in an inactive or resting state for the greater part of the time; that they are linked in relatively isolated conditioned reflex arcs and that they are activated only when the particular reactions for which they are specifically associated are called out. Such a view is incompatible both with the widespread effects of stimulation which can be demonstrated by changes in tonus and also with recent evidence from electrical recording of nervous activity. It is now practically certain that all the cells of the cerebrospinal axis are being continually bombarded by nerve impulses from various sources and are firing regularly, probably even during sleep. The nervous activity which they in turn elicit depends upon the current physiological state of the neurons with which they are connected. It is probably not far from the truth to say that every nerve cell of the cerebral cortex is involved in thousands of different reactions. The cortex must be regarded as a great network of reverberatory circuits, constantly active. A new stimulus, reaching such a system, does not excite an isolated reflex path but must produce widespread changes in the pattern of excitation throughout a whole system of already interacting neurons.

The facts of cerebral structure support such a view. The cortex is composed chiefly of neurons with short axons. Le Gros Clark (8) has found for the striate area of the monkey that Marchi degeneration extends for only a short distance from a point of injury. In the striate area of the rat, I have never been able to trace degeneration beyond three or four cell diameters from the margin of a lesion, and I believe that this lack of long transcortical fibers is true of other areas as well as of the visual cortex. Visual perception reveals close integration of different parts of the striate areas in spite of the absence of long association fibers. In the visual cortex of the rat there are only 19 neurons for each afferent fiber. To produce the animal's visual acuity, all of the afferent fibers must be firing continually. There are approximately 34,000 cell bodies in the lateral geniculate nucleus of the rat, and the minimum number of visual units necessary to produce the visual acuity of the rat is actually above this figure. (The acuity is determined by direct experimental tests.) These figures should be of interest in relation to the numerical values cited by Dr. von Neumann. The number of cells in the visual cortex of the rat is only about 10^6, and in some of my experiments where I have removed the greater part of the visual cortex the capacity for discrimination of visual forms has been retained when no more than 20,000 cells of the visual cortex remain. There is also evidence that no part of the cerebral cortex except the visual areas is essential for visual perception and memory.

These facts lead to the conclusion that the same cells in the visual cortex participate in a great variety of activities. Practically all of the cells of the area must be fired by every visual stimulation, and these same cells must be the ones which retain the visual memories. The conclusion follows that differential responses depend upon the pattern of cells which are excited in combination. The visual cortex is a network of cells of short axon without long interconnections between its parts or with other cortical areas. Its integrative functions are an expression of the properties of such a network.

The same conception must be applied to other cortical areas. There are, of course, long association tracts in the cortex, such as the corpus callosum, the superior longitudinal fasciculus, and the temporo-frontal tracts. Once, 26 years ago, I suggested facetiously that these might be only skeletal structures, since I could find no function for them. No important functions of these tracts have yet been demonstrated. Section of the corpus callosum produces only a slight slowing of reaction time, ipsilateral as well as contralateral (1); section of occipito-frontal fibers produces, perhaps, a temporary disturbance of visual attention but no other symptoms. The integrative functions seem to be carried out as well without as with the main associative tracts. The major integrative functions must, therefore, be carried out by the network of cells of short axon. The properties of such networks of cells must be analyzed before the mechanisms of the cerebral cortex can be understood. Something can be inferred from the characteristics of excitability of cells and their arrangement in recurrent loops. If, as seems a necessary conclusion from the histology of the striate area, all of the cells of the network are subject to constant excitation and are firing whenever they recover from the refractory state, then mutual interference of circuits will produce complicated patterns throughout the area, patterns which will stabilize in the absence of differential stimulation, as is perhaps indicated by the regularity of the alpha rhythm. Any new afferent impulses reaching the area can only produce a reorganization of the existing pattern. What happens at any particular point in the system, as at an efferent neuron, is the statistical outcome of the interaction of myriads of neurons, not of the transmission of impulses over a restricted path, of which that efferent cell forms a link. It is possible to isolate parts of the system by operative means or by anesthetics and so to get a one-to-one relation of stimulus locus and responding muscles, from which the reflex mechanism has been inferred. As Goldstein (12) has pointed out, however, the parts isolated in the reflex are influenced by a multiplicity of effects in the intact organism of which there is little or no trace in the isolated preparation.

I can best illustrate this conception of nervous action by picturing the brain as the surface of a lake. The prevailing breeze carries small ripples in its direction, the basic polarity of the system. Varying gusts set up crossing systems of waves, which do not destroy the first ripples, but modify their form, a second level in the system of space coordinates. A tossing log with its own period of submersion sends out periodic bursts of ripples, a temporal rhythm. The bow wave of a speeding boat momentarily sweeps over the surface, seems to obliterate the smaller waves yet leaves them unchanged by its passing, the transient effect of a strong stimulus. Wave motion is not an adequate analogy because the medium which conveys the waves is uniform, whereas the nerve cells have their individual characteristics of transmission which at every point may alter the character of the transmitted pattern.

The great number of axon terminations on every nerve cell has not been considered in theories of integration. It implies, of course, that the cell can be fired by impulses from a variety of sources. But it also suggests another possibility, more fruitful for understanding of integrative processes. A nerve impulse arriving over a single axon terminal may not fire the cell but may modify its excitability to impulses from other sources. In an elaborate system of neurons such subthreshold effects might establish a pattern of facilitation which would determine the combination of cells fired by subsequent excitations. The space coordinate system and various types of *set* or priming may be pictured as patterns of subthreshold facilitation pervading the network of neurons which is activated by the more specific external stimulus.

Such a view of the mechanism of nervous action certainly does not simplify the problems nor does it as yet provide any clue to the structuring that constitutes the set or determining tendency, or to the nature of such relations as are implied in the attribute-object, opposites, or other abstract concepts. A few relations seem reducible to spatial terms, part-whole, for example, but even for these there is no clear conception of the neural basis of their space properties. These considerations do not, I believe, contradict fundamentally the basic conceptions that have been formulated by Dr. McCulloch. They do, however, indicate a direction of necessary elaboration. The nets active in rhythmic and spatial organization are apparently almost coextensive with the nervous system. The analysis must be extended to the properties of such nets; the way in which they are broken up into reactive patterns in the spread of excitation, to give, for example, directional propagation or its equivalent. I strongly suspect that many phenomena of generalization, both sensory and conceptual, are products, not of simple switching, but of interaction of complex patterns of organization within such systems.

Summary

The problems of the syntax of action are far removed from anything which we can study by direct physiological methods today, yet in attempting to formulate a physiology of the cerebral cortex we cannot ignore them. Serial order is typical of the problems raised by cerebral activity; few, if any, of the problems are simpler or promise easier solution. We can, perhaps, postpone the fatal day when we must face them, by saying that they are too complex for present analysis, but there is danger here of constructing a false picture of those processes that we believe to be simpler. I am coming more and more to the conviction that the rudiments of every human behavioral mechanism will be found far down in the evolutionary scale and also represented even in primitive activities of the nervous system. If there exist, in human cerebral action, processes which seem fundamentally different or inexplicable in terms of our present construct of the elementary physiology of integration, then it is probable that that construct is incomplete or mistaken, even for the levels of behavior to which it is applied.

In spite of its present inadequacy, I feel that the point of view which I have sketched here holds some promise of a better understanding of cerebral integration. Attempts to express cerebral function in terms of the concepts of the reflex arc, or of associated chains of neurons, seem to me doomed to failure because they start with the assumption of a static nervous system. Every bit of evidence available indicates a dynamic, constantly active system, or, rather, a composite of many interacting systems, which I have tried to illustrate at a primitive level by rhythm and the space coordinates. Only when methods of analysis of such systems have been devised will there be progress toward understanding of the physiology of the cerebral cortex.

REFERENCES

1. Akelaitis, A. J. Studies on the corpus callosum: II. The higher visual functions in each homonymous field following complete section of the corpus callosum, *Arch. Neurol. Psychiat., Chicago,* 1941, **45,** 788–796.

2. Becher, E. *Gehirn und Seele.* Heidelberg: 1911.

3. Bethe, A. Plastizität und Zentrenlehre, *Handb. norm. path. Physiol.,* 1931, **15** (II), 1175–1220.

4. Boring, E. G. *A history of experimental psychology.* New York: Appleton-Century-Crofts, 1929.

5. Brown, T. G. On the nature of the fundamental activity of the nervous centers, *J. Physiol.,* 1914, **48,** 18–46.

6. Buddenbrock, W. v. Der Rhythmus der Schreitbewegungen der Stabheuschreke Dyxippus, *Biol. Zbl.,* 1921, **41,** 41–48.

7. Chamberlain, A. F. Indians, North American. In *Encycl. Brit.,* 1911, **14,** 452–482.

8. Clark, W. E. Le Gros. Observations on the associative fiber system of the visual cortex and the central representation of the retina. *J. Anat., Lond.,* 1941, **75,** 225–236.

9. Epstein, I. *La pensée et la polyglossie.* Paris: Payot et Cie (n.d.).

10. Fournié. *Essai de psychologie.* Paris: 1887.

11. Fritsch, G., and Hitzig, E. Ueber die elektrische Erregbarkeit des Grosshirns, *Arch. Anat. Physiol., Lpz.,* 1870, 300–332.

12. Goldstein, K. *The organism.* Boston: Ginn, 1939.

13. Holst, N. v. Vom Wesen der Ordnung im Zentralnervensystem, *Naturwissenschaften,* 1937, **25,** 625–631, 641–647.

14. Ingebritsen, O. C. Coordinating mechanisms of the spinal cord, *Genet. Psychol. Monogr.,* 1933, **13,** 483–555.

15. Jacobsen, E. Electrophysiology of mental activities, *Amer. J. Psychol.,* 1932, **44,** 677–694.

16. Lashley, K. S. The accuracy of movement in the absence of excitation from the moving organ, *Amer. J. Physiol.,* 1917, **43,** 169–194.

17. Lashley, K. S. The mechanism of vision: XVII. Autonomy of the visual cortex, *J. genet. Psychol.,* 1942, **60,** 197–221.

18. Lashley, K. S. The mechanism of vision: XVIII. Effects of destroying the visual "associative areas" of the monkey, *Genet Psychol. Monogr.,* 1948, **37,** 107–166.

19. Max, L. W. Experimental study of the motor theory of consciousness: IV. *J. comp. Psychol.,* 1937, **24,** 301–344.

20. Pick, A. *Die agrammatischen Sprachstörungen.* Berlin: 1913.

21. Sherrington, C. S. *The integrative action of the nervous system.* London: Constable, 1906.

22. Sherrington, C. S. Some functional problems attaching to convergence, *Proc. roy. Soc.,* 1929, **105B,** 332–362.

23. Thorson, A. M. The relation of tongue movements to internal speech, *J. exp. Psychol.,* 1925, **8,** 1–32.

24. Titchener, E. B. *Lectures on the experimental psychology of the thought processes.* New York: Macmillan, 1909.

25. Washburn, M. F. *Movement and mental imagery.* Boston: Houghton Mifflin, 1916.

26. Watson, J. B. Is thinking merely the action of the language mechanisms? *Brit. J. Psychol.,* 1920, **11,** 86–104.

31. CEREBRAL ORGANIZATION AND BEHAVIOR [1]

Today I shall discuss a subject which, like our Oedipus complexes, has probably troubled many of us but has been suppressed, especially in scientific meetings. Suppression is a sign of conflict, and I hope that I may be able to contribute something to lessen the tension. I refer to the problem of how the brain knows that it knows; what characteristics of neural activity constitute mind. The pioneers in neurology were not troubled by this problem. They accepted the metaphysics of their day, which regarded the brain only as the agent of mind. Mind was for them a little man, seated in the head, who did all the thinking and willed all the actions for the brain. The brain was really only an impediment to him since, by the doctrine of survival, he could get along even better without it. (No one seems to have noted that this concept involved an infinite regression, like puppy dogs and little fleas.) When Fritsch and Hitzig reported the excitability of the cortex, they readily interpreted the excitable areas as "the place of entry of single psychic functions into material." And students of cerebral localization, even when they did not subscribe to mind-brain interaction, were content to ascribe mental functions to specific areas, without inquiring how the areas carry out the functions. Even today this mixing of the mental and physical retards analysis of the actual functions of specialized parts of the nervous system.

In 1881 Bubnoff and Heidenhain wrote, "It seems to us absolutely necessary that investigations of the physiology of the brain be kept as distinct as possible from the accompanying psychological processes." Pavlov, who studied for a time with Heidenhain and was much influenced by him, developed this attitude still further in his attempt to construct a complete account of behavior in terms of conditioned reflexes without reference to mental phenomena. Bechterew, who anticipated Pavlov in the formulation of behavior in terms of associative reflexes, accepted a psychophysical parallelism. Pavlov was less explicit but came to regard mental phenomena as of no concern to the physiologist; a fit subject only for psychologists and

[1] EDITORS' NOTE: From *Proc. Ass. Res. nerv. ment. Dis.*, 1958, 36, 1–18. Reprinted by permission of the Williams and Wilkins Co.

philosophers, whom he held in slight esteem. The behaviorist school in America has carried this conception to its logical conclusion, not only denying that mental phenomena are relevant in the study of behavior, but asserting that they do not provide a basis for any scientific study whatever. Their position, however, still leaves them with the problem of how man ever developed the delusion that he is conscious.

Students of neurology might well be content to leave the problem in such hands, although it is certain that no solution will come from those sources. Mind, for psychologists since Watson, has become a naughty word. Metaphysicians and theologians have spent so many years weaving fairy tales about it that they have come to believe one another's phantasies.

There are indications, however, of an increasing interest in the problem of mind among neurologists. I would not intrude the question here, in what I am sure will otherwise be a serious scientific discussion, save that, within the past few years, three leaders in neurology, specialists in different fields, have asserted that mind cannot be explained by the activities of the brain and have sought to reseat the little man on his throne in the pineal gland.

Sherrington (14), after demonstrating that mind is not a special form of energy, wrote:

> The sun's energy is part of the closed energy cycle. What leverage can it have on the mind? Yet through my retina and brain it seems able to act on my mind. The theoretically impossible happens. In fine, I assert that it does act on my mind. Conversely my thinking "self" thinks that it can bend my arm. Physics tells me that my arm cannot be bent without disturbing the sun. My mind then does not bend my arm. Or, the theoretically impossible happens. Let me prefer to think that the theoretically impossible does happen.

Eccles (4) accepts Sherrington's conclusion that the mind is not a form of energy, then evolves an elaborate theory as to how non-energy mind can act on matter, appealing to telepathy as supporting evidence. He accepts Eddington's misrepresentation of Heisenberg's principle of uncertainty and makes elaborate calculations to show that a minute "influence," within the limits which Eddington sets to the uncertainty principle, can act upon a synaptic junction and modify behavior. As Heisenberg himself has told me, the principle of uncertainty is entirely irrelevant to the question of causal determination. It is a principle of unobservability, and as a basis for doctrines of will it is in a class with the belief that the invisible face of the moon is made of green cheese. Also, I still consider the gambling house odds more reliable than Rhine's statistics.

Walshe (16) bases his argument for reviving the soul chiefly upon the assertion that man is more wonderful and more dignified than the earwig.

I cannot quote the earwig but can quote Archy, the cockroach, in reply (Don Marquis). "A man thinks he amounts to a great deal but to a mosquito he is only something good to eat."

I am not ready to accept these doctrines of scientific despair and Christian hope. They are based upon a thorough misconception of the facts of consciousness. They fail to analyze the problem and show no conception of what phenomena are to be explained, or cannot be explained, by the action of the brain. The problem requires an entirely different approach; a thorough analysis of the phenomena of consciousness, oriented with reference to the phenomena of neural activity. Only when such an analysis has been made, will it be possible to test the correlation of mental states and processes with the brain's activity. I am confident that when the questions which are now held to be unanswerable are properly formulated, they will turn out to be capable of translation into physiological terms and will fall within the competence of present methods of physiological research. I shall try to illustrate the sort of analysis which is required and the conception of mental events to which it gives rise. I shall also speculate a little concerning the nature of the neural processes suggested by the mental organization.

Some thirty years ago I first tried to get a clear definition of the mind-body problem. I went through a mass of literature, chiefly the product of various schools of philosophy, and listed all the characteristics of mind which were cited as inexplicable in terms of neural action. I then turned to the psychological evidence to test the validity of these supposed characteristics. This is a procedure which has since acquired philosophic respectability by being christened an ism (operationism), which is merely questioning generalizations and extrapolations and going back to examine the data from which they were derived. I was forced to the conclusion that philosophers have been unreliable observers and that much of the difficulty of the mind-body problem is due to their incompetence as psychologists. The phenomena to be explained, as studied by psychologists, are mostly not what the philosophers have claimed them to be.

My original list of supposedly inexplicable traits was quite long, and I do not intend to inflict them all upon you. One of the most widely cited and heavily emphasized of them derives from Descartes's "cogito ergo sum." He thought this a statement of a fundamental truth, but as Bertrand Russell (13) has emphasized, it is only a false analogy. I, my body, does work. My body exists. Thinking is work; therefore there must be something to do the thinking. The analogy is false. The only conclusion that can be derived from experience is that thought exists. No psychologist has ever discovered the thinker. William James (7) reported that the search for the I reveals only feelings of tension, chiefly in the mouth and throat. There are neither empirical nor logical grounds for assuming that the existence of consciousness implies a distinct entity which is in the relation to it of a knower or doer.

The problems of mind suggested by the literature fall into two groups: first, the nature of the items, elements, or things which are present in consciousness; second, the arrangement or patterns in which these items occur. That is, experience consists of sensations, images, emotions, and perhaps some less clear items, arranged in an endless variety of combinations which are described by the laws of perception, of thought, or of logic. The problems arising from these two aspects of mind are different. The content of experience, the sensations and the like, constitutes all that is directly known. It is the material which has most stubbornly resisted description in the space-time system of the physical sciences. The ordering is not so certainly to be characterized as mental. I shall deal with it first because interpretation of the content of experience is derived from the ordering.

No activity of mind is ever conscious. This sounds like a paradox, but it is none the less true. There are order and arrangement, but there is no experience of the creation of that order. I could give numberless examples, for there is no exception to the rule. A couple of illustrations should suffice. Look at a complicated scene. It consists of a number of objects standing out against an indistinct background; desk, chairs, faces. Each consists of a number of lesser sensations combined in the object, but there is no experience of putting them together. The objects are immediately present. When we think in words, the thoughts come in grammatical form with subject, verb, object, and modifying clauses falling into place without our having the slightest perception of how the sentence structure is produced. If you question this, try to think a thought in dactylic hexameter; with the syllables correctly emphasized; in the rhythm of, "This is the forest primeval, the murmuring pines and the hemlocks."

Experience clearly gives no clue as to the means by which it is organized. If the organization were produced by a slide rule or by a digital computer, consciousness would give no indication of the fact nor any basis for denying it. If the brain is capable of producing such organization, then it may be considered the organizer.

The assertion is frequently made that the ordering of mental processes or the achievements of mind are such as no machine could accomplish. Specific characteristics of the organization have been cited as inexplicable. Some of these are based on a false interpretation of the phenomena; others present genuine problems; problems which can, however, be formulated in physiological terms. I shall review a few of these characteristics or attributes of mental organization to show the misconceptions which they involve and also the genuine problems which they raise.

The Unity of Consciousness

Kant held that the mind, being immaterial, cannot occupy space. The idea goes much further back, as in the scholastic discussion of how many angels can dance on the point of a needle. Psychologists, however, at least in recent times, have seen no reason to keep mind unitary. William McDougall (12), whom I regard as the most able student of these matters, although I disagree with every word he ever wrote, postulated an atom of mind adsorbed on every material atom. When the physical atoms are assembled in the brain, the mental atoms combine to form mind. (As I have mentioned elsewhere, this theory preceded the splitting of the atom.) The unity of mind, if it deserves that term, is a quite different thing. It is the unity of a system of interacting and interdependent parts; the same sort of unity as appears in any complicated machine.

There are temporal combinations which might be called unifying actions. The words of a spoken sentence may extend over a considerable interval of time, yet the sentence as a whole arouses further associations. Such facts present definite physiological problems, in this case the nature of the persistent aftereffects of neural activity.

The concept of mental unity seems to be responsible for the search for some center of consciousness, where information from all parts of the brain is brought together and synthesized. Such a notion violates what I believe to be a basic principle of interpretation of neural action. The neural processes constituting a percept, a memory, or an idea cannot have fewer distinct elements than the number of items present in consciousness. When one looks at a sheet of coordinate paper, there may be 300 or more squares seen clearly within the foveal field. The squares extend, progressively less clearly, to the edges of the paper, and dots or lines in the periphery are seen as breaks in the texture. Such a field may include 20,000 or more distinct visual items. Each item of the visual field must be represented either by a distinct neural event or by some simplified, symbolic representation of the entire visual field. The latter alternative implies as many distinct symbols as there are possible permutations of items in vision, and this presents an even greater task for any limited system of neurons in a center of consciousness, than does the assumption of a neural event for each item in consciousness. Only the cerebral cortex has a large enough number of elements to provide for such complexity.

Experience is a sequence of interrelated events, but the unity is only that of coexistence of elements belonging to the same order.

The Mind's Transcendence of Time and Space

The brain is only here and now, but mind leaps into the past and brings it into the present. Mind crosses the ocean when we think of scenes in London or Paris. Mind reaches into the future when we foresee events.

Yes, there are plenty of such statements in the literature, and E. B. Holt (5) wrote a whole book about them. But my mind can also pass through the looking glass, wander in the tulgy wood, and see the burbling Jabberwock. There is no more transcendence in the one case than in the others. There is a core of problems in these extravagant claims, though they are not often clearly formulated; for instance, the dating of memories. What places the memory of an event in the past? I have a memory of a day in school, or rather a completely isolated memory of a large and dangerous-looking woman bending over me and thrusting at me a contrivance of wooden balls strung on wires, a memory of slapping her and running. As a memory this has no date. It might have been a dream last night. But it is dated by hearsay; that I was sent to school at the age of four and ran away. That places it in the ordered series of memories of the places where I have lived. For me, places of residence form the major units of the time scale. We each have, I think, such a seried scheme of memories. The order is determined just as is the memory of the alphabet, polarized from a to z, and the pastness of memories is estimated by it. There is no very satisfactory theory of this polarization of memories, but Hull's adaptation of Pavlov's irradiation theory is a possible one (6).

A version of this notion of mind's transcendence appears in Sherrington's interpretation of binocular vision. He states that there is no evidence that the nervous paths from two corresponding retinal points in the two eyes reach a common mechanism in the brain. He denies that they do reach a common mechanism (14, p. 273) and concludes that binocular fusion is mental, not physical. He says, "The synthesis is a mental one in which the finite mind uses 'time' as synthesizer." (Whatever that may mean.) Sperry's studies show that anatomic connection is essential. The normal cat has binocular fusion like that of man. What is seen with one eye is recognized by the other. When the chiasma is severed, this interocular transfer still occurs, but if the splenium is also severed, reactions which are formed with one eye are not transferred to the other.[2]

The Selective Action of Mind

Of the multitude of things which might be in consciousness, only a very limited number are present at any one moment. It is held that this isolation has no parallel in the physical world and that energy changes, since they form a continuum, could not effect such isolation. This category of mental activity involves many problems, such as attention and dissociation, selective memory, and directed action. I can deal with them most readily by sketching the theory of cerebral organization that I have dreamed up in the course of years. It involves several postulates about integrative mechanisms.

[2] Reported at the International Physiological Congress, Montreal, 1953.

1. The billions of neurons in the cerebral network are organized into a large number of systems. Each system consists of the traces of a number of habits or memories. Knowledge of the moves and games of chess would constitute one such system; memories of neural anatomy another; and so on through all of the individual's varied interests. The traces or engramata in any system are more closely connected with one another than with other systems. The systems are not anatomically separate, and the same neurons, in different permutations, may participate in many systems. For brevity I shall call these "trace systems."

2. Such a trace system may be thrown into a state of tonic activity by an external stimulus which activates one set of traces within it. In the tonic state the traces of the system are readily excitable and available to recall. Other systems are in abeyance. Thus when one plays chess, the Evans gambit or Philodor's defense may be readily recalled. But if the player is interrupted by the question, "Who won the pennant last year?", he will take some time to "collect his thoughts"; that is, to organize the baseball trace system. Such a general tonic activation seems a plausible explanation of concentration upon a particular subject, limiting associations to that subject. Questions of preparatory adjustment, organization of purposive activities, and the like can be formulated in such terms. An activated trace system would limit associations of the flow of ideas to the topics included in that group of traces. As I have stressed elsewhere (10), grammatical structure and other ordered activities imply some sorting or arranging mechanism, active before the words reach overt speech or silent thought. The relations in thought structure are antecedent to consciousness. The tonic background might provide the basis for this preorganization. This leads to the problem of the neurology of logic, of which a bit more, later.

3. A system in tonic activity dominates the brain field, limiting the organization of other systems. It is relatively impervious to unrelated excitations. An intense stimulus, or an emotionally charged one, such as the sound of one's name, may break in, but the great mass of afferent excitations is excluded. This blocking might be either an active inhibition or the preemption of neurons which might otherwise be included in the blocked system. The phenomena of attention demand some such hypothesis.

4. The neurons in a trace system, under tonic activation, exert some mutual facilitation. The tonic state of the whole system is thus built up and maintained. This was the only sort of explanation that I could find for the reduction in efficiency of behavior in proportion to the extent of brain damage. The assumption is consistent with Woodworth's notion (19) that long practiced habits may be transformed into drives; that activities which have acquired many associations may become obsessive.

5. The level of tonus in the partially activated system may vary. Circuits which have just been fully activated may retain a high level of subthreshold activity and thus contribute to the temporal organization evident in the memory span.

6. Fixation in memory is generally possible only when the remembered material forms part of such a dominant system. Learning has been classified in two types: mechanical, produced by repetition; and rational, which is not dependent on repetition. We remember the content of a book, not in the author's words but in meanings which fit into previous knowledge of the subject. During the reading the meanings are not necessarily formulated clearly in verbal or other thought forms, but they may be so formulated later. That is, associations may be formed during reading with traces in the system which are not activated above tonic levels during learning.

This assumption would provide an explanation of some types of confusion in which the patient may show disconnected activities or disordered thinking, with no later memory of what occurred during the state.

Such a system of low level tonic excitation in a system of memory traces would provide a basis for many of the characteristics of mental organization. The circuits of the trace system which are actively firing at levels sufficient to excite other traces would constitute the content of experience, limited and changing from moment to moment. The background of tonic activity would determine the direction of attention and of the flow of thought, restricting it to related associations. It would provide the binding force that holds together the temporal sequences through memory span and more permanent associations. Reduction in the tonic level of the system, as in sleep or under anesthetics, or violent invasion, as in a convulsive seizure, would destroy the organization necessary for memory and the continuity of the conscious state. Partial incomplete disorganization in sleep would permit interaction of different partial systems with the bizarre contaminations that occur in dreams.

These assumptions concerning cerebral organization are, of course, purely speculative and mainly inferences from psychological events. There is no present direct evidence from physiology in support of them. However, they are not inconsistent with what is now known of the physiology of the brain, and I believe that some such mechanism is implied by our present knowledge of the structure and activities of the cerebral cortex.

As I emphasized at a previous meeting of the Association (11), it is probable that every neuron in the cerebral cortex, and indeed in the whole nervous system, is subject to a continuous bombardment by nerve impulses. This follows from consideration of cell number, of frequency of sensory input, and of the continuity of the cerebral network. The observations of Gray Walter (17) on synchronous firing of many areas of the cortex with driven alpha rhythms show how widespread the excitations may be.

Not all and perhaps not even a large proportion of the neurons are fired by the bombardment. It requires at least two and perhaps many more impulses from end buds to fire the cell. But partial depolarization with increase in excitability may result from subthreshold volleys and, because of decremental conduction in the cell membrane, may be selective for special connections. When one set of circuits is actively fired, it should be expected that some neurons in associative connection with it would receive too few impulses to fire them, but sufficient to prime them for response to impulses from other circuits. Sherrington's studies of overlap in motor pools revealed a condition of increased excitatory state which could provide a mechanism for the tonic state of associated neurons at higher levels. This would result in a sort of priming of an entire associative or trace system.

I believe that what is known of the learning process justifies these assumptions concerning the role of the tonic background in the formation of associations. The importance of repetition in learning has been greatly exaggerated. Thorndike, who was the most eminent American student of learning and for many years an advocate of the theory of learning by repetition, finally denied its importance. He substituted for repetition a somewhat vague concept of "belongingness" which implies, so far as I can interpret it, some unconscious relational structure or unconscious associations.

An organization of associated neurons excited at subthreshold levels seems not only a reasonable but an almost necessary consequence of the structure and known physiological properties of the cerebral cortex. As I have indicated, the interplay of such systems would provide a mechanism for a large proportion of the selective activities of mind.

A few other supposedly inexplicable mental activities can be mentioned only briefly.

The Will

Voluntary action is often cited as purely mental, chiefly because freedom of the will is indispensable to many established ethical systems. Voluntary action is usually defined as a choice between two foreseen alternative actions. This is beautifully illustrated by the spinal frog. If a bit of acid is placed on the midline of the rump, the preparation responds by alternate jerking of the hind legs; incipient wiping movements. Finally the motor system of one leg dominates, and that leg performs the complete wiping reflex, while the other is extended. Here is foresight; we often see a man making such tentative actions while he is reaching a decision, and his verbal debating (foresight) about it is only a substitute for other tentative actions. After the period of indecision, of vacillation, the spinal frog also reaches its decision. Save in the complexity of the alternatives, the procedures are the same.

The Self

It has been held that the feeling of personal identity implies a subject of consciousness, a self external to and possessing the consciousness. Clinical evidence strongly indicates that the self is a stereotype of memories centering about the body image. Distortion of the body image often produces a loss of the feeling of personal identity, and an analysis of the normal self strongly supports such a view. I have worn spectacles for as long as I can remember, guarding them from damage, adjusting them, and searching for them in the morning. They seem to have become the focus of my self. When I try to imagine my ghost, it has no face, its body is vague. I am sure only that it wears spectacles.

Creative Ability

Du Noüy (3) and Walshe, among others, argue that human achievements are so much greater than those of any animal that they cannot be accounted for by the slight differences in the size and structure of the brains. There is no objective measure of achievement or of its difficulty. The measurement of intelligence is based upon a time scale; the units of measurement are units of chronological age. There is no measure of adult achievements, and the statement that one is quantitatively greater than another is meaningless. If the time scale is applied to evolutionary development of intellect, as it is to individual development, then the increase in mental ability from the tarsiers to the first ape is at least six times as great as that between the ape and man. Comparing the abilities of monkeys and their brain sizes to those of the great apes, it seems not unlikely that the addition of two or three cell generations in the development of the ape brain might raise it to human capacity.

An example of the difficulty of correlating structure and function without adequate analysis is the search for a locus of intelligence. Early students located intellect in the frontal cortex. Subsequent studies have chased it out of the frontal regions to the parietal, to the temporal, and it now seems relegated to subcortical regions. Factor analysis by Spearman, Thurstone (15) and others has meanwhile broken intelligence down into a number of special abilities, visual, spatial, verbal, and the like. These "primary abilities" resemble the functions disturbed by lesions in different parts of the cortex closely enough to suggest that they represent functions of different areas. But the analysis has not yet been carried far enough. When the tasks which differentiate the various special abilities are compared, many of them seem to involve the same sort of logical manipulations. And the same sort of manipulations appear in animals which lack a cortex. They differ only with respect to the materials manipulated (visual, somesthetic, verbal). This suggests that the general principles of logical structure, the formation and manipulation of abstractions, are a general property of neural organization. The search for a center of intellect has been futile because the function was not adequately analyzed.

The problem of the neurology of logic must be faced eventually. Wertheimer (18) has analyzed the solving of problems in a range from that of young children to Einstein's own accounts of his methods. Trial and error plays a dominant role in all cases, but it is a trial and error in applying logical principles. The number of kinds of logical relations with which the mind deals is not great; few symbols are employed in symbolic logic. Instances of animal behavior fitting every logical symbol can be found. The limitations of animal intelligence are set by the nature and complexity of the materials dealt with, not by fundamental logical relations. The neurological problem is to define these relations among concrete processes so as to open them to physiological analysis. Most of the phenomena of abstraction and generalization are exhibited in the discriminatory behavior of animals, and some progress has been made toward physiological explanations at that level.

I have thus far tried to show that the organization of mental states does not reveal any operations which cannot be accounted for in principle by the mechanisms of the brain. I doubt that any of the models representing brain activities, that we have today, embody the principles of neural integration. The machines which compute or learn are almost all digital. The brain has been compared to a digital computer because the neuron, like a switch or valve, either does or does not complete a circuit. But at that point the similarity ends. The switch in the digital computer is constant in its effect, and its effect is large in proportion to the total output of the machine. The effect produced by the neuron varies with its recovery from refractory phase and with its metabolic state. The number of neurons involved in any action runs into millions so that the influence of any one is negligible. With perhaps a few exceptions, like Mauthner's cell in the embryo, any cell in the system can be dispensed with. I have made nearly a thousand stab wounds in the cortex of a monkey without producing discoverable symptoms. The accuracy of nervous activity is a statistical accuracy derived from the number of neurons involved. The character of variation in sensory thresholds and in accuracy of movement bears this out. The brain is an analogical machine, not digital. Analysis of its integrative activities will probably have to be in statistical terms. The mathematical analyses of spreading waves of excitation in a nerve net by Ashby (1), Beurle (2), . . . and others are a promising start in this direction. The fact that we have not yet duplicated the mechanisms of the brain is, however, no argument for the existence of a separate mind.

Of course the doctrine of psychophysical parallelism has involved the theory that the mind's activities are exactly duplicated in the brain, ever since recognition of conservation of energy, so that it may seem quite unnecessary to labor the point as I have done. But that doctrine does not provide any clue to the nature of the brain's operations. I consider it objectionable for several reasons. It admits a whole realm of events outside the scope of scientific explanation, providing a delightful playground for those who dislike science. More importantly, it takes a long step toward the mysticism of interactionism, and present-day neurologists seem only too ready to take the additional step. Finally, acceptance of the doctrine has definitely retarded the analysis of thought processes with an orientation toward the problems of neurophysiology.

Thought and Action

A word concerning the relation of the neural processes of thought to behavior. I once invented a thought-reading machine; a system of levers which magnified and recorded movements of the tongue. I first had my subjects speak a word, then think it silently. Movements of the tongue were minute but otherwise identical with those of speech. However, it was soon evident that when the subject thought for a few moments without speech, the tongue dropped to the back of the mouth and showed no movements, even when the subjects were doing mental arithmetic; squaring three place numbers and giving correct answers. If, during a mental task, I urged the subject to hurry or if I slapped him, the tongue came forward and identifiable word-curves, not always profanity, appeared on the records. A study of movements of the closed eyes during thinking of directions in space or of simple geometrical figures gave similar though less consistent results.

Such observations provide evidence that the neural activities in thought are identical with those of action, save for the lack of facilitation of the final motor path. The addition of emotional tension or facilitation increases the excitability of lower motor centers so that the neural activities of thought can fire them. The chief function of the pyramidal system is, I believe, to supply such facilitation and thus transform the thought to action.

The Content of Experience

I turn now to the nature of the items making up the field of consciousness, which are manipulated in unconscious ways. These items, as described by psychologists, are sensations or sensation-like images. Emotions reduce to somesthetic sensations; affects may constitute an additional class, but are too vaguely defined for treatment here. A few investigators have reported other elements: feelings of innervation and Vorbewusstseinslagen, feelings of being about to have an idea. These latter are, however, questioned by most observers. The problem of the content of experience boils down to accounting for the character of sensations. This has been thought to present the greatest difficulty for reducing mind to brain and has been most often cited in discussions of their incommensurability. "This red is my red. It is unique, indivisible, ineffable. By no stretch of the imagination can it be reduced to vibrations in the ether or to volleys of nerve impulses." I suspect that this proves only the inelasticity of the imagination, calcified by the senility of tradition.

What can actually be said of sensory qualities, of red and green? They are different, but the difference cannot be defined. They are recognizable, but the basis of recognition cannot be stated. They may have spatial extent, but within the limits of retinal sensitivity they may be reduced to extensionless points. Space is not inherent in the color. We may say that red is warm, exciting; but that is only adding irrelevant emotional content. Indescribable and undefinable differentness are the only attributes of sensory quality.

A quite simple neural mechanism would produce this condition. Assume that lights of different wave lengths excite volleys of different frequencies in the striate area. These volleys activate a neural system to produce patterns of activity which differ for the different volley frequencies but do not reproduce the frequencies. This system now excites another, say the verbal, which does not directly receive the incoming volleys. For the verbal system then, the sensory volleys are different, but they cannot be broken down into volley frequency. Like red and green they are different and identifiable, but they have nothing in common with volley frequency. They have all the attributes of sensory quality.

Does this still leave the ineffable red? Is your red still red? I can only give an illustration which may shake your faith in it. I knew a painter who, after a mild stroke, developed a red-green blindness. Her work became drab, a muddy combination of browns and greens, in contrast to her former use of vivid colors. I got a clue to the trouble when she copied a portrait but painted the face a sickly green. It was not an attempt at modernism. She had laid on a green foundation, a technique sometimes used to give depth to flesh colors, and had failed to cover it up. She had no inkling of the trouble but only felt hurt that some of her former pupils received prizes while her work was ignored. To her, her models and paintings still looked alike, since the color defect applied to both, though she now confused reds and greens. What then of her ineffable red? Has the red of normal vision any more constancy or significance? These same considerations apply to all sensory qualities.

I cannot pretend to have formulated a complete and satisfactory account of how the brain thinks. I recognize gaps and inconsistencies in my formulation of the problems, and the hypotheses that I have suggested will probably collapse under the weight of additional evidence. But I do have faith in the point of view and the method that I have tried to illustrate. Research on the brain has revealed a network of cells, organized in various structures and systems, subject to constant excitation from the sense organs, and capable of developing and maintaining a great variety of patterns of activity. On the physical side the phenomena can be described, and although the picture is far from complete, the essential elementary processes for the production of behavior have been defined. In contrast, the conception of mind has been extremely vague and has not provided a basis for asking meaningful questions about its relations to the neural events.

As long as mind is thought of as a special kind of being, obeying an all-or-none law in its presence or absence, or as some special type of energy, such as Sherrington sought and failed to find, so long will its relation to the brain be incapable of investigation. Mind is a complex organization, held together by interaction of processes and by the time scales of memory, centered about the body image. It has no distinguishing features other than its organization. The mental phenomena must be subjected to an analysis as complete and detailed as that which is being made of neural activities. Only as progress is made in such an analysis, and as the picture of the brain's activities is completed, will it be possible to make significant correlations between the two organized systems. Meanwhile, there is no logical or empirical reason for denying the possibility that the correlation may eventually show a complete identity of the two organizations.[3]

REFERENCES

1. Ashby, W. R. *Design for a brain.* New York: 1952.
2. Beurle, R. L. Properties of a mass of cells capable of regenerating impulses, *Philos. Trans.*, 1956, **240B**, 8–94.
3. Du Noüy, L. *Human destiny.* New York: 1947.
4. Eccles, J. C. *The neurophysiological basis of mind.* Oxford: 1953.
5. Holt, E. B. *The concept of consciousness.* New York: 1914.
6. Hull, C. L. *Principles of behavior.* New York: 1943.
7. James, W. *Principles of psychology.* New York: 1910. Vol. I.
8. Köhler, W., and Wallach, H. Figural after-effects: an investigation of visual processes, *Proc. Amer. phil. Soc.*, 1944, **88**, 269–357.
9. Lashley, K. S. The behavioristic interpretation of consciousness, *Psychol. Rev.*, 1923, **30**, 237–272, 323–353.
10. Lashley, K. S. The problem of serial order in behavior. In Jeffress, L. A. (Ed.) *Cerebral mechanisms in behavior.* New York: 1951.
11. Lashley, K. S. Functional interpretation of anatomic patterns, *Proc. Assoc. Res. nerv. ment. Dis.*, 1952, 529–552.
12. McDougall, W. *Body and mind.* New York: 1911.

[3] EDITORS' NOTE: The discussion following the oral presentation of this paper has been omitted.

13. Russell, B. *A history of western philosophy.* New York: 1954.
14. Sherrington, C. *Man on his nature.* Cambridge: 1941.
15. Thurstone, L. I. Primary mental abilities, *Psychometr. Monogr.,* 1938, 1–121.
16. Walshe, F. M. R. Thoughts upon the equation of mind and brain, *Brain,* 1953, **76**, 1–18.
17. Walter, W. G. *The living brain.* New York: 1953.
18. Wertheimer, M. *Productive thinking.* New York: 1945.
19. Woodworth, R. S. *Dynamic psychology.* New York: 1918.

PUBLICATIONS OF K. S. LASHLEY [1]

1. Visual discrimination of size and form in the albino rat, *J. Anim. Behav.*, 1912, **2**, 310–331.

2. Biparental inheritance and the question of sexuality in paramecium, *J. exp. Zool.*, 1913, **14**, 393–466. (H. S. Jennings and K. S. Lashley)

3. Biparental inheritance of size in paramecium, *J. exp. Zool.*, 1913, **15**, 193–200. (H. S. Jennings and K. S. Lashley)

4. Notes of the development of a young monkey, *J. Anim. Behav.*, 1913, **3**, 114–139. (K. S. Lashley and J. B. Watson)

5. Reproduction of inarticulate sounds in the parrot, *J. Anim. Behav.*, 1913, **3**, 361–366.

6. Literature for 1912 on the behavior of vertebrates, *J. Anim. Behav.*, 1913, **3**, 446–463. (J. B. Watson and K. S. Lashley)

7. A note on the persistence of an instinct, *J. Anim. Behav.*, 1914, **4**, 293–294.

8. Recent literature of a general nature on animal behavior, *Psychol. Bull.*, 1914, **11**, 269–277.

9. An historical and experimental study of homing, *Carnegie Instn. Publ.*, 1915, **7** (211), 9–60. (J. B. Watson and K. S. Lashley)

°10. Notes on the nesting activities of the noddy and sooty terns, *Carnegie Instn. Publ.*, 1915, **7** (211), 61–83.

11. The acquisition of skill in archery, *Carnegie Instn. Publ.*, 1915, **7** (211), 107–128.

°12. Inheritance in the asexual reproduction of *Hydra viridis*, *Proc. nat. Acad. Sci., Wash.*, 1915, **1**, 298–301.

13. Recent literature on sensory discrimination in animals, *Psychol. Bull.*, 1915, **12**, 291–299.

14. Inheritance in the asexual reproduction of hydra, *J. exp. Zool.*, 1915, **19**, 157–210.

15. Results of continued selection in hydra, *J. exp. Zool.*, 1916, **20**, 19–26.

16. Observations on ciliary current in free-swimming paramecia, *J. exp. Zool.*, 1916, **21**, 281–293. (S. O. Mast and K. S. Lashley)

17. The color vision of birds. I. The spectrum of the domestic fowl, *J. Anim. Behav.*, 1916, **6**, 1–26.

18. Sensory physiology of animals, *Psychol. Bull.*, 1916, **13**, 209–315.

---

[1] Lashley's master's essay, The bacteriology of eggs with special reference to the mode of contamination, University of Pittsburgh, 1911, was never published.

° Reproduced in whole or part in this volume.

19. The human salivary reflex and its use in psychology, *Psychol. Rev.*, 1916, **23**, 446–464.

°20. Reflex secretion of the human parotid gland, *J. exp. Psychol.*, 1916, **1**, 461–493.

21. Changes in the amount of salivary secretion associated with cerebral lesions, *Amer. J. Physiol.*, 1917, **43**, 62–72.

°22. The accuracy of movement in the absence of excitation from the moving organ, *Amer. J. Physiol.*, 1917, **43**, 169–194.

°23. The retention of habits by the rat after destruction of the frontal portion of the cerebrum, *Psychobiology*, 1917, **1**, 3–18. (S. I. Franz and K. S. Lashley)

24. Sensory physiology of animals, *Psychol. Bull.*, 1917, **14**, 276–283.

25. The effects of cerebral destruction upon habit-formation and retention in the albino rat, *Psychobiology*, 1917, **1**, 71–140. (K. S. Lashley and S. I. Franz)

26. The effects of strychnine and caffeine upon the rate of learning, *Psychobiology*, 1917, **1**, 141–170.

27. The criterion of learning in experiments with the maze, *J. Anim. Behav.*, 1917, **7**, 66–70.

28. Retroactive association and the elimination of errors in the maze, *J. Anim. Behav.*, 1917, **7**, 130–138. (H. B. Hubbert and K. S. Lashley)

29. A causal factor in the relation of the distribution of practice to the rate of learning, *J. Anim. Behav.*, 1917, **7**, 139–142.

30. Modifiability of the preferential use of the hands in the rhesus monkey, *J. Anim. Behav.*, 1917, **7**, 178–186.

°31. A simple maze: with data on the relation of the distribution of practice to the rate of learning, *Psychobiology*, 1918, **1**, 353–367.

32. Sensory physiology of animals, *Psychol. Bull.*, 1919, **16**, 159–164. (K. S. Lashley and J. D. Dodson)

33. Studies of cerebral function in learning, *Psychobiology*, 1920, **2**, 55–135.

34. A consensus of medical opinion upon questions relating to sex education and venereal disease campaigns, *Ment. Hyg.*, N.Y., 1920, **4**, 769–847. (J. B. Watson and K. S. Lashley)

35. Sensory physiology of animals, *Psychol. Bull.*, 1920, **17**, 178–187.

36. A psychological study of motion pictures in relation to venereal disease campaigns, *Publ. U.S. Interdepartmental Social Hygiene Board*, 1922, 1–88. (K. S. Lashley and J. B. Watson)

°37. Studies of cerebral function in learning. II. The effects of long-continued practice upon localization, *J. comp. Psychol.*, 1921, **1**, 453–468.

38. Studies of cerebral function in learning. III. The motor areas, *Brain*, 1921, **44**, 255–286.

39. Studies of cerebral function in learning. IV. Vicarious function after destruction of the visual areas, *Amer. J. Physiol.*, 1922, **59**, 44–71.

40. The behavioristic interpretation of consciousness, *Psychol. Rev.*, 1923, **30**, 237–272, 329–353.

°41. Studies of cerebral function in learning. V. The retention of motor habits after destruction of the so-called motor areas in primates, *Arch. Neurol. Psychiat., Chicago,* 1924, **12**, 249–276.

42. Physiological analysis of the libido, *Psychol. Rev.,* 1924, **31**, 192–202.

°43. Studies of cerebral function in learning. VI. The theory that synaptic resistance is reduced by the passage of the nerve impulse, *Psychol. Rev.,* 1924, **31**, 369–375.

44. Studies of cerebral function in learning. VII. The relation between cerebral mass, learning and retention, *J. comp. Neurol.,* 1926, **41**, 1–58.

°45. Temporal variation in the function of the gyrus precentralis in primates, *Amer. J. Physiol.,* 1923, **65**, 585–602.

°46. The survival of the maze habit after cerebellar injuries, *J. comp. Psychol.,* 1926, **6**, 423–433. (K. S. Lashley and D. A. McCarthy)

°47. Spinal conduction and kinesthetic sensitivity in the maze habit, *J. comp. Psychol.,* 1929, **9**, 71–105. (K. S. Lashley and J. Ball)

48. *Brain mechanisms and intelligence.* Chicago: Univ. Chicago Press, 1929.

49. Learning. I. Nervous mechanisms in learning. In Murchison, C. (Ed.) *The foundations of experimental psychology.* Worcester, Mass.: Clark Univ. Press, 1929. Pp. 524–563.

°50. Basic neural mechanisms in behavior, *Psychol. Rev.,* 1930, **37**, 1–24.

°51. The mechanism of vision. I. A method for rapid analysis of pattern-vision in the rat, *J. genet. Psychol.,* 1930, **37**, 453–460.

52. The mechanism of vision. II. The influence of cerebral lesions upon the threshold of discrimination for brightness in the rat, *J. genet. Psychol.,* 1930, **37**, 461–480.

53. The mechanism of vision. III. The comparative visual acuity of pigmented and albino rats, *J. genet. Psychol.,* 1930, **37**, 481–484.

54. The mechanism of vision. IV. The cerebral areas necessary for pattern vision in the rat, *J. comp. Neurol.,* 1931, **53**, 419–478.

55. Cerebral control versus reflexology: a reply to Professor Hunter, *J. gen. Psychol.,* 1931, **5**, 3–20.

56. Mass action in cerebral function, *Science,* 1931, **73**, 245–254.

57. The mechanism of vision. V. The structure and image-forming power of the rat's eye, *J. comp. Psychol.,* 1932, **13**, 173–200.

58. The mechanism of vision. VI. The lateral portion of the area striata in the rat: a correction, *J. comp. Neurol.,* 1932, **55**, 525–529. (K. S. Lashley and M. Frank)

59. Studies of cerebral function in learning. VIII. A reanalysis of data on mass action in the visual cortex, *J. comp. Neurol.,* 1932, **54**, 77–84.

60. Massenleistung und Gehirnfunktionen, *Nervenarzt,* 1932, **5** (3), 113–120, 180–184.

61. Studies of cerebral function in learning. IX. Mass action in relation to the number of elements in the problem to be learned, *J. comp. Neurol.,* 1933, **57**, 3–56. (K. S. Lashley and L. E. Wiley)

62. Studies of cerebral function in learning. X. The effects of dilatation of the ventricles upon maze-learning, *Amer. J. Physiol.,* 1933, **104**, 51–61. (K. S. Lashley, W. T. McDonald, and H. N. Peters)

°**63.** Integrative functions of the cerebral cortex, *Physiol. Rev.*, 1933, **13**, 1–42.

64. Learning. III. Nervous mechanisms in learning. In Murchison, C. (Ed.) *A handbook of general experimental psychology.* Worcester, Mass.: Clark Univ. Press, 1934. Pp. 456–496.

65. The mechanism of vision. VII. The projection of the retina upon the primary optic centers in the rat, *J. comp. Neurol.*, 1934, **59**, 341–373.

°**66.** The mechanism of vision. VIII. The projection of the retina upon the cerebral cortex of the rat, *J. comp. Neurol.*, 1934, **60**, 57–79.

67. The mechanism of vision. X. Postoperative disturbances of habits based on detail vision in the rat after lesions in the cerebral visual areas, *J. comp. Psychol.*, 1934, **17**, 355–391. (K. S. Lashley and M. Frank)

°**68.** The mechanism of vision. XI. A preliminary test of innate organization, *J. genet. Psychol.*, 1934, **45**, 136–144. (K. S. Lashley and J. T. Russell)

°**69.** Studies of cerebral function in learning. XI. The behavior of the rat in latch-box situations, *Comp. Psychol. Monogr.*, 1935, **11**, 1–42.

70. The mechanism of vision. XII. Nervous structures concerned in the acquisition and retention of habits based on reactions to light, *Comp. Psychol. Monogr.*, 1935, **11** (52), 43–79.

71. The mechanism of vision. XIII. Cerebral function in discrimination of brightness when detail vision is controlled, *J. comp. Neurol.*, 1937, **66**, 471–480.

72. The mechanism of vision. XIV. Visual perception of distance after injuries to the cerebral cortex, colliculi, or optic thalamus, *J. genet. Psychol.*, 1937, **51**, 169–207.

°**73.** Functional determinants of cerebral localization, *Arch. Neurol. Psychiat., Chicago*, 1937, **38**, 371–387.

°**74.** The thalamus and emotion, *Psychol. Rev.*, 1938, **45**, 42–61.

75. The mechanism of vision. XV. Preliminary studies of the rat's capacity for detail vision, *J. gen. Psychol.*, 1938, **18**, 123–193.

°**76.** Conditional reactions in the rat, *J. Psychol.*, 1938, **6**, 311–324.

°**77.** Experimental analysis of instinctive behavior, *Psychol. Rev.*, 1938, **45**, 445–471.

78. Factors limiting recovery after central nervous lesions (Hughlings Jackson Memorial Lecture, Montreal), *J. nerv. ment. Dis.*, 1938, **88**, 733–755.

79. The mechanism of vision. IX. The numerical relations of cells in the visual system of the rat, *Ukr. Psikhonevrol. Akad.*, 1938.

°**80.** The mechanism of vision. XVI. The functioning of small remnants of the visual cortex, *J. comp. Neurol.*, 1939, **70**, 45–67.

81. Studies of simian intelligence from the University of Liége, *Psychol. Bull.*, 1940, **37**, 237–248.

82. Coalescence of neurology and psychology, *Proc. Amer. phil. Soc.*, 1941, **84**, 461–470.

°**83.** Patterns of cerebral integration indicated by the scotomas of migraine, *Arch. Neurol. Psychiat., Chicago*, 1941, **46**, 331–339.

84. Thalamo-cortical connections of the rat's brain, *J. comp. Neurol.*, 1941, **75**, 67–121.

85. Correlated developments in neurology and psychology, *Science,* 1941, 93, 465–466.

°86. An examination of the "continuity theory" as applied to discriminative learning, *J. gen. Psychol.,* 1942, 26, 241–265.

87. The mechanism of vision. XVII. Autonomy of the visual cortex, *J. genet. Psychol.,* 1942, 60, 197–221.

88. The problem of cerebral organization in vision, *Biol. Symp.,* 1942, 7, 301–322.

89. Olfactory discrimination after destruction of the anterior thalamic nuclei, *Amer. J. Physiol.,* 1943, 139, 446–450. (K. S. Lashley and R. W. Sperry)

°90. Studies of cerebral function in learning. XII. Loss of the maze habit after occipital lesions in blind rats, *J. comp. Neurol.,* 1943, 79, 431–462.

91. Studies of cerebral function in learning. XIII. Apparent absence of transcortical association in maze learning, *J. comp. Neurol.,* 1944, 80, 257–281.

92. Sensory control and rate of learning in the maze, *J. genet. Psychol.,* 1945, 66, 143–145.

93. The Pavlovian theory of generalization, *Psychol. Rev.,* 1946, 53, 72–87. (K. S. Lashley and M. Wade)

94. The cytoarchitecture of the cerebral cortex of Ateles: a critical examination of architectonic studies, *J. comp. Neurol.,* 1946, 85, 223–306. (K. S. Lashley and G. Clark)

95. Structural variation in the nervous system in relation to behavior, *Psychol. Rev.,* 1947, 54, 325–334.

95a. Translation in Spanish of article 95. Las variaciones estructurales del sistema nervioso en relacion con el comportamiento, *Rev. Psicol. gen. apl., Madrid,* 1948, 3, 25–49.

96. The mechanism of vision. XVIII. Effects of destroying the visual "associative areas" of the monkey, *Genet. Psychol. Monogr.,* 1948, 37, 107–166.

°97. Persistent problems in the evolution of mind, *Quart. Rev. Biol.,* 1949, 24, 28–42.

98. The problem of interaction of cerebral areas, *Trans. Amer. neurol. Ass.,* 1949, 187–194.

99. Psychological problems in the development of instrumental aids for the blind. In Zahl, P. A. (Ed.) *Blindness.* Princeton: 1950. Chap. 31. Pp. 495–511.

°100. In search of the engram. In *Symp. Soc. exp. Biol.* No. 4. Cambridge, Eng.: Cambridge Univ. Press, 1950. Pp. 454–482.

101. Physiological psychology. In *Encycl. Brit.,* 1950, 18, 687–690.

102. An examination of the electrical field theory of cerebral integration, *Psychol. Rev.,* 1951, 58, 123–136. (K. S. Lashley, K. L. Chow, and J. Semmes)

°103. The problem of serial order in behavior. In Jeffress, L. A. (Ed.) *Cerebral mechanisms in behavior,* New York: Wiley, 1951. Pp. 112–136.

104. Functional interpretation of anatomic patterns. In *Patterns of organization in the central nervous system, Proc. Ass. Res. nerv. ment. Dis.,* 1952, 30, 529–547.

105. Neuropsychology. In *Survey of neurobiology,* Natl. Res. Council, Wash., 1952 (237), 18–23.

106. Dynamic processes in perception. In Adrian, E. D., Bremer, F., and Jasper, H. H. (Eds.) *Brain mechanisms and consciousness.* Springfield, Ill.: Charles C. Thomas, 1954. Pp. 422–443.

107. Instinct. In *Encycl. Brit.*, 1956, **12**, 429–431.

108. An exchange of views on psychic energy and psychoanalysis, *Behav. Sci.*, 1957, **2**, 231–240. (K. S. Lashley and K. M. Colby)

*109. Cerebral organization and behavior. In *The brain and human behavior, Proc. Ass. Res. nerv. ment. Dis.*, 1958, **36**, 1–18.

NAME INDEX

551

SUBJECT INDEX